Bitten by the Tarantula
and other writing

Bitten by the Tarantula
and other writing

JULIAN MACLAREN-ROSS

with an introduction by Paul Willetts

BLACK
SPRING
PRESS

Published in 2005 by Black Spring Press Ltd
Curtain House
134–146 Curtain Road
London EC2A 3AR

www.blackspringpress.co.uk

The Dark Diceman published courtesy of the manuscript holder, the Harry Ransom Humanities Research Center, The University of Texas at Austin.

Bitten by the Tarantula first published by Allan Wingate, 1946; 'Edward: A Detective Story', 'The Money Makers' and 'The Nine Men of Soho' first published in *The Nine Men of Soho*, Allan Wingate, 1946; 'Action 1938', 'Civvy Street', Part 1 of 'Funny Things Happen' and 'The Rubber Cheque' first published in *Better Than a Kick in the Pant*s, Lawson & Dunn/Hyperion Press, 1945; Part 2 of 'Funny Things Happen' first published in *Christmas Pie*, 1943; 'The Boy Who Might Have Been with Luck the Chess Champion of the World' first published in *Selected Writing*, 1944; 'Five Finger Exercises' first published in *Fortune Anthology*, 1942; 'The Honest Truth' first published in *Christmas Pie*, 1943; 'The Almighty Dollar', 'Affairs of Honour', 'Frank Harris Revisited', 'Mystery Magazines', 'Of Gorse' and 'So long, My Buddy' first published in *Punch* (14 October 1953, 11 April 1956, 10 October 1956, 13 November 1957, 28 December 1955 and 30 November 1955 respectively); 'The Triple Life of Major Trask' first published in *Spring Pie*, 1943; 'The Gem', 'Good Lord, Jeeves', 'Reading', 'A Cable', 'A World of Women' and 'The Peach' first published in *The Funny Bone*, Elek Books, 1956; 'Gas', 'The High Jump', 'The Phantom of the Cookhouse' and 'Seven Days of Heaven' first published in *The Stuff to Give the Troops*, Jonathan Cape, 1944; 'A Mirror to Darkness' and 'The World of Alfred Hitchcock' first published in *New Writing and Daylight* (6, 1945 and 7, 1946 respectively); 'A Brief Survey of British Feature Films' and 'Parade of Violence' first published in *Penguin New Writing* (29, 1947 and 30, 1947 respectively); 'A Totem of the 1920s' and 'Griffith, Stroheim and the Decline of Realism' first published in *Encounter* (March 1954 and August 1954 respectively); 'A Poet of Fear', 'Story of a Full Life', 'Robert Louis Stevenson', 'The Surrealist Movement', 'From a Chase to a View', "A Saga of the Deep South', 'The Simenon Cycle', 'Mr Wodehouse and Others', 'Out of the Ordinary', 'The Awful Child', 'The Hunted and the Heather', 'A Beginning, a Middle and an End', 'Story-telling and the Screen' and 'Hornblower in Command' first published in *Times Literary Supplement* (25 December 1948, 11 November 1949, 26 May 1950, 28 July 1950, 16 February 1951, 13 February 1953, 20 March 1953, 29 May 1953, 25 February 1955, 18 November 1955, 1 June 1956, 12 October 1956, 15 August 1958 and 17 August 1962 respectively); 'Mr Hamilton and Mr Gorse', 'The Black Romances of A.E.W. Mason', 'Seventy Years of Sexton Blake', 'Mary McCarthy and the Class of '33', 'The Dark Glass of Sheridan Le Fanu', 'Chandler and Hammett', 'The World of Robert Bloch', 'Ernest Hemingway' and 'The Strange Realm of M.P. Shiel' first published in the *London Magazine* (January 1956, March 1963, November 1963, January 1964, February 1964, March 1964, July 1964, August 1964 and September 1964 respectively).

ISBN 0-948238-32-1

A full CIP record for this book is available from the British Library

Cover design Hanna Sundén and Angela Lee; front cover: detail of *Portrait de Madame Allen Bott* by Tamara de Lempicka © ADAGP, Paris and DACS, London 2005, reproduced with permission; back cover: Julian Maclaren-Ross, sitting in the garden of Greenleaves, Bognor Regis, 1940, © C.K. Jaeger.

Typeset in Minion by Dexter Haven Associates Ltd, London
Printed and bound in Great Britain by Cox and Wyman Ltd, Reading

CONTENTS

Introduction
Paul Willetts

THE LIFE AND LITERARY CAREER OF JULIAN MACLAREN-ROSS (1912–64) are inextricably entwined with Soho's bohemian heyday, with the era of rationing, basement drinking clubs, and smog-shrouded streets. Still, it's easy to imagine Maclaren-Ross thriving in today's media-dominated world. If he was a young writer now, he'd be the subject of countless fawning magazine profiles, dissecting his flamboyant wardrobe, quoting his droll comments, as well as savouring his aura of unbreachable self-confidence and deadpan cool. Such profiles would be accompanied by dramatically composed photos of him. I can just see him posing in the memorabilia-lined French House pub or on some neon-lit West End street. He'd be dressed in his trademark outfit: a pale suit, gaudily patterned tie, and aviator-style sunglasses, his famous teddy-bear coat draped round his shoulders, a silver-topped cane clasped in one hand and a cigarette-holder in the other.

Though his habitual get-up harked back to the sleek sartorial style of the 1890s dandy, it also looked forward to the fancy-dress posturing of pop stars from the 1960s onwards. He was, in many ways, ahead of his time, not least in his literary output. As a writer of fiction, he pioneered a style that was often slangy and conversational, its unpretentious clarity, casual tone and mordant humour contributing to its enduring appeal. What's more, in short stories such as 'The Rubber Cheque', he indulges in jokey formal games that prefigure the postmodern tricksiness of many current writers.

His essays on film and literature were similarly innovative, yet their originality is less conspicuous. Despite penning only a limited amount of film criticism, all of it reproduced here, he broke new ground in that genre. As a literary essayist, the enthusiasm, knowledge and seriousness with which he treated both high art and the easily dismissed products of popular culture anticipated the approach taken by so many subsequent critics. *Bitten by the Tarantula and other writing* provides a showcase not only for these little known and under-appreciated aspects of his career but also for his versatility. Difficult though his life was, alcoholism, drug-fuelled paranoia and lack of money being among the obstacles strewn across his path, he maintained a surprisingly high output that spanned numerous literary genres. During the latter half of the 1950s, for instance, he juggled novel-writing with work as a journalist, screenwriter and radio dramatist. But he is now remembered chiefly for his memoirs and fiction, the boundary between which tends to be indistinct.

Like innumerable other major writers, ranging from Christopher Isherwood to John Updike, he relied on direct experience as the source of the majority of his best work, an obvious exception being the short story about colonial India that brought him to prominence. For inclusion in this volume, I've chosen a cross-section of Maclaren-Ross's fiction, encompassing a novella, nineteen frequently brief and pungent stories, not to mention several previously unpublished fragments of novels. In all but one case, the stories have been plucked from his 1956 miscellany, *The Funny Bone*, plus his three published collections – *The Stuff to Give the Troops* (1944), *Better than a Kick in the Pants* (1945) and *The Nine Men of Soho* (1946). The stories, few of which have ever been reprinted, explore four main periods in his strange and troubled life. These comprise his upbringing on the French Riviera between 1921 and 1933; his early adult years on the south coast of England; his unhappy spell as an army conscript, culminating in his desertion and subsequent incarceration in a military psychiatric hospital; and his itinerant post-war existence, much of it spent in the pubs and clubs of Soho. Of the stories featured here, the latest is 'The Gem', dating from the beginning of 1955. And the earliest is the cheekily titled 'Five Finger Exercises', an apprentice-work describing his brief romantic entanglement with a fellow guest in the seaside hotel in which he'd been staying after he left the Riviera and moved back to England. By the standards of the mid-1930s when 'Five Finger Exercises' was written, its subject-matter was sufficiently risqué to make magazine editors reluctant to publish it. Thanks to Maclaren-Ross's growing reputation, it finally appeared in print in *Fortune Anthology*, a 1942 collection issued by the shady publisher L.S. Caton, later lampooned in Kingsley Amis's *Lucky Jim*. Caton's unwillingness to pay contributors led Maclaren-Ross to joke about how the *Fortune Anthology* should be known only by its initials.

As you'd expect from a selection of stories written over a period of almost twenty years, there's considerable variation in their style, form and tone. At one end of the spectrum, there are such stylistically and structurally conventional stories as 'Five Finger Exercises' and 'Action 1938', told from the point of view of omniscient third-person narrators. In sharp contrast, Maclaren-Ross also produced playful stories such as 'Funny Things Happen', narrated in the lean, chatty, anecdotal style with which he became synonymous. It's a style that makes you feel as if he's talking to you over a glass of black-market whisky in the basement bar of some after-hours Soho dive. Of course these stories bear the imprint of the American writers Dashiell Hammett, Ernest Hemingway, Damon Runyon, James M. Cain and William Saroyan, yet their tone is unambiguously English and unmistakably his own, by turns flippant, sardonic, matter-of-fact and disenchanted. With rare exceptions, the army stories that established him as one of the brightest British literary talents to emerge during the Second World War were written in this deceptively easy manner. Another distinctive facet of his army stories is the way in which they hover near the border between fiction and reportage, sometimes erring on one side, sometimes on the other. Nowhere is the element of reportage more apparent than in 'Seven Days of Heaven', his melancholy depiction of a week's leave spent with his girlfriend in Bognor Regis. It could be seen as a touching companion-piece to 'Are You Happy In Your Work', which features in the recently published *Collected Memoirs* (Black Spring Press). Together with this documentary account of day-to-day life in a wartime garrison, 'Seven Days of Heaven' foreshadows the comparable work of the 1960s 'New Journalists' who are credited with inventing the now routine technique of presenting factual material in a vivid, novelistic style.

Part of the reason for the revival of interest in Maclaren-Ross's fiction and memoirs is that his prose remains fresh and astonishingly modern. *Bitten by the Tarantula and other writing* offers the swelling ranks of Maclaren-Ross fans the chance to enjoy a great deal of entertaining and illuminating work, hitherto uncollected, unpublished or available only in rare and expensive first editions, changing hands for as much as £650. Among the unpublished material, there's a story entitled 'I'm Too Old to Play the Violin', an amusing curiosity to which I was alerted by a reference in *The Lesser Infortune*, Rayner Heppenstall's *roman-à-clef* about life in Northfield Military Hospital where he and Maclaren-Ross had been inmates. 'Dorian Scott-Crichton', Maclaren-Ross's fictional counterpart, was said to have published a couple of short stories in the newly launched hospital magazine. One of these was described as 'a mere sketch' with which 'Scott-Crichton was not pleased'. Sure enough, tucked away in perhaps the only surviving copy of the May 1943 issue of *Psyche*, the magazine's real-life equivalent, its mimeographed typescript faded and brittle, I found 'I'm Too Old to Play the Violin'. There's no denying that it *is* 'a mere sketch'. All the same, it's imbued with both Maclaren-Ross's wry humour and familiar exasperation with military bureaucracy, which prompted the critic Bernard Bergonzi to describe his army stories as being like 'Kafka rewritten by the Marx Brothers'.

Humour of an altogether different variety pervades the surviving section of his first novel, *A House of Cards*. In the wake of the book's completion during the autumn of 1935, he submitted the manuscript to the publishers Jonathan Cape, but it was rejected. When he found himself stationed at an army depot in Southend seven years later, he used some of his spare-time to rework its opening chapter, which is published in this volume. The chapter, presented – unusually for him – from multiple viewpoints, was drafted in one of a stack of army-issue exercise books that he'd rescued from the waste-bin. Though he had been given official permission to use them, he ended up being charged with theft and gaoled.

Staged against the backdrop of a seaside hotel, the first chapter of *A House of Cards* is populated by characters who are imaginatively distorted versions of real people, Maclaren-Ross included. He appears in the guise of 'Gerard St John', a film extra and would-be writer, working on 'a book called *Women I Have Proposed To* which, although he described it as a fictional treatise, was based largely on personal experience'. Lighter in mood and more overtly comic than any of his published fiction, *A House of Cards* is narrated with urbane, breezy charm that's a world away from the clipped, acerbic style of so many of his wartime stories.

A much more substantial example of his fiction is provided by the long out-of-print novella, *Bitten by the Tarantula*. I was recently encouraged to re-read it by the writer Jonathan Meades, who regards it as being far superior to Cyril Connolly's much better-known book *The Rock Pool*, also set against the Riviera's sybaritic, inter-war bohemian scene. I soon realised that I'd been wrong to bracket *Bitten by the Tarantula* with Maclaren-Ross's disappointing late novels. True, it isn't in the same league as his 1947 masterpiece, *Of Love and Hunger*, but it has plenty to recommend it. Like *Of Love and Hunger*, it was written during the 1940s, yet its sparse, dialogue-laden style and bleak hedonism belong to the pre-war period in which it's set. As if to emphasise this, the narrator is reading *Vile Bodies* and there's a scene, involving a sportscar speeding round the local market square, that carries a touch of the nihilistic symbolism of Evelyn Waugh's novel.

In the disingenuous 'note by the author' that prefaces *Bitten by the Tarantula*, Maclaren-Ross describes how the book 'was written in 1942 as a relaxation from writing the series of army tales afterwards published in a volume called *The Stuff to Give the Troops*'. Possibly because he was ashamed of the novella's apparent frivolity, he chose to distort the truth, portraying its composition as a form of literary holiday. *Bitten by the Tarantula* – which originally bore the ironic title *The Simple Life* – was, in fact, started shortly before Maclaren-Ross's conscription into the army during the summer of 1940. As the preface makes clear, the book was rooted in his own experiences. The autobiographical component is underscored by a cross-reference to his – most likely pseudonymous – childhood friend, 'Gene Flood', who crops up elsewhere in his fiction.

Once Maclaren-Ross had completed the first half of the novella, by which time he had been posted to a military training camp in Dorset, he showed it to Cyril Connolly, editor of the influential magazine *Horizon*, where he had just made his triumphant debut. Connolly responded very positively to the manuscript. On condition that the book ended up being no longer than 10,000 words, Connolly was prepared to set aside an entire issue of the magazine to it, an honour only bestowed on Evelyn Waugh's *The Loved One*. But *The Simple Life* soon expanded way beyond the specified limit, probably because it offered Maclaren-Ross a nostalgic escape from army life, which had soon lost its novelty. Even so, the completed manuscript was still too short to be regarded as a full-length novel, ensuring that it was hard to place with a suitable publisher, irrespective of Maclaren-Ross's status as a marketable young author.

Under the more catchy title *Bitten by the Tarantula*, it was eventually published in 1946 by Allan Wingate Ltd, a new imprint launched by the young André Deutsch, to whom Maclaren-Ross had been introduced by Graham Greene. The book scored a commercial hit, no doubt aided by its subject-matter and the relative exoticism of its pre-war setting, so far removed from the prevailing austerity of post-war England.

Bitten by the Tarantula was the first of three Maclaren-Ross books that appeared under the Allan Wingate banner. Well before *Of Love and Hunger*'s release in the autumn of 1947, its demanding and sometimes paranoid author – whose record of feuding with publishers proved so deleterious to his career – had fallen out with Deutsch. In the meantime he negotiated an alternative deal with the more established firm of Eyre and Spottiswoode, then under the managing directorship of Graham Greene, who shared his passion for vernacular thrillers. So highly was Maclaren-Ross rated by Greene that he obtained a hefty advance for just such a thriller. This was to be based on the crimes of Eugen Weidmann, a multilingual, German-born serial killer who had been tried and executed in 1939. Ever since reading the extensive newspaper coverage of the trial, Maclaren-Ross had wanted to write a novel about Weidmann's lethal crime-spree. Never shy about his literary ambitions, Maclaren-Ross would often stand at the bar of the Wheatsheaf, his favourite Soho pub, regaling fellow drinkers with tales of how he was going to dramatise the story. Using the advance that Eyre and Spottiswoode had paid him, the profligate Maclaren-Ross installed himself and his current girlfriend in a plush West End hotel, where he set about writing the novel, entitled *Death and His Sweetheart*, its action transplanted from France to England. But he ran out of money before he could finish the book, retitled *The Dark Diceman*, a phrase culled from William Faulkner's *The Sound and the Fury*.

As Maclaren-Ross came to discover, he required a prolonged period of unbroken concentration in order to complete a novel. His recurrent financial problems forcing him into the embrace of freelance journalism, he found that the book's initial momentum was dissipated. Despite selling an option on the film rights and receiving a confidential grant from an unlikely saviour, none other than Prime Minister Clement Attlee, he was unable to regain the lost impetus, compelling him to concede that the novel would never be completed. Over a decade afterwards, by then homeless and so mentally unbalanced that he became convinced his personality had been taken over by the villain from Robert Louis Stevenson's *Dr Jekyll and Mr Hyde*, he sold the pristine manuscript to raise money.

Along with Alex Maclaren-Ross, who owns his father's literary copyright, I was presented with an ethical dilemma about whether such uncompleted fiction should be included. Our qualms were overridden by the conviction that each of the featured novel-fragments contains something to admire, something that would be of interest to fans of Maclaren-Ross's work. In common with *A House of Cards*, the existing 12,000 word section of *The Dark Diceman* gives us a tantalising glimpse of a fresh literary direction that its author might have taken. More to the point, it deserves to be rescued from obscurity. Though the chapter seen from the point of view of 'Trégi' – the Soho French low-life – lacks conviction, the menacing atmosphere and suspenseful, cinematic cutting more than compensate for that defect.

Clearly, *The Dark Diceman* has the makings of a memorable thriller in the mould of Patrick Hamilton's revered Gorse Trilogy, which Maclaren-Ross admired and which it predates by several years. Its depiction of a socially disparate group of characters, interconnected by the impact of crime, demonstrates that it also had the potential to be a forerunner of the sweeping, so-called 'social crime' novels of the contemporary American writers Richard Price and George P. Pelecanos. One thing is for sure, though: there's something exceptionally sad about all that unfulfilled potential, about the way *The Dark Diceman* stops in mid-sentence, echoing the premature ending of Maclaren-Ross's life.

The two other much shorter fragments of novels published in *Bitten by the Tarantula and other writing* offer a similarly poignant reminder of the unfinished projects that littered his nevertheless productive career. He appears to have written no more than the first few pages of either *Astrid: A Long Story* or *Business and Desire*, both of which exist in several versions, the most polished and, by implication, latest of which are presented here.

In all probability *Astrid* dates from 1957, not long after he'd returned to London, following an unhappy sixteen-month sojourn in Oxford. While he was there, recovering from the trauma of yet another failed relationship, he spent a great deal of time in the company of the New Zealand writer Dan Davin and his wife Winnie, who appear in *Astrid* as 'Matt' and 'Maggie McCarthy'. Whether the book would have evolved into a worthy addition to the Maclaren-Ross œuvre is unclear, but the initial, self-contained pages hark back to his earlier stories, within which he displays the rare knack of transmuting ostensibly inconsequential everyday experience into sharp, well structured fiction.

On the evidence of the various chapter-plans of *Business and Desire*, it too was destined to be a *roman-à-clef*. Next to the names of the characters, Maclaren-Ross had even jotted down their flesh and blood equivalents, among them Reggie Smith, the BBC producer who would later provide the model for the character of 'Guy Pringle' in the novelist Olivia Manning's Balkan and Levant Trilogies. Armed with a brief outline, Maclaren-Ross was, in 1951, able to persuade Hamish Hamilton, owner of the eponymous publishing firm, to issue an advance for the mooted novel, the focus of which shifted over the ensuing years. By the late 1950s, he envisaged it cutting between his professional life and his many romantic entanglements. But a frustrating and, for him, unprecedented bout of writer's block prevented him from bringing the project to fruition, progress being limited to the few obsessively rewritten pages reproduced here. These describe his initial encounter with Leonard Woolf's bohemian niece, Diana Bromley, who would become his second wife and the mother of his only child. The meeting took place in the Caves de France, a famously dingy drinking club on Dean Street, patronised by the likes of Gerald Hamilton, model for the titular anti-hero in Christopher Isherwood's *Mr Norris Changes Trains*. For Maclaren-Ross's literary purposes, the club was renamed the 'Claire de Lune'. Brief though the completed chunk of *Business and Desire* is, it conjures the down-at-heel ambience of the Caves and affords an eerie insight into what would be one of the pivotal moments in his rackety existence. Previous girlfriends had tended to exert a stabilising influence. Diana Bromely, on the other hand, would turn out to be every bit as erratic and rootless as her new partner-in-penury. The romance that followed their chance encounter in the Caves was by far the most turbulent of his life, bitter arguments provoking frequent separations.

No matter how chaotic his relationships and domestic arrangements were, Maclaren-Ross never allowed himself to be distracted from his *raison d'être*, namely his literary vocation. From 1945 right through until his death, he subsidised both his heavy drinking and creative work with journalism. This consisted of book reviews, literary parodies, essays on the cinema, facetious profiles of fictional characters, and lengthy ruminations on writers he admired. In one of the many intriguing paradoxes evident in his career, he was capable of writing with level-headed clarity even when his life was in disarray.

Years earlier when he was an aspiring writer ensconced with his parents on the Riviera, he'd had a brief theatre review published in the *Monte Carlo and Menton News*. But his first serious foray into criticism came in 1945 when he was commissioned to write an article on contemporary American cinema for *New Writing and Daylight*, one of the many miscellanies and literary magazines flourishing during that period.

Drawing on his lifelong passion for the cinema, the article – entitled 'A Mirror to Darkness' – was not only perceptive but also original in its assessment of such 1940s thrillers as *The Maltese Falcon*, *The Glass Key*, and *Double Indemnity*. In these, he discerned a shared, uncompromising vision of violence, greed and sexual deviance. It was a vision that would, the following year, lead a French cineaste named Nino Frank to label this sub-genre of doom-laden movies 'film noir'.

On the strength of 'A Mirror to Darkness', Maclaren-Ross landed another commission from *New Writing and Daylight*, this time for a piece about Alfred Hitchcock, in whose work he teased out a consistent theme. He took a similar approach in his next item of film criticism, written anonymously for *Penguin New Writing*, a high-circulation magazine edited by John Lehmann. Once again, the article – presumably uncredited because Maclaren-Ross already had another piece in that issue – concentrated on movies that would become known as film noir: movies such as *The Blue Dahlia*, *The Dark Corner*, and *Scarlet Street*. In these he perceived 'a cinematic world of violence and corruption [...which] may well be considered existentialist'.

Ever the egotist, Maclaren-Ross could seldom resist garnishing his film criticism with autobiographical anecdotes, though these are always pertinent and engaging. The unappealingly titled 'A Brief Survey of British Feature Films', his penultimate contribution to John Lehmann's *New Writing* stable of publications, begins with a captivating, typically conversational reminiscence of his childhood excursions to the cinema just after the First World War. Demonstrating characteristic lightness of touch and authorial sleight of hand, he moves on to rail against the classbound inadequacies of the British film industry. With startling prescience, he points out the seeds of its imminent decline. And, in passing, he gives a nod in the direction of the now little-known James Curtis, pseudonymous author of *They Drive By Night* and fellow exponent of vernacular English prose.

Regrettably, Maclaren-Ross was under-employed as a film critic. By the 1950s, he had made the transition from being a critic to being a screenwriter. His experiences on the practical side of the film business informed his two remaining contributions to the genre. For *Encounter* he wrote an expansive, well-informed essay on the silent films of D.W. Griffith and Erich von Stroheim. For the *Times Literary Supplement*, he wrote about 'Storytelling and the Screen', his comments permeated by the resentment he felt towards the film companies and producers who had employed him on a series of ultimately disappointing assignments.

Screenwriting was not, however, Maclaren-Ross's only sideline during that period. Towards the end of 1947, his friend the novelist Anthony Powell, who was working part-time for the *TLS*, helped him out of his latest financial mess by employing him as a book reviewer. Maclaren-Ross insisted on the *TLS* defying both convention and its accounting system by paying him 'cash-on-delivery', his payment all too often finding its way with disconcerting speed into the cash-registers of favoured West End pubs and clubs. Self-conscious though he was about his lack of a university education, he rapidly demonstrated his abilities as a critic. He was soon pressed into supplying so-called 'middles' for the *TLS* – essays on individual writers, literary forms or movements. His initial contribution was devoted to Henry Green, whose books he rated highly, their abrupt rhythms reverberating through his own work. He went on to produce middles on a diverse selection of other cherished subjects. Whatever he was commissioned to write about, be it the arcane fiction of Jean Cocteau or the popular novels of C.S. Forester, he offered fresh observations as well as tangential insights into his own life and work. Within only a few years, he was regarded as a literary critic of sufficient stature for Oxford University Press to give him the chance to expand his *TLS* middles into a collection of essays on modern novelists. But he never seized the opportunity, preferring to pursue other ventures.

Throughout the rest of his life, literary criticism provided him with an invaluable source of much-needed ready cash. Besides writing for the *TLS*, he received regular commissions between 1953 and 1959 from *Punch*, the humorous magazine that was enjoying a resurgence under the editorship of Malcolm Muggeridge. In addition to dashing off short book reviews, he wrote pieces on specific themes, amusing reminiscences, comic articles and literary parodies, several of which are reproduced here. These include his parody of H.E. Bates's work, a seemingly innocuous send-up that led Bates to instigate a successful High Court libel action against him.

For all Maclaren-Ross's well-documented self-absorption, he was both receptive to other writers' work and keenly aware of their stylistic nuances, his output in this field prompting Malcolm Muggeridge to hail him as 'the best living parodist'. To his delight, Maclaren-Ross even earned appreciative responses from P.G. Wodehouse, Georges

Simenon and William Faulkner, whose work he had spoofed with such obvious affection.

When word got round that he was a contributor to *Punch*, the entrance to the magazine's premises became blocked by a jostling crowd of bailiffs hunting the elusive, debt-ridden Maclaren-Ross. Incensed by the consequent inconvenience, the owners of *Punch* were keen to dispense with his services. But he was saved from dismissal by the generous intercession of Anthony Powell, by then installed as its Literary Editor.

Maclaren-Ross combined his work for *Punch* with book reviewing for other publications such as the *Sunday Times*, the *Listener*, and John Lehmann's recently launched, bi-monthly *London Magazine*. A staunch believer in his talent, Lehmann commissioned him to write what would be a shrewd overview of Patrick Hamilton's Gorse Trilogy, his familiarity with which enabled him to parody the novels for *Punch*.

Preferring to concentrate on his creative writing, Maclaren-Ross opted out of his role as a critic near the end of the 1950s. But it was a role that he couldn't escape for long. Early in 1963 his precarious circumstances compelled him to solicit work from the poet Alan Ross, who had taken over the *London Magazine*. It was to be a fortuitous, mutually beneficial association. During the remaining months of his life, which came to an unforeseen conclusion in November 1964 when he suffered a fatal heart-attack, Maclaren-Ross became a regular visitor to the magazine's offices. He delivered a succession of dazzling reviews and essays, along with instalments of his *Memoirs of the Forties*. His critical writing for the *London Magazine* covered such wide-ranging subjects as the Gothic stories of Sheridan Le Fanu, the work of Mary McCarthy, and Ernest Hemingway's posthumously published *A Moveable Feast* which, most likely, inspired Maclaren-Ross's own memoirs of bohemian Soho. Even when the chosen topic is as obscure as the florid fantasy novels of M.P. Shiel or the pulp fiction of Robert Bloch, Maclaren-Ross's criticism is always worth reading. As a rule, he tended to write about books or writers who interested him. For that reason he seldom delivered the type of scathing verdicts which are the stock-in-trade of many of his fellow critics. Though he had a reputation for being abrasive when encountered face-to-face, his essays are erudite, incisive and, more often than not, appreciative. Like all the best critical writing, they nourish the reader's understanding of the work in question.

Whether Maclaren-Ross was producing reviews, essays, fiction or memoirs, he had that happy knack of being able to make his prose feel vibrant, immediate, effortless and individual. His writing conveys the unmistakable voice of what his friend the critic Anthony Cronin called 'one of the doomed men of Soho'. Reading his work now is akin to viewing some miraculously untarnished film footage, the colour undimmed by the intervening decades. Ahead of the game in so many respects, Maclaren-Ross's time has, it seems, finally arrived.

Paul Willetts
June 2005

BITTEN BY THE TARANTULA:
A STORY OF THE SOUTH OF FRANCE

AUTHOR'S NOTE

Several people who read this story in manuscript seemed to think the choice of subject – life in the South of France during the summer of 1930 – called for some kind of explanation. It had no topical significance: was the book, therefore, written out of a sense of guilt? As an indictment of the 'Bad Old Days' when one lived for pleasure alone?

The answer to both these questions is No. I haven't a sense of guilt; I am in no way responsible for the war and have little hope of being responsible for the peace; nor did I ever find the type of life described in the following pages particularly pleasurable.

The story itself was written in 1942 as a relaxation from writing the series of army tales afterwards published in a volume called *The Stuff to Give the Troops*. It was written under service conditions, and it amused me at the time to alternate between describing the two ways of life, the past and the present. As the action takes place fifteen years ago, I fail to see how it can be expected to have topical significance.

That the book has not been printed until now is partly due to the manuscript's habit of absenting itself from my possession for long intervals, and partly to prejudice in the publishing trade against books under 70,000 words in length.

All the characters, including the narrator, are entirely imaginary.

London 3.3.45
J.M.-R.

PART ONE

'What Ho! What Ho! This Fellow is Dancing Mad...'

*   *   *

1

I THOUGHT IT'D DO ME GOOD TO GET AWAY FOR A BIT. THAT summer in Nice there was a heat wave on, and everyone wore pitch helmets and white drill, as though in the tropics. By August almost all of our crowd had cleared out: the town had become literally too hot to hold them. The heat was really appalling. It was almost too hot to move. The nights were no cooler: the air felt sticky and there was a smell of tar all over the town.

When Armstrong suggested this trip I accepted at once. The idea of staying a month in the mountains appealed to me tremendously. No worries. Nothing complicated. The simple life. That suited me fine.

'Where shall we stay?' I asked him.

Armstrong said: 'There's a choice of two hotels. The Royal is the best.'

'You've been there before, then?'

'Last year. It was very restful.'

'That's just what I need, a good rest.'

'You never have anything else.'

'Nonsense. My life is a turmoil. I often think of entering a monastery.'

'Or a convent,' Armstrong said. 'Have you never thought about that?'

'A convent would be too complicated.'

'Yvonne was brought up in a convent wasn't she?'

'I believe she was.'

'How is that progressing?'

'She's away in Geneva.'

Which was another reason for leaving. With Yvonne away, life seemed much less complicated but on the other hand much less exciting. She

3

wouldn't be back for months, and in the meantime there didn't seem anything to do.

But two days later Armstrong rang up with a change of plan. Instead of an hotel, why not stay for a while with Spider: he had a châlet up there.

'Are we invited?' I asked.

'Of course.'

'All right.'

'It should be amusing,' Armstrong said.

'Not so restful though.'

'It'll be pretty restful. Practically in the wilds. Miles from anywhere.'

'Splendid. When do we start?'

'Tomorrow afternoon.'

2

Spider's servant Vaska met us at the bus stop in the boulevard MacMahon. He was a gigantic young Russian with close-cropped curly hair and a broken nose. He wore a sleeveless blue singlet and the muscles bulged like a blacksmith's in his brown arms. His mother, an immensely stout woman employed as cook at a pension in the town, was supposed to be a countess in exile; but other Russians strenuously denied the truth of this story, and certainly Vaska's low forehead and pleasantly pugnacious face gave no indication of aristocratic descent.

Vaska greeted us with great heartiness, banging Armstrong on the back and almost breaking the bones of my hand. He took our valises and hoisted them without effort on top of the bus, which was drawn up outside the Café de l'Univers. Nearly all the seats were already taken: stout peasant women laden with baskets of provisions predominated among the passengers.

'What time does it start?' Armstrong asked Vaska.

'Five sharp,' Vaska told him.

'Time for a drink first.'

It was cooler inside the café. Vaska and a friend of his called René, who wore a knitted pullover, white plusfours and a white polo képi, played belote with the bus-driver until it was time to start. They banged on the table and made a good deal of noise. All of them drank cognac. Standing at the bar, Armstrong and I drank pernod.

'Tell me about Spider,' I said. 'I've only met him twice.'

Armstrong said: 'Spider is SO. He writes poetry. They say he poisoned his wife but I don't believe it myself. Anyhow there was an enquiry and Spider lost his job in the administration. He didn't mind much as he'd inherited quite a bit from his wife. After that he went to Algiers and lost all the money gambling.'

'How does he live then?'

'Borrowing from friends.'

'What else?'

'He takes drugs and has a daughter aged ten.'

'Quite a character in fact.'

'Definitely a character.'

'He speaks very good English for a Frenchman.'

'He's supposed to have been to Oxford, but no one knows for certain.'

'Will there be a big party staying with him?'

'No, quite small I believe.'

'Anyone interesting?'

'You mean women?'

'Possibly.'

'I shouldn't think so. But anyway we're going there for a rest.'

'That's true.'

Armstrong had just returned from excavating dead cities somewhere in Egypt. Before that he had been in New Guinea studying the sexual customs of Papuan tribes. His book on this subject, *Phallic Fetish*, sold very well indeed. People bought it to look at the photographs.

But Armstrong wasn't really an explorer or a writer: these activities with him were purely incidental. He had a wide range of interests, and a large private income, inherited from his father, absolved him from the necessity of earning a living in any particular sphere of life. He was thirty-five and still a bachelor, having successfully eluded the efforts of many determined women to marry him. The most importunate of these at the moment was a Canadian girl staying at the same hotel in Cannes, and it was to escape from her that he was making this trip to the mountains.

In appearance Armstrong was imposing: even bigger than Vaska.

He stood six feet two and weighed sixteen stone. He had a round bland smooth-shaven face, hair sleekly centre-parted and heavy-lidded somnolent eyes. He spoke in a slow drawl and I had never seen him excited or angry, although I had known him for several years.

Bronzed and imperturbable in white ducks and solar topi, he personified the legendary English globe-trotter as portrayed by Jules Verne; only the long green cigarette-holder, through which he smoked incessantly, struck an incongruous note. The cigarette-holder was a let-down. It wasn't in character. One felt he should have smoked a pipe.

'Are you writing anything now?' I asked him.

'Some articles for a Sunday paper.'

'The Curse of the Pharoahs and so on?'

'More or less.'

At that moment the bell rang inside the café. It was five o'clock. The bus-driver stood up and threw down his cards, at the same time striking the table a tremendous blow with his fist.

He shouted: 'Merde alors!'

'That's ten francs you owe me,' Vaska told him.

The bus-driver paid up grumbling, while René grinned in the background. We all went towards the door, Vaska carrying a bottle of cognac with him. The bus-driver walked a little unsteadily.

'Don't drive us all over a cliff Jules,' Vaska said to him.

'Over a cliff my arse,' the driver said. He was still very angry at losing. Breathing hard, he took hold of the handle and started to crank the engine. It gave a sudden roar and the body of the bus pulsated.

'All aboard!' the driver shouted, waving his arms wildly.

'En voiture!'

We climbed in carrying Armstrong's portable gramophone and the portfolio containing the new records. Vaska and René got up beside the driver. Armstrong and I sat wedged in between two fat housewives who stank of garlic.

The bus started off suddenly; its route lay along the promenade des Anglais. Rows of empty white chairs were drawn up outside the Méditerranée and Kiki Baranov was talking to Damia Bellini on the steps of the Grande Bleue as we flashed by. I called out to her but she didn't hear. Then the bus branched off by the Californie.

3

The journey took four hours. At first I attempted to read *Vile Bodies*, which I had brought with me, but this was impossible because a basket was banged into my ribs by one of the fat women at every lurch of the bus and finally I gave up in disgust. The bus drove madly on across bridges, through gorges and archways tunnelled in red rock, the road dipping away to gullies on either side. At one point there was a great gap in the wooden railings where a car had skidded and struck some months before; it had been precipitated into the ravine and two of the passengers had been killed. The two fat women on either side of us discussed this incident with relish, shouting across at each other above the roar of the engine. The smell of garlic became more offensive as the sun made the women sweat. Armstrong and I lit cigarettes in a chain, one from the other: the rushing air extinguished matches when struck.

I wondered what staying with Spider would be like. The intelligence conveyed to me by Armstrong, coupled with what I had already heard from other sources, didn't seem to promise a particularly peaceful time. I wondered if we should all be poisoned or else expected to join in an orgy of opium smoking: neither of these possibilities appealed to me.

A sudden scream from one of the fat women interrupted my train of thought. I looked round. Her eyes were fixed on the road ahead. An enormous lorry, unheralded by hoot, had appeared all at once from round a bend in the road. It was bearing down on us at a fair speed. A collision seemed inevitable. The fat woman threw up her hands and let out a shriek like a siren. The other woman next to Armstrong was too appalled to scream, but more passengers shouted behind us. Armstrong took his cigarette-holder out of his mouth as the bus-driver jammed on his brakes. There was a tearing scraping sound as the front mudguard grazed the parapet at the side of the road, and the bus stopped with a sudden jerk, flinging me forward in my seat. The lorry-driver had braked too, and the two vehicles slid to a stop alongside each other, with scarcely an inch in between. Both drivers leaned out, cursing in Niçois; the lorry-driver shook his fist. Vaska and René joined in: the air became full of flying oaths. I could feel the sweat coming out cold under my armpits and my forehead prickling. I looked round at Armstrong, who nodded and raised his eyebrows. It was impossible to tell whether he had felt any emotion: his big brown face remained expressionless. He put his cigarette-holder back into his mouth and puffed at it as the bus began to move forward again: there was just room to pass. All the passengers became very voluble; the two fat women praised God piously for their narrow escape. The lorry-driver leaned forward and spat a final insult, at the same time allowing a dense cloud of poisonous fumes to explode around us from his exhaust, with the effect of a defiant and derisive fart. The bus swung out from the parapet into the middle of the road again; its gears ground up a steep gradient, leaving the lorry behind. The bus-driver looked round and grinned reassuringly to show that he had been in complete control of the situation. Vaska put the bottle of cognac in his hand and he drank with his head tipped back and his other hand on the wheel. The bus thundered across a steel bridge spanning a viaduct; below, a waterfall tumbled into a valley. I could have done with a drink myself.

4

Halfway up we stopped at a village partly rebuilt after a recent landslide. Evidence of destruction could still be seen all around: wooden shacks half demolished, beams poking up through shattered roofs, mounds of brick and rubble where houses had been squashed flat by the collapsing hillside. The ruined streets sloped downwards, knocked awry; new huts with tin roofs had been hastily erected among the ruins; a few grubby barefoot children pattered forlornly about in the dust and wreckage of their homes.

We drank at the bar of the village café while the bus-driver recounted the lorry incident to all and sundry, praising his own presence of mind, growing boisterous and boastful under the influence of more brandy. Armstrong and I ate bread and cheese: we were both hungry.

'How far is it now?'

'Another hour.'

We climbed back into the bus; the two fat housewives had disembarked and I could now read undisturbed. I read the part where Adam calls on the colonel at Doubting Hall, chuckling to myself as the bus climbed higher into the hills and the sun dipped behind the pine trees. The air grew definitely cooler as we approached the village.

The bus drove down a long avenue lined with plane trees and swung in a semicircle into the public *place*, where a few loafers in cloth caps and chokers tended tethered donkeys. René was met by the old Frenchwoman who was keeping him and they went off to an hotel together. The bus-driver and Vaska said goodbye, banging each other on the back for some time, while Armstrong and I stood by our valises, which contrary to expectation had not fallen off the bus-top.

'Fou Châlet's about four miles from here,' Armstrong said.

'Is it called that?'

'What?'

'Fou Châlet.'

'Actually, no. It's called Lou something. A patois name that I can never remember. Fou Châlet's far more appropriate.'

'Why? Are they all mad up there?'

'Mad as hatters. Bound to be.'

At this moment Vaska approached us, dragging behind him by the bridle a pack-mule of formidable aspect. This animal exhibited immediately all the worst characteristics associated with its species. It laid back its ears, forefeet firmly planted, baring long yellow teeth and snapping with them savagely at Vaska's shoulder. Undeterred by these demonstrations, Vaska proceeded to load onto its back most of the luggage. The mule bucked and reared round at him, kicking up with its hind hooves like a bronco attempting to shake its rider from the saddle. Grinning goodhumouredly, Vaska dodged in under the gnashing teeth and wrenched its head back by the bridle, at the same time bringing his knee up into the animal's stomach several times.

'Sacré vieille!' he shouted, 'Keep still, blast you!' wrenching at the bit. He panted over his shoulder at us: 'She's a temperamental old bitch! Too full of spirit!' The mule flailed about furiously, kicking up a cloud of dust all around them. Vaska, releasing the bridle, stepped back out of reach and struck the mule a blow with his fist across the snout, following this up with a terrific kick in the stomach. The animal subsided at once: the wind had been knocked out of it. It stood still, rolling its eyes in alarm, and shaking its head from side to side.

Vaska turned round and grinned at us, spreading his hands and shrugging his shoulders deprecatingly.

'What can you do with an animal like that?' he asked. 'I hate to hurt her, she's not a bad old bitch! Too much temperament, that's her trouble. Like me!' He flexed his muscles once or twice and patted the mule affectionately on the muzzle. 'Poor old Mireille! Never mind. We understand each other, don't we? Hein?'

Mireille rolled her eyes at him and essayed a tentative snap at his fingers, but without much decision. Vaska slapped her across the buttocks and laughed uproariously. 'That's right,' he said. 'Good old girl!' Mireille now suffered him to strap onto her the remaining pieces of luggage, all except our valises and the gramophone.

'I've rung up the taxi,' Vaska told us. 'It'll be along in a minute.' He unslung a haversack from his back and handed it to Armstrong. 'You better take this,' he said. 'It'll be safe with you,' and winking with an air of great secrecy, added: 'Take care of it – it's very important!'

Armstrong nodded understandingly and slung the haversack over his shoulder. A tremendous tooting from further down the road announced the arrival of the taxicab. Rocking and jolting from side to side, it advanced precariously down the empty street, the horn sounding furiously, as though to clear a passage through dense crowds. It shuddered to a standstill beside us, the engine expiring with a cough as if it had conked out altogether.

Vaska assisted the decrepit driver to gather up our belongings and stow them inside. This operation took some time as Vaska was obliged in the middle of it to foil an attempt on the part of Mireille to lie down and roll over in the middle of the road. A further delay ensued while the engine was coaxed again into life, but finally we got under way, Vaska waving and shouting: 'See you later!'

Our displacement took place in a series of jerks. Then the taxi gathered speed, bouncing crazily up and down over pits and craters in the roadway. Inside we were tossed about like peas in a can. Our valises slid to and fro across the floor of the cab. A cold wind blew in on us through a broken pane. The taxi rattled on towards open country. The driver honked his horn unceasingly.

About a mile up the road we came to a halt, so abruptly that I thought an accident had occurred. The taxi gave a convulsive shiver and stopped dead, its wheels embedded in a rut. The driver climbed down and pulled the door open with a flourish, spilling us out, breathless and shaken, into the road.

'Voilà messieurs,' he said.

I said: 'Are we here already?' It didn't look like it. We were standing on a barren stretch of rubble, ending in a barrier marked by a red lamp and a sign which said: 'ROUTE BARREE'. The forest brooded dark and menacing above us.

'Fifteen francs,' the driver said.

'That's too much,' Armstrong said.

'It's my price.'

'It's daylight robbery,' Armstrong said in English. He asked me: 'What's the French for daylight robbery?'

I translated: 'Monsieur says you are a bandit.'

'Peut-être bien.' The driver was unconcerned. He held out a clawlike hand for the money. Armstrong gave him a twenty franc note. The driver put it in his pocket and muttered 'Merci bien.'

'The change,' Armstrong said.

'I have no change.'

'Have you got any?' Armstrong asked me.

I searched through my pockets. 'No.' The driver grinned at us in toothless triumph.

'Vous êtes un bandit,' Armstrong told him.

The driver shrugged his shoulders up very slowly and smiled. 'Ah bah! Faut bien vivre.'

'I don't see the necessity,' I told him.

We left the old ruffian struggling to start the engine and took a few steps forward, carrying the luggage.

'What happens now?' I asked.

'We've got to walk. The new road's not finished yet.'

'How far?'

'About three miles through the forest. I know the way.'

'En avant, then.'

5

We plodded in single file along the path, the valises weighing down our arms. A wind had sprung up, shaking the tree-tops. It struck cold through my thin trousers. Armstrong, accustomed to hacking his way through the jungles of New Guinea, plunged without hesitation into a sort of thicket; branches snapped back into my face as I followed behind. We emerged from the trees onto a narrow track skirting a cliff. Foothold was very insecure. Sometimes the brashy soil crumbled away from us, a few loosened rocks bumping down the steep slope behind. Carrying the suitcases further impeded progress.

'This is bloody,' I said. 'How far now?'

'A fair stretch,' Armstrong said cheerfully. He advanced ahead, planting his feet carefully down along the edge of the cliff. I followed without enthusiasm. Suddenly Armstrong gave a startled cry. His foot had slipped on a loose stone. He lost his balance, let go of his valise, and clutched with both hands at the grass bank above. His legs slid from under him, dangling over the cliffside. I parked my luggage and dashed forward to help him. I got hold of his shoulders and managed to haul him up onto the path again, where he stood clinging to a projecting tree-stump and cursing. A portion of the path had fallen away altogether under his weight: it crashed down in a miniature avalanche over the cliff: our valises were now islanded away from us on the further side, with a sheer drop in between.

Armstrong recovered his calm almost immediately. 'That was a near thing, by God,' he said.

'What are we going to do now?' I asked him.

Armstrong took stock of the situation. We were now standing on a thin ledge of rock which might at any moment collapse beneath us. The path joining onto this also appeared extremely unsafe. Neither of us felt inclined to proceed under such conditions. On the other hand we couldn't stand on the ledge all night.

Already I fancied I could feel it crumbling. There was also the problem of recovering our luggage to be considered.

But these dilemmas were speedily solved for us. A pattering of feet along the path heralded the appearance of several uncouth shapes dressed in blue dungarees. A combination of guttural sounds and outlandish grunts emanated explosively from them. Two of these figures leapt lightly over the gap: Armstrong and I found ourselves unceremoniously seized and propelled from behind along the path into safety on the other side. We stood in a clearing ringed round by dark savage faces, some of them wildly bearded. More shapes loomed up out of the gathering gloom: our valises and the gramophone were dumped down beside us.

A furious babble of sound, accompanied by excited gestures, broke out in answer to our bewildered thanks. Brown hands plucked at our clothing: the white ducks and solar topis were examined with fierce astonishment. To a spectator we would undoubtedly have presented the picture of two explorers ambushed, in the course of an expedition, by an aboriginal horde: our clothes lent colour to this impression.

A tall man with a ragged black beard cleared a space around him by hurling back the others, and confronted us, one hand raised impressively to command silence. The chattering subsided immediately: this seemed to be the spokesman, a person of some importance. Like the others he wore dungarees; a béret basque was perched incongruously on his woolly head. He tapped himself on the chest and said in a deep growl: 'Moi – Mahmoud!'

I acknowledged this introduction and answered him in French. Mahmoud shook his head. The personal pronoun had apparently exhausted his knowledge of the language. A flood of grating gutturals poured from him. I shook my head in turn and tried again in English. The tall man grew impatient. He flashed his teeth and pointed angrily to the cliff. The others crowded round again, gibbering and gesticulating at us. Things seemed to have taken a threatening turn. I fully expected to have our throats cut at any moment. There was a sheath knife in the spokesman's belt that I didn't much like the look of. No other weapons were in view, but the others doubtless bristled with arms under their clothing.

I looked round at Armstrong. He was calmly engaged in lighting a cigarette. When he had got it well alight, he screwed it down to his holder, smiled lazily at the tall man and held out his cigarette-case. The tall man took one, barking out a word of thanks in his own tongue. To my surprise Armstrong immediately replied in the same language. The tall man threw up his hands in delight. He let loose a torrent of words, clapping Armstrong on the shoulders and laughing. Armstrong turned and pointed up into the forest: he seemed to be asking the way. The tall man's face darkened. He shook his head and pointed in the opposite direction. The others all joined in with advice at this point and were hushed peremptorily. The tall man took Armstrong earnestly by the arm. He appeared to be urging some course upon him. Armstrong smilingly demurred. The tall man stepped back and jerked his knife from its sheath. I thought our last hour had come. Then he sprang suddenly forward, grappling some unseen adversary and stabbing viciously with the knife into thin air. At the same time his face, reverted in Armstrong's direction, nodded up and down, the mouth opening to emit a blood-curdling howl. He stabbed with his knife once more and straightened up with the gesture of one flinging a limp body away from him. He slapped the knife into its sheath and crossed over triumphantly to Armstrong. The violent pantomime was evidently at an end. It appeared to be the description of some scene which had been previously enacted. Armstrong nodded once or twice. The tall man rolled up his sleeve and pointed to a scar on his bare arm as though to clinch the argument.

Armstrong turned to me. He said: 'These men are Algerians employed to make the new road. They say the woods are very dangerous after dark. Infested with wolves. This man Mahmoud was attacked by one. He killed it after a struggle.'

13

Mahmoud had got the gist of this translation. He nodded vigorously and invited me in dumb show to examine the scar on his arm. It had been a long jagged wound. I nodded and said to Armstrong: 'So what?'

'They want us to spend the night with them in the canteen.'

'I'd sooner risk the wolves.'

'So would I on the whole.'

Armstrong turned back and interpreted our decision to the tall man. They argued for some time. The tall man, Mahmoud, glared and gestured furiously in my direction. He was obviously denouncing me as an imbecile. Armstrong smiled but remained firm. At last the tall man, after a final terrific protest, abandoned the argument. He gave us up, with a sweeping dramatic gesture of disgust, to the wolves. The other Algerians watched the scene, huddled gloomily together in groups. They had lost interest in us. Armstrong produced from an inside pocket his notecase. At sight of this all the Algerians, except Mahmoud, again became galvanised. They executed an excited dance around Armstrong, uttering shrill cries. I personally thought that Armstrong had made a false move. Now, I expected, we would surely be murdered.

Armstrong took two ten-franc notes from his notecase and tendered them with a smile to Mahmoud. This latter, standing haughtily apart, waved the money away. He was offended at having his advice rejected. Persuading him to accept the twenty francs took some time, but it was eventually accomplished. Mahmoud stuffed the notes into his shirt and nodded a curt goodbye. He spoke a few words of farewell to Armstrong but did not say anything to me at all. Marshalling his men around him, he strode away with a dignified gait into the forest. The trees swallowed them up. The clamour of their voices faded gradually to silence.

I took out a handkerchief and mopped my forehead. 'We're well out of that, anyway,' I said to Armstrong.

'We weren't in any danger.'

'I'm not so sure. When you got out the notecase I thought we were done for.'

'Oh no. I understand these fellows. They're fundamentally honest.'

'That's fine,' I said. 'And now for the wolves.'

Picking up the suitcases again we trudged on through the trees. It had now become quite dark. There was no moon as yet and the air was very cold. I felt myself shivering. In these circumstances our sun helmets and white drill appeared actively silly. I hoped Fou Châlet was not too far away, as hunger was also beginning to make itself felt. We stumbled on across rough ground, tripping over the roots of trees. Suddenly Armstrong stopped in his tracks and looked wildly around him.

'My God!' he said. 'The dope!'

'What dope?'

'The dope for Spider.' He said: 'It was in the haversack that Vaska gave me. Now I haven't got the haversack.'

'Where is it then?'

'I must have dropped it over the cliff.'

We looked at each other for a moment in silence. There was obviously nothing to be done. To return and hunt for the haversack was quite out of the question.

Armstrong said: 'My God. Spider'll be furious.'

'What kind of dope is it?' I asked.

'Morphine. About a month's supply. He can't get it up here.'

'That's certainly awkward,' I said.

'Awkward? He'll go off his head.'

'As bad as that?'

'He's got the habit.'

'Well,' I said, 'It can't be helped.'

'I suppose not, but still. It's damned awkward.'

'Yes.'

6

We came safely through the forest without encountering any wolves. Once I heard what I thought was one, but Armstrong identified this as an owl. The trees thinned out into marshy meadows; we walked knee-deep in tall grass that rustled with the movements of invisible reptiles. Armstrong said: 'Ware snakes.' Moisture soaked up from the ground through the rope soles of my canvas shoes. I was cold and hungry.

At last, over a ragged hedge running the length of the field, the pointed roof of a wooden building showed, and pointing at this Armstrong said: 'Fou Châlet.'

We toiled up a slope towards it, lugging the valises. The châlet, as we approached it, seemed much smaller than I had expected. Its exterior was unimpressive. A light showed in a long window on the ground floor. I hoped to God they had got a meal ready.

Armstrong set down his suitcases and banged on the door, at the same time shouting: 'Open in the name of the law!'

Feet shuffled across the floor inside. The door was unbarred and flung open, rattling on rusty hinges. Spider himself stood revealed in the opening, a tall gangling figure dressed as usual in stiff black. Words of vociferous welcome bubbled up out of his fan-shaped beard of a pre-war Frenchman.

'Armstrong!' he shouted. 'You old devil! You too, Christopher,' he added, grasping my hand. 'Come inside!'

He put his hands on our shoulders and drew us both in through the doorway. It opened directly into what appeared to be the living-room. A long wooden table ran down the length of this, cluttered up with packs of cards and chips and counters. Gambling of some sort had evidently been in progress, but the room apart from ourselves was now empty. An oil-lamp standing on the table provided the only illumination, its glass funnel clouded with smoke. It smelled powerfully. A wooden staircase, built into the centre of the room, wound upwards into the darkness above.

Spider said: 'I thought you'd got lost. We were about to organise a search-party. I'm glad you found your way all right!'

He stood by the table, grinning at us: a single tooth gleamed out from the tangle of his beard. In view of his appearance, the apparently authentic nature of his Oxford accent gave one a distinct shock at first meeting.

'You're looking very well, Spider,' Armstrong said. 'You look younger than ever.'

Spider laughed and waved his hand. He said: 'But you must both be famished. I'll get you some food.'

These words struck a responsive chord in me. Spider limped across the room, his shadow wavering fantastically on the wall behind him. He threw open a door at the far end that led to the kitchen. A blast of hot air came out of it and Vaska was revealed, tucking into a meal at the kitchen table. He waved to us and called out something cheerfully, his mouth full of food.

'Raoul!' Spider shouted. 'Raoul!'

An answering call came back from the kitchen: 'Oui msieu!'

'They've arrived,' Spider said. 'You can dish up now.'

'Bien msieu,' the answer came back.

Spider returned, his left foot, encased in a thick-soled surgical boot, dragging along the floor. He said: 'The others have gone to bed. They retire early because of the children.'

'Children?' I said.

'Yes, we have four staying with us, including my own Marie.'

I was vaguely relieved at hearing this. The presence of children at the châlet seemed to preclude the chance of any orgies such as Spider might otherwise have been expected to indulge in. It looked as if we were going to have a peaceful time after all.

'How is the ghost, Spider?' Armstrong asked.

Spider shook his head. 'I never hear it,' he said.

'Is the châlet haunted?' I said.

'It's supposed to be.'

'I've always wanted to see a ghost.'

'You won't see this one,' Armstrong said. 'You can only hear it.'

'What form does it take? Clanking chains? Or just things that go bump in the night?'

'It's footsteps,' Armstrong said.

Spider said: 'Everyone hears them but me. It's really most amazing.'

Raoul, a boy of about seventeen, now came in from the kitchen with the food. It was some kind of ragoût, that smelt pretty good. Raoul started to clear a space at one end of the table. He was a typical Niçois from the Old Town, with a cheerful cheeky face and black oiled hair. I'd often seen him hanging about the Music Box in Nice with other corner-boys of the same type, or trying to peer round the screens they put up outside the Savoy when outdoor dancing was in progress. That's probably where Spider picked him up.

We started to eat while Spider grinned at us from the other side of the table.

'What made you so late?' he asked. 'We expected you hours ago.'

Armstrong said: 'We were delayed on the way up. For one thing I nearly fell over the cliff. Some Algerians rescued us. It all took time.'

Spider said: 'Those Algerians are pretty tough customers. They're always knifing one another for various reasons. It's a wonder they didn't hold you to ransom.'

'They're all right if properly handled,' Armstrong said. 'One's got to understand them.'

He added: 'That reminds me, Spider. The most awful thing. I don't quite know how to tell you.'

'What?'

'A haversack that Vaska gave me to look after.'

'You don't mean –'

'Yes.'

Spider now began to exhibit signs of alarm. About to help me with more stew, he stopped with the ladle suspended in mid-air, staring at Armstrong across the table.

He said: 'What about the haversack?'

'I'm frightfully sorry, old man...'

'Tell me! What has happened?'

'I've lost it.'

'Lost it?'

'Over the cliff.'

The ladle dropped from Spider's hand into the stew. Some of the gravy splashed up over the tablecloth. Spider started to rise to his feet. His mouth fell open. He leaned forward supporting himself with both hands on the tabletop. Twice he struggled to speak but his voice got caught up in his throat and no words came. At last he got out in a strangled whisper: 'You can't have lost it.'

'I'm most awfully sorry, old man,' Armstrong said again. Spider slammed his hand down on the table. With a contorted face he shouted: 'Sorry?' His eyes were starting out of his head. He swayed as if about to fall in a fit. Vaska loomed up in the kitchen doorway, the startled face of Raoul peering around his shoulder.

Spider put up a hand and wrenched at his stiff white collar. It came away in his fingers, the back stud broken off. He began to bawl blistering oaths in French, raising his clenched fist with the collar clutched in it. His English had given way altogether under the strain.

Armstrong sat stunned by the fury of this outburst. Vaska detached himself from the doorway and came lurching towards Spider. He put a hand on Spider's shoulder and tried to force him to sit down. Spider twisted furiously in his grasp, trying to get free. They struggled halfway across the room. Raoul gaped at them open-mouthed from the kitchen door. Somewhere upstairs a child started to cry. Spider struck Vaska heavily in the face. Vaska released him and took a step back, shaking his head. I wondered if he were about to employ the same methods that he had used in subduing the mule.

These proved unnecessary, however. Spider had shot his bolt. He now collapsed onto a chair and began to sob with a hard racking sound in his throat. Vaska stood by making soothing noises and patting him on the back.

Armstrong said: 'This is all most unfortunate. I wouldn't have had it happen for anything.'

Doors opened upstairs along the landing. There was a mutter of voices and someone started to descend the creaking stairs. The sound of the child crying mingled with Spider's sobs. A man's head wearing a woollen nightcap protruded over the banisters, looking down. A woman's voice enquired from above: 'Mais que se passe-t'il, donc?'

Vaska called up: 'Rien. Ne vous en faites pas, madame. Ce n'est rien!'

The nightcapped head withdrew, after a long curious look at Spider. Feet ascended the stairs again slowly and the woman could be heard again demanding in lower tones what was going on. A gruff rumble answered her and the door closed. The child continued to cry. So did Spider. Tears ran down his gaunt furrowed cheeks into his beard. He raised his head and said in a despairing wail: 'But what shall I do? What shall I do?'

Vaska said: 'It'll be all right, don't you worry, I'll go down in the morning first thing. We'll find it all right, you see!'

Spider shook his head. He refused to be comforted. He put his hands in his head and mumbled: 'It's no good, I'm done for. Foutu. Finished!'

'You'll be all right,' Vaska told him.

I couldn't help feeling that Armstrong had chosen a very bad time to announce the loss of the haversack. He should have waited until after we had finished eating. I was still damned hungry but to ask for a second helping in the present atmosphere would have seemed in bad taste, if not actually heartless. I wondered how long this scene was likely to continue. Already it appeared to me unendurably protracted. Spider had now stopped crying, but he still sat in the chair with his shoulders hunched up and his head in his hands. An occasional 'Foutu' issued from out of his beard. At last Vaska persuaded him to go to bed. Leaning heavily on Vaska's arm he limped towards the staircase with his head hanging down.

'Goodnight, old man,' Armstrong called out to him.

Spider muttered something in reply but without looking round at us. He had gone to pieces terribly. Vaska had to half carry him upstairs, his feet dragging from step to step. Raoul followed in the rear, to lend assistance if needed.

I said to Armstrong: 'For God's sake.'

'I feel terribly sorry about it,' Armstrong said.

'It wasn't your fault.'

'Of course it was.'

'Well,' I said, 'we won't argue the point.'

'Do you think we shall find the haversack?'

'No.'

'Neither do I.'

'Have some more to eat.'

'I'm not hungry.'

'Well, I am.'

I ladled out some more stew onto my plate. There was a little grease congealed on the top by now but it still looked good. I ate two more platefuls, dipping my bread into the gravy. Armstrong smoked cigarettes. He looked worried and slightly upset.

Vaska came downstairs again and crossed over to the table.

'How is he?' Armstrong asked.

'Pretty bad. Raoul's with him.'

'It's a rotten business,' Armstrong said.

'Yeah. I hope to Christ we find that dope.'

'So do I.'

'Is there anything else to eat?' I asked.

'There's some trifle,' Vaska said. He fetched it from the kitchen. I felt better when I had finished eating, but I'd become very tired. Vaska and Armstrong discussed the possibilities of finding the haversack. I stood up and said: 'I'm for bed.'

'I'll show you the way up,' Vaska said. He lit a candle from the lamp and took my suitcase in the other hand.

'Goodnight Christopher,' Armstrong said.

'Goodnight,' I said.

Vaska preceded me upstairs with the candle. A sound of sobbing came from behind Spider's door as we passed it. The other rooms were now quiet. The child had ceased altogether.

Vaska said: 'Your room's up here.'

'Up this ladder?'

'That's it.'

'Christ.'

'The others are all taken.'

The ladder was negotiated with some difficulty. We crawled through a trap door at the top into a kind of loft. Vaska opened a door onto a small room full of boxes and coils of rope. An iron bed stood in one corner of it. The moon had risen and shone bright through the barred window.

'Got all you want?' Vaska said.

'Yes I think so.'

'The lavatory's outside by the kitchen.'

'What about the bathroom?'

'There isn't one.'

This is the simple life all right, I thought. I sat down on the bed, which sagged alarmingly under me.

Vaska said: 'See you in the morning then.'

'That's right,' I said. When he'd gone I unpacked my pyjamas and got into bed straightaway. It wasn't so uncomfortable as I had expected, or perhaps I was too tired to care. There were no curtains on the windows and I turned over to keep the moon out of my eyes. I went to sleep at once. It had been an eventful day.

7

Raoul woke me in the morning with my hot water. The sun was shining in the window and the air was sharp and clear.

'How'd you sleep?' Raoul said.

'Like the dead.'

'D'you hear the ghost?'

'No. Did you?'

'No.'

'Where are the others?'

'Out looking for the dope. They've had breakfast.'

'What's the time?'

'Ten.'

'I'd better get up.'

'Righto.'

I washed and shaved quickly. The mountain air coming in through the window had given me an appetite. It was very excellent air. I felt really splendid. Looking back, the events of the night before seemed some sort of curious nightmare which the morning sun had dispelled. I put on a pullover and climbed down the ladder.

Downstairs in the living-room Armstrong's gramophone was playing 'Happy Days are Here Again'. A tall woman in crimson silk pyjamas stood beside it. She turned round as I came in and said with a brilliant smile: 'Good morning.' She spoke English with a Russian accent.

'Good morning,' I said, taken slightly aback. I hadn't expected anything like this. I examined her with interest.

She was thin but supple, with high pointed breasts and well defined buttocks. The crimson silk pyjamas outlined all that sufficiently. She had bold dark eyes bulging out brilliantly on either side of an aquiline nose. Her face was high-boned, tapering to a pointed chin above which her mouth was painted in a double curve of crimson lipstick. It was set in a flashing smile which in conjunction with her fierce intense stare gave her a rather rapacious expression. Her hair was dark with a bleached blonde streak in it.

She said: 'Since our host is absent we must introduce ourselves. I am Madame Mollinov.'

'I'm called Christopher.'

'Have you not another name?'

'Barrington-ffoulkes.'

'Barrington...?'

'ffoulkes. With two small 'f's.'

'It is not easy to pronounce.'

'No.'

'I shall call you Christophaire.'

'Please do.'

'My name is Véra.'

'You are Russian?'

'But yes.'

'I know many Russians.'

'On the Riviera it is difficult to avoid them.'

I laughed politely. Mme Mollinov said: 'I am serious. There are too many Russians along the Côte. Do you not think so?'

'I like them.'

'But still there are too many.'

'Perhaps a few.'

The gramophone started to run down. Mme Mollinov wound it up again and reversed the record. On the other side was 'Singing in the Rain'.

Mme Mollinov said: 'The gramophone is yours, yes?'

'No. It's Armstrong's.'

'The other Englishman? The big one?'

'Yes.'

'He is very fascinating.'

'Very.'

I wondered whether Armstrong reciprocated her feelings in this regard. It seemed unlikely. Mme Mollinov was the type of woman he disliked most. On the other hand I found her amusing.

Humming the tune she said: 'You like music?'

'Very much.'

'Dancing?'

'Yes.'

'When you have eaten we will dance.'

'With pleasure.'

Raoul came in with a pot of coffee and a large loaf of new bread. The coffee smelt alluring. I said: 'You will excuse me?'

'Of course.'

I sat down and started to eat, spreading fresh honey thick on the new bread. It went down well. The coffee was also excellent. Mme Mollinov, sitting on the other side of the table, said: 'You have good appetite.'

'It's the air.'

I went on eating ravenously. Mme Mollinov lit a Turkish cigarette which she smoked through an expanding cigarette-holder of alarming length. Some of the smoke blew across the table towards me. The gramophone played a tune called 'Coz I'm Ka-razy for You'. I finished my last cup of coffee and sat back feeling marvellous. It was the first time in many years that I had eaten breakfast. I had forgotten what it tasted like.

Mme Mollinov said: 'And now we will dance, if it does not interfere with your digestion.'

'No. I have an excellent digestion. I've been known to eat nails.'

'Nails?'

'It's a figure of speech.'

'You do not in reality eat nails?'

'Hardly ever. I was just joking.'

'Ah, a joke.'

Mme Mollinov shook her head back and laughed understandingly. She swayed lightly into my arms and we began to dance, while Raoul beat time on the table with the bread-board. He also kept the gramophone going so that we did not have to disentagle ourselves every five minutes to put on new records. Mme Mollinov pressed herself tightly against me as we danced. She did not feel as thin as she looked.

I said: 'It's a wonder we have not met before. In Nice.'

'I do not live in Nice. My home is in Paris.'

'And Monsieur Mollinov?'

'He is dead.'

A child's voice made itself suddenly heard outside, calling: 'Maman!'

'My little girl,' Mme Mollinov explained, detaching herself and turning to the door. A small swarthy child of about four suddenly burst into the house, calling out incontinently: 'Maman! I want to pi-pi!'

'Véra!' Mme Mollinov said, pretending to be shocked. She grimaced at me: 'Children are so indelicate.'

'Fais vite Maman!' little Véra said warningly.

Mme Mollinov took her hand and led her out through the kitchen, smiling back at me over her shoulder. Other children now came running in from outside. There were three of them. Two were quite small; the other, a thin undersized girl of about ten, was plainly Spider's daughter Marie. She stood staring at me with large mournful eyes, standing on one leg, and rubbed her foot against the other.

'Hullo,' I said to her.

'Hullo,' she said in French. 'You're an Englishman aren't you?'

'Yes.'

'Can you talk English?'

'Of course.'

'My papa talks English.'

'I know.'

Marie coughed explosively, with a hollow sound in her chest. I said: 'That's a nasty cold you've got.'

'It's not a cold. It's my lungs. My lungs are weak.' She coughed again and said: 'The air is good for them.'

'Yes.'

Her thin sharp face became flushed when she coughed. She did not really resemble Spider at all and yet there was something in the shape of her features that made their relationship obvious.

She said: 'The doctor says I should go to Switzerland. Papa can't afford it though.'

The other children, bored with this conversation, now began to tug at her frock, shouting: 'Come and play, Marie! Come and play?'

Marie said: 'You will pardon me, Monsieur?'

'Sure. Run along.'

They dashed out into the sunlight again, Marie coughing violently as she ran, with her thin knees knocking together. Véra scampered through the kitchen and joined them. Her mother came up and stood beside me in the doorway, looking out.

'That's sad about Marie,' I said.

'What?'

'Her lungs.'

'Yes. It is a tragedy.'

'Perhaps she will get better, though.'

'It is possible.'

I said: 'And these others? Are they yours also?'

'My God no. They belong to Mme Paillon.'

'Who is that?'

She pointed to two deck-chairs set out on the grass slope in front of us. They were turned so that I could not see the people in them.

Mme Mollinov said: 'They are French people. Very dull. I am glad that you have come. I was annoying myself before you came. Now I shall have company.'

'You certainly will.'

In front of us the green countryside sloped downwards to the valley and the village far below; above the hollow ran a chain of mountains capped with clouds; behind us rose the forest, of which Spider owned a few acres. The sun was dazzlingly bright but the air remained pleasant and cool.

A group of figures came into view, climbing the slope. It was Spider and the others, returning from their search for the dope. As they came nearer I guessed from their demeanour that the search had been successful, even before I could distinguish Spider waving the haversack in the air at me.

'They appear very excited,' Mme Mollinov said.

Marie had recognised her father and ran forward to embrace him. Armstrong and Vaska stopped to exchange a few words with the people in the deck-chairs. Spider limped on towards the house with one arm around Marie and the other triumphantly holding up the haversack.

'We found it! We found it!' he was yelling.

'Thank God for that,' I said.

Mme Mollinov and I went forward to meet them.

'Were the contents intact?' I asked.

'All the phials unbroken. It was caught up in a tree. A miracle!' Spider said, giving an insane cackle of laughter and slapping my shoulder. He seemed quite drunk with elation. Mme Mollinov aimed an enticing smile at Armstrong, who came up looking very British in a brown tweed jacket and white flannel trousers. Spider, waving the haversack, went on into the house to break the good news to Raoul. Vaska, winking at me, followed him in. Marie plunged off to play with the other children.

Mme Mollinov said: 'You must present me to your friend, Christophaire. We have not yet been introduced.'

'I'm sorry. Mr Armstrong, Mme Mollinov.'

'How d'you do.'

Mme Mollinov held out her hand in such a way that Armstrong had no alternative but to kiss it. She smiled ravishingly at him but had no time to get really started before we were again interrupted by the child Véra, whose demands this time were of an even more urgent nature than before. Slightly annoyed, Mme Mollinov led her off into the house.

Armstrong said: 'I don't envy your taste.'

'How?'

'Taking up with that tart.'

'Don't you like her?'

'I'm surprised that you do.'

'She has so few inhibitions.'

'That's a mild way of putting it.'

'She is a bit of a man-eater,' I admitted.

'She'll have you swallowed up in no time.'

'Not me. I'm too tough.'

Vaska came out of the house carrying an enormous bucket and joined us.

'How is Spider now?' Armstrong asked him.

'Fine. He's just taken a shot. He'll be okay by lunchtime.'

'How'd he first take to it?' I asked.

'After his operation,' Vaska said. 'Doctor gave it to him to stop the pain and then he got the habit.'

'They all say that.'

'It's true of Spider. He's all messed-up inside. His tripes are held together with cat-gut.'

'Well I'm glad he got the dope back, anyhow.'

'So am I,' Armstrong said, 'You know I felt awfully bad about that.'

'He'll be right as rain now,' Vaska said.

Armstrong said: 'My God here's that woman again.'

We watched Mme Mollinov approaching from the house. She came down the slope in a graceful sinuous swagger, her hips swinging and her head held high.

Vaska said: 'She's a hot number all right.' He winked at us and walked off carrying the bucket and whistling. He was going to fetch water from the stream. Mme Mollinov, coming level with us, stared after him admiringly.

'What a beautiful boy that is,' she said.

'Not quite how I should describe him,' Armstrong said.

'Beau garçon. Il est beau garçon.'

'You think so?'

'Don't you?'

'Please don't insinuate,' Armstrong said.

Mme Mollinov laughed. 'He has a beautiful body,' she said. 'So male.'

'His sex is certainly not in doubt.'

Mme Mollinov laughed again, but with less confidence this time. She was beginning to find Armstrong a puzzler. He didn't react in the right way.

He said: 'You are interested in the male body, Mme Mollinov?'

'Only as an artist.'

'Are you an artist?'

'Just a little.'

'Mr Armstrong is a writer,' I said. 'He has written a book.'

'But, how interesting. What is the title?'

'*Phallic Fetish*.'

'I must read it.'

Armstrong said: 'I am sorry I haven't a copy here at the moment. You would find the photographs most edifying.'

He smiled slowly as he said this, but his smile did not make the words any the less insulting. I could see that he had taken a definite dislike to Mme Mollinov. He turned and left us at once, walking off towards the house. We watched him go in, stooping his head under the lintel of the door. Mme Mollinov frowned slightly.

She said: 'He is a great friend of yours, yes?'

'I've known him for years.'

'A very great friend perhaps?'

'Not in the way you mean.'

Mme Mollinov said: 'But he has particular morals, no?'

'Not at all.'

'You are sure?'

'Absolutely.'

Mme Mollinov shook her head, unconvinced. Like many women of her type she was obsessed by the idea of homosexuality and ready to suspect any man of it who did not show immediate signs of being attracted to her.

'And you?' she asked.

'And me what?'

'Vous n'en êtes pas?'

'No.'

Mme Mollinov squeezed my arm. 'Do not be angry if I wondered... there are so many these days. It is difficult to tell.'

'Yes.'

'I am glad.' She gave my arm another squeeze. 'I am glad you are not like that.'

'Shall we take a walk through the woods?'

'Perhaps later. Now I must go and dress.'

She patted my hand, smiled at me quickly with a sidelong glance, and went on up the slope, still walking with that slight swagger as though she were wearing very high-heeled shoes.

After a while I followed her indoors. Armstrong beckoned me from the window of his room on the ground floor. His room opened off the living-room. He sat down on the edge of the bed and lay back with his arms behind his head.

'How's the intrigue getting along?' he asked.

'You were pretty rude to her.'

'I can't stand that kind of woman.'

'She thinks you're *so*.'

'I don't give a damn.' He lay back smoking calmly with his cigarette-holder pointed up to the ceiling.

I said: 'This is a better room than mine.'

'Where've they put you?'

'In the loft.'

'What!'

'It's up a ladder.'

'Good God. We can't have that. What are they thinking of?'

'It isn't so bad really.'

'I'll speak to Spider after lunch. He's no idea of how to treat a guest. I'll get him to shove another bed in here.'

'No, don't bother. It's quite all right.'

'My dear fellow, I insist.'

Through the window the voices of the children floated up faintly to us, calling out to each other.

'What d'you think Mme Mollinov is doing here?' I said.

'Can't place her. Perhaps she's blackmailing Spider.'

'Or she might be after the plans.'

'They're a queer lot.'

'I haven't met the French people.'

'They don't seem to fit in either.'

'Funny.'

'I expect they're lending Spider money.'

'It's possible.'

8

I met the Paillons at lunch. They were a typical French bourgeois couple. M. Paillon was a thickset middle-aged man with grey hair and a shaggy grey moustache. It was his head that I had seen the night before, protruding over the banisters and wearing a woollen nightcap. His wife was thin and had a worried expression. At lunch she attended exclusively to the food on her plate, in the intervals of attempting to coax her children to eat up their cabbage. All the children sat down to table with us, and only Marie was able to eat without assistance. Little Véra, whose existence seemed to centre solely round the needs of nature, required frequent attention on the part of her mother.

Mme Mollinov had changed into a flowered frock without sleeves and her face was freshly painted. She talked with great animation to everyone, even managing to make eyes at, and flirt with, M. Paillon. Armstrong she ignored, however.

Spider sat at the head of the table in really terrific form, his eyes with their pin-point pupils sparkling from under shaggy eyebrows. His beard had been combed out and he had a new stiff white shirt collar on. He drank heavily and I began to be a bit nervous. I didn't know how well morphine and wine mixed. He kept pressing Armstrong and I to fill our glasses. The wine was white and sweet. It was called Camp Romain and Spider had provided it specially for Armstrong. The Paillons drank only Vichy. Mme Mollinov drank water and ate a tomato salad. She was on some sort of diet. I ate pretty well myself: I was hungry.

Raoul, who did the waiting, cleared away the dessert and served coffee. At once an outcry arose from the Paillon children.

'Papa! Papa! Le p'tit cochon!' they demanded.

M. Paillon smiled fondly. He took a small china pig from his pocket and set it down on the table. All the children became very excited, except Marie, who sat smiling wearily and with her hands folded, in an attitude of faint tolerance.

M. Paillon said to Spider: 'Vous permettez?'

Spider made an expansive gesture of assent which just missed knocking the wine bottle over. M. Paillon said: 'You will excuse me Mme Mollinov?' He explained: 'It is perhaps a little rude. Un peu polisson.'

Mme Mollinov gave her consent graciously and everyone craned forward to watch as M. Paillon struck a match and applied it to the little pig's behind. A puff of smoke was ignited and a strip of black paper curled out from under the pig's tail and dropped onto the table-cloth, to represent excrement. The children clapped their hands and crowed.

Little Véra exclaimed: 'Caca! Caca!' recognising immediately a familiar element in her daily life. She danced about in delight. Spider roared with laughter and slapped his hand down on the table. He tossed from side to side in his chair shouting: 'Ah ça, c'est inouï! C'est marrant, ça!'

Armstrong was deeply disgusted. He did not laugh at all and muttered to me behind his hand: 'We shall have the children doing it on the table next.'

M. Paillon now proceeded to do a series of tricks with matches, some of which were in questionable taste. He cocked an apologetic eye occasionally towards Mme Mollinov, but she did not seem to mind very much, and Spider continued to laugh and applaud extravagantly.

When M. Paillon had exhausted his repertoire, Raoul started to clear the table. I made an excuse and went up to my room. I felt I needed a rest. The food weighed heavy on my stomach. I hadn't had such a big meal for months. In Nice it was always too hot to eat much.

I lay down on the bed and started to read *Vile Bodies*. I read up to the part where the motor-racing takes place, while terrific detonations from outside periodically shook the house. It was the Algerians dynamiting rocks to make the new road.

My stomach continued to feel queasy, and after a while I went downstairs to look for the lavatory. There was no one about at all and the house was very quiet. I went through to the kitchen and out to the lavatory. In front of this, our old friend Mireille was tethered, cropping grass. She lifted her head and gave me a baleful look as though daring me to approach nearer. It seemed as though she would only allow me to pass into the lavatory over her dead body. There was nothing for it: I made my way quickly into the wood behind the châlet.

Returning later I came upon Mme Mollinov, encamped with an easel in front of the house. She was engaged in painting the view. A small canvas was already clotted with masses of blue and green. It was too early yet to predict what form the picture might finally take, or to say whether or not Mme Mollinov possessed any great talent. Standing beside her I managed to make the appropriate admiring noises, however. Mme Mollinov laughed. She had changed her clothes again and now wore a green sun-bathing top and shorts. Her body, though thin, was well-rounded in the right places and richly bronzed.

I said: 'You have a very nice tan.'

'You think so?'

'I always peel, myself. Bright red patches. Most unsightly.'

'That is because you are so blond.'

'Probably.'

'Englishmen are always blond.'

'Not always. Armstrong isn't blond.'

'I do not like Mr Armstrong. I always like men blond. That is because I am so dark.'

'No doubt.'

She said: 'Tonight after dinner, we will take a walk together, yes? You would like that?'

'Very much.'

'So.'

She smiled at me and I went back inside again. I thought I really must write a letter to Yvonne. Up in my room I started on this task but the words would not come easily. I looked out of the window and watched Mme Mollinov sitting at her easel, painting. I wondered if life at Fou Châlet was going to be as simple as I anticipated.

9

That evening, after dinner, we all played baccara and Spider won quite a lot of money. He was very elated at this, and explained to us an infallible system which he had perfected and which he proposed to try out at the Casino during the following season, if he could manage to get together the necessary capital. He looked at us all meaningly and added that anyone who cared to act as his partner in this enterprise could be sure of substantial profits. The suggestion was received in silence, and Spider shook his head sorrowfully. He could see a fortune sliding out of his grasp.

In the kitchen Vaska and Raoul were playing some complicated gambling game of their own. They quarrelled frequently over the score, but Vaska put an end to all argument by thumping the table with his fist and scooping up the money, which he then shovelled into his pockets. Raoul could be heard muttering sulkily to himself, but he did not raise any active objection and the cards were dealt out for another round. The kitchen door was open, and the heat which came out from the stove was terrific.

Mme Mollinov, who had been fanning herself furiously for some time, now rose and tugged at the outer door. She got it open and the flame of the oil stove on the table shot up in the draught, flickering and smoking over the top of the funnel.

Standing in the doorway Mme Mollinov said: 'It is a wonderful night.'
I said: 'Shall we go for our walk now?'
'Why not.'
She ran upstairs to look for a wrap. Armstrong, sitting at the table smoking through his holder, grinned and raised his eyebrows at me. Spider continued to expound his system to M. Paillon, who listened stolidly, stroking his moustache, while Mme Paillon, who had not joined in the baccara, did some knitting. Mme Mollinov came downstairs with a wrap on.

'What about your child?' I said.

'She is asleep.'

We went out. After the heat in the living-room the night air struck very cold and Mme Mollinov shivered slightly as we walked up through the pine trees behind the house. The moon had risen, an enormous yellow globe shining down on the valley. It was a really tremendous moon.

Mme Mollinov stumbled over something and took my arm. She said: 'They tell me there are wolves in the forest. You will protect me if we are attacked?'

'Of course.'

I slipped my arm round her to give tangible assurance of protection. She laughed and said: 'But perhaps you are yourself a wolf, no?'

'And you are little Red Riding Hood?'

'Please?'

'It is an English fairy-tale. A fable.'

'Ah so.'

It was very quiet in the wood. The smell of pine needles mingled pleasantly with Mme Mollinov's scent. We walked on together with the moon shining down on us through the tree-trunks. I said: 'Then you are afraid of me?'

'No.'

'That isn't very complimentary.'

'Why should I be afraid of you?' She opened her eyes very wide at me. In the yellow light of the moon the make-up on her face looked purple.

'I am very dangerous' I told her.

'You are a nice boy.'

'Not so nice and not a boy.'

'Yes. You are a nice-looking boy. Beau garçon. You know that?'

'I've been told so.'

'By many women?'

'One or two.'

'You are conceited, also.'

'Not a bit.'

'Oh yes. You are very conceited.'

'Have it your own way.'

'I am sure that you have many women.'

'No.'

'I do not like to be one of many.'

'No one suggested that you should.'

We had stopped walking now but I still had my arm around her.

She said: 'But why do we quarrel? A night like this was not made for quarrelling.'

'What was it made for then?'

She touched me on the arm. 'You are not angry with me, no?'

'Of course I'm not.'

'You are sure?'

'Yes.'

I drew her closer to me and bent my head to kiss her. It proved to be a long kiss but her mouth, large and cool, remained closed. She drew away and said: 'Now we are friends again, yes?'

'Of course.'

'More than friends?'

'Perhaps.'

'Let us sit down.'

We sat on a rotting tree-trunk by the side of the path. After a moment she said: 'You are very passionate for an Englishman.'

'Am I?'

'I had not expected you to be like this.'

'What did you expect?'

'Kiss me again. No, not like that.'

'Why not?'

'I do not like to kiss like that. It is not hygienic.'

'How silly.'

'No, not like that.'

'I insist.'

'Just once then.'

' . . .'

Mme Mollinov let her head fall on my shoulder and sighed. I sat with my arm around her watching the moon between the trees. It was deep yellow and simply terrifically large. An outsize in moons. I was reminded of another night with Yvonne, in the woods above the boulevard Tsarevitch. I wondered what she was doing now.

Mme Mollinov opened her eyes and said: 'What are you thinking of?'

'You.'

'No. You were thinking of somebody else.'

'I do sometimes. It's my unselfish nature.'

'Another girl?'

'No.'

'You were! I am sure you were.'

'Kiss me.'

'I will not kiss you while you think of another girl.'

'Don't be silly.'

'What is her name? Is she a Russian?'

'No. An Eskimo.'

'An Eskimo?'

'She lives on candles and blubber.'

'Now you are joking me.'

'Yes.'

'But seriously, you have another girl?'

'Only you.'

'Dar-ling.'

She put her arms round my neck. Some time passed. Mme Mollinov said: 'No, you must not do that.'

'Why shouldn't I?'

'Your hand is cold.'

'I was trying to keep it warm.'

'You men are all the same. You want only our bodies. You do not want our souls.'

'Let's not talk about our souls.'

'You want only the body. That is not love.'

'Nobody said it was.'

'You do not love me then?'

'Yes I do.'

'You do not love me at all.'

'All right.'

'Do not be angry.'

'You were angry, not I.'

'Kiss me dar-ling. Say you love me.'

'I love you.'

'Dar-ling. Good-night, dar-ling. We must go in now.'

'Already?'

'It is late and I am cold.'

'Righto.'

Saying goodnight satisfactorily took a long time, but we arrived back at the châlet at last. Everyone had gone to bed and the living-room was in darkness. Mme Mollinov kissed me again quickly and ran upstairs.

I was groping around for a candle when the door of Armstrong's room opened and he appeared swinging a big stick threateningly in his hand.

'Oh it's you. I thought it was the ghost.'

'Why the stick?'

'I'd have beaned you in another minute. What are you doing in the dark?'

'Looking for a candle to get upstairs with.'

'You're in here now. I had your things shifted.'

'Thank God for that.'

I went past Armstrong into his room. It had two beds in it now and my luggage had been brought down. Several ferocious-looking insects had managed to penetrate the barred window and were now climbing the walls and depending from the ceiling. Armstrong looked at me and laughed.

'What's the joke?'

'Look at your face.'

'Lipstick?'

'You look like the rue de Lappe.' Armstrong, who was wearing green silk pyjamas, lay down on his bed and lit another cigarette.

The room was lit by an oil-lamp smaller but less smelly than the one in the living-room. Armstrong said: 'How was it?'

I finished wiping the lipstick off my face and said: 'Not so bad.'

'You'll get in a mess with that woman.'

'I doubt it.'

'Wait and see.'

10

I'd been asleep for about ten minutes when something woke me. I opened my eyes and did not at first realise where I was until I saw Armstrong sitting up in the other bed.

'Listen!' he said.

Heavy footsteps were descending the ramshackle wooden staircase. The treads shook under them and a board cracked sharply.

'The ghost!' Armstrong said. 'Come on!'

He took a large electric torch from under his pillow and jumped out of bed. I followed suit, blinking and rather cross. I thought what fools we should look if it proved to be merely Spider on his way to the lavatory.

On the other hand the footsteps did not limp. Still, it might be Vaska, or M. Paillon. The footsteps were too heavy for anyone else in the house. They came to the bottom of the stairs and began to cross the floor in the direction of the outer door.

The moon was shining brilliantly in through our bedroom window. Armstrong advanced on tiptoe to the door and stood there with his stick in one hand and the torch in the other. He waited until the footsteps paused directly outside and then threw open the door, at the same time pressing the button of his torch.

A beam of light clicked on across the living-room, but looking over Armstrong's shoulder I could see no one at all. Armstrong flashed his torch round the room. It revealed the long table, the scattered chips and unemptied ashtrays, the gramophone and the grandfather clock. Except for these inanimate objects the room was quite empty.

Armstrong went out and tried the outer door. It was still locked as I had left it when I came in. In any case no one could conceivably have escaped from it in such a short space of time. Whoever had caused the footsteps must have been standing directly outside our bedroom when Armstrong opened the door.

We looked at each other in silence, absolutely dumbfounded. Then Armstrong said: 'That was the ghost all right.'

'I don't see what else it could have been.'

I discovered that I was shivering. The floor was icy cold on the soles of my bare feet.

Armstrong said: 'We may as well go back to bed now.'

'Supposing it returns?'

'It only walks once a night.'

He closed the door again and climbed back into bed. He went to sleep almost at once, but I did not find it so easy. I lay awake for some time listening for a repetition of the footsteps; but apparently Armstrong was right, for the remainder of the night passed undisturbed.

Next morning I had a letter from Yvonne, forwarded from my flat and dated a week before. I read it sitting up in bed while eating my breakfast.

Armstrong, who was also having breakfast in bed, had received several letters. The longest of these was written in a large sprawling script on sheets of a very brilliant blue paper, and Armstrong frowned thoughtfully as he read it, sucking at his cigarette-holder.

Yvonne's letter was also long, having been completed in several sections, each bearing its own date and the last one written in pencil. It was clear from the tone of this that Yvonne was getting impatient. She was evidently not prepared to continue our relationship on its present basis without some sort of definite understanding, if not an actual engagement. That was her convent upbringing reasserting itself. She finished up with a threatening bit about a major who danced quite divinely and who was staying at the same house-party as herself.

I tossed the letter over to Armstrong. 'What d'you make of this?'

'Yvonne?'

'Yes.'

'Mine's from that Canadian girl.'

'Let's have a look.'

'Here you are.'

The Canadian girl wrote in violet ink and her letter itself was quite extraordinarily purple. It was eight pages in length, the last one almost completely covered with small crosses, representing kisses. She signed herself 'Your ever-loving Laura.'

I said: 'I'd like to meet her someday.'

'You're welcome. In the meantime Mme Mollinov will keep you occupied.'

'I've no doubt she will.'

Armstrong said: 'I suppose you'll marry Yvonne eventually.'

'I can't make up my mind.'

In the living-room the gramophone started up suddenly. It must have been Mme Mollinov who set it going, as a sort of signal that she was up and about, because shortly afterwards I saw her pass the window in her sun-bathing top, carrying her easel and making for the woods behind the house.

I got out of bed and started to wash with the hot water which Raoul had brought in at the same time as the breakfast. Armstrong said: 'Tally-ho. The hunt is up.' I left him in bed, smoking and finishing the remains of the Keiller's marmalade, and went out through the kitchen, where Vaska was stoking the furnace with big blocks of pine wood.

I found Mme Mollinov up in the forest, sitting on a camp stool and with a new canvas, also unfinished, propped up on her easel. She did not turn round though she had obviously heard me approaching, and I bent down and kissed her bare shoulder. Her skin was very smooth and warm where the sun, shining down through the trees, had caught it. She leaned back her head and put her cheek against mine, but when I went to kiss her she said: 'No.'

'Why not?'

'It is too early for that. Also I have been very angry with you.'

'Angry?'

'You are a very naughty boy. You did not come to say good morning to me.'

'I was in bed.'

'You are a lazy boy.'

'Not at all. The ghost kept me awake half the night.'

'The ghost?'

'Didn't you hear it?'

'No.'

I told her about the footsteps which Armstrong and I had heard. Mme Mollinov shuddered. 'Were you not afraid?'

'Perhaps a little. But I don't believe in ghosts.'

'You are not spirite?'

'Not a bit.'

'Did you think of me last night?'

'Yes.'

'Nice thoughts?'

'Naturally.'

'Dar-ling,' she said. 'Kiss me good morning dar-ling.'

I shifted my position, which had begun to be rather cramped, and sat down on the ground, pulling Mme Mollinov sideways off the stool so that her body was braced back across my knees. Her eyes, wide and bold under thin plucked eyebrows, stared into mine. Her face at these close quarters did not look so young: there were tiny lines on her cheeks and at the corners of her eyes. Her mouth this morning was outlined in magenta lipstick; it tasted scented and soapy in my mouth.

She leaned her head out of reach, shaking the bleached blonde streak of hair out of her eyes and laughing. I bent forward to kiss her again but she put her hand across my mouth. Her fingers tasted of turpentine and the stuff which she put on her nails. It was a not unpleasant mixture.

She said: 'You must not kiss me anymore now.'

'Oh yes.'

'No. Somebody might see us from the châlet.'

'Why worry?'

'It would make a scandal. You must be correct. I thought the English were always so correct.'

'Sometimes they are very incorrect indeed.'

'I see that now.'

Spider and Vaska appeared suddenly out of the wood behind us, Vaska leading the way and swinging an axe in his hand. He grinned at us as he went past with his heavy lurching stride; and Spider, limping behind him, gave us a really terrific sideways leer, his one visible tooth waggling in his beard. He was hatless and his sparse grey-black hair was twirled up on his forehead like horns. He looked so much like a satyr that I shouldn't have been surprised to find that he concealed a cloven hoof inside his surgical boot.

Mme Mollinov said to me: 'You see? Now they will think bad things.'

'What kind of things?'

'They will think that we are – how do you say – having an affair.'

'Well aren't we?'

'We shall see. You must have patience. And you must be more discreet.'

'All right.'

From the forest we could hear the clop-clop of Vaska's axe, cutting down trees. Occasionally Spider's voice was also audible, directing operations.

Mme Mollinov said: 'Monsieur Bertrand does not like women.'

'Who?'

'You call him Spider.'

'Oh yes.' I had never consciously heard Spider's real name before.

Mme Mollinov said: 'Il en est, je crois.'

'So they say.'

Somehow it seemed incongruous in Spider's case, partly owing to his beard. With a beard like that one expected him to be the typical

Frenchman of tradition, with at least five mistresses somewhere in the background. There were no apparent signs of homosexuality that I could see; though his relations with Vaska – and probably Raoul – seemed open to suspicion.

I asked: 'Have you known him long?'

'No. We are only here en pension.'

'En pension?'

'Sixty francs a day, tout compris. It is because of Véra. My child. In Paris she was not well. I thought in the mountains she would be better. And then there are the other children for her to amuse herself with.'

'Are the Paillons en pension too?'

'Of course. Did you not know?'

'It's news to me.'

'You are not en pension?'

'No. We're just ordinary guests.'

I was trying to calculate how much money Spider was making out of the ill-assorted persons whom he had collected under his roof. It should amount to quite a tidy sum. Not a bad method of augmenting one's income, providing that one did not mind a crowd of strangers cluttering up one's house all day long. At the same time quite a lot of people might not care for the conditions of life at Fou Châlet.

Mme Mollinov said: 'You are en vacance?'

'That's it.'

'You think you will enjoy your visit?'

'I'm sure I shall.'

I slipped my arm round her waist again. Despite her pretended fear of being overlooked, she made no opposition this time to being kissed. Quite the reverse in fact. At length she took her mouth away from mine, but without removing her arms from around my neck. Her eyes were half-closed; the whites rolled up, showing between her lids. She drew a long shuddering breath and rubbed her cheek against mine.

'Dar-ling,' she said, 'You want me dar-ling?'

'Of course I do.'

'I want you also.'

'Tonight?' I said.

'It will be difficult. My child sleeps in the bedroom with me.'

'Hmm. That's awkward.'

'Yes.'

'Never mind. We're bound to find some way.'

41

I turned my head. Mme Mollinov sat up straight, taking her arms from around my neck. Her face was flushed and irritable. In French she snapped out: 'Yes? What is it?'

Little Véra had come scampering up and now stood in front of us, twisting her legs ominously together. 'Maman,' she said, 'I want to pi-pi.'

12

We were sitting around in the living-room after lunch when the kitchen door crashed suddenly open and Raoul rushed out, shouting something unintelligible in a shrill voice. Startled by this abrupt entrance, Mme Paillon dropped her knitting and the ball of wool began to roll away across the floor, unwinding itself as it ran. Only Armstrong, stretched in a long chair smoking through his holder, made no movement of surprise.

Raoul threw the door to and fumbled for a moment at the lock, trying to find the key, which was on the other side. Realising this, he gave a wail of despair and crossed the room at a stumbling trot, his hands outstretched imploringly towards Spider. His face was puckered up with fear. He stammered: 'Monsieur. Monsieur.'

Spider started to say: 'What…?' when the door was again flung back and Vaska bulked huge in the opening. Raoul gave a shriek like a girl's and backed round to the other side of the table. Vaska lunged purposefully into the room. The lines stood out in hard red ridges across his forehead. Through clenched teeth he roared out: 'You little rat! Call me a thief?'

Raoul began to blubber. He backed against the wall and stood flattened against it, flinging up both arms to protect his head. Reaching him in two strides Vaska delivered a shattering buffet with his open hand, which knocked Raoul backwards over a chair and stretched him out on the floor at Armstrong's feet.

Raoul rolled over on his back and without attempting to rise began to drum his heels on the floor, shrieking all the time at the top of his voice. At this point Mme Mollinov also began to scream. The noise was deafening. Spider had risen to his feet and was shouting impartially at Vaska and Raoul to stop, but at the same time making no active effort to interfere.

Vaska roared again: 'Call me a thief?' He kicked the fallen chair out of his way and made for Raoul with one leg drawn back as though to score a goal in a football match.

It was at this moment that Armstrong took command of the situation. He reached out a hand and clamped his fingers on Vaska's arm as Vaska lurched past his chair. Without apparent effort on Armstrong's part, Vaska's progress was effectively arrested. He tottered from one leg to the other, lost his balance, and landed heavily on one knee. He clutched at Raoul with both hands and missed as Raoul, now on all fours, scuttled quickly back out of reach.

Armstrong heaved himself out of his chair and grappled Vaska from behind. His cigarette-holder was still gripped firmly between his teeth. It waggled up and down as Vaska essayed vainly to dislodge Armstrong from his back. The struggle was soon over. Armstrong hauled Vaska to his feet and flung him into the chair which he himself had just vacated. There was a splintering crash and the wooden supports of the chair gave way altogether, letting Vaska down with a tremendous bump onto the floor. He lay there on his back, for the moment dazed.

Armstrong said: 'Will someone now explain what all this is about?'

He turned enquiringly to Raoul, who stood by the stairs sobbing and snivelling through his nose. Everyone now gathered round and began to bombard Raoul with questions. M. Paillon, who had removed himself to a safe distance during the scuffle, became particularly vociferous in this connection. Mme Mollinov had now stopped screaming and looked rather pleased with herself. I think that on the whole this display of primitive violence had not been entirely distasteful to her. She put out her hand and squeezed mine hard as we stood in the crowd round Raoul.

A red bump had begun to swell up on Raoul's forehead where he had struck it in falling. Otherwise he appeared unhurt. In reply to M. Paillon's reiterated enquiries he stammered out between sobs something about a hundred francs. M. Paillon, standing in front of him with legs straddled and stomach outthrust, raised his eyebrows enquiringly. 'A hundred francs?'

Raoul nodded violently. The incredulous note in M. Paillon's voice seemed to make him more definite in his assertion. 'Cent francs,' he repeated.

M. Paillon pursed his lips, assuming a sceptical expression. 'A hundred francs,' he said. 'Sure you don't mean a hundred *sous*? Cent sous, hein? C'est ça n'est-ce pas? Cent sous, non pas cent francs!'

Raoul shook his head even more violently than before. 'Cent francs,' he insisted. That, no less, was the sum involved. His hundred francs had been stolen. That saligaud Vaska, that brutt'accidente, had snaffled it out of the sock where he kept it hidden.

A strangled roar of rage interrupted this tale of woe. The familiar words 'Call me a thief?' assailed our ears once more. Raoul ducked his head with a terrified squeal and took cover behind Armstrong as Vaska swayed to his feet amongst the wreckage of the smashed chair.

'You dirty little bastard! Me steal your mucking money?' Vaska's face was crinkled, his eyes sunken into his head with fury. There were flecks of foam on his thick pink lips. Mme Mollinov shivered and clutched my arm convulsively for protection. M. Paillon clicked his tongue and shook his head reprovingly at the bad language. 'Allons, mon vieux! Ladies present tu sais!'

Vaska paid no attention to this reproach. He marched menacingly towards Raoul. 'You filthy little sod, I wouldn't wipe myself on your bloody dough!'

Armstrong interposed his bulk between. 'Now now,' he said. 'Take it easy old fellow.'

Vaska drew himself up with dignity. 'I am an honest man. Of noble blood!' He thumped his chest with a clenched fist. 'My mother is a countess. Related to the Romanovs. And that sale tapette there accuses me of pinching his cash. I ask you Mr Armstrong, as an Englishman – is it likely? Listen!' He appealed to the rest of us. 'Call in the police. Have me searched. Look here!' He started to turn his pockets inside out. 'Have I a hundred francs? No! Maybe you think I've hidden it. Okay – search my room then! Go ahead! I give you permission.'

Spider stepped into the circle, pushing M. Paillon aside. He laid his hand on Vaska's shoulder. 'Listen, old man. There's no reason to lose your temper. Perhaps Raoul's mistaken. The money may have been mislaid...'

'Money! Mislaid!' Vaska shook off Spider's hand and turned to him with a snarl. 'It's my belief he never had a hundred francs. Anyhow, one thing's certain: I don't stay in the same house with that little swine. He goes or I go, see? That's my last word!'

He swung round and stamped out through the kitchen, slamming the door behind him with a crash that shook the house. For a moment there was silence, and then Raoul suddenly burst into tears again. I thought that scenes of this sort were becoming far too common at Fou Châlet.

Spider sat down in his chair at the head of the table. He was stroking his beard and looked distinctly worried. Armstrong started to screw a fresh cigarette into his holder. M. Paillon said: 'Let us consider the matter calmly. If Raoul has in reality lost a hundred francs...'

I saw that the discussion was about to begin all over again. I felt heartily sick of the whole lot of them. For some reason even Mme Mollinov was included in this feeling of general disgust. She had withdrawn her arm from mine and was standing looking down at Raoul, with her back turned to me.

Seeing my chance to escape unobserved, I stepped past Mme Paillon, who was gathering together her ball of wool, and out through the front door. I walked quickly away from the house up into the woods where I had been with Mme Mollinov that morning. I did not walk very far, as so much excitement after a heavy luncheon had upset my stomach. I lay down in a patch of sunshine with my back against a tree-stump and took Yvonne's letter from my trouser pocket. I re-read it twice but was still unable to reach a decision regarding her. The sun on my face was hot but without being oppressive like the sun in Nice.

I closed my eyes and thought about Yvonne. Marriage appeared to me a pretty grim possibility: like the thought of death, to be instantly dismissed from the mind. On the other hand it might be pleasant to become engaged for a while. I had never been formally engaged. I wondered what Yvonne's mother would think about it. She did not entirely approve of me. Of course I had money and a double-barrelled name. Yvonne Barrington-ffoulkes. It was a bit of a mouthful but it would look all right in the gossip-column of the *Monte Carlo News*. Gene Flood could report the wedding. It would be a scoop for him. Mr and Mrs Barrington-ffoulkes. Confetti and Nôtre Dame Cathedral. Yvonne in gold. They'd call us a handsome young couple. And afterwards what? The honeymoon. Sleeping with Yvonne would be very pleasant. I had never slept with her but it was quite easy to imagine.

I sat up abruptly. Who the hell said anything about honeymoons? An official engagement was as far as I was prepared to go. I was surprised to find, however, that the idea of marrying Yvonne had seemed so pleasant. That was only in theory though. In practice it would never work. We should be at each other's throats the whole time. Still, thinking about it had helped to pass the time quite nicely.

I lay back and began to formulate the terms of my letter to Yvonne. Proposing marriage by letter was not an easy task. I supposed that one would have to propose before becoming engaged. I had never proposed marriage to any woman as yet. That seemed a good beginning for the letter, and I decided to go on from there.

A shadow fell across me and I looked up. It was Mme Mollinov, wearing a wide-brimmed straw hat and smiling down at me.

'Hullo,' I said. I found that I was quite glad to see her again. The feeling of revulsion had passed away entirely. It was possibly due to the disordered condition of my stomach, which by now had also subsided.

Mme Mollinov stretched herself with a single graceful movement on the pine-needles beside me. The wide-brimmed hat, with its suggestion of Longchamp racecourse, looked incongruous in conjunction with her sun-bathing kit. It emphasised her rather predatory profile.

'Do I disturb you?' she asked.

'Not at all.'

'If you wish to be alone I will go away.'

'Don't do that.'

I took her hand. Her fingers were very smooth and cool. I tickled her palm and she giggled and pressed her shoulder against mine.

She said: 'Why did you go away just now?'

'I felt fed-up.'

'You had eaten too much?'

'That also.'

'You are a gourmand.'

'What's going on at the châlet?'

'The dispute continues.'

'Have they found the hundred francs?'

'No,' Mme Mollinov said. 'That Vaska is a savage. He is very brutal.'

'That attracts you no doubt.'

'He is very strong. You are not strong like Vaska.'

'I'm not a thieving Russian thug, if that's what you mean.'

'Now you are jealous.'

'Not in the least.'

'You are being very foolish.'

'All right.'

Mme Mollinov laughed. She took from her vanity box a box of Gitanes Vizir.

'I will light a cigarette for you.'

'Thanks.'

She lit a cigarette and placed it in my mouth. It tasted of her lipstick and the end was slightly moist. 'You like that?' she asked.

'Yes.' Lying back in the sun, smoking the Turkish cigarette and holding her hand. I felt lazy and content, but not really like love-making.

I said: 'Your husband is dead, isn't he?'

'Why? You are afraid he would shoot you?'

'He's had no cause to shoot me up to now.'

'If he had been alive he would have shot you. Poor Grigori. He was very jealous.' Mme Mollinov sighed. 'We were married very young.'

I tried again to compute her age, but unsuccessfully. The child Véra was about four but that made no difference as I did not know how long the husband had been dead. There was also the chance that M. Mollinov was not the child's father at all. She was probably thirty-four, but the wide-brimmed hat made her look older than she usually did.

'Poor Grigori,' she sighed again. 'He was so handsome. So big and blond. But terribly jealous. He would kill anybody who looked at me.'

'He must have killed a good many people.'

'Silly boy.' She laughed and pressed my hand. 'It is a façon de parler.'

She leant towards me and desire revived suddenly with the smell of her perfume. I threw away my cigarette and put my arms around her. We lay there kissing while the cigarette fumed away on the ground, sending up a thin thread of smoke. Mme Mollinov said: 'The forest will take fire.'

'Damn the forest. Let it burn.'

'Darl-ing,' she said, 'why are we doing this?'

13

Mme Mollinov combed out her hair, tugging her head sideways and smiling at me over her shoulder. I held the mirror up while she applied lipstick and powder to her face. I felt sleepy and satisfied and rather sentimental towards her.

She said: 'You are happy, dar-ling?'

'Very happy.'

'You love me?'

'Yes.'

'I am glad.'

She sheathed her lipstick and peered closely into the mirror, outlining her eyebrows with charcoal.

'What is the time?'

'My watch has stopped.'

'It must be late.'

The sun had slipped round behind us now, throwing a golden glow up into the sky. I thought it must be about six. I hoped we hadn't missed tea as I felt ravenous. The air was certainly doing my appetite a lot of good.

Mme Mollinov held up her hat and made a moue. The hat had a big dent in the crown. 'Naughty boy. Look what you have done.'

'Never mind. I'll buy you a new one.'

'Will you? Dar-ling.'

I put out a hand and pulled her erect beside me. Her face, freshly made-up, was flushed and all the lines seemed to have been smoothed out of it. She looked marvellous. She leant forward and touched her lips very lightly to mine. Her rouge felt slightly sticky and left behind it a taste of almonds. She shook her head and smiled brilliantly.

'I am so glad that you love me, dar-ling,' she said.

14

Vaska gave us tea when we got back. Everyone else seemed to have vanished. Vaska was in good form again, grinning from ear to ear as he walked around the table, banging down plates. At Mme Mollinov's request he put a record on the gramophone and the needle ground out 'Happy Days are Here Again' while I ate enormous slabs of plum cake and Mme Mollinov's foot pressed mine lightly under the table. There was no sign of Raoul.

After tea Mme Mollinov said: 'I must look for Véra. Poor child, I am neglecting her. That is your fault.'

'I suppose so.'

'You must not forget that I am a mother.'

It seemed a curious time to remind me of this fact, but I did not feel disposed to argue the point. She got up from the table and patted my cheek.

'I will see you later, dar-ling.'

'Righto.'

She went out and I could hear her slightly metallic voice calling: 'Véra! Véra!' outside. I lit a cigarette. On the whole it had been a satisfactory afternoon. So far things had turned out all right. I did not allow myself to think beyond the immediate future, which probably entailed another walk with Mme Mollinov during the evening.

I went through to the bedroom, where Armstrong, lying on his bed, was writing a letter.

'How do you spell "Mortgage"?' he asked me.

'With a "t",' I told him. 'Writing to the Canadian girl?'

'No, a business letter.'

'What happened about Raoul?'

'He leaves tomorrow morning. Vaska refuses to stay on otherwise, and as he does most of the work here Spider can't afford to let him go. And then there are other reasons, as you can imagine.'

'Quite.'

'Spider is very upset about it all,' Armstrong said. 'He wanted me to buy the châlet from him so that he can send his little girl to a sanatorium.'

'What did you say?'

'Nothing doing. Particularly as I've already lent him twenty thousand francs for that purpose.'

'What did he do with the money?'

'Gambled it away.'

'Spider seems to me a bit of a sod.'

'He has his bad points.'

'Did you know that he ran this place as a pension?'

'Yes, he told me today. Anyhow I didn't feel inclined to take it on. I've already got three houses.'

'He can always sell the forest if he needs cash.'

'He raised money on that three months ago.'

'Good God.'

'I feel sorry for him in a way.'

'I don't. I feel sorry for the child though.'

'Yes.'

A sudden hullabaloo made itself heard outside. Looking out through the wire mosquito curtain which covered the window I could see Mme Mollinov, plainly in a furious temper, hauling little Véra along by the hand, while Marie and the Paillon children followed, slightly subdued, at a distance.

49

'What's going on?' Armstrong said.

'I don't know.'

Through the window I could see Mme Mollinov shaking a furious finger in the face of her recalcitrant offspring: the words 'méchante', 'new frock', and 'ruined' could be distinguished above little Véra's howls as, kicking and squalling, she was hauled into the house. The noise continued up the stairs, punctuated by the sounds of slaps and a really terrific roar from little Véra; after which a door slammed, cutting off most of the clamour.

I sat down in a chair and took a Chesterfield cigarette from the tin open at Armstrong's elbow. The truly demonical expression on Mme Mollinov's face had given me food for thought. I did not care for women with tempers like that. Stories of the Russian temperament which I had heard at various times now came back to me with misgiving. I remembered that girl of Jean Germain's who, after a quarrel over uncooked sausages, had split his face open with the edge of a frying pan. She had been a Russian too. I began to wonder what I had let myself in for.

Armstrong said: 'Been out with the Mollinov?'

'Just for a stroll.'

Armstrong shook his head. He obviously disapproved of the whole affair. From upstairs a faint wail of pain and fury from little Véra filtered down to us. She had been beaten and put to bed.

Marie and the Paillon children ran past the window. The sad fate of their playmate forgotten, they were engaged in a game of tag. I could hear Marie coughing as she ran past. I pulled a sheet of notepaper towards me and unsheathed my fountain-pen.

Armstrong said: 'Yvonne?'

'I owe her a letter.'

But I did not propose to Yvonne after all. Instead I wrote her a detailed account of life at Fou Châlet, ending up with the row between Vaska and Raoul. The letter, I thought, would amuse her but she would probably be annoyed too, as the tone of the letter was not at all what she was obviously expecting.

Naturally I left out of the letter any mention of Mme Mollinov.

15

Raoul went off early next morning, and none of us were up to see him go. I heard afterwards, however, that he had managed to blackmail Spider into giving him a hundred francs to replace the sum which he claimed to have lost.

16

Next day Armstrong proposed an excursion to the village. Mme Mollinov was in bed with a headache, so she did not accompany us.

We set off together soon after lunch. The weather appeared inauspicious. It was unbearably close and the sky was banked with big black clouds. Luminous shafts of thundery sunshine spread out fanwise from beneath them, pointing fingers of light at the valley and the village below us.

'Big storm going to break,' Armstrong said, screwing up his eyes at the sky, with a recollection of tropical tempests.

'Should we turn back?' I said.

My collar was limp with perspiration and the air felt sticky on the backs of my hands and on my neck. We continued on down a beaten track between lush rolling prairie, which undulated in natural terraces towards the valley. It was a different route to the one we had taken when we came up the first day, and supposed to be quicker.

The sun had been eclipsed altogether now and an icy wind blew suddenly across from the mountains, bending the grass flat and biting through our thin drill suits. An enormous drop of rain splashed down from the black sky and hit the brim of my solar topi.

'Run for it!' Armstrong said.

Turning against the wind we set off at the double towards a group of rocks thrown up on the hillside, which afforded the only nearby shelter. The thunder rolled like a big drum behind us and the drops of rain solidified into a thin hissing sheet, blown sideways by the wind and soaking us to the skin. We were wet through by the time we reached the rocks. A sort of cave hollowed out beneath a big boulder afforded us room enough to sit down under cover, although Armstrong's bulk made the space more cramped than it would otherwise have been.

He said: 'What perfectly bloody weather,' opening his tin of Chesterfields. There was only one cigarette left in the tin: he had almost exhausted his supply.

The thunder cracked again and the rain blew past in clouds. I counted ten between the crashes. A fork of lightning flickered down the valley in front of us, leaving its sudden blinding imprint on my eyeballs. A truly tremendous crash followed, a crack of breaking wood, and a puff of smoke went up from a group of trees down the valley.

Armstrong said: 'That hit something.'

As the smoke cleared away, we saw one of the trees bent and withered into a gnarled grotesque shape where the lightning had struck it. I remembered the two men whom my sister had come upon one day in the country, after a storm, standing rigid by a haystack, their steel implements still clutched in stiffened fingers. They were quite dead and their faces had turned as black as negroes' faces. My sister had been ill for weeks after this incident. She had been an impressionable girl.

Armstrong continued to smoke calmly. He said: 'Of course, if the lightning strikes this rock we're done for. We'd be completely buried underneath it.'

'That's right,' I said. 'Let us by all means be cheerful.'

'They'd have to dig our bodies out,' Armstrong said. 'But on the other hand no one would know where to look. We'd simply have vanished off the face of the earth.'

'Strange Disappearance of Famous Explorer,' I said. 'Edwin Armstrong Vanishes from Man's Ken.'

'What about Christopher Barrington-ffoulkes?'

'The name's too long to make a headline. And anyway I'm not important enough.'

'They'd put Riviera Playboy Passes From Public Eye.'

'That's a good one.'

'It would be a major mystery,' Armstrong said.

'What's a minor mystery?' I asked him.

'Your attachment to that Russian tart.'

'I have my reasons.'

'They're not hard to guess.'

Thunder rolled out seemingly above our heads and the lightning forked again somewhere out of sight: we could just catch the flicker of it across the sky. Hailstones as big as marbles bounced off the rock and the rain poured steadily down. The cold wind had ceased and the air was hot and clammy once more, but my wet drill suit clung to me like an icy shroud. The storm seemed likely to go on forever.

I wondered how Mme Mollinov was feeling. Her headache had come on early the night before and I had hardly seen her since our interlude in the wood behind the house. It was almost the first time I had thought of her since. That, apart from the obvious one, was her principal attraction for me at the moment. I could put her completely out of my mind whenever I wanted. That was because our affair was not so far complicated by love. Yvonne, on the other hand, was far too often in my thoughts. When we were together we quarrelled continually and yet when I was alone I could not entirely forget her. With Mme Mollinov it was entirely different, and to me preferable. I did not want to be in love with anyone. Directly one became serious things began to go sour. I did not want to be serious. I am not a serious person at all, I thought.

Armstrong, interrupting my introspection, said: 'Have you got any cigarettes?'

'Yes.' I passed over my case and Armstrong struck a match.

The hailstones rattled like machine-gun fire, rolling together in little clusters on the ground in front of our rock. Then they ceased abruptly and the thunder rumbled away in the west. It seemed to be receding into the distance. The rain, reduced to a thin drizzle, still pattered down, however.

Armstrong said: 'Il ne pleut jamais sur la Côte d'Azur.'

'It looks like clearing though.'

'Yes.'

Patches of blue sky showed between the black clouds and the sun broke through again, arching an enormous rainbow above the houses grouped in the valley. The rain stopped its thin trickle as though suddenly dried up, and we crawled out from under the rock.

The air had cooled off considerably but the sun was hot. Moisture steamed up from the ground and from our wet drill suits as we started off again towards the village, while the rainbow spanned the sky and water squelched up from the grass under our rope-soled espadrilles.

The village had a main street, running downhill, with water flowing in a grooved gutter down the centre. It led down into the public square where the donkeys were tethered and where the band played on summer evenings.

Armstrong and I sat on the porch of the hotel belonging to Laurie Staynes, the private detective and parliamentary candidate, President of the Society for the Prevention of Cruelty to Girls. The hotel was not the Royal and the one supposed to be the best. It was a new venture for this man of many interests, and managed mainly by his wife, a fair and faded Englishwoman whom he was supposed to neglect.

Staynes himself was French. He owned two cars, one of them a racer and the other a kind of covered van, for professional purposes, on which was painted the legend LAURIE STAYNES, CONSULTING CRIMINOLOGIST, and a picture of himself smoking a Sexton-Sherlock pipe, menaced on left and right by fearsome hooded figures from the sales-compelling dust-wrapper of an Edgar Wallace novel.

It is doubtful, however, that Staynes' detective work in reality brought him into contact with dangers of this sort. His activities were mostly limited to shadowing co-respondents and securing evidence for divorce proceedings, out of which he sometimes managed to levy blackmail on a small scale.

Sitting on the porch of the hotel, we watched Staynes careering crazily around the *place* at the wheel of his racing car, the back of which was packed with blonde girls shouting 'Whoopee' and drinking from bottles, whom he had no doubt rescued from some cruelties that were being inflicted upon them.

Mrs Staynes also watched from the doorway of the hotel, but her rather pale well-bred face showed no emotion whatever. Doubtless she was accustomed to this kind of thing.

Staynes circled the square three times, crouching over the wheel, hooting and tooting at his horn as hard as he could. The third time he passed the hotel, a girl in white who was tighter than the others threw an empty bottle out of the car, splintering it in fragments on the kerbstone. Then Staynes, honking his horn heartily, headed the car for the open country.

His wife went indoors again. We could hear her giving orders to the waiter about the wine which we had ordered for dinner. She had a pleasant voice but she spoke French with a very English accent.

Armstrong said: 'Have you heard that story about Staynes? The time when he went to America?'

'To get evidence for someone?'

'That's it.'

'And then the client wanted his money back.'

'Yes.'

'The way I heard it, Staynes didn't go himself. He sent an assistant.'

'No no. He went himself and had a damn good holiday on the retaining fee.'

'I hear he only got ten votes at the last election.'

'Do you wonder.'

Vaska's friend René came up the steps of the veranda and greeted us with a terrific display of good fellowship. He still wore his white plusfours and polo képi. He threw himself into a chair and attempted at first to stand us drinks, but gave way gracefully to Armstrong's suggestion that he should have one with us.

Mrs Staynes served the drinks herself. She was of aristocratic appearance but rather anaemic. René said: 'Alors madame! Comment ça va?'

Mrs Staynes smiled frigidly and said: 'Très bien, merci.' She pronounced the last word 'mercy'.

René threw up his hands and said, making a comical face: 'Ah, les anglaises!' as Mrs Staynes disappeared into the hotel. 'Always reserved. Cold as ice! But she is distinguished, that one.' He gripped my arm and said, bending his face forward until I could smell the garlic on his breath: 'I wouldn't mind consoling her for the infidelities of her husband. They say she's very rich! But,' he shook his head regretfully, 'avec les anglaises ça ne marche pas!'

Outside it was growing dark. People began to appear on the *place* forming groups and laughing. I began to fear that we would have to invite René to have dinner with us. These misgivings proved unjustified, however. Having drunk three brandies and smoked two of Armstrong's cigarettes, René rose to his feet.

'I must be moving now. Anastasie awaits!'

'Who is Anastasie?'

'My bonne-amie.' He winked and, waving his hand to us, ran down the steps of the porch. The waiter came out carrying plates of soup; we started to drink it while swarms of flying ants descended upon us in a sudden cloud, crawling all over the table.

Armstrong said: 'Spider talks of giving up the drug habit.'

'Talk's about as far as he'll get.'

'He says he'll turn over his stock of dope to me.' Armstrong fished the corpse of a drowned ant out of his soup and continued: 'I'm to dish it out in small doses, less and less every day until he's cured.'

'That'll never work.'

'We can but try.'

After dinner we walked around the *place,* where a crowd of people congregated, sitting in rows of chairs round the bandstand. Among those present were René and his old French paymistress, who had been an actress and was still farded as though for the footlights. The musicians played something out of *Tosca.*

About nine o'clock we hit the homeward trail. Our clothes had dried on us now but they felt stiff as tarpaulin and had completely lost their shape. Laurie Staynes rushed past us at the wheel of his racer, going back to the village. The back of the car was empty, and I wondered what he had done with the girls.

18

Next day I had a streaming cold and stayed in bed, dosing myself with aspirin and reading a book. I had finished *Vile Bodies*, and the book I was now reading had been lent to me by Spider. It was a French *roman de moeurs* called *Les Adolescents Passionés*, and the first part of it dealt with sex-perversion on a gigantic scale at a French lycée. The story seemed to me slightly exaggerated as although I had myself been to a lycée I had never encountered anything like this. I had always understood that homosexuality was more likely to flourish at an English public school but here again I was only going by what I had read and by Armstrong's highly coloured accounts of his public schooldays.

The book was interesting, however, and I continued to read on in the intervals of blowing my nose and attempting to clear my head of the singing noises which invaded it. Armstrong had gone out for a walk, but in the living-room the gramophone, animated by M. Paillon, ground out a French comic song about artichokes, alternating with La Caravane and La Fille du Bédouin. M. Paillon always played these three records, as the remainder were American and he did not like what he described as le djazz.

The children were playing somewhere on the grass in front: I could hear Marie's cough and little Véra sending up an occasional temperamental yowl whenever she was thwarted in any respect. Somewhere in the distance the Algerians were dynamiting again and the glass of the window rattled every now and then. It was late afternoon.

A light tap sounded on the bedroom door. It opened and Mme Mollinov slipped in, closing the door behind her and holding one finger to her lips with the air of a conspirator.

'Ssh!' she hissed in a penetrating whisper.

'What's the matter?' I said.

'They must not know I am here. It would make a scandal.'

'But didn't M. Paillon see you?'

'No. He has gone to the water.' She pronounced it 'vataire'. 'You understand?' she said. 'The vater-closet. He must not know I have come to see you.' She sat down on the bed beside me and stroked my forehead with her fingers. 'Poor dar-ling. You have fever.'

'A little.'

'You must take aspirin.'

'I've taken six already.'

'Six! That is too many. You will kill yourself!'

'No fear.'

'You must not kill yourself dar-ling. I want you to live – for me.' She took one of my hands and pressed it, gazing at me with her slightly protuberant eyes: a soulful Russian look. 'You must not die, dar-ling.'

'Of course I shan't. It's only a cold.'

I was getting a little tired of this. I reached for my handkerchief from under the pillow and blew my nose again. To change the subject I said: 'And how are you today?'

'My headache has gone. But yesterday: bon dieu, how I suffered! And today it is you, poor dar-ling. We have both of us suffered.'

She seemed determined at all costs to make a drama out of it. She was evidently in a dramatic mood. She started up in alarm as M. Paillon's heavy footsteps crossed the living-room outside again.

'Bon dieu! What shall I do?'

'It's all right.'

'He may enter and discover me.'

'Of course he won't.'

'Ssh. You must not talk so loud.'

I thought that if we were overheard Mme Mollinov's sibilant whisper would sound far more suspicious than if we spoke in normal tones. It did not seem worth while to argue about it, however. The singing in my ears had suddenly become redoubled. I wished that Mme Mollinov would go away and leave me alone. I was in no mood for romance.

The gramophone started up again in the living-room: it was the artichoke song once more. I made up my mind to break that record at the first available opportunity. Mme Mollinov reseated herself on the bed and took my hand again.

'See. I will take your pulse. I know how. During the war I was a nurse.'

'What is my pulse?'

'It goes ve-ry fast. But perhaps that is because I am near you, yes?'

'Might be.'

'Dar-ling.' She said: 'I will not kiss you because of your cold.'

'All right.'

The record came to an end and the gramophone stopped. We heard M. Paillon crossing the room again and then his feet ascending the stairs. Mme Mollinov jumped up off the bed, smoothing down her skirt which had got rucked up above her knees.

'I must go now. Goodbye, dar-ling. Get well quickly.'

She kissed the tips of her fingers and laid them for a moment against my lips. Then she opened the door, stood listening for a second, and slipped out, closing the door behind her softly.

I took a cigarette out of my case and tried to smoke, but the cigarette tasted of absolutely nothing. It made my head swim and I crushed it out again in the ashtray by my bed. I went on reading *Les Adolescents*. The plot had now resolved itself into a sort of bisexual triangle-drama, with Massias, a homosexual of a particularly virile type, in love with a boy called Yves Chantrié, who in turn burned with an unavowed passion for Massias' nymphomaniac sister. Some terrific climactic scene was obviously to be expected from such a situation.

I blew my nose for the umpteenth time and reflected that no condition was so perfectly bloody as a really bad cold in the head. The door opened and Armstrong came in.

'My God,' he said, 'What a fearful stink.'

'What kind of stink?'

'That woman's scent.'

'I can't smell it.'

'You're lucky.' He threw open the window as far as it would go and said: 'That's better.'

'Is it hell. I'll freeze to death.'

'A little fresh air will do you good.' Armstrong sat down on his bed, puffing out a protective cloud of smoke around him as a precaution against germs.

I said: 'How is Spider's cure progressing?'

'It started today. I'm going to limit him to two shots a day to begin with.'

'He'll never stand that.'

'He'll have to get used to it.' Armstrong got up and said: 'Now I shall have a wash in the stream before dinner.'

'Close that damned window as you go out.'

I picked up *Les Adolescents* again. My head felt as though someone had stuffed a wet dishcloth inside it. The singing noises had given way to an absolute deafness. I read on to the part where Massias, having induced his sister to drug Yves, was preparing to rape him in his sleep. It was clear what the end would be. Yves, after this, would have to kill himself. There was no other way out.

About eight o'clock, when the others were having dinner, Vaska brought me in a bowl of soup with some toast in it. I drank the soup without tasting it at all, but the high seasoning left my mouth very hot afterwards. In the light of the oil-lamp which Vaska had lit, I could see the insects already motionless on the walls. They were strange stick-like shapes and did not seem to have any wings. One of them was squatted within reach of my hand, but I hesitated to knock it down in case it proved to be poisonous and attacked me, like the big green lizards which inhabited the mountain region and which were supposed to leap upon travellers out of trees and inflict a deadly wound.

I drank a glass of water and settled down to finish *Les Adolescents*. Yves killed himself all right.

19

Someone was knocking at the door. I opened my eyes with difficulty. They felt as though someone had rubbed sand in them and then tried to gum down the lids. I blinked at Armstrong getting out of bed with a lighted candle in his hand. The knocking continued frenziedly and the door handle rattled. I wondered hazily if this was the ghost demanding admittance; and then, muffled by the deafness in both my ears, came Spider's voice calling out: 'Edwin! Edwin! Open!'

I sat up in bed and immediately my nose began to run again. I took out my sodden handkerchief as Armstrong started to unfasten the door which he had locked presumably in expectation of this visit. Spider pushed past him into the room. He wore long flannel nightshirt and a nightcap and looked almost inconceivably grotesque. He clutched Armstrong by the arm and shouted: 'Give it me quick! I must have it.'

'Steady on, old fellow,' Armstrong said soothingly.

'I tell you I've got to have it.'

'Remember your promise.'

'Damn my promise. I must have it now, I tell you!'

'It's for your own good.'

Spider's face was working. The jaws moved up and down like the jaws of those wooden images that Damia Bellini had in her flat, bearded hillmen of some sort, which could be worked by wires and which Spider in a way rather resembled.

He pleaded in a broken voice: 'Edwin. For the sake of our friendship. You have got to let me have it. Please! I implore you.'

He advanced, clawing at the front of Armstrong's pyjamas. Again his game leg gave his movements the jointed jerkiness of the bearded dolls. As Armstrong retreated, holding up the lighted candle, Spider missed his balance and fell forward on his knees; he tried to get up, failed, and abandoning the effort, began to drag himself along the floor, his clasped hands stretched up to Armstrong in an attitude of supplication.

'Edwin! Please! Have pity!'

'Get back to bed, old man. You'll catch your death of cold.'

Spider's voice went up warningly. 'You better let me have it. You'd better.' He appealed to me: 'Christopher, please! Make him give it to me.'

He began to sob and scream, beating the flat of one hand on the floor. 'Blast you. Blast you. Blast you.'

Saliva dribbled down his beard. His whole body began to twitch as if on the verge of an orgasm.

Doors opened on the landing above. The staircase shook as though someone was sliding down the banisters – the sudden eruption of Vaska into the room, in singlet and stockinged feet, proved this to have been indeed the case.

Vaska wasted no words. Spider, kicking and screaming, was hoisted clear of the floor and lifted bodily onto his back. They vanished together through the doorway, Spider emitting a strangled shout of surprise and fury as he was carted off. Armstrong closed the door and locked it again. He blew out the candle and got back into bed.

I said: 'I suppose we shall have this sort of thing every night now.'

'Vaska can handle him,' Armstrong said.

I blew my nose in a desperate attempt to clear my ears of the deafness. I was unsuccessful. Sounds of movement upstairs. M. Paillon's voice and Spider sobbing and moaning came to me muted as though through cotton wool. But for these noises I might easily have dreamt the degrading scene which had just been enacted. The sense of unreality and nightmare persisted into my sleep: knockings and groanings and phantom figures pursuing me through successive layers of clammy cobweb festooning a long stone corridor.

20

Much later the following year I went to the cinema in Nice and saw a sound-film featuring Lon Chaney, which we called in French *Le Talion*. I never found out what the English title was.

The setting was a bungalow standing on wooden piles somewhere in a tropical swamp, fitted with trapdoors through which Lon Chaney, representing a paralysed fiend of incredible malignity, would suddenly appear, dragging useless legs behind him and holding a knife between his teeth. Despite the plot, a complicated melodramatic affair with a revenge motif, the action and atmosphere of this picture adequately symbolised to me the conditions of life at Fou Châlet.

It brought everything back very vividly: Mme Mollinov and Vaska and Spider hysterically demanding from Armstrong another shot of the dope; the ghostly footsteps on the stairs, apparently a trick of acoustics which remained to the end unexplained; and for a moment I seemed to feel the presence of another ghost beside me in the darkened cinema, to hear a voice whisper 'Dar-ling' and a gramophone playing 'Happy Days' above the strident clamour of the sound-apparatus.

But that, as I say, was much later.

21

Time passed pleasantly enough at Fou Châlet, despite the comparative discomfort, the difficulty of obtaining a decent bath, and the nightly visitations from either Spider or the ghost. In the afternoons and evenings there were always walks with Mme Mollinov or excursions into the village with Armstrong to enliven the tedium; once, returning on a moonless night, we got lost in the forest and were obliged to spend the night in a clearing, keeping in turn an hourly watch against wolves, which we could hear howling but which did not materialise. My relations with Mme Mollinov seemed to have become fairly stabilised, but I still thought a certain amount about Yvonne. I had not received any reply to the letter which I had written her.

22

One day after dinner Armstrong drew me aside.

'I foresee complications for the Spider,' he said.

'Of what kind?'

'Vaska is threatening to leave. He says the work here is too much to handle on his own.'

'What rot. He's as strong as a horse.'

'Nevertheless he threatens to pack in unless he has some help soon.'

'It's his fault Spider got rid of Raoul.'

'Oh quite.'

'Well, what's going to happen?'

'That's just it. Spider proposes to get Michel up here to lend a hand.'

'Who is Michel?'

'Spider's ward. Haven't you heard about him?'

'No.'

'Nothing at all?'

'Absolutely not.'

Armstrong proceeded to enlighten me. It was a long and discreditable story. Apparently Spider, having been appointed Michel's guardian by the boy's parents who were of good family and who were killed in a motor accident, had somehow got his hands on the inheritance and as usual had gambled it away. Michel, sent to a communal school instead of to the expensive college which his people had in mind, developed bad ways and eventually landed himself in a juvenile offender's court, from which Spider managed to extricate him with money borrowed from Armstrong. At liberty again, Michel immediately cut loose and after serving a short apprenticeship with a gang of dope-traffickers in Marseille turned up in a villa in Monte Carlo, living on an elderly English art critic of dubious moral reputation.

The art critic's jewellery and some of his antiques disappeared in suspicious circumstances and were traced to a pawnshop by Laurie Staynes; but the critic, whose personal relations with Michel did not bear investigation, declined to prosecute. (It cost him 20,000 francs to hush the matter up with Staynes.)

Michel, emerging triumphantly from this incident, was now living somewhere in the Old Town: it was believed, with a negress. He was nineteen years old.

I said: 'So you think there'll be trouble.'

'If Michel comes up here there's bound to be.'

'How is Spider getting on with the dope?'

'Admirably. I've started mixing water with the morphine now. He doesn't notice the difference.'

'When does Michel arrive?'

'Tomorrow afternoon. Spider sent him a wire.'

23

'A letter for you,' Mme Mollinov said. She stood there holding out the long blue envelope with the Geneva postmark and Yvonne's hand-writing on it. 'From a woman,' she added in a threatening tone.

I took the letter and said: 'It's from my mother.'

'You have told me that your mother is dead.'

'I mean my stepmother. My father married again.'

'Do not lie to me, please.'

'I beg your pardon!' I tried to simulate indignation at having my word doubted. Mme Mollinov saw through this at once.

'Ne joues pas la comédie. Ce n'est pas necessaire, tu sais!'

When Mme Mollinov went off into French things were very bad indeed. Already she had assumed the expression which came over her face on discovering that her small child had committed some peculiarly revolting misdemeanour. Her eyebrows hooked down menacingly over her nose, she glared at me with a vicious look reminiscent of the mule Mireille when about to start on someone: the equivalent of laying back her ears.

I said: 'My dear Véra, I'm not obliged to discuss my personal correspondence with you. Please understand that. Whoever writes to me, it's my own affair.'

'Affair?' Mme Mollinov said. 'Affair?' She laughed wildly and continued rattling out in rapid French, rolling the R's with a Russian accent: 'Affair. Yes, that's the word you want all right. You think you can tromper me behind my back with some stupid English miss, writing her love-letters no doubt while all the time you're making love to me. Yes – no, don't interrupt! Doubtless it is she whom you intend to marry when this interlude is over, hein? Well, I'm not playing – understand that? If you want to act the Casanova on the quiet you'll have to find another partner: I'm through! Comprends-tu? C'est fini!'

'But listen…'

'I've done enough listening. After all we've been to each other you can do this.'

'But I haven't done anything.' Going off into French myself, I said: 'Voyons, Véra, sois raisonnable. C'est idiot de prendre cette attitude.'

'Idiot?' She gave another high-pitched histrionic laugh. 'So I am *idiote* now, when only last night I was your *chérie* and your sweet and God knows what. You can safely call me names now that you have a letter from your English miss to console you. Yes – you are right. I have been indeed *idiote* not to have seen through you before!'

She turned without more ado and marched off again into the house. I sat back in my deck-chair, feeling rather annoyed. I had the idea that this was only the first of many similar scenes. If Mme Mollinov was going to turn possessive on me it would be just too bad. I made up my mind to take a firm line with her in the future.

I tore open the letter from Yvonne. As I had expected she was angry with me. The tone of the letter was distinctly tart. The major's name was mentioned in it with increasing frequency. He was not only a divine dancer, but also very charming and *galant*. Yvonne had an irritating habit of using a French word where an English one would suffice. Recollection of this mannerism brought her image suddenly before me. I remembered the way she had of craning her rather long neck forward when she asked you a question. I did not want to lose her to any god-damned big-game-hunting British major.

I did not know whether or not I loved her, but I certainly didn't want to lose her.

I went back into the house and wrote her off a letter immediately. I didn't find the task of putting together a proposal as difficult as I had imagined it would be. It was a pretty good letter really.

I gave it to Vaska to post. He was off to the village to meet Michel, who was due to arrive on his motorbike that afternoon. Mireille, laden with baskets intended to contain a week's supply of food, was with him, tugging at the bridle and baring her teeth.

I said: 'Here's five francs to get yourself some fags. But see this letter gets posted – it's important.'

Vaska grinned. 'Okay boss,' and banged Mireille across the backside with a big stick, in an excess of exuberance.

'Gee-up, you bitch. We're on our way.'

24

Supper that night was an awkward meal. Mme Mollinov and I were not on speaking terms, and Michel sat glowering at his plate in sullen silence most of the time, only speaking in order to demand fresh helpings of food, which he ate voraciously. He was handsome in a dark rather brutal way, with black hair plastered down on his forehead and grey circles under his eyes. He wore a leather jerkin with a zip-fastener on the collar and spoke in a loud voice with a meridional accent. He looked much older than nineteen.

Spider, keyed up for the occasion with a double-shot of dope administered by Armstrong as a special treat, cracked jokes nervously with one eye on his ward. His attitude towards Michel was one of rather cringing deference. The conversation, out of politeness to Michel, was conducted entirely in French: with the result that Armstrong, who might otherwise have helped cope with the situation, got rather left out of things.

After supper Spider proposed to read us one of his poems. It was a long pastoral dedicated to an abstract someone who, like the Onlie Begetter, was of equivocal sex. Michel, hunched up in his chair, scowled sulkily as his guardian's voice boomed on. He was furious because he had been obliged to leave his motorbike down in the village. This machine appeared to constitute his major interest in life.

Spider turned over the last page of his manuscript and looked up at us, awaiting applause. Michel growled out under his breath the French equivalent of 'balls', but this verdict was fortunately drowned by a polite admiring patter from the Paillons and Mme Mollinov, and by Armstrong clapping and saying 'Magnificent, my dear fellow. Magnificent!' I don't suppose he had understood a word of it.

Spider, bowing his head in acknowledgement, turned to Michel with a rather timid smile. 'What did *you* think, dear boy?'

'Oh it's all right I suppose. I don't know anything about poetry.' Michel stood up, stretching his arms above his head. 'I think I'll turn in. I'm fagged out.'

Spider staggered to his feet with embarrassing promptitude. 'Of course! After a long journey…my dear boy, you really must excuse me. I hadn't thought.'

He turned towards the kitchen, yelling for Vaska to help with Michel's luggage. Michel, with a brief 'Bonsoir,' slouched off towards the stairs. Apparently he was to sleep in the loft.

Seeing the prospect of a partie of bacarra ahead of me, at which I was certain to lose some money, I got up and walked over to the outer door. I thought I would smoke a cigarette and take a stroll round the house before retiring.

Outside it was very dark and cold, but the air, after the stuffiness of the living-room, was refreshing. I found that I had a slight headache. I walked up into the wood and sat for a few minutes on a fallen tree-trunk, reviewing the events of the day. Having taken a decisive step with regard to Yvonne had rather eased my mind. I felt better now that the decision was taken out of my hands.

Looking up I saw the lighted end of a cigarette advancing towards me through the darkness. From behind it Mme Mollinov's voice called out: 'Christophaire.'

'Hullo,' I said.

She sat on the tree-trunk beside me and took my hands in hers.

'Dar-ling, I have been so foolish. Will you forgive me?'

'Of course I will.'

'I have been *idiote* as you said. But it is because I love you that I become jealous. You understand?'

'Yes.' I knew perfectly well that she did not love me, but to say so would involve us both in tiresome recriminations which I did not feel disposed to enter into. It was better to accept the declaration as a formal convention such as writing 'Yours sincerely' at the foot of a letter. A form of words which one used but did not necessarily believe in.

She said: 'You sound so cold. So phlegmatic. Are you not pleased that I love you?'

'Of course I am.'

'You do not kiss me?'

I leaned towards her in the dark. Her face was very cold but her lips were burning hot. Some smoke which she had just inhaled came into my mouth. She threw her cigarette away and pressed her arm tight about my neck, holding the kiss. Her lips opened wide; she relaxed her body against my arm, swooning with her head back, a trickle of saliva running from her mouth into mine.

She whispered, her breath hot in my ear: 'You will love me tonight, yes?'

'What – here?'

'Silly boy. No. In bed,' she whispered. 'It would be more comfortable in bed, yes? You would like that?'

'Definitely,' I said.

I was rather surprised though, being accustomed to the most elaborate precautions on her part against possible scandal. To go to bed together at Fou Châlet seemed uncommonly like throwing all caution to the winds. However, it wasn't my worry.

'Kiss me again like that,' I told her.

25

We tiptoed upstairs in pitch darkness. All the others had gone to bed. Mme Mollinov pushed open her door and, taking me by the hand, guided me carefully across the room. She seemed able to see in the dark.

She whispered: 'We must be very quiet.' A sound of breathing came from somewhere on my left. I had forgotten the child Véra. Mme Mollinov whispered: 'She is asleep. She will not awake if we are quiet.'

As though to belie this statement, little Véra turned over restlessly in her cot, but it proved to be a false alarm. I put my arm around Mme Mollinov and felt, through silk, her skin hot against my hand. It felt as though she had fever. She drew me down onto the bed, the sheets giving me an icy shock like a cold shower.

She whispered: 'You love me dar-ling? You love me?'

'Yes,' I said, 'Yes,' feeling for her mouth with mine. I did not want to talk at all. The bedsprings creaked; simultaneously a board on the landing outside cracked as though in sympathy. I lifted my head and listened. A soft thudding sound followed: someone stealthily descending the stairs, placing their feet carefully from step to step.

'What is that?' Mme Mollinov whispered in alarm. 'The ghost?'

'I don't know.'

Next moment came an appalling crash. It was succeeded by Spider's voice swearing furiously in French. Afterwards I learned that, attempting to descend in stocking-feet, without the support of his surgical boot, he had slipped and fallen down five stairs, bumping his behind severely.

Mme Mollinov gave a little startled scream and clutched hold of my arm. The child Véra awoke, crying and calling 'Maman.' The stair-rail rattled and shook as Spider held onto it to haul himself upright. He continued to curse all the time. Mme Mollinov let go of me and slid off the bed to comfort the child.

The bedroom door opened downstairs and Armstrong's voice called up to enquire what was wrong. At once Spider stopped cursing and began his usual demand for an extra supply of dope. The voice of Michel cut in angrily from the landing, telling Spider to go to bed.

'Va t'coucher, vieux con! T'as pas fini de chiauter là? Nom de dieu, j'veux dormir, moi!'

I sat on the bed listening to Spider tearfully accusing both Armstrong and Michel of cruelty towards him. Vaska's voice joined in, and sounds of a scuffle indicated that Spider was being forcibly removed from the scene in the usual manner, Michel apparently assisting with kicks and blows from behind.

Little Véra, refusing the ministrations of her mother, began to howl her lungs out; and I could hear Marie coughing and one of the Paillon children crying next door. M. Paillon's voice penetrated the wall in a thick mumble, remonstrating with his wife, who seemed disposed to go out and interfere.

Gradually all these sounds abated as a series of closing doors shut them out. Only little Véra kept up her yelling, and I could tell by Mme Mollinov's tone that she was speedily losing patience. Holding up my trousers, which had slipped down, with one hand, I tiptoed over to the door and out onto the landing.

Armstrong's door opened as I finally reached the ground floor, and the beam of his torch shone full in my face.

'Turn that bloody thing off,' I told him. I felt tired and fairly furious. My headache had come on again with a renewed throbbing.

Armstrong laughed, lowering his torch. 'A night of love?' he said.

'Almost,' I told him.

Inside with the door shut, Armstrong said: 'Michel's a bloody nuisance. He's upsetting Spider's nerves. Just when I'd got him down to one shot a day, too.'

Pulling on my pyjamas, I said: 'Yes.'

'You don't sound very interested.'

'For all I care Spider can go to hell.'

'He probably will,' Armstrong told me. 'It's only a question of time.'

26

Severed by the teeth of the saw, the log dropped in two halves; and Michel, stepping forward, cleft one half viciously with a stroke of his chopper. Vaska, who had been wielding the saw, stood back and Michel swung up the hatchet to deal with the second half; as he did so, the head, which had been loose for some time, flew off leaving the haft in Michel's hand, while the blade buried itself deep in the kitchen door.

Michel threw the haft down and swung round on me as I stood watching them at work on the grass plot at the side of the house. He said: 'You see? I told the old fool that axe was damned dangerous. Why I might have killed someone!'

He went over to the door and wrenched at the blade, breaking it free with a crack of splintering wood. He stood for a moment brooding with the blade in his hand, running one finger along the edge to test its sharpness. Then he flung it down so that it stuck point-foremost in the earth, and spat out of the side of his mouth.

'Ah-bah!' he said, stretching.

'There's another axe in the kitchen,' Vaska told him.

'Hell. I've done enough bloody work for one day. You carry on.' He said abruptly to me: 'Come for a walk. I'd like a talk with you.'

'All right.'

We walked away from the house towards the stream. Michel stopped on the brink of it and swung round suddenly, one hand flying to his hip pocket as though to pull out a pistol and hold me up. It was only a packet of cigarettes, however, which he produced. A packet with the head of an Indian chief reproduced on the outside: the kind that Spider smoked. 'Have one of these. They're not bad – I pinched them from the old bastard this morning. Hell, why shouldn't I? What's a packet of fags? He's done me out of more than that. All my money gone down the drain. I could have lived like a gentleman.'

He used the English word. He spoke very quickly in short sentences, spitting out his words as though they were the seeds of a fruit. He said: 'I can talk to you. You're an educated man. Same's I'd have been if it weren't for that old swine. A bloody board-school. Left me to rot in the gutter, sod him. To live as best I can. Bon! Je suis débrouillard. I get along. But I'll be even with him, mark my words. Just you wait.'

He stared down at his hands: big and blunt, stained with grease and with dirt under the nails. The skin of his face, seen in daylight, was pasty and studded with blackheads; but he was still handsome in an animal way.

He said: 'So I have to work for him like a bloody servant. To earn a few filthy francs. If I hadn't been broke he'd never have got me here.' And, spitting savagely into the stream: 'The old bastard,' he added.

Mme Mollinov's voice called my name from the direction of the house. She stood at her window looking out and waving. Michel, seeing her, said: 'Smart dame, that. She's got chic. I could go for her in a big way. She's – what's the word?' He snapped his fingers. 'Exotic! That's it: exotic.' He added: 'Léonie's exotic too.'

'Who is Léonie?'

'My mistress. Like to see her photo?'

He took a snapshot from his pocket and passed it across to me. Léonie was undoubtedly exotic. She was a full-blooded negress. She only needed a few more bangles and a stick through her nose to compete with the femmes à plâteaux who were being exhibited that summer at Cros de Cagnes Zoo.

Michel said defiantly: 'Sure she's black. So what? I don't give a damn. La nuit tons les chats sont gris. Have you a mistress yourself?'

'No.'

'What about that Russian woman?'

'Mme Mollinov?'

'Yes.'

'What about her?'

'Isn't she your mistress?'

'Not that I know of.'

Michel said 'Hmm,' sceptically.

Mme Mollinov appeared in the doorway of the house and began to walk towards us across the grass. She was all dolled-up in a white linen suit with a short tight skirt, which, as she stepped out, outlined emphatically her long rounded thighs.

Michel leered and said: 'I'll leave you to it.' He slouched off, nodding to Mme Mollinov, who shot him a brilliant seductive smile as they passed each other, at approximately the attitude of eyes-right.

Coming up to me she said: 'You have been talking to Michel?'

'The other way round, really.'

She laughed, looking back over her shoulder at Michel. 'He is joli garçon. Many women would like him.'

'He lives with a negress.'

'Like Baudelaire?'

'That's the only resemblance.'

Mme Mollinov laughed again. She said: 'You are ready, dar-ling?'

'When you are.'

'So.'

'Where is your child?'

'She is with Mme Paillon.'

'Let's go then.'

'Very well.'

We started off arm-in-arm down the slope towards the village, where we had arranged to spend the day.

Mme Mollinov, squeezing my arm, said: 'You still love me, dar-ling?'

'Yes.'

'More than your English-miss?'

'Don't let's start that again.'

'No. We must not quarrel today.' She started to giggle suddenly.

'What are you laughing at?'

'Last night. It was very droll.'

'You think so?'

'Yes. Then, I was angry also, but now I think it is very droll. Very funny.'

'You've got a peculiar sense of humour.'

She kissed me lightly on the cheek, still giggling. 'Never mind, dar-ling. Perhaps tonight.'

'I'm not going through all that again.'

'You do not want to love me?'

'Yes. But not at the châlet.'

'We could stay at an hotel.'

'In the village?'

'Why not?'

'But we have no luggage.'

'It is of no importance. We could invent an excuse.'

'That's a good idea.'

'You see? I am not so *idiote*, hein?'

She smiled at me and I slipped an arm round her, halting our progress in the middle of a field.

She said: 'No. You must wait until tonight.'

'One kiss.'

'Only one, then.'

27

Mrs Laurie Staynes looked askance at us when we asked for rooms at the hotel. She seemed about to refuse, when her husband, arriving suddenly upon the scene, overruled all objections and offered to conduct us personally upstairs.

He was a short stocky man with a red face and a black moustache and he smelt very strongly of cognac. He led the way up, talking all the time in highly incorrect English with a mixed French and American accent. I wondered how he had come by his name. (I found out afterwards that he had it changed by deed-poll as being more befitting for a private enquiry agent. His original name was Blod.)

He stopped on the first landing and threw open a door with the triumphant air of someone who had successfully performed a difficult conjuring trick.

'There you are! Pretty good, ah? All comforts. You like? That's swell. And here is the room for madam. With a door communicating. Electric light, everything modern. All right? Okay! We got bath too, same as America. First door on left. Anythings you want: whisky, cocktails, just ring. I come directly.'

He backed out, grimacing at us with great good humour: the genial host.

Mme Mollinov said: 'I do not like that man. He looks – how do you say – louche.'

'He's very louche indeed. He's a detective.'

'But detectives are not louche.'

'This one is.'

'I do not like him at all.'

She went across into her bedroom and almost immediately a piercing scream rang out.

'What's the matter?'

'Come quickly. There is a beetle in my bed.'

'We'll soon settle that.'

The beetle, a large black cockroach, was eventually dispatched; Mme Mollinov standing in a corner with her skirt pulled up until the deed was done.

She said with a shudder: 'I do not like to sleep in that bed now.'

'You're not going to sleep in it anyway.'

'But perhaps your bed has also beetles.'

'I doubt it.'

I pulled back the covers and had a good look inside. The bed was innocent of beetles. A perfunctory knock on the door announced the sudden reappearance of Laurie Staynes.

'I thought madam called.'

'She did. There was a cockroach in her bed.'

'Cockroach?'

'Un cafard.'

Staynes threw back his head and roared with laughter. It was obvious that he thought Mme Mollinov had screamed for another reason altogether. 'Un cafard!' he said, stamping his foot and spluttering. 'Un cafard!' He was highly amused. We could still hear him laughing as he went away along the corridor.

Mme Mollinov said angrily in French: 'The sâle bête. Does he find it amusing that his hotel is infested with insects?'

'He didn't believe it about the beetle. He thought you were calling for assistance.'

'Assistance?'

'He thought I was trying to seduce you.'

Mme Mollinov did not at first understand this. When it finally penetrated she also began to laugh. It struck her as a really tremendous joke. The people downstairs probably thought she was having hysterics. I went over and locked the door, plugging the key-hole with my handkerchief as a precaution against the detective proclivities of

Laurie Staynes. Mme Mollinov lay across the bed, watching me and shaking with laughter.

'Are you going to seduce me, dar-ling?' she said. 'Shall I call for assistance?'

28

In the morning I left her still asleep, and went along the corridor to have a bath. This proved to be a tub made of tin, and the hot water had to be fetched up from downstairs in buckets. Still it was better than washing in the stream outside the châlet.

Mme Mollinov was not awake when I came back. She looked very attractive lying in bed, but I decided not to awaken her and went downstairs to have some breakfast. Laurie Staynes came out onto the veranda while I was finishing my coffee.

'Ha, there you are, mister! Sleep well? No more cafards?' He roared with laughter and rubbed his hands. 'Madam not up?'

'No.'

'Have a whisky?'

'Not yet, thanks.'

'Cigarette then. American cigarette. You not American?'

'No, English.'

'I bin to America. Los Angeles, Frisco. Know them?'

'I've never been there.'

'You miss somethings. America's swell place. Plenty drink, plenty dough. And dames.' He rolled his eyes upward. 'Dames *everywhere*!'

'That must be nice.'

'I'll say.' He bent confidentially across the table. 'When I was in Frisco…'

Mrs Staynes called him sharply from the doorway of the hotel. 'Okay. I come,' he shouted back and got to his feet with a regretful sigh. '*Dames*,' he said, but this time in a tone of disgust.

A large new shining motorbike snorted round the corner and shuddered to a standstill outside the veranda, almost colliding with Staynes' covered van which was drawn up at the kerb. The driver dismounted and came up the steps of the hotel. Disguised in mica goggles and a leather greatcoat, with the addition of an airman's crash helmet, I did not immediately recognise Michel until he halted in front of my table.

'Hullo. I've been looking for you.'

'Why?'

'You didn't come back last night. Spider got worried.'

'So you've been sent to fetch us back.'

'Not exactly. I'd a row with the old bastard this morning and mucked off out.'

'Mme Mollinov was afraid to go back in the dark. She didn't feel equal to the journey.'

This was the alibi which we had decided upon the night before. Michel made no pretence of believing it, however. He merely winked and said: 'Have a nice time?'

'Tolerably.' To divert him from this topic, which I did not really feel inclined to discuss with him, I said: 'Is that your motorbike down there?'

'Yeah. Like to have a look at it?'

'Very much.'

His dark sullen face alight with enthusiasm, Michel walked around the machine explaining the mechanism and pointing out various in-novations, gadgets which he'd had specially affixed. I nodded, trying to look intelligent and not too bored.

'She's a nice job. I'll take you for a spin one day.'

I thought that nothing was less likely, that is if I had any say in the matter. I said: 'I should like to come very much.'

'Care to jump on now?'

'I must wait for Mme Mollinov.'

'Another time then.'

'With pleasure.'

Michel straddled the bike and kicked the self-starter. The engine roared and the machine shot forward, Michel turning hazardously to wave a gloved hand as he rode off, bouncing over the uneven surface of the road and vanishing finally in a cloud of dust and carbon monoxide.

I looked up to find Mme Mollinov standing beside me. 'Who was that?' she asked.

'Michel,' I told her.

'What did he want?'

'They got anxious about us and sent him down.'

'But it is not their affair.'

'Perhaps they thought we had been eaten by wolves.'

'Now they will make a scandal.'

'To hell with them.'

I took her hand and pressed it. Mme Mollinov said: 'You have had breakfast?'

'Yes.'

'Why did you not wait for me? It would have been nice to eat together.'

'I didn't want to wake you.'

I sat back against the rail of the veranda and watched her eat. Outside the plane trees threw their shadows across the *place*, but the sun was already beginning to encroach upon it. A peasant woman with a shawl round her head was drawing water from the pump into a tin pail. I felt pleased and at peace with everything: this enviable frame of mind was only disturbed by the presentation of the bill, made out by Mrs Staynes, which proved to be out of all proportion to the actual hospitality which the hotel offered. I wondered if they were charging us up for the cockroach which Mme Mollinov had found in her bed.

Before leaving I had a drink with Staynes in the bar. He insisted on treating me to this: I reflected that he could well afford to. I had a double whisky. Staynes said: 'I give you my card. Maybe one day you want a divorce. Okay, I fix it see? I fix everything.'

'Thanks. But I'm not likely to get married.'

'You never know. Me, I say that too one time. But,' he shrugged his shoulders and gestured towards his wife, who was watching us disapprovingly from the veranda: 'You see? I'm a sucker. You too maybe.'

'I doubt it.'

Staynes shook his head. 'All men are suckers,' he said philosophically.

'Well, you should know,' I told him.

29

Three days later. 'Another letter from your English miss.'

'How do you know that she's English or a miss?'

'I am not a fool. She is English and blonde and she plays bridge and has long teeth.'

'As a matter of fact she's dark and hates bridge like poison.'

'Ah! Then you admit that the letter is from a girl?'

'Certainly. Why not? Is there any reason why a girl shouldn't write to me. Or perhaps she should ask your permission first?'

'So! She is dark. Naturellement, I should have known you prefer brunettes. I have noticed that. It was forced upon my attention.'

'Are you suggesting that I forced my attentions upon you? In any case I didn't find you exactly unwilling.'

'Oh!' She gave a little outraged gasp and slapped me hard across the face with her open hand. One of the rings which she wore cut across my cheek and opened it up. I turned and walked into the bedroom and slammed the door. I fumbled at the envelope which I was holding in my hand. My hand was shaking, and not entirely with anger. I realised with astonishment that I was trembling with anxiety lest Yvonne had decided to reject my proposal. I knew then that I was in love with her and had been all along.

I sat down on my bed and started to read the letter. I was still re-reading it ten minutes later when Armstrong entered.

'What the devil have you done to your face?

I realised that blood was running from my cheek: a few drops of it had dripped down on the counterpane. I took out my handkerchief and pressed it against the cut. I said: 'Mme Mollinov.'

'Another row?'

'Exactly.'

'What news from Yvonne?'

'We've just become engaged.'

Armstrong took the cigarette-holder out of his mouth. He was tremendously surprised, and also pleased. It was the first time I had ever seen him exhibit any emotion.

'Congratulations, my dear fellow! What d'you want for a wedding present?'

'I thought you might be best man.'

'My dear fellow, of course. I've had enough practice.'

'The thing is, how am going to get away from here without any more trouble? I've got to' go immediately because Yvonne's coming back this weekend.'

'Send yourself a telegram. That's what I always do.'

30

Michel said: 'So you're going to leave us?'

'Unfortunately I have to.'

'Fed up?'

'Not at all. As you know, I received a very urgent telegram calling me back.'

'Don't blame you getting sick of this blasted hole. I'll go bloody crazy myself if I stay here much longer.'

They all assembled outside the châlet to see me off, including Mme Mollinov. There had been a partial reconciliation the night before, in which I had acquiesced in order to avoid further trouble. She had decided not to accompany me to the bus, however, and I set off alone carrying my suitcase with a chorus of farewells ringing out behind me. It was my last sight of Fou Châlet, but my connections with it and its inhabitants were by no means over, as I was to find.

PART TWO

'…He Hath Been Bitten by the Tarantula'

*　　　*　　　*

1

THE TELEPHONE BELL RANG BESIDE MY BED. 'HULLO,' I SAID.

'Hullo. That you Christopher?'

'Armstrong! Where are you?'

'Back in Cannes.'

'I didn't expect you so soon.'

'The party at Fou Châlet broke up. There's been the hell of a row and Spider's in a nursing home with a nervous breakdown.'

'Good God. What happened?'

'Michel beat it with all his available cash and Mme Mollinov.'

'What!'

'They're supposed to be in Paris.'

'Well I'm buggered.'

'I hope not.'

'What an extraordinary thing.'

'Spider had a fit on the spot. You'd better come over tonight and I'll give you the details. Don't bring Yvonne though.'

'No of course not. What time?'

'Let's say seven.'

2

It was in all the papers a week afterwards, under the heading 'Un Crime Horripilant à L'Avenue de Clichy'.

I read about it in *Le Petit Parisien* one evening while waiting for Yvonne to return from the cloakroom at a restaurant where we had been dining. At first impact I could not at once take in what I had been reading: the names Mme Mollinov and Michel Dessanges, staring at me from a column of smudged print that came off on the hands, seemed to have little connection with reality or with people whom in one case at least I had known intimately. And yet, after the news of Michel's elopement with Mme Mollinov, this sequel did not come exactly as a surprise. It was as though in my subconscious mind I had been expecting all along something of this sort to happen.

Yvonne's voice said from behind me: 'What are you so absorbed in?'

I said: 'One of the people from Fou Châlet has just been murdered.' My voice did not sound quite as though it belonged to me.

Yvonne said sharply: '*What?*'

'A Russian woman called Mme Mollinov.'

'Murdered?'

'Yes.'

'Who by?'

'A boy called Michel. Spider's ward. He was staying at the châlet too.'

'You knew them?'

'Of course.'

My mind was not really on the questions which I was answering. It was fully occupied in attempting to disentangle from the highly coloured account of the crime some relation to the circumstances in which its protagonists had become familiar to me. The butcher's knife, the blood-stained suit and the partially dismembered body belonged strictly to the works of Georges Simenon and Ashton Wolfe; to reconstructions of famous French crimes and the adventures of Inspector Maigret: a world where violence was *de rigueur*. One does not readily associate one's acquaintances with events of this nature.

Yvonne, looking over my shoulder, said: 'I see they haven't caught him yet.'

'No.'

'How d'you get to know these awful people. They'll probably call you as a witness.'

'I don't think so.'

'Getting mixed up in a murder case.'

'My dear girl it's nothing to do with me.'

'You seem very interested in it.'

'Naturally.'

'Did you know the woman well? I suppose you made love to her.'

'No.'

Yvonne gave a sceptical sniff. She said: 'Well, hurry up anyhow. It's past nine now. We'll be late for the party.'

'All right. Garçon! L'addition!'

3

I rang up Armstrong directly I got back.

'Have you seen the papers?'

'No. Why?'

'Michel has murdered Mme Mollinov.'

'Holy smoke.'

'They quarrelled over something. A diamond bracelet that she had.'

'Have the police got Michel?'

'Not yet. He's still at large.'

'This'll kill Spider. I must see him at once.'

'You can't now. It's two a.m.'

'I'll have to see him tomorrow first thing.'

'I hope to God they don't haul us all into court.'

'That's very unlikely.'

'It's a terrible thing.'

I felt too tired to go into all the details. I said: 'Bye-bye. See you tomorrow,' and rang off. My head was aching like hell. Sweat trickling down my body had made my stiff shirt go limp. It was still very hot weather. I mixed myself a pernod-and-water and sat down in an arm-chair by the window. I had not turned on the light in the apartment, and the moon shining in through the pane reminded me of Mme Mollinov and the wood behind Fou Châlet. I could not think of her as being dead. Death was a fact which I had never found easy to apprehend, especially when it occurred at a distance and in circum-stances as remote from reality as the murder of Mme Mollinov. It was all very confusing. I did not know what I felt.

I put a hand in my pocket and took out the cigarette-case which Yvonne had given me for an engagement present. This reminded me that we were soon to be married, and that I had quarrelled furiously with her in the taxi coming back. It was obvious that a reconciliation would have to be effected. I pulled the phone towards me and dialled her number. There was a click at the other end and Yvonne's voice said 'Hullo.'

'Hullo,' I said. 'Is that you darling?'

4

Michel was arrested in Marseille. He pleaded guilty at the trial but placed most of the blame on Spider for his early upbringing and environment. Spider received the censure of the judge; although it went to his credit that he paid for Michel's defence: with, of course, money provided by Armstrong. Michel's advocate was eloquent enough, but failed to get him off since the prosecution had pulled a masterstroke by producing in court the child Véra, who had been adopted by impoverished relatives of Mme Mollinov living in the Russian colony in Nice.

Michel managed to escape the guillotine, however. In view of his age he was awarded instead fifteen years in the penal battalions. I did not attend the trial myself, being at that time very busy getting married; and it was not until six months after that I heard the end of the story.

Walking along the avenue de la Victoire one February evening, I felt a hand grip my arm and turned to look into the grinning face of Vaska.

'Hullo, skipper! How's it going?'

'Not so bad,' I told him; although this answer at the time was far removed from the truth. In point of fact I felt bloody awful.

Vaska wore a new double-breasted blue suit with very padded shoulders. He looked like a boxer dressed up in his best clothes. He said: 'Come and have a drink with us. Spider's been looking for you for ages.'

We crossed the road, which was slippery with the confetti left over from last night's carnival celebrations. Spider was sitting at a café table on the opposite sidewalk. He had on a grey cloth cap and a pepper-and-salt suit, and in these garments I did not at once recognise him. At close range, however, his hollow hairy cheeks and fan-shaped beard, now liberally flecked with grey, were unmistakable. At the same time he looked ten times better than when I had last seen him. I knew that in the nursing home they had finally cured him of the drug habit, but I was unprepared for this radical change in his appearance. It was as though, in shedding his habitual black, he had assumed with the pepper-and-salt suit another and more genuinely genial personality.

'Christopher! My dear fellow!'

'Please don't get up.'

'I'm sorry I couldn't attend your wedding; but as you know at the time circumstances did not permit.'

'Quite.'

'You got my present all right?'

'Yes thanks.'

'Congratulations! I never expected to see you settle down.'

'No.'

'What are you having to drink?'

'A pernod, please.'

'Good! Garçon, trois pernods.'

'You're looking extraordinarily fit, Spider.'

'I *feel* extraordinarily fit. As a matter of fact I've had a big stroke of luck lately. I managed to sell the châlet!'

'Who to?'

'M. Paillon. He bought it up lock stock and barrel. Ghost and all! For quite a respectable sum too.'

'Oh, splendid.'

'Yes indeed. I was able to send Marie to a clinic in Switzerland. They say she'll be cured in six months.'

'That's excellent news.'

'It's a great load off my mind. Of course after that unfortunate affair of Michel's, I was pretty depressed, as you can imagine.'

'Yes.'

'If it hadn't been for dear Edwin I don't know what I should have done.'

'No.'

'One day I must repay all I owe him.'

A shadow darkened Spider's face for a moment at this thought, but the prospect of repayment was sufficiently remote to cause him no prolonged anxiety. He said: 'Poor Michel. It was a terrible blow to me when they sentenced him. Fifteen years in the Batt d'Af. One might as well be dead.' He shook his head sadly to and fro, but almost immediately brightened up again as the waiter approached bearing the drinks.

'Well, it's no good brooding over the past. Here's to the future! To your happiness, my dear fellow!'

'Thanks.'

We downed the toast. A wind blew down the avenue, scattering the confetti on the sidewalks and shaking the awning of the café. Inside, the window-panes were misted with steam, and shadows of people moved behind them as though imprisoned in an aquarium. I shivered slightly. It was a cold night: too cold really for outdoor drinking.

'Will you have another?' Spider said.

'No, really. I must be getting along.'

'Already?'

'I've a business appointment.'

'Well look us up soon. You know my address. Although I may be moving shortly. A larger apartment. Something more spacious.'

We shook hands all over again, Vaska grinning and banging me heartily on the back: 'So long, skipper!'

I turned and walked on up the avenue towards the place where Laurie Staynes had his office. I had to see him about my divorce.

SHORT FICTION

Edward: A Detective Story

*   *   *

I WON'T TELL YOU WHAT HIS SURNAME WAS. THE WAY THINGS turned out you might not believe it: it really was too much of a coincidence. Just think of him as Edward. We all did.

Edward had hair that looked as hard and shiny as the back of a black beetle. There was something, too, of the beetle in his odd sidelong scurrying walk, and his black butler's tailcoat, divided at the back, looked from behind like a beetle's wing-cases about to unfold. He was not deformed: the twist of his shoulders made you think so at first. His face was twisted too. It was a swarthy face. Black brows hooked down over a hook nose. One eyebrow went up when he smiled. He smiled with one side of his face only. You'd expect his voice to be sleek, suave. Wrong. It was harsh and full of gutturals. A touch of the ghetto? I couldn't say.

The hotel was short of staff. It was on the South Coast and this was the season. Servants were always leaving, bribed by rival hotels with bigger wages. The chef was always threatening to leave. His wages had already been raised three times. He cursed in the kitchen but the food was good. Edward and his wife didn't threaten and they didn't leave. They'd been there a month already. Edward acted as a waiter also. He was deft, attentive and polite. Other waiters, not so deft or polite, helped him. They came and went. Sometimes they went because the chef threw things at them. He never threw anything at Edward. I think he was wise not to.

Edward's wife, Mildred, made the beds and carried jugs of water up and down stairs. She was a plump little thing with a face like a pie. Nothing to look at, but Edward adored her. You could see it in the twist of his head whenever she came in sight. His face softened up and

87

became yearning: a lover's face, eyes like velvet – astonishing. When this happened, Mildred herself cast down her eyes and looked demure. I never heard them speak to one another: they might have been carrying on an illicit love affair instead of being man and wife.

I was having tea in the lounge the afternoon they came for Edward. Gravel crunched on the path outside. Looking through the window I saw two men in bowlers. It was hot but they had on mackintoshes. Edward saw them same time as I did. He made a croaking sound in his throat and dropped a plate of cakes. The plate broke and the cakes rolled away across the floor. It was the only time Edward ever dropped anything. He didn't stoop to pick up the cakes either. He turned and plunged through into the hotel restaurant. An old colonel shouted: 'What the hell!' and a Pekinese started to yap. One of the bowler-men shouted: 'Round the back. Head him off,' and came diving through the lounge. I stood up. The detective fell over the Pekinese. The Pekinese tried to bite the detective. I ran outside; several others came too. We watched the second detective tugging at the door of a shed by the tennis court. A third detective ran up from a car parked by the gate. He shouted: 'Stand back, lays an' gents, he may be armed.' The first detective now joined his pal, having shaken off the Pekinese. They both tugged at the shed door. The handle came off and the door flew open with Edward attached to it on the inside. There was plainly no fight in him: he collapsed immediately on the ground, calling out something about a wound.

The detectives hauled him up, one on each side. He drooped limply between them while they patted his pockets. Apparently he wasn't armed after all. They had to half-carry him to the gate: he couldn't, or wouldn't, walk. His feet dragged along, making grooves in the gravel. The third detective held the door of the car open. Just as they were getting him inside, Mildred appeared. She shrieked and fainted. She would. The chef, who'd been cooking the dinner, came out at this and started to curse. The car door slammed and the detectives drove off. At least, two of them did. One stayed behind. This one said: 'Who's the proprietor of this hotel?'

The proprietor, Donald Blair, was bathing on the beach. So were his partner and the partner's wife. They had to be fetched. Water was thrown over Mildred. With a final curse, comprising everybody, the chef returned to the kitchen. In the lounge the Pekinese was licking sugar off the cakes Edward had dropped.

Donald Blair arrived in a towel and bathing trunks. He was a great swimmer and proud of his body, which was richly bronzed. There was only one thing wrong with it: no hair on his chest. He minded terribly. I've no hair on my chest, either, but I don't mind. Donald Blair did. When dressed he sometimes wore a black shirt. He wasn't a Fascist, though. Not a member of the Party, that is.

Hansen, his partner, though built on a much smaller scale, had plenty of hair on his chest. He looked like the Hairy Ape. With him was his wife, Enid. They all wanted to know what the hell. They disappeared with the detective into Donald Blair's office. Mildred also. I wondered whether they'd arrest her as well. I rather hoped they would, but they didn't.

Dinner that evening was bad. All the shouting had upset the chef. Over this bad dinner everybody talked about Edward. The hotel guests were astonished at his arrest. That he turned out to be a well-known criminal, with his photo (wearing a beard) in the *Police Gazette*, nearly bowled us over. His being so sinister made it doubly surprising: as though the obvious red herring in a detective story turned out after all to be the master villain. If he'd been a meek, kindly-looking man it would have seemed far more credible. We all felt rather cheated.

After dinner I went for a walk with Peter. In those days almost everyone disliked me. In turn I disliked almost everyone. Perhaps they – and I – still do, but that's beside the point. The point is, Peter didn't dislike me, and I didn't dislike her.

Peter was fifteen and to her I, at twenty-four, appeared immeasurably old and wise. I liked this, since to other people I often appeared young and silly. Also she was an attractive child. Black curly hair, slanting grey eyes, and a high-boned face vaguely reminiscent of a girl I'd been in love with two years before. Perhaps it was that too. Anyhow, I liked her.

We walked along the promenade. There were coloured beads of light strung from poles along it and behind them the sky was electric blue. Peter wore a flame-coloured pullover. The other girl had also been addicted to pullovers of this colour.

Usually we talked about dance-music. It was our one topic of conversation but we could keep it up all day. Both of us were mad on jazz. We bought records and played them to each other on our respective gramophones. Fats Waller was our favourite at the moment and Carroll Gibbons came second. Nat Gonella was all right with us, too.

Tonight, however, we didn't talk about dance-music. We talked, naturally, about Edward.

'Did he get anything?' Peter asked me.

'Nothing so far's they know.'

'Not even spoons?'

'I expect he was after more than spoons. According to the detective he's quite a big shot. They've been after him for years.'

'A jewel-thief, wasn't he?'

'That's it.'

'I was disappointed in the detective,' Peter said. 'He looked so ordinary.'

'Did you expect him to speak with an Oxford accent, like in Edgar Wallace? They're ordinary people.'

'Of course they are,' Peter said. She always agreed with me. I liked that, too. Who doesn't? After a bit she said 'D'you think Mildred was his accomplice? That she knew?'

'They can't prove it. Anyway, she's not his wife. He's got a wife in Somerset.'

Peter whistled. 'Bigamy!' and then: 'I never did like Mildred.'

'Neither did I.' We both giggled. 'Well, anyway, it was exciting,' Peter said. 'I wish I'd been there.' She was on the beach with her parents when it happened. I said: 'How the chef cursed.'

'I like to hear him curse,' Peter said. 'You can hear him out in the hall sometimes.'

It had got dark. The tide was hissing thinly in along the shore. On the way back we did our crooning act. We crooned two songs: 'The Scene Changes' and 'These Foolish Things'. I always put my arm round Peter while we crooned. Her body had almost no weight against me. She sang with her face upturned to the sickle moon that figured itself in so many of our songs. Then we came up the steps towards the hotel and I took my arm from around her. The long windows were all lit up and her father and mother were standing by the garden gate.

Mr Bates smiled and waved the stem of his pipe as we came up. He was a tall thin man in reddish tweeds and he seldom spoke. In any case he never got a chance. His wife did all the talking. Mrs Bates was half-Irish and liked to remind you of it. She had grey hair straggling out from under the brim of a close-fitting cloche hat. Peter got the grey eyes from her and Mrs Bates' hair might once have been black. The high-boned face belonged, with the addition of lines and a moustache, to her father.

'Been for your walk?' Mrs Bates said. 'It's a broth of a night,' and she said broth with a bit of a brogue. Neither of them gave the impression of keeping an eye on us. They were indulgent parents and Peter was an only child. Anyway, they'd no cause to worry. She lived in her own dream of dance-music and had no thought for boys, though her shape under the flame pullover showed she was growing up.

'Is it time for the late dance-music yet?' she asked.

'Ten-thirty,' Mr Bates said. 'Are you going to sit up and listen to that again?'

'Oh, please!' Peter said. 'It's Nat tonight.'

Mr Bates winked at me and waved his pipe.

Mrs Bates said: 'What do you think about that Edward? The scamp. Poor Mildred, what she must be suffering.'

I thought rather: Poor Edward, and later I said so to Donald Blair as we played snookerette on the table in the hall.

'Poor Edward be damned,' Blair said, chalking his cue so hard the chalk squeaked. 'Fellow's an utter swine. Just like you to feel sorry for him.'

Blair didn't like me. He said I needed a toughening process. It was his boast that when drunk he used to walk along the sidewalk knocking people into the road if they didn't get out of the way quick enough. But as I say, he didn't belong to the Party.

'I'll tell you something about Master Edward.' He put screw on red and scored 200. 'You know he has a wife in Somerset. Well, she hadn't seen him for close on seven years. After seven you can presume death, and she wanted to marry again. Then the day before the seven years is up, comes a post card from Edward. 'I'm still alive in case you don't know it.' Now isn't that the action of an absolute swine?'

For some reason this story made me laugh. Blair blew up. From saying I was soft he veered round and said I was a hard-hearted swine. He got so angry he knocked a skittle down and lost his score. The table ticked over.

'That'll be half a dollar,' I told him.

'Time for Nat Gonella,' Peter said, coming in from outside. Blair ground his teeth and paid up. We sat in the lounge with the wireless on and Georgia came through. The coloured bulbs beyond the window went out because it was eleven. Night was no longer deep blue. Black now and the small waves broke.

Georgia,
Georgia,
You're on my mind.

Mildred went about for days afterwards with her eyes red. A new butler arrived: Alfred. He looked mild and the chef hurled a soup tureen at him. Wages went up immediately, including the chef's. Peter and I sat in deck-chairs on sun-scorched grass. Fats Waller's voice croaked out of the horn of my gramophone. One day we looked up through our sunglasses and saw the detective coming in the gate.

There was news. Edward had escaped. He'd gone sick with a wound incurred in the 1914 war and had been lodged in the prison infirmary at Portsmouth. One night he got away in pyjamas with a pinched overcoat over them, but they didn't find out till the morning after. By that time it was too late. Edward slept the night in his old digs. The landlady had let the room to a commercial gent, but he was away on business; so Edward, who'd climbed in through the window, was able to have a good sleep in his own bed. When he'd finished sleeping, he put on an old suit of the commercial gent's that was hanging up in the wardrobe, and left: again via the window. He left the prison pyjamas behind: that's how they found he'd been there.

The detective himself believed that we were unlikely to see Edward again: it seemed probable that he'd stowed away on a boat or that associates in Portsmouth had fixed him up with a hide-out in London. Mildred was questioned again, and went about with her eyes redder than ever: they now seemed to be positively swimming in blood. I myself admired Edward tremendously for this exploit; so did Peter. Discussions about it frequently interrupted our talks on dance-music. I'd lent her Constant Lambert's *Music Ho* because of the section on jazz, and she said he seemed to have the right ideas.

I made up my mind to marry Peter in two years' time, when she was old enough. Why not? True, we only had one thing in common; but that was better than nothing, which was what I had in common with most girls. I thought it all over and it seemed to me a good plan. The idea of marriage attracted me a lot at this time. Later I got married and then it attracted me much less. But that was later.

Meanwhile I said nothing to Peter about marrying her. We sat in deck-chairs, we played tennis and bathed; went for walks along the beach and the promenade; listened to dance-music and danced together in the lounge late at night when the guests had gone to bed. Two years did not seem a long time to wait.

I was playing snookerette with Blair and Hansen one evening when Mrs Bates suddenly came rushing into the hall.

'Quick, quick!' she said, and she was so excited she forgot to speak with a brogue. 'Edward's outside. Catch him quick.'

Hansen, whose shot it was, nearly cut the cloth at this. 'Edward?' he said. 'Outside?' and looked towards the door as though expecting Edward to walk in.

Blair said quickly: 'Where is he ?' and laid down his cue.

'Walking down the promenade, past the house. I saw him.'

A woman called Mrs Wills chimed in. 'That's right. Thought I saw him myself earlier on. He was sitting in a shelter but I saw his feet. I come from up North and I can always recognise anyone by their feet.'

There was no time to lose, Blair said: 'Come on you chaps,' and led the way at the double. Peter wanted to come with us, but Mr Bates asserted himself for once and stopped that. We came out on to the promenade and there in front of us was a figure that seemed to be Edward's. And yet: was it? The figure wore a dark overcoat and the back of its head was beetle-black; but it walked erect, with no twist in the shoulders, no servile stoop, and we were none of us sure. The figure wasn't hurrying and we gained on it rapidly. This part of the promenade was deserted; we'd walked so fast the hotel was far behind. We drew level; Blair and Hansen closed in on either side; I came round in front. The man stopped. I saw his face: horn-rimmed spectacles, a dark moustache. My first thought was, it's not him.

The man said: 'Yes?' sharply. It wasn't Edward's voice.

Blair said: 'You're Edward, aren't you?' and I could tell he wasn't sure, either.

'My name's Barnes,' the man said. 'I think you've made a mistake.'

'If so, it's easily rectified,' Blair said. 'If you wouldn't mind coming along with us.'

'Why should I?' the man said, still not in Edward's voice. Light glinted off the lenses of his spectacles. 'I don't know you.'

We all stood firm. I felt the need for a cigarette, and took one out. As I bent my head to light it there was the sound of a scuffle and Blair shouting: 'Oh, no you don't!' I looked up in time to see Edward kick Hansen in the thigh and turn to bolt. Blair grabbed him by the arm and coat collar and held him fast. Edward went limp at once and yelled out about his war wound. Hansen, rubbing his thigh, straightened up and grabbed the other arm. I came round in front again in case he tried another bolt. Edward started to sob. He pleaded with Blair and Hansen to let him go. Blair was inflexible. 'I stand for law and order,' he said sternly. He was enjoying himself. His jaw stuck out, his eyes were narrowed, and if he'd been an animal he'd have laid his ears back. Edward saw no possibility of pity there, and he'd just kicked Hansen. He appealed to me. 'What've *you* got against me, sir? Didn't I always look after you well?'

True enough. He had. I began to feel bad. Still, I wasn't holding him, and it'd take more than me to persuade them to let go. Then Edward went too far. He said his old mother was dying and he'd come back all this way to see her. You couldn't refuse to let a man see his old dying mother; you wouldn't have the heart. At this even I was sickened. 'Bring him along, boys,' I said to them.

From the road above came a squeal of brakes and a car stopped. It contained local plain-clothes men telephoned for by Enid Hansen from the hotel. A large man in a soft hat vaulted over the parapet, came up to Edward, and snatched his spectacles off. The tears dried immediately on Edward's cheeks, his eyebrow went up, and he smiled with one side of his face only.

'All right,' he said in his old guttural voice. 'It's a fair cop.'

Later we all sat round drinking Scotch with the plain-clothes men after Edward had been removed by car to Portsmouth. He kicked up something awful when they refused to let him see Mildred. The room was full of tobacco-smoke and the plain-clothes men looked slightly embarrassed without their hats. Peter sat with her ear almost glued to the radio, listening to Carroll Gibbons. She was again disappointed in the detectives. When they'd gone Blair had a brain-wave. He rang up the *Express* about Edward, so as to get his name in the paper. He did, but it came out 'Blane' and their ages were reversed, so that he became forty and Edward twenty-four.

Everybody except Peter and I sympathised more and more with Mildred. Two days later she disappeared and so did the cash-box containing twenty quid. Then everyone stopped sympathising. We never heard from her again: she didn't even testify at Edward's trial, where he was awarded seven years for bigamy. The day he was sentenced he got hold of a knife and tried to sever the veins in his wrist. He did succeed in inflicting a slight cut on his hand.

The Bates' holiday came to an end. They had to go back home. The night before they left, Peter and I walked along the promenade as usual. Peter was depressed; she didn't want to leave.

'You'll be coming back,' I said, to cheer her up.

'Not till next year. And then we may not.'

'The chef did some good cursing today,' I said. 'Did you hear him?'

'Damn the chef,' Peter said. She didn't feel like crooning either. We came to a part of the promenade where it was not well lit and no one about, and there she turned to face me. She was wearing her flame-coloured pullover, and in the bad light it seemed more than ever that other girl's face upturned.

'Aren't you going to kiss me?' she said.

I hesitated; the two years weren't up yet. Then I thought: we've got to start sometime. So I kissed her. She didn't like it. She broke away and ran, and next morning when I came down to breakfast she and her parents had gone.

That's the end of the story.

Except for one thing: Edward's surname. I'd better tell you that now, after all. His surname was Crook. You don't believe it? No. All right. Neither do I.

The Money Makers

*　　　*　　　*

AS A CHILD I LIVED A LOT IN FRENCH HOTELS. ONE DAY I WAS standing on the balcony of one of these hotels looking down into the street, when I heard a voice jeering up at me from the garden of the hotel next door. 'Yah, Froggie!' the voice said. It was an English voice. Looking round I saw it belonged to a small boy about my size and age dressed in a Lord Fauntleroy suit, who stood grinning up at me from below with his hands on his hips.

I was outraged. 'Yah, Cissie!' I bellowed back. I turned and charged down the stairs of the hotel into the street. Lord Fauntleroy met me at the gate of his hotel. We clinched without further ado and fell together on the ground. The fight went on for some time and neither of us won. At length we stood up, panting for breath. Lord Fauntleroy's suit was covered with dust and his knee breeches torn. We looked at one another warily. Then Fauntleroy said: 'You don't fight badly for a Frog.'

'I'm not a Frog. I'm English.'

'Oh, are you? I'm English too. My name's Bartholomew. I thought you were a Frog.'

'No,' I said. Since the fight appeared to be based on a racial misunderstanding, we shook hands. 'How old are you?' I asked him.

'Eight and a half.'

I was eight and three-quarters, so I had the advantage there. On the other hand Bartholomew had two fathers. One of his fathers was a soldier in India, the other lived at the hotel with his Mamma and was a financier.

'What's that?' I asked.

'He makes money. Can you make money?'

'No,' I said.

'I can,' Bartholomew said. 'I can make as much money as I like.'

'How d'you do it?' I asked him.

'I'll show you,' he said. 'D'you want to make some?'

I said I did, so first we collected together some leaves. Bartholomew showed me which leaves to pick; they had to be a special sort. At last we had enough leaves: Bartholomew looked at them with satisfaction. 'We can make enough money to last us with that lot,' he said. 'Now put them in this tin.'

He went and fetched a watering-can which he placed carefully beside the tin full of leaves. 'Now the formula,' he said. The formula was a crumpled piece of paper which he drew from his pocket; it had some pencilled figures on it which, he said, would enable us easily to turn the leaves into money. He'd pinched the piece of paper from his second father who made money every day by just writing down figures like this: it was sure to work. First thing was to pour the right quantity of water on the leaves. He did this with great care, muttering to himself and glancing from time to time at the paper in his hand.

'Now help me to mix it,' he said. This was done by scooping up handfuls of dust and adding them to the water and leaves in the can. I helped him to stir the mixture into a thick brown paste on the top of which a few leaves floated. I looked forward happily to the moment when this mixture should transform itself by magic into glittering golden pieces such as I'd read about in *Treasure Island*. 'What'll we do with all this money when it's made?' I said.

'We'll buy ice cream cornets with it,' Bartholomew said.

That seemed a good thing to do; I nodded. Luncheon interrupted our labours; we agreed to meet immediately afterwards. 'It'll have had time to change into money by then,' Bartholomew said.

'What the devil have you been doing with yourself?' my father asked angrily when he saw me. 'You're all over mud.'

'I've been making money,' I told him.

'Making money? What d'you mean?'

'With leaves and water. It's easy if you have the formula.'

'I wish I knew how to make money,' my father said.

'I'll show you how to do it later on,' I told him.

But when I rejoined Bartholomew in the next door garden we had a shock. The mixture hadn't turned into money at all. Bartholomew stared down at it with a frown, and I could see he was perturbed.

'Better stir it up some more,' he said. We stirred and stirred, but the mud remained mud, without even the smallest glint of gold.

'We must've mixed it wrong,' Bartholomew said at last.

Under his direction we mixed another lot. Still nothing happened. Bartholomew turned pale. He drew out the formula and glared at it unbelievingly. 'Perhaps it's that,' I said. 'Perhaps the formula's wrong.'

'That must be it,' Bartholomew said. He turned and kicked the tin of leaves into the air. A shower of mud poured down on the garden. He kicked the watering-can over and tore the formula into shreds. 'I'll get a new formula tomorrow,' he said.

But next day he wasn't there. I called at the hotel and was told that he and his Mamma and second father had left that morning. I never met him again. Pity, because I've been trying ever since to make money all my life, without success. It must be because the formula's the wrong one. I'm sure Bartholomew must have got the right formula by now, if only we could run across each other.

The Nine Men of Soho

*　　　*　　　*

I GOT TALKING TO AN ATS IN A PUB OFF OXFORD STREET THE other night. She looked a fairly typical ATS; service respirator slung, buttons bright and shining, white lanyard: all that. It was the last day of her leave, she told me.

'Thought I'd come and have a squint round the old place before I went back.'

'D'you know this part of the world well?' I asked her.

'Lord, yes,' she said. 'I lived in Charlotte Street for seven years before the war.'

And she added: 'You may not know it, but I was one of the original Nine Men of Soho.'

'Never heard of them,' I said.

'What, never heard of the Nine Men?'

'Absolutely not,' I said. 'Who were the other eight?'

'I can't remember all their names now it's too long ago. But only one of them was a woman, besides myself. That was Queen Zoe, who afterwards shot some man in a mews. I daresay you remember the case?'

'Vaguely,' I said.

'All of us were distinguished in one way or another. There was Roddy Penn-Venn, the pavement artist, for instance. At that time he had a job painting glass jars to contain bath-salts. It was I who actually helped him to burgle the bath-salts factory later on.'

'Why did he want to do that?' I asked.

'They were very expensive bath-salts,' she explained, 'and poor Roddy was always hard up. Anyhow, he came to me one day and said he'd got hold of a key to this place and would I come and help him carry some of the jars.

'I said I would, so we started off. The bath-salts factory was in Hampstead. Completely deserted, all in darkness. Roddy let us in with his key and we started feverishly stuffing our pockets with the salts.

'When we were absolutely bulging with them and Roddy had got into a most awful flap, starting at every sound and so on, we thought it time to go.

'Luckily I took a last look round before we beat it. And on the table what do I find?

'Roddy's visiting-card! The darn fool would have gone off and left it there but for me.'

'Perhaps he wanted to,' I said. 'Like the master criminals in the stories, you know, who always leave some sign behind them on the scene of the crime.'

'They don't leave their visiting-cards,' she said. 'Besides Roddy wasn't a master criminal.'

'Evidently not,' I said. 'But what did you do with all these bath-salts?'

'Roddy sold them to various swell pals of his. Actresses and so on, half-a-crown a time.'

'And did no one ever find out?'

'Never. The burglary was discovered, of course, but who would suspect Roddy, with the angelic face he had in those days?'

'Hasn't he still got an angelic face?'

'Well, not quite so much now, poor darling. It's got a bit bloated and bashed about since then.' She sighed. 'Alas, we none of us get any younger.'

'You look young enough,' I said.

'I'm preserved in brandy,' she said. 'Lord, when I think of all the stuff I used to put away,' and she looked down at her empty glass.

I ordered her another bitter.

'Tell me more about the Nine Men,' I said. 'Did they do anything besides pinch bath-salts and murder people in mews?'

'Oh, plenty of things. Bath-salts and murder were only side-issues with us. We used to pretend that we were the only real people in Soho, and that the others were only a mirage.'

'I wish you'd been right,' I said, looking round at various people in the pub.

The ATS laughed. 'In a way we were, you know. For example, we were the first to discover that Greek place off St Giles High Street, where everyone goes for coffee.'

'D'you mean the cellar?'

'That's it.'

'No one goes there now,' I told her. 'It's been closed down by the police.'

'Has it?' she said; 'I didn't know. How times change.'

'Indeed,' I said. 'And we none of us get any younger.'

'You're dead right,' she said. 'I'll be twenty-six next year. You can't tell me anything about the ravages of age.'

'I wasn't,' I said. 'You were telling me about the Nine Men.'

'Oh yes. Well, we used to meet in the cellar every evening and drink coffee. Then one night the Greeks told us very politely we'd have to stop as they wanted to use it for gambling. So we decided to all take a house together.'

'In Charlotte Street?'

'Yes. Somebody burnt it down in the end. I forget who. But at first we all lived there and had a terrific time. I remember once we sat in one room and laughed solidly for an hour.'

'Why did you do that?'

'Somebody said something funny.'

'Reasonable enough,' I said. 'What happened then?'

'The neighbours objected in the finish. Said they couldn't get a wink of sleep. Extraordinary man, too, called Mr Macphail used to wander in and out asking us if we could give him half a potato.'

'Was he one of the Nine?'

'No, he was an undertaker. Lived next door. He wanted the potato to keep his pipe-tobacco dry.'

'You certainly saw life,' I said. 'Ever meet any of these people nowadays?'

'None except Roddy, and you can see him almost any day at Hyde Park Corner, except when it rains. Last time we ran into each other he was trying to raise money to perfect a new invention: a doodle-bug trap.'

'Couldn't he raise it by pinching some bath-salts?'

'The factory's closed down, unfortunately. Wartime restrictions.'

'Shame.'

'You ought to talk to Roddy sometime, though. He could probably tell you what happened to the rest of the Nine. I joined the ATS shortly after the house was burnt down, so I rather lost touch with things. The group broke up not long after that, I believe.'

'Pity,' I said. 'I thought I might make a story out of it. Have another beer?'

'Thanks,' she said. 'Of course there were another nine men I could tell you about.'

'Who were they?' I asked.

'They were a man named Tom Wilkins,' she told me.

'What, all of them?' I said.

'Every one,' she said. 'You see he was mad. He believed he was nine people at the same time.'

'Must have made life very difficult for him.'

'It certainly did. Particularly as one of the people was Ethel Barrymore and another Harpo Marx.'

'Were most of them film stars?'

'Directors as well. He'd been a script-writer you see.'

'Enough to drive anyone off his rocker,' I said, remembering my own experience.

'Exactly,' the ATS agreed. 'He had a sister who was on the films, too. Altogether it was all too much for him, and funny things began to happen.

'He went mad slowly and then quickly. The nine people he represented began to figure more and more in his life. One morning they all rolled up at the office together, and you can guess the result: poor Tom was out of a job. You'd have thought that being nine people he could have got another easily, with all that combined talent. But the trouble was, the nine didn't get on any too well together. At times it was practically war to the knife, and he got nearly torn apart. Anyway, no one would employ him and finally he had nowhere to sleep.

'I remember the night it all came to a head. I was staying at a flat called the Square Hole: that was before the house that got burnt down.

'One night I heard a thunderous knock and there stood Tom Wilkins. He had flaming red hair and a black eye. He stood there declaiming poetry for about half an hour; it was a thing he often did.

'Then he sat down and played the piano, at the same time talking to himself in nine different voices.

'I didn't know what to do with him. All sorts of people came up to complain: they thought I was throwing a party. None of them cared to tackle Tom when it came to the point, though. He looked pretty wild, and, of course, being mad he had the strength of ten. Nine, anyway.

'At last I got him to lie down on the sofa; I thought he'd go off to sleep. But no, he kept asking for music. Music to soothe the savage breast.

'In desperation I switched on the radio, but all that came through was a voice saying: "D'you mean to tell me that your goldfish spoke to you at twenty past two in the morning?"

'I switched it off hastily, too late. Tom'd heard. He was sitting bolt upright on the sofa, with his red hair standing on end and his black eye bulging out of his head.

'"It's my sister," he said. "She's being persecuted. I can tell: those were code-words."

'Nothing I could say would pacify him. His sister was being persecuted, he had to go at once and rescue her.

'"But you don't know where to find her," I protested. "She's somewhere in Hollywood."

'"Don't you believe it," Tom said. "She's in Shenley Mental Hospital. Been there some time. Hollywood's only a blind to put people off the scent. She's in hiding see?"

'Then he said: "I must get to Shenley at once. Lend me eight-and-six."

'"There's no trains running at this time," I told him.

'"All right," he said, "then I'll walk."

'And off he went, just like that, in the middle of the night.

'The police picked him up about half way there,' she said, finishing her bitter and setting down the glass. Poor old Tom. He got to Shenley all right.'

Action 1938

*   *   *

WE WERE IN THE 'SUSSEX' ONE EVENING WHEN TWO FASCISTS came in, one of them tall and thin and tough looking; the other smaller, with only one arm and an empty sleeve pinned up to his shoulder. Both of them were quite young and they both wore black shirts. The taller one had a black raincoat on over his shirt and was carrying a big bundle of newspapers under his arm. He put these down on the counter and said to the barmaid: 'Two halves of bitter, please.'

There was nobody in the bar but us; most of them were in the billiard-room, watching the snooker.

The tall tough fascist looked over at us and said something to the smaller fascist, who shook his head. The barmaid served them and sitting down on a stool started to file her nails. She wasn't interested in any of us.

The tall fascist leaned across the counter towards me, tapping the bundle of newspapers with his finger. 'Have you seen these?' he asked.

'What are they?' I said.

'Today's papers.'

'I've seen some of them, yes.'

The tall fascist nodded to himself. He looked at me searchingly and then nodded again, as though satisfied.

'Did you know that most of the newspapers in England are owned by Jews?' he said.

'No, I didn't. Are they?'

'Of course they are. Haven't you ever thought about it?'

'I can't say I have.'

'Well, it's a fact. The Jews are getting control of the British Press. They're a menace!'

'In what way?'

'In every way!' shouted the tall fascist. 'How can impartiality and freedom of speech continue to exist when our press organs are controlled by an alien race? I ask you that!'

'I can't answer it.'

'Of course you can't,' the tall fascist said. 'There *is* no answer, that's why. It's unanswerable.' He looked at me with sudden suspicion. 'You're not a Jew, I suppose?'

'No,' I said. 'Why? Do I look like one?'

'You can't go by looks nowadays,' the tall fascist said. 'It's difficult to tell them, they have ways of disguising themselves.' He turned for confirmation to the smaller, one-armed fascist, who nodded, drinking his bitter.

'A disguised Jew is the most dangerous kind!' the tall fascist said, staring at me.

'Well?' I said. 'D'you think I'm a disguised Jew?'

'No,' the tall fascist said finally, making up his mind. 'You're dark and you've got curly hair, but on the whole I think you're an Aryan.'

'Come to that, you have dark hair yourself.'

'Ah, but being a fascist I am above suspicion.'

'Caesar's wife,' I said.

The fascist looked briefly at Randall, but without much interest; he was obviously Aryan. Randall, who looked bored with the blackshirts, asked me if I'd have another bitter. I said all right, and the barmaid got up and drew the beer, afterwards sitting down to file her nails again.

'Tell me,' I asked the tall fascist, 'why do you hawk those newspapers around with you. Are you trying to sell them?'

'No. I keep them as evidence.'

'Evidence?'

'Every copy of these papers,' the tall fascist said, 'contains some evidence that the controlling policy is in the power of the Jews.'

'That so?'

'I can prove it,' the tall fascist said. 'Eh?' He appealed to the one-armed fascist, who nodded solemnly.

'You see? It's true!' the tall fascist said. I nodded.

'Have another bitter?' Randall asked me; he'd finished his quickly.

'All right,' I said, finishing mine.

'Miss!' Randall shouted, rapping with his glass on the counter. He looked very fed up with the fascists. The barmaid got up without hurrying and drew the beer. We could hear the balls clicking faintly in the billiard-room.

'So now you know,' the tall fascist said.

'Can you suggest a remedy?' I said.

'Clear the Jews out of the country. Get the reins back into our own hands.'

'That will take a long time, won't it?'

'Not so long as you think,' the tall fascist said darkly. 'Eh?' He looked at the one-armed fascist, who nodded again.

'You'd be surprised,' the tall fascist said. He looked at me very hard for a moment and then nodded curtly. He picked up his bitter and drank it off at a gulp. 'Come on,' he said to the one-armed fascist, and picking up the bundle of newspapers he walked to the door. The one-armed fascist nodded to me and followed him.

'Goodnight,' I said.

'We'll be seeing you,' the tall fascist said.

'I hope to Christ not,' Randall said, as the door closed behind them. He said to me: 'For Christ's sake, why do you want to get mixed up with those mugs?'

'Why not? They amuse me.'

'You're easily amused.'

'I've got a happy disposition,' I told him.

Randall finished his bitter. 'What about this night-life you were going to show me?' he said.

'All right,' I said. 'Come on.'

'Goodnight,' Randall called to the barmaid, who answered without looking up from her nails. We just didn't interest her at all.

Outside, the high street was completely deserted, not a soul in sight.

'For Christ's sake,' Randall said, 'this is the big city right enough. You ever get lonely living here?'

We walked along the high street until the sign saying 'FREE AND EASY' showed up; it was next to a hairdresser's shop and we could hear dance-music playing inside. The first thing we saw when we got in was the two fascists. They were dancing with a couple of peroxide blondes up on a sort of platform at the end of the room. There was another girl sitting at the counter eating a ham sandwich; she wore a short-sleeved frock and looked very cold. Otherwise the place was empty, except for the man in the chef's cap behind the counter, who was cutting more sandwiches for something to do.

'This is the life,' Randall said. 'What are you going to have?'

'We can't get a drink here. They haven't a licence.'

'What! No licence?'

'No.'

'For Christ's sake,' Randall said. 'Let's have some coffee then.'

'Two coffees?' the man in the chef's cap said.

I looked at the girl sitting by the counter. She was dark and none too pretty, with thick eyebrows and rather muscular arms, which had gooseflesh all over them from the cold; the place wasn't too well heated.

'What about it?' I asked Randall.

'No damn fear.'

'Why don't you have a stove in this lousy hole?' the girl asked the man in the chef's cap.

'Feeling cold?' he said.

'Not half. I'm darn near frozen.'

'It's colder outside,' the man said significantly.

'Give me another sandwich,' the girl told him. She'd seen at once we weren't having any, so she took no notice of us.

The two fascists were still dancing up on the platform, while the radiogram played a slow foxtrot. The tall fascist saw me and waved his hand. He was smiling and seemed to be having a good time.

'Oh, God,' Randall said, 'those two mugs again.' He drank coffee gloomily.

The record ran down and stopped and the two fascists got down off the platform, followed by the peroxide blondes, neither of whom were much to look at.

'Well,' the tall fascist said to me quite heartily, 'we meet again.'

'As you say.'

'Not dancing?'

'No. I'm surprised that you are.'

'Why is that?'

'I shouldn't have thought you'd dance to Jewish music.'

'*Jewish music!*'

'That foxtrot was composed by a Jew,' I told him.

'What!' said the tall fascist. He seemed very shaken.

'Look for yourself,' I told him.

The one-armed fascist went up on the platform and took the record off the radiogram. He read the name on the label very carefully, holding the record up to the light in order to do so.

'Aw, what's it matter?' one of the blondes said. 'Let's have something to eat.'

'Wait,' the tall fascist told her. The one-armed fascist came towards him holding out the record. He looked very worried.

'Is it true?' the tall fascist asked, taking the record from him and looking at the label. The smaller fascist nodded.

'I'm surprised at you both,' I said.

'It was a mistake,' the tall fascist said. 'It won't happen again.'

'Say, aren't we going to have some eats?' the blonde asked him.

'No,' said the tall fascist. He threw the record on the floor, where it smashed to bits.

'Here, what are you doing!' the man in the chef's cap said.

'Shall we smash the place up?' the tall fascist asked the other one. The smaller fascist hesitated, then shook his head.

'What are you doing!' the man in the chef's cap said, coming out from behind the counter.

'Shut up,' the tall fascist told him. He drew back his fist and struck the man hard in the chest with it, sending him flying backwards onto the floor.

'What the hell!' said one of the blondes.

'Come on,' Randall said to me, 'let's blow.'

'Wait a minute,' I said.

The dark girl up the counter went on calmly eating her sandwich. She wasn't disturbed at all.

'Listen,' said the tall fascist, 'we don't want any trouble, so just keep quiet, see?'

The man in the chef's cap didn't say anything. He just sat where he'd fallen, looking very surprised.

'Come on,' the tall fascist said to the other one. He picked up his bundle of newspapers and started to go out.

'That's a nice lousy way to treat a girl,' said one of the blondes, but she didn't say it very loud. Randall threw some money on the counter to pay for the coffee, and we got out. In the street, the tall fascist was waiting for us.

'Thanks for telling me that,' he said. 'I didn't know.'

'You ought to be more careful,' I said.

'The Jews control everything nowadays,' said the fascist. 'That's why we want to clear them out.'

'D'you think you'll succeed?'

'Certainly. We have a very powerful following. Even in this town we are very strong.'

'I know. I went to a meeting once. A fellow got slung downstairs and broke his leg.'

'That's the trouble,' the tall fascist said. 'There's always such a lot of hooliganism, it gives us a bad name. But we're putting a stop to it gradually.' The one-armed fascist had come up and he nodded his head in confirmation of this.

'Why don't you join us?' the tall fascist asked me.

'I'm not interested in politics,' I told him.

'Well, you ought to be,' the tall fascist said. 'We'll be in power next year!'

'Will you?'

'It's a cert.'

'I'll wait till then before joining you.'

'It'll be too late then,' the tall fascist said. 'Eh?' He looked at the other fascist, who nodded.

'You think it over,' the tall fascist told me.

'All right. I will.'

'Come on,' Randall said, 'here's our bus.' He was very fed up.

'Cheerio,' I said to the fascists.

'So long,' said the tall one.

The other one-armed one didn't speak, but he put up his hand in the salute. He hadn't said a word all evening. Maybe he wasn't able to; maybe he was dumb. I don't know, but I certainly never heard him talk.

I looked back as we got on the bus; the two fascists were walking away down the high street together, and the tall one was still hawking that bundle of newspapers under his arm.

The Boy Who Might Have Been with Luck the Chess Champion of the World

*   *   *

I HARDLY EVER PLAY CHESS NOWADAYS. BUT AT ONE TIME, WHEN I was thirteen years old, I used to play a terrific lot of chess. In fact, with luck, I might have become the chess champion of the world.

I taught myself to play really. Of course, I had some co-operation at first, chess being a game for two players, like love. Co-operation in this case was supplied by two boys called Flood, who lived in a villa next door to ours, in the South of France. It was the eldest boy, Gene, who co-operated most, because he played chess with me. Phil, his younger brother, didn't co-operate much. He used to stand about and watch us play.

It was one summer and very hot. We were sitting in the garden of Gene's villa wondering what the hell to do. It was too hot to do much.

'We could play poker,' Gene said.

'We played poker last night,' I said.

'What about draughts, then?'

'I'm sick of draughts.'

'That's because you always lose,' Gene said.

'I beat you last time, anyway.'

'A fluke,' Gene said.

'All right, get the board then,' I said, 'and we'll see.'

It was a French draughts board with ten squares to a line. But it was reversible, and on the other side there were only eight squares. I hadn't noticed them before.

'What's this for?' I said. 'English draughts?'

'No,' Gene said. 'That's for chess. Good game, chess.'

'D'you know how to play?' I said.

110

'Sure,' he said. 'I can play chess. Boy coming over on the boat taught me.'

'All right,' I said. 'Let's have a game now. I'll soon learn.'

'We've got no chessmen.'

'We could play with halma-men,' I said.

'No good,' Gene said. 'You got to have proper chessmen. Otherwise you can't play.'

'The horse,' Phil said. He'd been listening. 'You got to have the horse.'

'The knight, you fool,' Gene said. 'That horse is called the knight.'

'What about the castle?' I said.

'You mean the rook,' Gene said. 'We chess-players call that the rook.'

'Why do you?' I asked.

Gene shook his head. 'It's a chess-playing term,' he said.

'Well, how can we get hold of some men?' I said. I was very eager to start playing.

Gene shook his head again. 'Chessmen are hard to get hold of,' he said. 'Short of buying them.'

'Let's buy some then,' I said. 'I've got ten francs saved up.'

'They'd be more than that. They're very expensive. Made of ivory.'

'I've seen ones made of wood,' I said.

'That's no good,' Gene said. 'You got to have ivory. They're the best sort. Can't break 'em.'

'That boy on the boat had some that folded up,' Phil said. 'They weren't ivory.'

'They were painted on ivory, though, weren't they?' Gene said.

'They were painted on something,' Phil said. 'Flat ones, in a case.'

'Ivory,' Gene said. 'There you are.'

I was disappointed. Ivory chessmen seemed out of the question. Then Gene had an idea.

'How about your father?' he said. 'He might have some chess.'

'I don't know if he plays.'

'He *looks* as if he played,' Gene said. 'He's got a beard, hasn't he?'

'Yes, he's got a beard.'

'There you are then,' Gene said. 'Always tell a chess-player!'

'All right,' I said. 'I'll go and ask him.'

My father was sitting in his study reading the deaths column of *The Times*.

'Chess?' he said. 'No. I don't play chess. Why should I?'

'We thought you might have some chessmen,' I said.

'What on earth d'you want chessmen for? You can't play.'

'No, but Gene can,' I said. 'He's going to teach me.'

My father was astounded. 'Gene play chess?' he said. 'Are you trying to make a fool of me?'

'No, Father,' I said. 'It's true. We want some chessmen so we can start playing.'

'Well, I'm damned,' my father said.

'Ivory ones,' I said.

'You're sure you don't want ones made of gold?'

'No, ivory,' I said. 'They must be ivory, otherwise you can't play.'

My father had started to read the deaths column again. He was no longer interested. I went back into the next-door garden.

'No good?' Gene said.

'No. He hasn't got any. And he doesn't play chess.'

'That's bad,' Gene said. He stroked his chin. He was annoyed. He didn't like to be wrong. He felt that my father's beard had misled him.

'Listen,' I said. 'I've got an idea. My birthday's quite soon. I might get some chess for a present.'

'Who'd get them for you?' Gene said. 'Your father?'

'No, he wouldn't. But my aunt might.'

'Ivory?' Gene said.

'I'll try.'

My aunt came to dinner that night, and afterwards I tackled her about the chessmen.

'But good gracious,' she said. 'Can you play chess?'

'I'll be able to when I get the men.'

'Don't listen to that nonsense,' my father told her. 'Of course he can't play. It'd be sheer waste of money buying him chessmen.'

'I don't see why he shouldn't learn,' my aunt said. 'Perhaps he'll be an infant prodigy. Wasn't it Capablanca who became a chess champion at sixteen?'

'But he isn't sixteen,' my father said. 'He's only thirteen.'

'I'll be fourteen soon,' I said. 'Besides, it takes time to be a champion. It might easily take three years.'

'Or thirty,' my father said. 'In my opinion the whole idea's a pack of nonsense.'

'I don't think it's nonsense,' my aunt said. 'I think it's a very good idea. After all, Capablanca was a Spaniard, wasn't he? And we've got Spanish blood. What do you think, Mary?' she asked my mother.

My mother on the whole was neutral. But she said: 'It'd stop them firing off pistols and throwing those bombs like they did last year.'

'I put a stop to the bombs without buying them chessmen,' my father said. 'However, if Jane wants to waste her money it's her own affair. Not mine.'

My aunt winked at me across the table. She'd always been my favourite aunt. I made up my mind that if she gave me the chessmen I'd become the champion in less than three years, in order to repay her faith in me.

My birthday came, and with it a large packet from my aunt. I tore at the wrappings feverishly. An ivory casket was disclosed. Inside it was a set of chessmen. They were red and white ivory and they were enormous. The more important pieces had faces carved on them. Even the knight had a face. It was a horse's face, of course. Only the rook and the pawns hadn't faces.

I put them back in the box and rushed next door to Gene.

'Look!' I said. 'The chessmen!'

'By gosh,' he said. He stared at the carved pieces with his eyes bulging out. 'Look at their faces,' he said.

'Look at the King!' Phil shouted, rushing up. 'Look at his beard!'

'Course he's got a beard, you fool,' Gene said. 'Beards go with chess. All chess-players have beards.'

'We haven't beards,' I said.

'We're not chess-players yet,' Gene said. 'We can grow beards later.'

'All right,' I said. 'Let's have a game first.'

We got out the board and Gene set up the men. The board was too small really for the size of men we had, and it looked very crowded when he'd finished.

'Now,' I said. 'How do we start?'

But Gene was a bit hesitant about starting. He stared hard at the board and stroked his chin as though a beard already grew on it.

'Some time since I played,' he said in explanation.

'Sure you can remember it?' I asked him anxiously.

'Yes,' he said, 'but there's a lot to remember.'

'What are the rules?'

Gene stroked his chin. 'We'd better start playing,' he said. 'You'll pick it up as we go along.'

'All right,' I said. 'What's the strongest man on the board? Which can do the most damage?'

'The queen,' Phil cut in. 'Queen's the strongest.'

'You shut up,' Gene said. 'We're playing this. You can play afterwards.'

'Your move,' he said to me.

'Righto,' I said. 'I moved the queen, jumping over the pawns to do it.

'Can't do that,' Gene said. 'Put her back.'

'Why?' I said.

'You can't jump over things. This isn't draughts. You got to move the pawns first.'

'These things?'

'That's it.'

We started to move. It went on a long time and nothing happened. Gene did not always remember the way the pieces moved, and once he even called in Phil to decide the move of the knight. Phil wasn't certain about this either, and they argued until I got fed up with it.

'When do we start taking pieces?' I said. 'Killing some of these off. We've been playing half an hour and we haven't killed anything yet.'

'You got to have patience,' Gene said, stroking his chin. 'It takes a long time to play chess. Sometimes a game takes three days.'

'Three days?' I said.

'At the least.'

'That's too long,' I said. 'I've got to become the chess champion in three years' time.'

'The world champion?' Gene said.

'In two years, now,' I told him. 'I'm fourteen to-day. I've got to be the champion before I'm sixteen. I'll never do it at this rate.'

Gene looked thoughtful. He said: 'I've a good mind to become the champion myself.'

'You can't,' I said. 'You're going to be an explorer, aren't you?'

'Doesn't matter,' Gene said. 'I could be a chess-playing explorer.'

'Let's get on with the game,' I said.

I decided to force a decision on Gene. I thought I'd become a lightning chess-player. I started to move all my pieces forward so that I could get the queen out, as according to Phil she could do the most damage. At last the way was clear and I waited impatiently my turn to bring the queen up and start killing Gene's men off.

Meanwhile it was Gene's move. He gave a shout of triumph and brought a bishop swooping diagonally down the board. Before I knew what was happening he'd whipped off my king and put the bishop in its place.

Phil danced about excitedly. 'The king!' he shouted. 'He's taken your king!'

'What of it?' I said. 'I've still got all my other men.'

'That's nothing,' Gene said. 'I've taken your king, the game's over. You can't go on playing without a king.'

'What about all these others, then?' I said.

'No good,' Gene said. 'Game's finished once the king's killed. Check, we chess-players call it.'

I glared furiously at the bearded king in his hand. I was so indignant that I seized one of the pawns and bit its head. Luckily the pieces weren't wood, otherwise I should have bitten off the head for certain. As it was, I nearly broke my teeth.

'That's not fair!' I shouted. 'You never said anything about the king before. Why didn't you tell me?'

'I only just remembered it,' Gene said.

There was no answer to that, so I said: 'What about another game?'

'All right,' Gene said. 'But you'll never be the champion if you let other people take your king.'

'I didn't know anything about it,' I said.

We set the pieces up again. Since I now knew that the whole point of the game was to kill the king, I surrounded him carefully with every man I was able to move. I had him bottled up. Nothing could possibly get at him.

Gene was also bent on the same idea and soon it became impossible to move anything. The board was completely cluttered up with pieces protecting our respective kings.

'No good,' Gene said at last. 'Neither of us can move at all.'

'A draw,' I said. 'Nobody wins. What do you chess-players call that?'

'Stalemate,' Gene said.

'All right, it's stalemate. Let's have another.'

We had another, with the same result.

'Stalemate again,' Gene said.

Phil said: 'When am I going to play?'

'All right, you have a game now.'

Gene sat and watched us play. It was again stalemate. Our respective kings were absolutely enclosed. Then Gene and Phil had a game. Phil lost. He slipped up somehow and left an open square in front of his king. Down came Gene's rook with a shout of triumph, and the game was over.

'Check!' Gene shouted. 'Check!' waving the red king at his brother.

I was disappointed and a little jealous. It looked as though Gene was going to be the champion after all, instead of me. Nor did chess seem an awfully interesting game played this way. It was too slow.

I went to bed very fed up that night, but next morning I'd an idea. I was determined to teach myself to be the champion. I went down to the English library and started to look for a book on chess. I couldn't find one at first. There were several books, but they were all full of chess problems. I wasn't concerned with chess problems. My problem was to learn how to play chess.

At last I found one that had the rules and everything in it. I took it home and read it for two hours. I wanted to read it at lunch, too, but my father stopped that. I bolted my food and rushed next door. The Floods were just finishing lunch.

'Hullo, Jay,' Mrs Flood said. 'Have you had anything to eat?'

'Yes, thanks, Mrs Flood,' I said. 'I just came to see Gene. I've got a book on chess.'

'Have you, by gosh,' Gene said. 'Let's have a squizz.'

'You and your old chess,' Gene's sister Geraldine said. She was almost sixteen and getting to be grown-up.

'Now, Geraldine, you mustn't be rude,' her mother said. 'I think it's very clever of the boys to play chess. You couldn't begin to play chess.'

'They haven't begun either,' Geraldine said.

'That'll do, Geraldine,' Mrs Flood said. 'Won't you have some pudding, Jay? It's apple pudding.'

'Well, thank you, Mrs Flood,' I said. I didn't really want pudding, I wanted chess, but one has to be polite. I ate the pudding impatiently. It was nice pudding, anyway.

When I'd eaten the pudding Gene, Phil and I adjourned to the garden.

'You've got the game all wrong,' I said.

'What?' Gene said. 'Impossible!'

'Look at the book then,' I said. 'You're not supposed to kill the king. The king can't be taken at all. You've got to get him cornered so's he can't get out. That's called checkmate.'

Gene frowned down at the book. He stroked his chin. He didn't like to admit defeat, but he couldn't get away from the facts. At last he said: 'Oh, well, I couldn't remember *everything*. Besides, I only played twice.'

'How about a game the new way?' I said.

We got out the men. We played three games the new way, although the book had to be frequently consulted. I won two of the games. The third was stalemate. Then I played Phil and beat him three times. I was happy. I thought with a start like this I couldn't fail to become the champion of the world at chess. I looked forward to becoming the champion in less than a year. Six months, perhaps.

After that, we played nothing but chess all day long. We became completely absorbed in the game. We got books from the library and did chess problems. I even got as far as doing the problems in the evening papers.

Then one afternoon I was walking through the public gardens, thinking out a problem, when I ran into a man called Mr Macgregor. He was the headmaster of the English school and did not sound Scotch, except for his name. I liked him, but I didn't go to his school. I went to a French school. My father always said there was no point in living in France if you were going to go to an English school.

'Well, Jay,' Mr Macgregor smiled, 'I haven't seen you about lately. What have you been doing with yourself?'

'I've been playing chess, sir,' I said.

'Have you really? I didn't know you played chess.'

'We only started to play this summer,' I said. 'We taught ourselves, Gene and I.'

'Does Gene play, too?'

'Oh, yes, he plays. We both play.'

'Care for a game now?' Mr Macgregor said.

'Do you play, sir?' I said. I was astonished. Apart from Gene and Phil, I'd never come across any other chess-player before. I'd begun to believe we were the only people in the South of France who played chess.

'I play a little,' Mr Macgregor said. 'Let's have a game, shall we?'

'But where will we get the men?' I said.

'I know where we can get some,' Mr Macgregor said.

He led the way down a side turning and stopped outside a house with a pillared façade. Over the door it had a sign, 'CHESS CLUB', and an arrow pointing inside. I hung back at sight of this.

'It's all right,' Mr Macgregor said. 'Nothing to worry about. I'm a member here. Nobody's going to eat you.'

I squared my shoulders and followed him in. I was rather angry with myself for hanging back. I thought it was no way for a future chess champion to behave.

I followed Mr Macgregor into a long room full of men sitting silently over chessboards. There were also some men not sitting, who stood watching those who were. The room was full of smoke from their pipes. I noticed one thing about these men at once. They had no beards. There wasn't a bearded man in the room. I was relieved that Gene had been wrong about this business of chess-players having beards, as I didn't think I'd be able to grow one by the time I was ready to become a chess champion. I hadn't begun to shave yet.

I sat down opposite Mr Macgregor at a table in the window. On the way there he had been greeted by some of the members. They did this by nodding or waving their pipes. None of them spoke and none smiled.

Mr Macgregor set up the men. They were large men, but made of wood. I didn't think much of them really.

'These men haven't got faces carved on them,' I said.

'No, why should they have?' Mr Macgregor said.

'Mine have,' I told him.

'These have got lead in the base,' he said.

'Mine are just as heavy without lead,' I said. 'They're bigger too.'

'They must be very expensive men,' he smiled.

'Ivory,' I said. 'A birthday present.'

We started to play. Mr Macgregor beat me in fifteen moves. It was a setback and I was surprised. We had another game and he beat me again. This time it took him twenty moves. I was no longer surprised, I was chagrined. I gritted my teeth. The tobacco smoke stung my eyes. The silence of concentration in the room weighed me down. I bent over the board, determined to concentrate, too. But by this time I was so rattled that it only took Mr Macgregor ten moves to beat me.

I sat back. 'Are you the club champion, sir?' I asked him.

'Lord, no,' he smiled. 'Far from it. Look, I tell you what. I'll give you pawn and move. How's that?'

So he gave me pawn and move, and again beat me. Then he took off two pawns, then a knight, then both of his bishops. It was like playing strip poker. He played me without a queen. He still won all these games and I was beginning to wonder whether he would still beat me if he took off all his pieces and had only the king.

Then at last I won a game. It was when he was playing without rooks. I was so surprised I nearly fell off my seat. Then I recovered, and shouted 'Checkmate!' All the chess-players turned and frowned at our table. I was a little abashed.

'Yes, that's mate right enough,' Mr Macgregor said. He seemed less surprised than I was. I'd a sudden idea that perhaps he had let me win, but I dismissed this as unworthy.

Playing the games had taken up all afternoon, and it was quite late when I left the club. But before I left I had become a member of it. Mr Macgregor had proposed me and also paid my initial subscription on the spot. I offered to repay him out of my savings, but Mr Macgregor wouldn't hear of this.

'No, no,' he said. 'You must accept it as a birthday present. From a fellow chess-player.'

We arranged to play again, and I went home very bucked. My father was less bucked. He wasn't bucked at all. He was angry. He wanted to know where the devil I'd been all day.

'With Mr Macgregor,' I said. 'At the chess club. I'm a member now.'

I whipped out my membership card and showed it to him. He put on his spectacles and read it. Then he took the spectacles off again and said, 'God bless my soul.' He was thunderstruck. He called my mother in.

'Mary, what d'you think? The boy's been made a member of the chess club. Perhaps he's a genius after all.'

'Good gracious,' my mother said.

They both looked at me very searchingly, as though they'd never seen me before. They were impressed.

At last my father said quite mildly: 'Well, well. You'd better go in next door when you've had supper. Your friend's been looking for you all afternoon.'

Gene had. He was annoyed. He'd been wanting a game of chess. When I told him where I'd been he didn't believe me at first. He said Oh yes, he'd spent the day playing with Capablanca. But when I showed him my membership card he changed his tune. Phil came and they all gaped at the card in silence. Even Geraldine had nothing to say.

'Perhaps you *will* be the champion,' Gene said.

Later we sat down and played, and I won by a move that Mr Macgregor had taught me. I won all the games that evening, and Gene shook his head sadly.

'You'll be the champion all right,' he said.

'I'll need some practice, of course,' I said. 'You must come down to the club and have a game sometime. As my guests.'

After that I played regularly with Mr Macgregor at the club, and once Gene came and played, too. Phil came as well, but not into the club. I got him as far as the door, and then he bolted.

Quite soon I got to be a passable chess-player. I played in the tournament, but got knocked out in the second round. I gritted my teeth and went into training. There was another tournament coming off in a month's time. I stayed in all day long doing chess problems and swotting up gambits and end games. In the next tournament I got as far as the fourth round.

Then, all of a sudden, there was great excitement. The world champion himself was coming to the town and had agreed to play at the club. I went into furious training. I hardly went out at all. I dreamt of chess all day and all night. My parents thought I was going out of my mind.

I gave up playing with Gene altogether. He was saddened, but he understood I had to think of my career. He and Phil played with a set of very inferior wooden men that they'd bought between them.

My aunt, by now in England, wrote to ask how was I getting on with my chess. Was I the champion yet?

I wrote back no, but I was going to play the champion next week in the tournament.

The day came, and through a thick screen of tobacco smoke I faced the champion at last across the chessboard. He made a move and walked round the room to another table. He was playing the whole of the club really, not only me. He wore big spectacles and was a young man, but certainly more than sixteen.

He came at length to my table again and poked a piece forward, moving almost immediately to the next table. I felt rather resentful. He did not seem to realise at all that I was his future opponent in the world tournament.

The evening wore on. One by one the champion polished off all the members of the club, including Mr Macgregor and the club champion, a man called Pritz. I was the only one left. I hadn't made a move for two hours. I was playing a waiting game. The champion had come to my table several times, but seeing I hadn't moved, had passed on again. I thought surely by now he must be getting tired out. I watched him cross the room towards me, and everyone was staring.

I slowly put out a hand and made a move. I'd been calculating this move for the last two hours. I moved a knight to K4. But as soon as I'd done it I was horrified. I realised that through overconcentration I had moved the wrong piece. I'd meant to move the bishop, not the knight. Worse still, by this move I'd left my queen unguarded.

While I watched, numb with horror, the champion's hand came slowly down and removed the queen. In its place he substituted his rook and stepped back. By all the rules of chess etiquette I was now in honour bound to give up the game. There was no point in continuing without a queen, especially against the world champion. But at this moment my British bulldog spirit asserted itself. *I wouldn't give in*. I insisted on continuing the game. I made another move. The champion immediately countered it by checking me.

I gritted my teeth and interposed a pawn wildly. All the members had gathered round to watch. They were outraged. The champion checked me again. I'd no more pieces to interpose, so I moved the king. The champion's rook pursued him into a corner. I held on in a frantic hope of making it stalemate. No use. The champion was relentless. He pushed forward a pawn. There was no way out. It was checkmate. I bent over the board with my face quite close to it in case I'd overlooked a possible outlet, but there was none. The champion was already walking away from the table. He hadn't even bothered to say 'Mate.'

I got up and went towards the door. There was a supper to follow, but I couldn't face it. Besides, the members were muttering angrily about me.

I was angry, too. 'You wait,' I kept repeating to myself on the way home. 'Just you wait. We'll meet again one day.'

'How did it go?' Gene asked when I got back.

'I got beaten.'

'Never mind,' Gene said. 'I suppose there'll be a return match?'

'I don't know,' I said.

I was too fed up to talk about it. I still had to tell my parents I'd lost. And then, two days afterwards, came a letter from my aunt asking had I beaten the champion?

I wrote back no, not this time, but there'd be a return match.

There wasn't a return match. The chess club was pulled down shortly after. It re-opened in new premises and named after the champion in honour of his visit. But by the time that happened I'd given up being a member. I'd given up being a chess champion, too. I'd decided to become a writer instead.

Civvy Street

*   *   *

ARMISTICE DAY, MUNICH YEAR

THE STREET LEADING TO THE LABOUR EXCHANGE WAS A BLIND
alley, ending in a high brick wall; the queue stretched some way along
it. As Alan turned the corner, groups of men were standing about
talking, despite the printed notice hanging inside the exchange which
said: 'DO NOT LOITER IN THE STREET TO THE ANNOYANCE OF THE
RESIDENTS.' It was Armistice Day and all the men wore artificial
poppies in their coats; the woman selling them had done such a brisk
trade that she was now on her way to fetch fresh supplies. She hurried
past Alan, a stout woman with a beaming face, her empty tray held in
front of her and the coppers rattling in her collection box.

Alan asked one of the men: '10.45?'

'You're late,' the man said; '10.45's up front.'

Alan pushed his way in further down. He was the only man in the
queue not wearing a poppy. The two behind him were discussing the
football pools.

'Three draws last week; not a one come up.'

'I was two down.'

'We can't all win,' the first man said philosophically.

'You're right there.' The second man spat and blew his nose. It was
a sunny morning but bitterly cold.

'Blowing up for snow if you ask me.'

'Pipes are all frozen our way.'

The first man stamped his feet to keep warm, swaying from side to
side and whistling through his teeth. The queue moved up slowly. A
man with a purple nose, wearing a beret, pushed through the door of

the exchange past the queue, tucking a pound note into his pocket. 'See you in the boozer, Bill.'

'Backed a winner?' Bill said.

'I'm good for a pint.'

The man in the beret hurried off down the street. Alan's hand in his pocket clutched a yellow card. His face felt stiff with the cold. He wondered if his application to the Unemployment Assistance Board had been considered yet; it was three weeks since the Inspector had called on him.

'Any means of support?'

'None, I'm afraid.'

'Previous occupation: salesman. Is that correct?'

'I've had two jobs as a salesman.'

(Carrying vacuum-cleaners from door to door, demonstrating the latest model to prospects either unable or unwilling to buy; a weekly pay-cheque for £2, less insurance; 'No sales'; the sack.)

'Prior to that, you were unemployed?'

'I had a private income.'

'What happened?'

'The slump.'

'I see.' The Inspector wrote 'Now destitute' across the form in front of him. 'Sign here, please.'

Since then Alan had heard nothing more; for three successive Fridays the clerk at the exchange had shaken his head. Alan's landlady was growing restive; four weeks owing already and everyone has to live; even Mrs Sleath, crouching in her kitchen over the gas-ring and the inevitable kipper.

A young clerk came to the door and called out 'Any more 10.45s?' There was a sudden stampede and Alan found himself jammed in the entrance against a man in a blue reefer jersey. It was warmer inside the office and smelt of sweat; the men queued up for payment and the head clerk, wearing a hat, threw the coins on the counter: 'Ten-fifteen-seventeen.' A grizzled man with a beard said in a loud voice: 'There's only one way: wipe out the lousy capitalists.'

The head clerk looked up and shouted: 'D'you mind not talking so loud! It's like the Tower of Babel in here, I can't hear meself think.'

Dead silence supervened, and Alan found himself in front of the desk. He signed his name with a stub of pencil and looked across at the young clerk, who shook his head.

'Nothing yet.'

'Nothing?' Alan's lips were still numb: he couldn't speak clearly. 'But it's three weeks,' he tried to say, and a man behind jogged him in the back: 'Sorry, mate.'

'We've heard nothing,' the young clerk said.

The head clerk stopped paying out and glared at Alan over his spectacles. 'What's the trouble, mister?'

'Three weeks,' Alan said, 'and nothing's come through.'

'We can't help that,' the head clerk said. 'It's nothing to do with us. And you're holding up the queue.' He pouted his lips angrily. 'Pass along, please.'

Alan turned away from the counter and pushed his way towards the door. A disturbance was in progress outside; a man in a bowler put his head in and called out 'Hey, mister!'

'What's up?' the head clerk growled. 'What is it now?'

'Bloke fainted out here.'

'Fainted?' the head clerk said, his eyes bulging out behind his spectacles. 'What's he want to faint for?'

'Hunger, I shouldn't wonder. He's smashed his head on the kerb. A proper mess,' the bowler man said with relish.

The head clerk grunted in disgust. 'Better phone the ambulance,' he said to the young clerk over his shoulder.

All the men who had been paid started to crowd out towards the entrance, talking excitedly. 'Quiet, please!' the head clerk shouted, but this time without effect.

The young clerk said: 'Hullo. Hullo,' into the telephone. The queue had broken up and Alan could not see the man who had fainted and struck his head on the kerb, because of the dense crowd around him. He turned right towards Woolworth's in the High Street. He had sixpence in coppers left and was on his way to buy a packet of Tenners and a cup of coffee. As he turned the corner the gun went off bang; traffic stopped all over the town and two dogs ran yelping up the road; Alan stood stiffly for the two minutes' silence. A second explosion, louder this time; the ambulance started off for the labour exchange; people in the streets became galvanised, hurrying along towards the cenotaph, where a service was being held and the clergyman spoke about peace. 'The crisis is over,' and the man bled in the gutter by the kerb and someone shouted 'Give the bloke some air.' Everybody must live; Alan thought about his landlady. Perhaps she'd wait another week.

A young girl in a short fur coat smiled at him: 'Buy a poppy?' holding out her tray. Alan paid his penny for patriotism and went on into Woolworth's, making for the counter where they sold cigarettes. Fivepence left; he'd have to cut out the coffee.

Five Finger Exercises

*　　　*　　　*

'I DON'T BELIEVE IT,' JOCELYN SAID.

'It's quite true,' she said. 'Honour bright. I'm sixteen.'

'You can't be,' Jocelyn said. 'You must be older than that.'

'Well, I'll be seventeen soon,' she said with satisfaction.

'Even so,' Jocelyn said, 'you're not sixteen now. You simply must be more than sixteen.'

'It's very rude of you not to believe me.'

'But it does sound incredible.'

He thought she looked fully twenty-three when he first saw her looking at an illustrated paper in the lounge, before lunch. They did not take any notice of each other; Jocelyn stared out the window at the steady-falling rain and thought my god, the Sussex Riviera, comparing it unfavourably in his mind with Monte Carlo or Cannes. He did not look at the girl at all; she might not have been there insofar as he was concerned. He stared out at the rain which splashed in puddles on the drive. Then the luncheon-gong sounded and they went through to the restaurant. Walking behind her Jocelyn noticed the set of her shoulders in the blue openwork jumper that she wore, but without interest, abstractedly. After lunch they sat in the lounge again. Jocelyn talked to an old lady named Mrs Bliss, who was the only other person staying in the hotel. She was very withered, with untidy white hair and a glass eye. She spoke dogmatically and continuously about her past glories and titled relations; her thin drawl drifted tirelessly on as the rain dripped down the window-panes outside. Jocelyn said 'Yes' and 'Quite!' and 'Definitely,' having found it a good plan to agree with everything that old people said, as that sometimes prevented them from saying it more than once.

While they talked the girl sat across from them, reading a bulky novel which she held upon her knee. Presently she rose and went out.

'What a quiet girl,' Mrs Bliss said. 'I haven't heard her say a word. I expect she's terribly shy, poor thing.'

'She didn't look shy to me,' Jocelyn said.

He did not see her again until dinnertime. Mrs Bliss never came down in the evenings so they were alone in the lounge afterwards. For something to do, Jocelyn offered her a cigarette.

'Thank you,' she said. 'I don't smoke.'

'Isn't it dreadful weather?'

'Yes. I suppose it's still raining.'

'Yes.'

'I tried to go for a walk this afternoon but it rained so hard I went to the pictures instead.'

'What was on?'

'It was a gangster-film. You know: full of machine-guns and molls.'

'And tough-guys saying Okay Chief.'

'That's right.'

Jocelyn laughed. 'D'you like the pictures?'

'Not much.'

'I suppose you're keen on dancing and that sort of thing.'

'Well, I haven't done a lot of it. I only left school last year you see.'

'Last year?'

'I ran away.'

'Good god.'

It was at this point that Jocelyn enquired her age and received his second surprise. He looked at her more closely. She was a big buxom girl and she had a round face. She had a smooth golden skin, a snub nose, and straight black hair, bobbed and held back from her forehead with a circular comb. She had changed into a long yellow frock that went well with the colour of her skin. Jocelyn saw that she was younger than he had at first supposed, but she still looked more than sixteen.

'And how old are you?' she asked him.

'Guess.'

'Thirty.'

'Got it first time.'

The girl nodded her head complacently.

Jocelyn said: 'Tell me. Why did you run away from school?'

'I just got tired of it. I ran away and took a job in London.'

'But don't your people object?'

'They don't know where I am.'

'Well, I'm damned. You're a most extraordinary girl aren't you?'

'I'm pretty extraordinary.'

'Good. I like extraordinary people.'

'You're not very ordinary yourself.'

'Of course I'm not.'

'When I saw you first I didn't think you were English.'

'I've lived a lot abroad.'

'Where? In Paris? I've been to Paris.'

'Yes, I was in Paris for years studying art.'

'Are you an artist then?'

'Of sorts.'

'I thought you were.'

'Why did you think that?'

'You look very Bohemian. Not respectable.'

'Do you like respectable people?'

'No. They're too dull.'

The evening passed pleasantly. The girl, whose name turned out to be Jill, told Jocelyn some amusing stories about the department store where she worked, and in return he recounted several of his experiences on the continent.

Jill said: 'You *have* had a hectic life. Don't you find it very boring down here after all that?'

'A bit. I shall be going back to London soon. I have a studio there.'

'I suppose you paint women in the nude.'

'Occasionally.'

Jill smiled. She had good teeth. She had widespaced grey eyes and a wide mouth with full lips. Jocelyn, who held unconventional views about girls' looks, found her attractive. He wished she were not so young as this made things more complicated than they would otherwise have been. To establish contact he took her hand and began to tell her fortune by the lines on her palm, predicting all kinds of unlikely events for the future. Outside it continued to rain heavily. At last Jill drew away her hand, which Jocelyn had been holding all this time, and said she must go to bed.

They went up together; their rooms were not far apart. Outside her door Jocelyn said: 'Goodnight, my dear,' and as she smiled at him he bent his head to kiss her. She stepped back and evading his arm, slipped into her room and gently closed the door.

Jocelyn retired to bed rather annoyed.

Next morning it was bright sunny weather, although everything was still wet from the rain. Jocelyn did not see Jill until after lunch, when he came upon her in the lounge, reading *The Good Companions*. He sat down beside her and immediately opened siege. 'Why were you so silly last night?'

'You mean I wouldn't let you kiss me?'

'Yes.'

'Men like you always want to kiss girls. I knew you wanted to long before that, when you were reading my hand.'

'Why wouldn't you let me?'

'I wanted to see you blow up.'

'I never blow up. I'm a very good-tempered man. At the same time I'm very persistent. I always get my way.'

'You're very conceited. That's one of the reasons why I wouldn't let you kiss me.'

'Are you going to let me do it now?'

'No.'

He leaned over and took her wrists. She was wearing a scarlet open-work jumper and he could see her flesh through it. Her breasts were prominent, with pointed nipples. She had a strong body and well-shaped. Jocelyn had always liked heavily-built girls. He looked down into her face. She was smiling with her full lips pursed up and did not look at all frightened or disconcerted. He kissed her cheek and felt the skin firm and smooth under his lips. She turned her mouth away.

'Dear me,' she said, 'you certainly *are* persistent.'

'Have other men tried to kiss you?'

'Oh, yes. One of the salesmen in our department is always trying.'

'And do you let him?'

'No.'

'Darling.'

At last he succeeded in kissing her mouth. 'It was closed and completely unresponsive.

'Now are you satisfied?' she said.

'Far from it.'

He was kneeling by her chair and he pulled her down and put his arms round her shoulders.

'It'll be funny if Mrs Bliss comes in and catches us like this,' Jill said. 'She's gone for a walk.'

He pressed his lips against hers several times. The result was again disappointing. He said: 'Do kiss me, darling. You should be able to with a mouth like that.'

'I'm afraid I haven't your experience.'

The sun struck through the glass of the window and made a pattern on the carpet. Jocelyn drew her forward so that she was sitting on the floor beside him, with her back against the chair. 'Now kiss me.'

'I don't think I can.'

She did not know much about kissing but she improved a little as the afternoon progressed. At teatime they were interrupted by the entrance of Mrs Bliss. She did not notice anything peculiar about them, although they were still sitting on the floor; she was as usual too occupied with her own affairs. Tea was brought in by the waiter. Mrs Bliss told Jocelyn and Jill of the walk she had taken, describing the scenery with a wealth of unnecessary detail. Jill ate a number of cream cakes and returned to reading *The Good Companions*. Mrs Bliss talked to Jocelyn about her girlhood in Ireland, touching briefly on various men, all wealthy and goodlooking, who had wanted to marry her.

When she went up to change for dinner Jocelyn said to Jill: 'We'll come in here afterwards, shall we?'

'If you like.'

'Keep on your jumper; I love you in that.'

'I'm glad somebody appreciates it.'

Later they spread cushions in front of the fire and sat down on the floor. As he was kissing her, the lock of hair which he wore over his forehead, to show he was an artist, fell forward into his eyes and she smoothed it back with her hand. He kissed her throat and neck and felt her body firm and heavy against his as he strained her to him. She drew away with a gasp. 'Let me get my breath back.'

'You're very sweet, Jill. I love you.'

'How many girls have you said that to?'

'You funny thing. Don't you believe me?'

'No. You just want someone to kiss.'

Jocelyn laughed and put his cheek against hers. 'Do you like me, Jill?'

'Course I do. Else I wouldn't let you do this.'

'Say you like me then. Say "darling".'

'I never say "darling". It's one of the things I can't say.'

'Why not?'

'I just can't.'

'Let me kiss you while you smile.'

Very much later, Jocelyn said: 'The fire's gone out.'

'I've got a gas one in my room.'

'Let's go up.'

'All right.'

The gas fire lit with a pop and the sticks of asbestos began to glow red.

'Don't let's have the light on,' Jocelyn said.

He led her over to the bed. They lay back across it and he started to kiss her. She was less shy in the dark.

'Kiss me properly, Jill.'

'How's that?'

'Not bad. Try again.'

'Mm.'

The gas fire glowed and hummed in the darkness. The eiderdown quilt on the bed became warm from the impress of their bodies. Jocelyn put his hands on her breasts through the woollen mesh of her jumper. She shivered slightly and said: 'You know too much for a man.'

'It's just as well.'

He continued to stroke her breasts and she began to breathe quickly. She held him to her with her arms round his neck and her lips worked slowly under his.

'Am I doing better?' she asked him presently.

'Very much better. You're a wonderful girl. You'll be at the top of the class soon.'

'Thank you, professor.'

'Take off your jumper, darling.'

'I thought you liked me in it.'

'I want to see you without it.'

'All right.'

She sat up and wriggled out of the jumper, dropping it on the chair beside the bed. He kissed the firm flesh of her shoulders and breasts, which gleamed faintly in the dark. Suddenly she buried her face on his chest and he could feel her trembling all over against him.

'Don't be frightened, darling,' he said. 'It's nothing to be afraid of.'

'I'm not afraid.'

'What's the matter then?'

'Nothing's the matter.'

Afterwards he said: 'You've got a lovely body, darling.'

'Please don't laugh at me.'

'I'm not laughing at you. Really. I'm speaking as an artist. You'd make a very good model.'

'D'you think so?'

'You'd make a lovely model. You must come and sit to me in London.'

'Oh, I should love that. Will you really? I've always wanted someone to paint me.'

She rolled over and kissed him several times. She was overjoyed. He held her in his arms. What he said about her body was quite true. She had a magnificent body.

'When will you come to London?' she said.

'Fairly soon.'

On Monday morning Jill came into the lounge, dressed for the journey. She looked different in her hat and coat and very grown-up. Jocelyn took her hands and said: 'I'm sorry you're going, dear. I wish you could stay.'

'Truly?'

'Yes, truly.'

'I wish I could stay too. But we'll meet again soon, shan't we?'

'Of course we shall.'

He kissed her and she kissed him back in the way he had taught her. 'Have you enjoyed your holiday, my sweet?' he said.

'Yes. Everything. I've enjoyed it all frightfully.'

'Good.'

She smiled up at him. 'And have I been a good pupil?' she said.

'A splendid pupil. You're a credit to the school.'

'I never was a backward girl,' Jill said.

He kissed her again and the sun was warm on her face and the porter came in to say the taxi was waiting outside.

'I'll come and see you off,' Jocelyn said.

In the afternoon, at tea, Mrs Bliss said: 'Has that little girl gone?'

'She went this morning.'

'She was rather peculiar, wasn't she?'

'Yes, she was rather. She was only sixteen.'

'Really? Is that all? It reminds me,' Mrs Bliss said, 'of an experience I had in Ireland when I was a girl ...'

Two days later, Jocelyn received a letter addressed to him in a large round handwriting.

JOCELYN DEAR,

How are you. It is very cold in London. I started work well on Tuesday morning. I jammed my little finger in a swing-door. It looks so funny now, it's got a huge bandage on it. I quite shocked the first-aid man because instead of crying I swore. I didn't even know some of the words before, they just came naturally. I felt rather proud of myself afterwards. I'm afraid I'm not a very good letter-writer, this one seems to be all about myself. Please write and tell me all that is happening at the seaside, I wish I were there to-day. I feel most jealous of you, being there. I haven't forgotten my five-finger exercises yet, tho' I haven't gained any further experience. (Take that which way you please.) Don't get conceited because I have written to you, I've seen so many respectable people to-day that I had to provide an outlet to my feelings by writing to someone who was not!

> With lots of love and kisses,
> JILL

P.S. I hope you come to town soon. (No conceit about this please.)

P.P.S. A girl told me yesterday that one of the sales men in our department is rather fast. I don't quite know what this means, but if it means 'quick work' then you must be fast.

Funny Things Happen

*   *   *

1. THE SPY WHO WAS A CHARACTER FROM CONRAD

FUNNY THINGS ARE ALWAYS HAPPENING TO ME.

For example, no sooner was I discharged from the army than I got mistaken for a spy. Nearly got arrested, too.

I was staying with a friend in the country. Call him Peter. What he does is quite important, but he was not doing it then. He was on leave from the Ministry. I was on leave too. My twenty-eight days hadn't expired. As a reaction from three years of khaki and clean fatigue I'd bought myself a crimson corduroy coat. It was this coat that got me into trouble – on that and my beard. I'd grown a beard as well. It doesn't take me long to grow a beard. It was getting along nicely. I'd already started trimming the point.

Anyhow, we were in the local one night, it was a Saturday and pretty full up, and there were a couple of blokes in a corner staring at us hard. I thought they were just staring at my beard, so I didn't take much notice. Then one of them got up and came over to me.

'Can I see your identity card, please?' he said.

'You can't,' I said. 'I haven't got one.'

'You hear that, Joe?' he said, turning to the other man who'd come up behind him. 'He hasn't got one.'

The other one nodded and rubbed his hands, looking pleased. 'Got any papers at all?' he asked me.

'Yes,' I said, 'discharge papers.'

'Let's see them,' the first one said.

'You go to hell,' I said. 'Why should I show them to you.'

'We're police officers,' the second said. 'CID.'

'Show me your warrant card then,' I said.

People had started to turn round and look at us. This seemed to make both the men uncomfortable. The second one said in a low voice: 'This is a confidential matter. We're on special duty.'

The first one, however, raised his voice. 'Hell, Joe,' he said, 'why kid-glove him? He's our man all right. Look at the coat. Corduroy, ain't it?'

'There's the beard, though,' the other said. 'They didn't tell us nothing 'bout a beard.'

'Maybe false,' the first said. 'Stuck on.'

'If you pull it to see I shall certainly sock you,' I told him.

The second looked serious. 'Offering violence,' he said. 'Police officer. Execution of his duty.'

Peter had been getting drinks at the bar. He now came up with a pint in each hand and said: 'What's the row?'

'Do you know this man, sir?' the second said. Peter hasn't a beard: hence the sir. He was smoking a pipe, too. He said: 'Of course I do. Friend of mine.'

'Is his name MacWhirr?'

'It is not,' Peter said.

'MacWhirr's dead,' I said. 'He died with Joseph Conrad.'

The first man got excited again at that. 'Hear that, Joe?' he said. 'Comrade! A communist!'

'Conrad, not Comrade,' I said. 'Wrote books.'

'MacWhirr was one of his characters,' Peter said.

'Can't be the same bloke,' the second man said.

The first said: 'Books! You read books?'

'I write them too,' I said.

Everybody in the pub had gathered round by this time.

Peter said sharply: 'Time you told us what all this is about. Here are my papers, if you want to see them.' He got out his Ministry card. The second man started to apologise at sight of this. He backed away, grabbing his pal by the arm and muttering: 'Mistake, sir. No offence.'

Before we knew what was happening, they were on their way out. Peter said; 'Just a moment!' Too late: the door had banged behind them.

We didn't follow; we went back to our drinking. But a few minutes later I felt a dig in the ribs. A hoarse voice whispered: 'Your name MacWhirr, guv'nor?'

I whipped round, almost upsetting my beer. A sort of tramp stood beside me. Three days' growth on his chin, a jacket that came down past his knees and a bowler without a brim.

'Who the heck are you?' I said.

'Police officer,' he said. 'Special duty.'

Both Peter and I became very angry at this. We asked him for his warrant card. Out it came at once. He looked over our papers with his brimless bowler pushed back. 'Thank you, gentlemen,' he said, 'all in order,' handing them to us and bowing. 'Sorry to've bothered you.'

'But look here,' Peter said, 'we've just been questioned by police officers. Two men.'

'Don't know nothing about 'em,' he said. 'Probably spies.'

'Why should they be spies?'

'Man we're after's a spy,' he said. 'MacWhirr. Takes photographs. Makes sketches. All got up like an artist, see? Corduroys. That's how we come to make the error; they didn't give us no description.'

'Well, I'm damned,' Peter said. 'Have a drink.'

'Not on duty, thanking you, sir,' and he shuffled out.

We didn't see any more detectives that evening, but later on in the week Peter and I were out for a walk and there, in the valley below us, was a man in a green corduroy suit, sitting on a stool sketching.

'My God,' I said, 'look! MacWhirr!'

'How d'you know it is?' Peter said. He's by nature cautious. We argued for some time. I was all for going down and asking him, but Peter said one couldn't go up to a total stranger and say 'Are you a spy?' just like that. 'Besides, he might be armed.'

So in the end Peter stayed behind to watch he didn't escape and I went for the local Home Guard unit. But when I got there all I found was a corporal soaking his feet in a bath of hot water, and he'd never heard of MacWhirr. 'Oo?' he said.

'MacWhirr,' I said. 'The well-known spy!'

'Don't know nothing about him,' he said.

'Where're your officers?' I said.

'Captain's playing Badminton,' he said. 'Can't disturb him.'

'Listen,' I said. 'If you don't take action you're aiding and abetting the escape of a spy. And you know what they do to spies, don't you?'

That shook him. 'All right, all right,' he said, and lifted his feet out of the bath. It took him some time to get his boots on and there was a further delay while the captain was dragged from the Badminton Club.

Finally, however, the whole section fixed bayonets and went charging off. They wanted to arrest Peter at first. Two of them were already poking their points into his stomach when I came up. The rest were rushing down the slope at the man in the corduroy suit, who gave a wild yell and sprang up, knocking over his sketching stool as he saw them.

'Look out, men!' the captain shouted. 'He may have a gun on him!'

Alas, he hadn't. He wasn't MacWhirr at all. Some quite well-known artist taking a holiday in the country. And didn't he raise cain. Threatened libel and God knows what. We'd the devil of a job to smooth him down. Most unreasonable. As we told him, we were simply doing our duty as citizens. It was his own fault; wearing corduroys and so on, of course he got into trouble. He'd only himself to blame.

2. CALL A POLICEMAN

I can tell you another story about police and coats. This time the police were uniformed and the coat was a teddy bear one. I was wearing it because it's the sort of overcoat film magnates are supposed to wear, and I'd just gone into the film business myself. I wasn't a magnate of course, not yet: the coat was perhaps a bit premature. But still.

A man in a Soho pub offered to buy this coat off me for fifty quid.

'Fact,' he said. 'Fifty nicker. Ready cash.'

I looked him over. He didn't look as though he had fifty pence.

'Sorry,' I said. 'It's not for sale.'

'On the dot,' he said. 'Give it you now. Ten minutes' time.'

'Nothing doing,' I said.

He turned round to his pals. 'Listen boys,' he said, 'I just offered this geezer fifty nicker for his coat, half a hundred, and what d'you think? The basket won't sell out.'

The Boys looked grave. 'That's a fair offer, pal,' one of them said. 'Be wise to take it.'

'Your own good,' another said.

'No soap,' I said. 'Not selling.'

I turned to go out. I'd had enough of that pub. The beer was bad, too.

One of the Boys barred my way. 'Now be reasonable,' he said. I picked up a glass. The potman, a nervous type, called out: 'Please, gents, please.' I put my back against the counter.

'Ah, let the ignorant basket go,' a man with a Cockney accent said. He had on a kilt.

'Don't know what's good for him,' the man who'd made the offer said. He spat on the floor.

I walked through the Boys to the door. 'Be seeing you,' a voice said.

'Not if I can help it,' I called back.

Outside it was pitch-black and pouring with rain. I turned into a pub in the next street. Old Frank was leaning on the counter with what looked like a whisky in front of him. 'What you having?' he asked me.

'A Scotch,' I said.

'No Scotch, only Irish,' the landlord said.

'Do you take me for Liam O'Flaherty?' I said. 'I'll have a Scotch ale.'

'Bloody Nationalist,' Frank said.

'Cheers,' I said.

The door opened and the fellow who'd offered me fifty nicker came in.

'This bloke's pinched my coat!' he bawled, pointing at me.

'Don't talk rot,' I said. 'I've had this coat seven years.'

'You took it off the peg in the other pub and walked out bold as brass.' He caught hold of my lapels.

'Fetch a policeman then,' I said.

'I don't need no coppers,' he bawled. 'You give me back my coat.'

In no time we were surrounded. A woman with feathers in her hat joined in on both sides. 'Squabbling over fur coats when me boys is out fighting in Africa,' she said.

'Frank,' I said, 'fetch a policeman.'

'Sure,' Frank said and dived through the door. He was glad to get out.

The fellow who said I'd stolen the coat made to follow, loosing his hold. I in my turn detained him firmly. 'Let me go,' he said, 'you big bullying bastard.'

'Oh, no,' I said. 'You stay here and wait for the police.' He stopped struggling and whispered: 'Give me a quid and we say no more about it.'

'You give me fifty quid,' I countered, 'or I'll hand you over to the coppers.'

The woman with the feather hat screamed: 'Blackmail,' and aimed a blow at me with her umbrella. She hit the other man instead. A free-for-all started. I suddenly tired of the whole business and made a dash for the door.

A shout went up of 'Stop thief!' I turned left in the street and then right. The rain pelted down. One pair of running feet followed me, but I was gaining. 'Taxi!' I roared.

And there, miraculously, was a taxi! 'Where to, sir?' the driver said, slowing down.

'Guilford Street,' I said. But a hand caught the belt of my coat just as I was climbing in. It was that man again. I hit him and knocked him into the gutter. Alas, when I turned again, the tail-light of the taxi was vanishing in the blackout.

The man was starting to scramble up again. There was nothing for it, much as I dislike violence. I knocked him down and sat on his head. 'Police!' I shouted. 'Police!'

The man shouted 'Help,' but his voice was a bit stifled. He was trying to bite the seat of my pants.

It was a damn silly situation, when you come to think of it: sitting on a man in Soho, with rain gradually soaking me to the skin. A drunk American soldier staggered up. Several more people gathered round.

'This man's tried to pinch my coat,' I explained.

'But he hasn't a coat,' someone said, flashing on a torch.

'That's just it,' I said.

Then suddenly I heard Frank's voice. 'Round here somewhere, constable,' he was saying. Heaven knows where he managed to find a policeman that time of night, but he'd done it all right.

'Here!' I shouted. 'Help! Police!'

The policeman turned on his bull's-eye lantern. 'Now then, now then,' he said. The crowd melted away. I stood up. The man I'd been sitting on stood up, too. Both of us began shouting accusations at each other.

'Now then, now then,' the policeman said. 'Who's charging who?'

I started to explain. Frank shouted suddenly: 'Stop him!' We all turned. The man was in full flight, running down a side-street. The policeman at once gave chase. Frank and I were left.

'Come on,' I said, 'let's go to the tube.'

'Righto,' Frank said.

So we walked off arm-in-arm.

There's a sequel to this, though. When I got home I found my wallet had been pinched. About ten quid in it, too.

I tell you, it doesn't pay to get mixed up with the police.

The Honest Truth

*   *   *

THE CLOCK ON THE STREET CORNER SAID SIX BUT IT WAS REALLY five. They'd forgotten to put it back the night before, when summertime changed.

Five p.m. on a Sunday afternoon: never my favourite time of day. Nothing to do until the pubs opened at seven. The hand of the clock crawled, slow as time itself, to five past.

Simultaneously a voice beside me said: 'Hullo.'

The voice belonged to a stocky medium-sized young man in a padded dark suit and spotted tie, hatless, with blond hair brylcreemed back, who stood with his head on one side smiling hopefully up at me.

'Hullo,' I said. So far as I knew I'd never seen him before in my life.

'You remember me don't you?' he said.

'I'm afraid I don't,' I said.

'Think back a little.' His smile became more intimate and indulgent. The sun picked out glittering points of blond stubble on his chin. Perhaps he'd the same difficulty in getting hold of razor blades that I had myself.

'Just think. 1939. Surely you can't have forgotten?'

But I had. Who the hell was he? Someone from my former battalion, unrecognisable now in civvies? Someone I owed money to in peace-time? Someone from the studios – a cutter, a cameraman? Or just someone I'd met in the Swiss? It was no good: I couldn't call him to mind.

'My memory's not what it used to be,' I told him.

His face clouded, he ran a hand across the blond bristles.

'But aren't you Alan Lloyd?' he said. 'The actor?'

'I'm not even Alan Ladd,' I said. 'In fact I'm not an actor at all.'

'Not connected with the theatrical world?' He was taken aback.

'Absolutely no connection,' I assured him.

'You look awfully theatrical in those clothes.'

'Do I?'

He laid his hand on my arm. 'I'm sorry, I didn't mean to be rude,' he said. 'I'm in such a muddle, half the time I don't know what I'm saying. You must excuse my impoliteness.'

'Of course,' I said. 'Often feel the same myself. About not knowing what I'm saying I mean. Why, only the other day a girl rang me up and said I'd offered to help her get to South America the night before. Damned if I could remember it, though.'

Interest seemed to awake again in him.

'Can you help people get to South America?' he asked.

'Me?' I said. 'No. That's the whole point. I told her my connection with the white slave traffic ended in 1932.'

'White slave eh?' he smiled. 'You don't look like a slaver I must say. Why'd you go out of business?'

'Really,' I said, 'my dear fellow.'

His face fell. 'I'm so sorry, I've offended you again. I didn't realise you were joking. My sense of humour is rather blunted these days.'

'So's mine,' I said. 'Come and have a coffee.'

'Delighted,' he said.

We went to a Lyons. Sat on a red velvet settee, ordered a black and a white.

'This chap Lloyd,' I said. 'Was he a friend of yours?'

'A very great friend.' He smiled reminiscently.

'Then surely you must have known I wasn't him? Unless I'm his double.'

'Look here,' he said. 'I better tell you the truth. I never thought you were Alan Lloyd at all. Wouldn't I have known him a mile away. The dirty sneaking stuck-up swine, of course I'd have known him. Wasn't I his understudy for seven whole months, having to put up every day with his stinking ruddy insults? Wasn't I?'

'I don't know,' I said. 'Were you?'

'Tell you the truth,' he said, 'I wasn't.'

'Pardon me,' I said, 'I'm a bit fogged myself now. Were you his understudy for seven stinking ruddy months or weren't you?'

'I was not,' he said. 'Damn it, man,' he shouted suddenly, 'Why should I understudy anyone?'

A fellow on the opposite seat, reading a newspaper on a bamboo frame, lowered this and looked at us apprehensively over the top of it.

The young man dropped a lump of sugar into his coffee.

'Sorry,' he said shamefaced. 'I forgot myself. Please don't send me away. You don't know what it means to me just to talk to a person of culture. Please. You must bear with me a little longer.'

'How much money have you got?' I asked him. He put his cup carefully down in the saucer. 'You're right,' he said, 'I am broke. Half a crown and a hole in my pocket. How did you know? Can you smell it on me? Do I stink of it then?' His voice had started to rise again. 'Or is it my clothes? This is the only suit I have. Can I help that? Can I?' His eyes swivelled and he sucked his cheeks in.

The Sunday paper on the opposite seat rustled uneasily on its stick.

'Drink up your coffee,' I said. 'Can't you get a job?'

'Jobs!' He laughed hopelessly. 'When I think of the jobs I've missed. Why I could be earning eight quid a week this very minute, as a waiter.'

'Well, why aren't you?'

'I haven't the clothes. No coupons.'

'You could hire a suit.'

'No money.'

'Surely your employer would advance you some.'

'Listen.' He lowered his voice. 'I'd better come clean. I'll tell you the honest truth. I was in the RAF, see?'

'Yes.'

'I was a flight sergeant. Twenty-five operations. I kept on coming back. Then one day my nerve broke. Snapped, just like that. I couldn't stand it, the strain. I couldn't stand it any more. So...' He stopped. His hands were trembling.

The man opposite dropped a sixpence on the table, sprang up, and rushed out precipitately.

'So you deserted,' I said. 'How long you been adrift?'

'Three months,' he said. 'You can't imagine what its like. Cadging food. Sleeping anywhere. Being hunted, like a beast. And knowing all the time that one day they'll catch up with me. A court-martial, the glasshouse.' He shuddered, his face in his hands.

'So now you see why I can't get a job,' he said.

'You want my advice?' I said.

'Please.'

'Give yourself up. In your present condition they'll never court-martial you. You'd get an immediate discharge on medical grounds.'

'And you think I'd get a job if they did discharge me?'

'Of course.'

He'd started to smile again. A rather pitying smile. 'All right,' he said. 'Have a look at this, then.'

From his inside pocket he produced a creased and much folded piece of blue paper which, smoothed out, said that Aircraftman Frank Legrand, aged twenty-four, had been discharged from the Royal Air Force since August 1941, exactly two months after his enlistment.

Reasons for discharge: unlikely to become efficient in any form of military service.

'So you're out,' I said. 'Discharged.'

'Since 1941.'

'And you've never been a flight sergeant.'

'No.'

'Or on twenty-five operations.'

'Never.'

'Well I'm damned,' I said.

His smile now became rather dreamy. 'It's funny the way I keep on telling lies,' he said. 'Can't stop myself somehow. Become a habit. I'm an awfully good liar, though. Don't you agree?'

'Heartily,' I said.

His face contorted with sudden contrition. 'I'm sorry. I'm so muddled up you must forgive me. You don't know what it is to be up against it as I am at the moment. I've simply no idea what I'm doing. No sleep. Not enough food. And everyone hard, hard as nails, unsympathetic... nobody caring.' His mouth worked and his hands twisted together. 'It's a steel town,' he said in a whisper. 'Oh, I know. One doesn't expect anything...'

'Look,' I said. I took out a quid. 'That's all I can manage at present. Would it be any use to you?'

'Use?' he said. 'Use?'

He stood up and smiled, leaving the pound note where it lay on the marble-topped table. His eyes rolled. He appeared suddenly exalted.

'Keep your quid,' he said. 'Keep it, my dear sir. I don't need it, I don't need anything. Garçon!'

A waiter hurried up. 'Two coffees, monsieur.'

The young man flipped open a black leather wallet. From the inside of this the edges of a thick wad of pound notes protruded. He extracted from among them a ten shilling note and handed it to the waiter.

'Keep the change,' he said. 'For yourself.'

The waiter almost fell to the ground. Only the fact that I was already seated prevented me from following suit. Recovering himself, the waiter bowed. The young man bowed too. He waved his hand at me and walked out through the open door into the bright sunlit Sunday-afternoon street, in which he was immediately lost to sight.

I sat on in a stupor. Shortly afterwards I picked up my quid and followed him out. There was a pub just opposite. I dived across the road and through the now open door.

I plonked my quid on the counter and ordered a double Scotch and soda.

I felt I deserved it.

The Rubber Cheque

*   *   *

THIS CHEQUE FOR TEN QUID WAS ALL I HAD. THAT AND TWOPENCE. Never mind why; we writers are always hard up, as you know.

I got down to the bank and pushed my cheque across the counter. I had to wait; the clerk behind the grille was busy thumbing through pads of pound notes. At last he looked up. 'Yes?'

I indicated the cheque. It was for an advance on a story I'd been commissioned to do. The clerk examined it carefully. Then he said: 'What d'you want me to do with this?'

'Cash it, of course,' I said.'

'Can't do that.'

'Why not? This is the Charing X Branch, isn't it? That's what it says on the cheque.'

'Ah, but this is a *crossed* cheque. You can only pay it in to your own bank.'

'I haven't a bank.'

The clerk shrugged his shoulders. People without banks didn't interest him. He bent again over his pads of money. 'Listen,' I said, 'I want this cashed immediately.' The clerk jerked up his head, surprised to find me still there. He said sharply: 'I've told you. I can't cash a crossed cheque. It's against the rules.'

'Well, what's the good of giving me a cheque I can't cash.'

The clerk shrugged again, it was no concern of his. I went out furiously to phone the editor who'd sent me the cheque. Then I remembered he'd be at lunch. His lunch-hour lasted from one till about three-thirty, and sometimes till four. These editors eat well. They spend nearly all day at it.

As for me, I didn't eat at all. I walked about the Charing X Road until four and then rang his office. Yes, they told me, the editor was back from lunch but he'd just slipped out for a cup of tea. If I'd hold on they'd see if they could find him. I held on grimly: my last twopence had dropped in the box.

After a while this editor came to the phone. He was a bit put out at being disturbed in the middle of his tea, but finally agreed to write another cheque. 'I'll make it out to Bearer,' and he rang off.

I'd to walk all the way to Fleet Street to fetch that cheque. He'd left it in an envelope downstairs at the reception desk. I tore the envelope open. Yes, this one looked OK; it was crossed too, but between the lines he'd written 'Please Pay Cash'. And best of all it said 'Pay Bearer'. Satisfied, I walked all the way back to Soho again. Just as my legs were about to collapse under me from walking, I ran into Harry Hicks the poet, coming out of a cinema. I was never so glad to see anyone in my life.

'Harry, you owe me ten bob,' I told him.

He sighed: 'It's a fair cop.' We sat down in a café and he paid up. I explained about the cheque. Harry was very indignant.

'This is outrageous,' he said. 'Why a fellow could walk about with cheques for hundreds of quids in his pocket and still be starving.'

'If the cheques were crossed and he hadn't a bank.'

'It's the banking system to blame,' Harry said. 'Should be exposed. I'm doing a film-script on banks right now.'

'Does it expose them?' I asked.

'It does not,' Harry said. 'It's a film sponsored by the banks themselves.'

Well, next morning in I walked to the bank again. This time it was a different clerk on duty. He asked to see my identity card, I can't think why. Then he said: 'What d'you want done with this cheque.'

'I want it cashed,' I said. He took the cheque away and returned in a moment with the manager. The manager said: 'I'm sorry, we can't cash this.'

'Why not?' I said. 'It's made out to Bearer, isn't it?'

'Ah, but it's not signed.'

'Not signed, nonsense,' I said. 'There's the signature at the bottom.'

'This part isn't signed.' He showed me the bit where it said 'Please Pay Cash'. 'See? It's only initialled. Also he should have crossed out the lines that make it into a crossed cheque.'

'Well, is it my fault he hasn't made out the cheque correctly?' I said. 'I want this money now.'

'Sorry,' they said.

'You'll hear more about this,' I told them. They both turned their backs. I went out and rang up the editor again. But it was Saturday morning: I should have known. He'd already pushed off for a weekend in the country.

I swore and counted what was left of Harry's ten bob. It was mostly coppers. Then I'd a bright idea. I went home and packed a suitcase full of old clothes. I threw a pair of spats and a red woollen waistcoat in on top of them for good measure. I lugged this lot down to the nearest pawnshop; it was miles away and the case weighed a ton.

'How much d'you want on 'em?' the pawnbroker asked.

'I leave that to you.'

'We always want some idea,' he said.

I'd never been to a pawnshop before, so I told him at random: 'Five quid.' The pawnbroker disappeared with the case behind a curtain. From beyond this, after a few seconds, came the sound of a snigger. The snigger developed into a laugh. Then the pawnbroker came back but he wasn't laughing. In fact he seemed angry. He banged the case down and said: 'I dunno how you have the sauce.'

'Sauce?' I said.

'Asking a fiver for that lot. Why, they're worn out. Ain't worth five bob.'

'What d'you mean worn out. I paid six quid for that sports-coat this summer.'

'Well, all I can say you been swindled.'

I hawked the case round to several more popshops after that: no soap. Even the spats and the red waistcoat didn't tempt them. I staggered back home with the case and got straight into bed. There was nothing else for it. I needed some sleep anyway. I slept right through the week-end without stopping.

On Monday morning I woke refreshed and immediately rang the editor up at home. It was eleven a.m. and he was shaving.

'What d'you want?' he said. 'This lather's drying on my face.'

'That cheque,' I said, and told him all about it. But to my surprise he got angry. 'I can't keep giving you cheques,' he shouted.

Then I got angry too, and banged down the phone. I sent him back his cheque in an unstamped envelope and didn't write a story for him after all. I wrote this one instead.

And I'll want payment for it in cash.

The Almighty Dollar

*   *   *

THE LAST STORY I WROTE ABOUT THE BISHOP WAS PRINTED IN A popular magazine which has since ceased publication. A few weeks ago, while drinking in a Paddington pub, I was surprised to find a copy of that particular issue thrust on the counter in front of me, a plump index finger underscoring the title of the story and my name.

'The illustrations,' said the Bishop gently, 'scarcely do me justice. On the other hand, there is a certain resemblance, which a number of my friends noticed.'

'Are you going to sue?'

'An attorney I know – disbarred, poor fellow, unfortunately – has suggested that course, but I've a horror of litigation. You wouldn't care to settle out of court?'

'I'll buy you a pint of bitter.'

'Plus a slight consideration – say a lousy ten bob? Done, my dear boy, done!'

He set down the tankard and sighed. 'I often thought I could write myself – if I had the time. But the pressure of business, you know... still, if you are prepared to act as my Boswell, there are many other stories I could tell you. For instance, the other day...'

The Bishop had come into possession of some smuggled dollars: market value, about two hundred quid. A chap called Spanish Jock knew of a buyer, and offered to help dispose of them, fifty-fifty split. Together they went to a restaurant in Soho, and the Bishop waited outside while Jock did the deal with the proprietor, name of Schweizer. He waited two hours, then impatience overcame him and he went in. Schweizer denied all knowledge of Spanish Jock, but admitted there was a back door; when the Bishop finally ran Jock to earth some days later he told a story far from credible.

A copper who knew him by sight had entered the restaurant just as he was about to approach Schweizer; he had scarpered out the back with the bogey on·his tail, ditched the dollars up the alley for safety's sake, and returned later to find some rotten geezer had made off with the dough. When the Bishop indicated his disbelief, Spanish Jock doubled his fist menacingly, saying 'Think I'd cross up a pal?' and the Bishop, seeing that little was to be gained by argument, returned to the restaurant to interview Schweizer.

'Spanish Jock sent me. About those dollars you bought from him.'

'Don't know nothing about no dollars,' Schweizer said doggedly.

'They're forged,' the Bishop told him. 'Jock just found out. The police're after him – they may be here any minute. Better give me the stuff quick.'

Of course Schweizer thought he was being done; on the other hand there was a chance the Bishop was telling the truth – especially as a CID officer had just walked in and was sitting at a table outside. Schweizer settled for a promise that the Bishop would share with him if he managed to resell the dollars, and the Bishop beat it out the back way with the roll in his pocket.

'Lucky coincidence, the CID bloke turning up like that,' I said.

'No coincidence, dear boy,' the Bishop said mildly. 'I phoned the Station beforehand and told them Spanish Jock might be there – he's wanted on two counts. However, to continue. I'd found another purchaser – a theatrical manager named Brittlebank. He was going over to the States on business, and only too glad to acquire a few dollars cheaply. Needless to say, I did not feel obliged to share with Schweizer, since he had plainly been a party to that dirty deal with Spanish Jock, in which they attempted to leave me out in the cold. Nor could he do much about it, as he now believed the dollars were counterfeit. Judge of my astonishment and horror, therefore, when I read in the paper, some time afterward, that John C. Brittlebank, Esq., the impresario, had been arrested in New York for passing forged currency! The dollars *were* counterfeit, after all – unwittingly I had been telling the truth!'

'That must have shaken you,' I said.

'It did,' the Bishop said, 'I was petrified. Happily, Brittlebank was released almost immediately, as his reputation for honesty was beyond doubt, but I took good care to keep out of his way when he returned.

'And then, one day, coming along Shaftesbury Avenue, I came face to face with him. My dear boy, I thought my time had come. But no – my luck still held! Brittlebank believed my assurances – or pretended to. Of course, it had not escaped me that I now had a hold over him similar to that which I had on Schweizer – in the eyes of the law we were both equally guilty of dealing in counterfeit money. Apparently he still had some of the "slush" left in his London office, and all he asked now was that I should take it off his hands – which I duly did, with no regrets on either side.'

'What did you do with the stuff then?' I asked.

The Bishop said: 'Spanish Jock bought it from me for fifty quid. A measly price, when you remember that he was ignorant of the forgery – until, of course, he in turn tried to dispose of the dollars. Somebody must have informed on him – someone, perhaps, whom he had doubled-crossed in the past…'

The Bishop beamed down at his empty tankard. 'He got five years – very lenient, considering… Think you could run to another pint, dear boy? And please, if you manage to sell that story – don't forget my cut.'

The Triple Life of Major Trask

*   *   *

SUMMER 1941; AN INFANTRY DEPOT SOMEWHERE IN ENGLAND.
I'd just been posted there when the orderly corporal handed me a
telegram. My mother was ill; come at once.

With the telegram crumpled in my hand I made my way to Company
Headquarters. This was three floors up a stone staircase, in a red-brick
building with an iron veranda running along outside it. French doors
opened off the veranda into the various offices, and a group of accused
soldiers, with their caps off, were being lined up by the CSM for
company orders.

The Sarmajor glanced up at me from the Minor Offence Report
which he held in his hand.

'Who're you?' he barked.

'Private Ross, J., sir,' I told him.

He looked down again at Army Form B whatnot, then up once
more at me. 'You're not on it,' he said. 'Beat it quick before you are.'

I dumbly tendered him the telegram; he took a quick dekko, then
said: 'Compassionate, eh? All right, fall in the end o' them there.'

I'd not yet seen my Company Commander, and wondered what my
chances were. After the first capless soldier was marched into his office,
I didn't rate them very high.

A roar like that of a wild beast rattled the French windows after the
recital of each charge. Private after private was marched out, speechless
and staggering under the weight of the sentences awarded.

My turn came all too soon to suit me; I was trembling already. 'Left
– right – left – right – left – wheel – HALT.'

Across a desk piled high with charge- and conduct-sheets, I saluted
a major in battledress whose head was bent over a Manual of Military

Law. Without looking up he barked out: 'What's the charge, Sergeant-Major?'

I started to stammer something, the Sarmajor cut me short with a nudge in the ribs. 'This man isn't on a charge, sir,' he said.

The major at this raised his head: a lined liver-coloured face with a drooping grey moustache. A pair of malarial eyes peered at me malevolently.

'Not on a charge! Then what's he here for, eh?'

'Compassionate leave, sir.'

'*Leave!*' Major Trask shouted. 'Then he ought to be on a charge. *Leave when there's a war on!* March him out, Sergeant-Major. Case dismissed!'

Out again on the veranda, I asked the CSM: 'What do I do now, sir?'

'See the Welfare Officer. Stand over here, he'll fix you up in a jiffy.'

I stood facing a French window marked Welfare Officer. It was the next office; after a moment the Sarmajor said: 'Tap and walk in.'

I did so, and gave a gasp. Seated opposite me was again Major Trask. A communicating door between the two offices explained his reappearance, but it was not only this that took me aback. It was the change in the man's expression. Kindliness now radiated from him. The grey moustache drooped no longer: it flaunted gaily over a smiling mouth. Even the pouched eyes seemed less sunken and malarial: they held a benevolent gleam.

'Well,' he said heartily, 'what's the trouble?'

Still completely fogged, I held out the telegram. He read it and said: 'Of course! Of course you must have leave at once. Have you seen your Company Commander? Just show him this paper,' he scribbled a few words, 'and you'll find it's all fixed. Good day to you and good luck!'

I saluted, about-turned, and stumbled out. The Sarmajor said: 'OK? Make out your pass then, I'll whip it in for OC's signature.'

He took the pass and the paper which said: 'To proceed on compassionate leave forthwith (SIGNED) J.B. Trask, Welfare Officer,' and disappeared into the OC's office.

A roar of 'Disgusting! The Welfare Officer exceeds his duty!' told me that Major Trask had already assumed his other personality, via the communicating door. But the pass came out signed, although this second signature seemed even more angular and savage.

I was too eager to get off on leave to ponder this singular situation, and at home I forgot all about Major Trask.

But back at the depot, my seven days concluded, I met him one evening crossing the square. I saluted swiftly, not certain in which capacity he was serving at the moment; then I saw by his smile and the upward twirl of his moustache that he was temporarily the Welfare Officer.

He stopped to say hullo. 'Well, your mother better? Good, good, glad to hear it. Had a mother myself once, you know!' and he passed on, smiling and swishing his cane.

Next morning was Company Commander's inspection; the major's moustache drooped, his baleful eyes spotted my bootlace undone.

'Untidy on parade,' and up on orders he dished out fourteen days CB. I thought this a bit stiff, and told the Welfare Officer so next door.

'Quite, quite,' he smiled. 'I sometimes think the OC's a good deal too severe in his punishments. I don't approve at all; discipline's one thing; just give this paper to your CSM and I think you'll find…'

But on this occasion the Company Commander stuck by his guns. He shouted and screamed: the Welfare Officer was too softhearted altogether.

The communicating door banged; the Welfare Officer threatened to put the case up before the Colonel. In the end, after more shouting, the sentence was amended to three days instead of fourteen and the Welfare Officer won the day.

My case was the first of several of this kind, and the Company Commander began to bite the drooping end of his moustache and shout curses at the door between the two offices.

Then they made Major Trask Officer I/C OCTU Candidates as well.

This third personality, although outwardly impartial, seemed on the whole an extension of the Welfare Officer; or any rate at war with the OC Major Trask, who as Company Commander sent in the names of potential officers whom Major Trask, in his new appointment, promptly turned down.

Furious chits passed between the two departments and no one was going up to OCTU at all. Soon after this the end came quite suddenly.

One morning when the Welfare Officer had just sent on leave a man undergoing seven days' jankers at the order of the OC, Major Trask as Company Commander saw reflected in the veranda window his antagonist, who through some flaw in the glass appeared to be grinning at him. It was too much: he struck out with his stick.

Glass tinkled down and recruits passing in the street saw Major Trask fall in a fit on the veranda. It was positively his last appearance: he had a Board at Mill Hill shortly afterwards and vanished into a home.

In a way I regretted his departure, myself; I happened to be on another charge at the time. The new Company Commander was also a strict disciplinarian; they'd appointed Captain Blundell Welfare Officer: and it was no good appealing to *him*.

The Gem

*   *   *

OXFORD SEEMS TO ME PREDOMINANTLY A PLACE WHERE DIM men come into their own; and when Nott rang up to ask me to lunch, one morning last November, I wondered whether his outline had grown more distinct with the passage of time.

He had one of those faces that once seen is never remembered. In London I used to identify him only by a green tweed hat: of such a shape that, in order to wear it correctly, he'd been obliged to print 'BACK' and 'FRONT' in ink on the lining, afterwards adding 'SIDES' (at my suggestion) to preclude any possibility of error. Otherwise, with his duffle coat, thick homespun suit, and even thicker spectacles, he was indistinguishable from scores of other serious-minded young men who, just after the war, flocked round the pubs in search of intellectual companionship: later, like Nott himself, emigrating to university towns and jobs connected with rural economy or social science. That, however, was seven years ago; and as the moment of reunion approached I began to worry lest I fail to recognise him if, after all this time, the green hat had been laid to rest. But, though he now wore a beard and a beret, all the other features that I vaguely remembered had been retained; moreover, as I entered, he was stooped over in the middle of the restaurant, removing cycling-clips from the turnups of his trousers, which it was safe to assume that no one else would do.

I'd had enough presence of mind to insist on the place where I usually lunched, instead of 'the little café lots of undergraduates go to', initially proposed by Nott; and the prices on the menu made him blink: he even took off his spectacles to polish them, in the hope of an optical illusion. Then he said: 'Spaghetti,' in a tone of surrender; and to me: 'I suppose you've settled down in Oxford for good.'

'No fear. I don't feel I'm quite a Lost Cause yet.'

Nott stared at me dumbfounded. 'You mean you don't like it here?'

'That's putting it mildly.'

'Then you'll be off to London again?'

'Directly I can find a flat.'

Nott shook his head. 'Very difficult, these days.'

'As I've discovered.'

The head waiter appeared inexorably at our elbow: 'And to drink, gentlemen?'

Nott said, as one resignedly ordering champagne for an acquaintance with expensive tastes: 'I expect you'll want a lager, or something like that. I'll just have a small brown ale myself.' Though never, to my recollection, noted for his consumption of alcohol at any hour of the day, he added: 'Don't drink much at lunchtime, like I used to. I have to work now!'

'Well, so do I.'

'Oh of course, your writing. I meant a regular job, like mine.'

'But I've a job too. Doing TV scripts.'

'What, regularly?'

'For the next three months anyway.'

Nott passed a hand thoughtfully over his beard. Then, after shovelling up spaghetti for a few moments in silence, he seemed to come to some decision. 'You know,' he said, 'I believe I've the very thing to suit you. A flat. My flat. In London W1. Just off Wimpole Street. Second floor, self-contained, fully furnished, newly decorated, sitting-room, double-bedroom, kitchen, all-electric, radio, frigidaire, own telephone...' His speech had gathered momentum rapidly; there was no stopping him now. 'And the staircase! Wait until you see the staircase! Wrought iron! A scarlet and white carpet underfoot! Leading up! And on every landing – statues!' His cupped hands moulded feminine curves in the air. 'Just imagine – statues! With concealed lighting: in niches on the walls!' He fell back overwhelmed; a fit of coughing seized him in his chair. 'It's a gem!' he managed to get out. 'A perfect gem!'

'And the rent?' I asked; 'Ten guineas a week? Seven? Five?'

Nott continued to shake his head triumphantly until the cough subsided. Then he took a pull of brown ale and leant forward in his chair. 'Two-ten,' he said.

At first I thought I'd misheard him. Then I said: 'Where's the catch?' But it seemed there wasn't a catch. China, bed-linen, cutlery?

All provided. Who'd clean the place up? Housekeeper on the premises. As for the low rental, hell, he wasn't the kind of chap to make profit out of a friend. He'd his own rooms in Oxford, where he was anchored by his job, and it became expensive paying for two flats: still, he was naturally loth to give up the Gem, with its staircase and statues, apart from all the other amenities. Besides, it was useful when he came to town for a weekend: saved staying at an hotel. I wouldn't mind putting him up occasionally? It'd only happen once in a blue moon, and he'd let me know well beforehand.

'Of course not,' I said, though privately determined that these visits should be restricted to one a month, with a fortnight's notice at that.

Nott now became nostalgic: 'I often think back over those times I had, with you and the other bohemians. You see, in a way, you're part of my youth.' But the word bohemian evidently evoked other associations, for his tone abruptly changed: 'You'd have to be businesslike, mind. Rent slap down; monthly in advance; no waiting; no excuses; no owing and *no dud cheques.*'

I said, rather coldly: 'I don't use a bank account,' but Nott was in full swing again; his beard fairly bristled; his face had gone dark red; behind the spectacles, his eyes became suffused with blood. 'Because I won't stand for any of that stuff. I get real mad if anyone tries it on. *Real mad!*'

The arrival of the next course seemed, however, to bring him back to normal; he said: 'Nothing personal, of course. It's only that I'm not much of a businessman myself, so I have to be tough about these things.'

'Same here,' I said; 'so to avoid trouble you can have three months' rent in advance the day I move in...'

'But I wasn't doubting you in any way.'

'And we'll have a proper contract drawn up by a solicitor at the same time.'

'I say, you *are* being businesslike, old chap.'

But then we struck a snag: owing to present pressure of work, I wouldn't be able to move until after Christmas. Nott made a *moue*; that meant the London rent would be mounting up meantime: couldn't I manage a small deposit, say a fiver, to help him out a bit?

'Yes, when d'you want it?'

'Now.'

'This minute?'

'Yes.'

He'd assumed his businesslike look again, so I counted out the required sum; none the less, the lunch ended with his calling for separate bills ('Bit short, end of the month you know, so if you don't mind we'll each just pay for our own'), and when we met subsequently in pubs, to discuss the remaining details, he proved himself to be an economist in more than the professional sense. Sometimes, towards closing time, I'd cast a meaning glance at our empty glasses on the counter; but Nott always misinterpreted this, and got ready to depart at once. 'Awfully kind of you, old chap, but I don't want to drink any more tonight. My landlady's a bit straitlaced: doesn't approve if I come home tiddly... Well, pip-pip. If you want to see the flat any time you're in town, just ring the housekeeper and she'll show you over.'

But Nott had described the flat's splendours so often, and so enthusiastically, that an actual visit seemed superfluous: besides, I was too busy to make even a day-trip to London. When, however, my TV producer called a script-conference at a moment's notice one morning, I phoned the housekeeper immediately on arrival at Paddington. There was no reply; by three o'clock I'd grown slightly deaf in the left ear from listening, at frequent intervals, to the ringing tone, and had to sit with my right side turned towards the boss at the conference table. In the evening I reopened my siege; at about the twelfth attempt, the housekeeper answered, prim and faintly Scots: she couldn't help it if I'd been ringing all day, there was her household shopping to do and who was this speaking, anyway? I said: 'Mr Nott will have told you I'm taking his flat over soon, and I'd like to see it before I go back to Oxford tonight.'

'Oh, tonight wouldn't be convenient, I'm afraid. You see, my husband'll be home shortly, and he doesn't care for me to be disturbed once he's in.'

'Too bad. I'll be along right away.'

I was speaking from a club where some of the boys were assembled. Among the boys was a girl. She said: 'Did I hear you mention a man called Nott on the phone just now? Because, if you're planning to move into his flat, it's only fair to warn you. My brother Raymond had it until a month ago, and now he's in hospital, no visitors allowed.'

'You don't mean Raymond Lester?'

She nodded. 'A bad nervous breakdown.'

A chill crept over me. Raymond Lester is a man well known to have nerves of steel. The girl said: 'Perhaps you'd better hear the whole story'; having heard it, I rushed out of the club and hailed a taxi. 'New one on me, guv,' the cabby said when I gave him the address, but he was hopeful: hope, however, had died on both of us by the time every turning off Wimpole Street, many of them one-way, had been explored and passers-by, commissionaires, other cabbies, and finally a policeman, consulted to no avail. The fare, meanwhile, had ticked up to eight and six. 'Paddington Station,' I said.

Back in Oxford, I phoned Nott at his digs. 'I say, old chap,' he said, 'rather late to ring, isn't it? Some people have to get up in the morning, you know.'

'And others,' I told him, 'have nervous breakdowns owing to constant turmoil in the house where they're living.'

After a short silence, Nott said: 'Lester had no business to meddle in affairs that didn't concern him.'

'But surely it did concern him, if the housekeeper's husband is a psychopathic drunk who beats his wife because he doesn't like her cleaning the tenants' flats, and locks her in the lavatory or bathroom all night so that nobody can get in.'

'Look, old chap, I can't argue about this over the phone. Suppose we meet in the pub tomorrow, nineish.'

'All right. And bring the key to this flat with you.'

Nott was in the pub as appointed. He said: 'Don't bother to get me a drink, I've plenty here. Just buy your own.'

'That's very generous of you, but what I really came for was that key. I'm going to have a look round the place tomorrow.'

'Careful how you do it, then. The husband's an ex-Commando, you know. It's safer to keep out of his way.'

'Unless he keeps out of mine, he'll find himself in clink,' I said. 'Truth is, the housekeeper lets you have the place cheap, for a rake-off, and you're scared of losing it if there's any trouble.'

For a moment Nott looked as if he were about to get real mad once more, then he thought better of it just in time: though I'd a feeling, as he reluctantly surrendered the key, that the old days with the bohemians would remain a nostalgic memory no longer, nor I a part of his youth.

Next day I travelled to London again. Before parting from Nott, I'd made him point out the exact location of the house on a map; it was in a mews and some distance from Wimpole Street: though still, technically, in the W1 area. The front door was open; and inside a hand-printed notice said: 'TENANTS WILL BE HELD RESPONSIBLE FOR KEEPING THE HALL *CLEAN* AND *TIDY*. (SIGNED P.J. MACDOUGAL, HUSBAND OF THE HOUSEKEEPER.)' This hung at the side of a winding staircase made of some metal resembling black-painted tin rather than wrought iron; there were two landings altogether, with a black marble bust of Shakespeare on the first one: the stair carpet, however, did not start until the second flight and may once have been scarlet and white, though now so dingy and frayed that its original colour scheme was purely a matter for conjecture. Not a cough, nor even a rustle, sounded from behind any of the closed and numbered flat doors: either the tenants had all fled in terror, or the mad husband had killed the lot off in the night.

Nott's flat was at the end of a dark *cul-de-sac* on the second landing, past a niche containing a plaster cast of the Venus de Milo, with a broken electric bulb in a brass socket above it; I turned his key in the lock and was immediately confronted with the sitting-room: shrouded in a permanent dusk since the one narrow window faced on to a high brick wall. Its furnishings included, at the moment, empty bottles, unemptied ashtrays, sticky glasses, one cigar stub, and a sunken purple lipstick standing on top of the radio: evidently the relics of a party Nott had given, by the looks of it, months before. The bedroom was lit by a skylight high up in a mansard roof and operated by pulleys; the phone sat, its cradle askew and the directory lay open on a bed that had been slept in and not remade: in the tiny all-electric kitchen, plates were piled high with the remains of kippers and an army-issue shaving-brush stood clotted with dried soap on the draining-board. I didn't dare look inside the fridge.

There was nothing more to see: no bathroom or lavatory in the Gem itself; and out of curiosity I went in search of these, wondering if I'd find the housekeeper locked in one of them. The lavatory (unlocked) was on the first floor, next to a sort of cupboard containing a large sink and a shard of mirror nailed to the wall; but the bathroom eluded me completely. As I paused, perplexed, on the ground floor again, a female Scots voice that I recognised at once asked: 'Were you wanting something?'

'I was looking for the bathroom, actually.'

The housekeeper was a small, wiry, sallow woman, bearing no outward marks of ill-usage, with a brown cloche hat on her head and a string bag full of veg hanging over her arm.

'The household shopping?' I said.

Without a word she turned and, leading me into the yard, pointed to a kind of conservatory with rough planks nailed across where the glass should have been. 'It's locked,' she said, 'and my husband has the key. Just remember, you have to scrub your own bath out: that is, when my husband lets you use it, of course.'

I sent the key of the flat back to Nott that night; and, despite my friends' advice, made no attempt to reclaim the fiver deposit: it didn't seem worth all the trouble I'd have getting it back. During the remainder of my stay in Oxford, I never set eyes on him once. Someone told me recently that his salary had been raised to fifteen hundred a year.

Gas

IN THE GUARDROOM AT THE DEPOT, WHERE THE INLYING Picquet used to sleep, they had those double-decker beds in rows, and the springs of the beds were always getting broken. One night they had all new beds in, and the next night they were all broken again.

Of course, on Inlying Picquet you had to sleep with all your equipment on, and no doubt that helped to break the springs; anyway they hung down like nets and your equipment'd get inextricably caught up in them.

Naturally, as soon as you came off parade outside there was a dash for the guardroom, and the thing to do was to get a bed that wasn't broken, or at any rate less broken than the rest, and to avoid the beds that were sandwiched in the middle, because if you had one of those you were hopelessly bottled up when it came to your turn for going out on guard, or if the alarm went.

I remember one night I got in there last and all the beds had been bagged except a top one that had no springs in it at all. It looked as though I'd have to stand up all night, but then one of the military police came and said did I mind sleeping in a cell, and I said No, so he took me in there and said did I mind being locked in because of rules and regulations and also there was a prisoner in the next cell, the one who'd shot his thumb off and they weren't certain how; he'd been in the clink a month now awaiting court-martial.

Anyway, this MP locked me in and I went to sleep; they'd a smashing bed in there. I was due to go on picquet outside at four in the morning, and the sergeant banged on the door then and said, Wakey, wakey, rise and shine. I said, Let me out, I'm locked in, and the MP came and said, You've got the key. I said, No you've got it, and he said, I gave it to you.

Neither of us could find it though, and we all shouted and hammered and said we hadn't got the key, and the prisoner hammered on the wall of his cell and said, Here, want some mucking sleep – is it the invasion or what?

Eventually the key was found on the floor of the guardroom and everything was all right. Another man did my picquet because I couldn't get out in time. Lucky the alarm didn't go though, because I'd the Bren gun and the anti-tank rifle in there with me and most of the ammunition boxes that hadn't been used to prop up beds with as well.

However, that's another story, the night I got locked in the cell. This one is about Gas. I've got them mixed, it was a different night.

We'd each chosen a bed and were laying out our bedding when suddenly the runner came dashing in. He was a Category C man, a Cockney with all sorts of things wrong with him, and many of them wrong with his face. He'd a most extraordinary face, but you couldn't see it now because he'd his respirator on over it and through the respirator he yelled out, GAS!

We said, Cut it out, and the sergeant said, Pack it in, I've a mind to shove you on report play-arsing about a thing like that. But the runner said, Honest, sarge, it IS gas, no kidding. He was in a proper stew.

So sergeant went out and the corporal too, and they came back with their eyes streaming and shouted, He's right, lads, get 'em on. We out with our respirators and had them adjusted quicker than we'd ever done it on gas drill, and there was hell being kicked up. Then the sergeant shouted, SSH, and we listened and we could hear Jerry going over, and the sergeant said He must just have dropped it, and the runner said, See, I was right.

Well, we were all of a doodah, not frightened, we were too excited for that I think, but all rushing to and fro, and some of us went out and, yes, it was gas right enough, but what kind? How should I know, the sergeant said, I've never been on a gas course, get the gas sergeant.

The runner went off. Meantime I got out my notebook with all about gas in it and which smelt of rotten fruit and of musty hay, and they all crowded round trying to read it through their respirators.

Anyway, we said, it isn't DICK because that has no smell and this had; it was tear gas because you could feel it pricking your throat where you'd shaved, and the runner came back and said the gas sergeant had gone on the beer downtown, but that round the stores the gas was much worse and the gas sentry raising Cain. So the phone orderly rung up for the gas officer; nobody could remember which one it was though, because they'd changed them and one had been posted, but which?

Meantime the sergeant said, Come on, and five of us went with him up the Lines by the Company store, and you could feel the gas there, like when you went through the chamber.

There was a light on in the store, you could see it under the door. The sergeant shouted OPEN UP, and there was the storeman staggering about with his eyes running and no respirator on and the gas came from in there – it was terrific.

Anyway, it turned out he'd knocked over a crate of tear gas bombs, and some had gone off, and the storeman said, Why all this fuss, he'd got the worst of it anyway 'cause his respirator had been knocked off by some swine in the Naffy night before. The sergeant said, serve you right putting the wind up us that way, and then they argued and the sergeant said, Shut up.

By this time the gas officer had arrived, the one that hadn't been posted, and he heard the story and there was trouble. But in the end they decided not to make a Thing about it, and the sergeant said should he include it in his guard report, and it was decided No.

So maybe I shouldn't be writing about it now, as maybe it's SECRET and they might have me on a court-martial. But hell, why worry: it wouldn't be the first time I've been locked in a cell.

The Mine

*　　　　*　　　　*

DID I TELL YOU ABOUT THE SPOT OF EXCITEMENT WE HAD AT OUR HQ the other week?

One morning I was sitting typing at my desk in the downstairs office when one of the runners came flying in and said there was a big mine floating about in the sea opposite, you could see it plain as plain. Well, of course, I didn't take any notice, there's always some damn silly rumour going about. It wouldn't have surprised me if he'd seen Hitler bobbing up and down outside. I paid no attention, everyone else rushed off out, I just went on typing. It was a list of cricket fixtures I had to finish, and very important.

Then L/C Ritchie came in; he said there *was* something out there, he'd seen it through his binoculars, and did I know what a mine looked like. I said Yes, I'd once seen a mine being towed away from our beach at home after they'd taken the sting out so to speak: the detonator or whatever is it they do. So then Ritchie said Does it have horns on and I said Yes and he said Then that's a mine all right.

Corporal Gales was passing the office, he looked in and said What's the row? Ritchie said A mine outside, you come and look but Gales said Not likely, I've been blown up by a mine once already, that's why I'm Grade C. Why not phone the police he said if you're so sure about it, so they did that and presently the police arrived. Two enormous constables and an inspector.

The inspector said Are you the Regiment in charge of this coast? and we said No we had enough to do without that so he said Which is it then? and we said the S. So the inspector got on the S and they said It's nothing to do with us, get the Navy.

While the inspector was getting the Navy, a crowd had collected outside and some of our lads had climbed up onto the sea wall to get a good look at the mine and the constables were ordering them back; there was a terrific shindy going on and Ritchie kept shaking hands with everyone and saying Congratulate me on a buckshee fiver. I said What fiver? Ritchie said The fiver you get for reporting a mine isn't that right inspector? and the inspector nodded, he was getting the Navy. He rang off and said The Navy's on its way, yes you'll get your fiver all right lad and Ritchie said See? Then the runner who'd first seen the mine said Where do I come in and Ritchie said Shut up, you'll get half.

Through the window I could hear them shouting and an officer from the S was shouting and one of our officers too and then the Navy arrived, it was a captain and he said Clear the decks.

Meantime Corp Gales was saying What about me? After all I phoned the police and the post corporal came in with a sack of letters on his back and said Garn, if it's the mine your talking about I saw it from the balcony, when I got up first thing, only nobody'd listen.

This sort of thing went on for about an hour, with all ranks running in and out and then the Navy took charge and closed the road and said we'd have to clear out as they were going to operate on the mine and it might go off while they were doing it, we were all to move. We said Where to? and the Major came in from consulting with the naval Captain and said Down to the Grosvenor: that was a hotel about 200 yards along the sea-front, that the squads were billeted in.

So two of the runners took hold of the despatch books and the postage book and the typewriter and went off down to the Grosvenor, I gathered up the SECRET File and was about to follow when the Major came back and said No not you, you'd better take up your quarters in the QM's Stores temporarily and I said Very good sir.

The runners were out of sight so I sent another runner after them and went down to the QM's, it was in the other direction. The Messing Officer's staff was there as well, they were sitting round the office with all their stuff, and the QM's clerk said when he saw me Oh god how many more.

Then the despatch rider rolled up, he'd been sent out of his way, the naval authorities had arrested him, he was late, he was angry. Where're the despatches, the adjutant'll raise the roof.

They've gone down to the Grosvenor I said, you'll have to hang on. In the middle of this Q walked in, he was in a towering temper. Who're all these people. Clear them out the whole ruddy lot, Come on he said to me, you for a start, you water off.

Now the Q's a holy terror, you can't argue with him, so I said Very good sir, though I don't know what the Major'll say I'm sure. What's that he said, the Major? Oh all right then, you better stand by, but keep an eye on the pencils he told his clerk, last time this happened we lost five, and he stamped out.

Then the three runners appeared, they had the despatches, the mine was due to go up any moment, but the typewriter had got left in the coffee shop, one of them was now going back for it.

I cursed, the despatch rider cursed, he grabbed his stuff and rode away. We sat there waiting for the typewriter and the mine to go off. Nothing happened. The messing staff were playing pontoon. You can't work in these conditions they said. I sat down on the floor and watched them play.

Then the phone rang, we could hear Q shouting into it, the messing staff scooped up their cards and money and a packet of pencils and a pencil sharpener when the QM's clerk wasn't looking.

The Q appeared and said All right you can all water off the lot of you, the S have just phoned up there's no danger now.

What a game, eh, they said, what a ruddy mess-up, and we all got our stuff together, the runners took mine and on the way back we met the other runner with the typewriter he'd rescued from the coffee shop and all went back to the office we'd been turned out of.

An argument was going on inside about the mine and who'd seen it first, Corp Gales and Ritchie and the post corporal and the runner, all at it hammer and tongs, and I said Come to that if I hadn't told you how to recognise it by the horns you'd never have known it was a mine at all.

So in the finish it was decided we were all to write out separate reports and let the civil authorities or the town council or whoever was giving the fiver decide from them who should have it.

After that we settled back to work as usual and after work I went off downtown. When I came back I had a shock.

You got to move into the back, Corp Gales said soon as I came in.

Why? I said, What d'you mean?

Well you sleep in the front don't you? he said, and everyone's got to sleep in the back cause the mine's going off at four in the morning and it may blow the front of the house away.

But hell I said, I thought the mine was okay now?

Yeh he said, *that* mine's okay but it's still floating about see, and they reckon when tide comes in four o'clock it'll bump into some o' them smalls uns we got tethered up and blow the works.

Oh hell I said. I started to look for a room at the back but they were all full. All sorts of people had moved in that I'd never seen before, God knows where they came from. Even the back kitchen was occupied, there was a bloke sleeping in the sink.

In the end I moved into the runners room. We had three walls between us and the mine but I still didn't feel too safe. Why the building used to shake every time someone dropped a pair of boots.

I woke twice during the night. Zero hour yet Corp? they said. No I said, it's only three, and next time we woke it was reveille and the mine still hadn't gone off. And it never did go off, next day the Navy came and towed it away. We were disgusted, we said it was a wash-out, and so it was.

The reward was a wash-out too, we none of us got it. The council decided to pay nothing in the end because we were military personnel and only doing our duty in reporting the mine. We said What difference does that make, isn't it everyone's duty to report a mine and they said Yes but you don't get no fiver for doing it, that's the difference.

So it just shows, doesn't it. Eh?

The High Jump

*   *   *

THIS BLOKE, OLD BROWNIE, WAS DETERMINED TO GET OFF THE draft.

He wasn't windy, mind; it was his missus. His missus swore blind she'd do herself in if he went overseas; when he went home on embarkation leave she even picked up the carving knife to prove it. Got all hysterical, she did. My opinion, it'd have been a good thing for old Brownie if she'd used the knife, but course he couldn't see it that way.

So as I say he'd made up his mind to dodge the draft, come what may. He thought up all sorts of stunts, he even wanted old Dusty Miller, in the MT, to run him over one time. Offered him a packet of fags for doing it.

'Run you over?' old Dusty said. 'No bloody fear. I ain't swinging for nobody's murder, not me.'

'Murder?' old Brownie said, 'Don't be daft. Nobody mentioned nothing about murder. Just my leg.'

'Your leg?'

'That's it. I go and lay on the road, see, and all you got to do is run your truck over me leg. Simple.'

'Which leg?' old Dusty said.

'Doesn't matter. Either one.'

'Nothing doing,' old Dusty said. 'Not a chance.'

'I'll make it forty fags,' old Brownie said.

'Wouldn't do it for fifty,' old Dusty told him. 'Not for a hundred, neither.'

So old Brownie had to give that idea up in the finish. He tried getting hold of some poison next, only nobody'd give him any. He tried the MI Room, everywhere. No good. Then he tried drinking a bottle of bluebell, but all it did was make him spew. Reckon his guts got used to anything swilling that Naffy beer. What with that and the tea. Anyhow, old Brownie was at his wit's end.

Then one night I was in the canteen and he come up to me. 'Thought of a new way out,' he said.

'What's it this time?' I asked him.

'I'm going to jump off the Spotting Tower,' he told me.

'You're crazy,' I told him. 'You'll break your bleeding neck jumping off that. It's too high.' The Spotting Tower was what we used to do guards on, watching out for Jerry planes, see? I don't rightly know how high it was, but too high for any fancy jumps, take it from me.

But old Brownie shook his head. 'Fall soft,' he said. 'Sand all around it. Break a leg, not more. Nice little spell in dock. Just you watch.'

'When're you going to do it?' I asked him.

'Tonight,' he told me. 'Ten o'clock.'

'Why ten?'

'My lucky number,' he told me.

'It'll be your unlucky number if you break your neck,' I told him.

Well, naturally I never thought he'd do it. I thought he was having me on. But he did do it.

When the canteen closed, ten o'clock, we went along with him to the Tower, quite a crowd of us that he'd told what he was going to do.

'How're you going to get past the sentry?' we asked him.

'I'll just tell him I want to cadge a smoke from one of the guard,' old Brownie said.

Well that was nothing new, with him, and it worked a treat. He went off up the steps and pretty soon we saw him show up right on top of the Tower.

'Good old Brownie,' we yelled at him, and he waved his hand at us and then jumped. Just like that. The sand went up all around him when he landed.

We all started to run at that. We reckoned he'd broke his neck for sure, but no, when we got to him there he was picking his self up out of the sand and swearing blue murder.

'Too soft,' he said. 'Have to have another go.'

'You're never going up there again?' we said to him.

'Bleeding am,' he said.

And he did. The guard tried to stop him this time, knowing what he aimed to do, but he got through 'em somehow and slung his self over.

And this time he didn't get up, he just lay there groaning with one leg doubled under him.

'Okay,' he said. 'I done it proper. Get the MO quick.'

So someone phoned up the MI Room and they sent an ambulance down and off Brownie went to the Sick Bay. He went on the draft just the same though. It got put back see, and by the time it went, old Brownie was out of dock with his leg mended all right, and they got him again.

You must have seen his photo in the papers a day or two back: got the VC for some screwy thing he did out there. He was that kind of bloke old Brownie. Stands to reason, bloke who'd jumped twice off that Tower ain't going to be scared of a few bleeding Jerries.

As for his missus, she didn't do herself in after all. Course not. She's living with another bloke now. I always knew that bitch was no bleeding good. I could've told him.

The Phantom of
the Cookhouse

*　　　*　　　*

A RECRUIT CALLED PITCHER SAW IT FIRST, AND THEN CORPORAL
Swayne saw it. Nobody paid attention to Pitcher, but when Corp Swayne
saw it the blokes began to sit up and take notice, because, of course, a
NCO's word counts more. Besides Corp Swayne wasn't the sort of
chap you'd expect to see ghosts.

He was a sanitary man, an old sweat with a row of medal ribbons
and not a tooth in his head. He had dentures, but he was always taking
them out. He'd seen it the night before, standing by his bed bending
over him. Put the wind up him proper, he said.

'What'd it look like?' I asked him.

'It's a waiter,' he told me.

'That's it,' Corp Swayne said. 'Flicking waiter. You know, got up
posh, shirt front, black coat and all. Standing by me like it was holding
out summat.'

'Your Kensitas, sir?' I said. I gave him a Blue Tenner. 'What sort of
face had it got?'

'No face,' Corp Swayne said.

'None at all?'

'Not even eyes. 'Sides, it was too dark to flicking well see.'

'What did you do?'

'Didn't do damn all. Pulled the blankets up over me head and went
back to kip again.'

Next day more fellows had seen it, and the news began to get
around. 'It's haunted,' they said. 'The cookhouse.'

But it wasn't actually the cookhouse that was haunted; it was in the
rooms above that the ghost appeared, where Waterloo Squad slept. We
were billeted then in empty hotels along the sea-front, and the cookhouse

was one of them, and the ghost walked there every night. Some of the fellows began to get windy. Most of them agreed it was a waiter, although a chap I sat next to at tea had a different version.

'It's dressed like Shakespeare,' he said.

'Have you ever seen Shakespeare?' I asked.

'No, I ain't never seen him, but that's how it's dressed.'

One night Sergeant Hicks, a man afraid of nothing, took the matter in hand. 'I'll fix the bleeder,' he said, and sat up on the cookhouse stairs with a drawn bayonet, waiting for the ghost to show up. Round about midnight it did. But Hicks'd expected it to come *up* the stairs, and it didn't. It came *down* them instead, walking past him without a sound, 'like a shadder' he said. The sergeant was shaken; he didn't use his bayonet, and the ghost vanished in the blackout downstairs.

The Company Commander got to hear of it, then. 'What's all this about a ghost in the cookhouse?' he said.

'Well, if you arst me, sir, it's a lot of cock,' the sergeant-major said. 'Just a yarn the lads are starting to spread round. I ain't never seen it meself.'

'But Sergeant Hicks has, sergeant-major.'

'Yes, but how many pints'd he had first, sir?'

Well, the Company Commander couldn't answer that one. He decided to detail a ghost-watching party every night, to parade at 1900 hours IN FULL EQUIPMENT, until further notice. Everyone was shaken, but the ghost still walked and the ghost-watchers got the wind up and went to the Captain in a deputation to complain.

'It ain't right, sir, and that's a fact,' they said.

So ghost-watching was stopped, but soon after this there was an epidemic of pinching. First it was all the cap-badges. Then it was gloves. All the gloves at one go. Every pair. Next two overcoats disappeared. The police were called in, and everyone was questioned. Ghost-watching started again, and a fellow got caught in the act, with a pair of PT shoes in his hand. But he wasn't the ghost, because even after he went to detention the ghost continued to walk.

The Company Commander wrote to the Society for Psychical Research, but they didn't answer. Old George, who was a Red, got very bitter about that.

'It's a class distinction, that's what it is,' he said. 'Just 'cause it's a waiter. If it'd been a dook they'd have written soon enough, you bet your life. Blinking snobs, that's all they are,' he said.

Then one day I was in the office typing out Detail when a bloke rushed in green in the face. 'Quick, corporal,' he said, 'a geezer's shot hisself!'

'Shot himself?'

'Jones, of Waterloo Squad. Get the MO quick, he's hurt bad.'

I got the MO on the phone. 'Get transport,' he said. The MI Room was miles away and up hill; he'd never have walked it in time. So I got on to the MT, and they said they'd send down a pick-up straightaway. I rushed off to the Company Commander. He wasn't in, but Mr Slater was.

'What's wrong, corporal?' he said. 'Why the devil don't you knock?'

'Sorry, sir,' I said, 'a man's shot himself.'

'Shot himself? Where? What man?' He stood up.

'Jones of Waterloo Squad,' I told him. He grabbed his cap and stick and dashed out. The street was full of fellows who'd heard the news running towards the cookhouse, and round the cookhouse itself there was a crowd. I went back to the office, and all day long different rumours kept pouring in: it was suicide, it was murder, Jones was dying, Jones was dead.

I didn't get at the truth until late that night. It wasn't suicide and it wasn't murder, although Jones hadn't shot himself. Bardell, his mate, had shot him. Only he didn't mean to, they were just mucking about. They'd been on the range and Bardell had got hold of a live round. He shoved it up the spout and said he'd let the ghost have it that night. Well, anyway, the rifle went off and Jones got it instead.

But he didn't die, luckily; he got all right in about a month. There was a court of enquiry and a court-martial and Bardell got 28 days' detention for being in possession of live ammo. Of course he said the ghost-watchers have live ammo, but the CO said he'd heard enough about the ghost and from now on the ghost was OUT.

Well, a CO's order is a CO's order, and they closed up the cookhouse for keeps, and we never heard of the ghost again because the CO said anyone found talking about it'd get CB.

What do I think about it? I don't think anything. I don't believe in ghosts myself.

Seven Days of Heaven

*   *   *

1. THURSDAY

MY LAST LEAVE STARTED OFF BADLY. TO BEGIN WITH, I MISSED the train. When I got to the station it'd gone. The railway official said: '11.45 next one,' and started to walk away.

'Wait a minute,' I said. He paid no attention, he kept on walking. I had to run to catch him up. 'I must catch the connection,' I said. 'Where can I get a taxi?'

'Over there,' he pointed. 'Use yer eyes,' and disappeared through a door marked STAFF ONLY. So I used my eyes but couldn't see any taxis with them. The taxi rank was empty. Another railwayman passed me and I said: 'Where are the taxis, please?'

That stopped him. 'Taxis?' he said. 'Now what would you be wanting a taxi for?'

'I've got to catch that connection to London. The 10.30.'

'A taxi'll cost you all of fifteen bob.'

'I don't care about that. Where can I get one?'

He looked at me as though I were out of my mind. Then he said very slowly, 'You might find Old Bob at that caff out back.'

'Thanks,' I said. I started off, I could feel him looking after me. I'm sure he was scratching his head but I hadn't time to look back.

I found the caff; there were several men dressed as taxi-drivers drinking tea inside. 'Anyone here called Old Bob?' I asked.

One of the men said: 'What's to do.' He was evidently Bob but he didn't look particularly old. I said I wanted a taxi to the town station; it was about 12 miles. 'Fifteen bob,' he said.

'All right.'

'Let's see the dough,' he said. 'I been caught like that before.'

In case any of this astonishes you I should explain that I am in the army a private soldier and furthermore I was in uniform. I myself sometimes forget this, especially when I'm going on leave: even the weight of my equipment fails to remind me. I remain the same inside, and so I'm always surprised at the difference the private's uniform makes to people outside the army. But by now I'm used to being treated with suspicion and distrust, so I showed him a quid and we got going.

We drove along a country road; there was a broken-down windmill with a board outside saying TEAS and an overturned bus with a tarpaulin over it at the side of the road by a hairpin bend.

'Been there three days,' Old Bob said. 'Why they don't clear her away God only knows.'

He talked for a time about engine trouble; I kept my eyes on the clock. It was 10.15. 'Shall we make it?'

'If we don't break down,' Old Bob said. 'Can't be sure of nothing these days, you know.'

He said his son had gone to Singapore on a draft; they'd heard nothing since; not a word. 'He weren't due for abroad neither but another bloke went sick the day before.' Old Bob said he'd like to meet that bastard sometime. We passed a gasometer and stopped outside the station. I was in a hurry, I gave him the quid and jumped out.

Old Bob said: 'Thank you sir.' I'm used to these changes of front, they don't mean anything now. I ran through the barrier and got on the train just as it started. I walked along the corridor; every compartment was full. My pack got jammed in a doorway; I nearly put my rifle through a window. I stood in the corridor looking out; hoardings and cows and parallel rails; a line of trucks; FOR YOUR THROAT'S SAKE SMOKE CRAVEN 'A'.

Later some people got out; I sat in a carriage opposite a sailor who had three red stripes and a screw sewn on his arm. I read a book and smoked five cigarettes. It was a two-hour journey to London.

The terminus was full of uniforms and red caps; I went up a staircase, down a staircase, and got a bus outside. I went on top, my rifle got between someone's feet; I said 'Sorry,' he just glared.

I said: 'Victoria Station please.'

The conductor said: 'What say? Speak up carnt yer?'

'VICTORIA STATION,' I yelled.

Everybody looked round. A businessman in a black suit muttered something about martial law soon if we're not careful. The conductor said: 'Orl right orl right. No need to bust me blinking ear-drums.'

I said: 'Here, you've given me the wrong ticket.'

He swore and clipped his punch again. The bus bumped over craters in the road; we passed the cenotaph, the Army and Navy Stores; the clock at Victoria said one. My appointment was for one-thirty; lunch with an editor. I parked my kit in the cloakroom; a wash and brush-up made me feel better.

Over lunch I sold suddenly two short stories. Everyone was astonished: I think the editor too. After lunch Wingard turned up. He was on leave and in civvies.

'Why the hell are you wearing those clothes?' he said. I said I'd just arrived. Later he said he wanted to eat buns. I said I knew where we could get French croissants. It was some way and the shop, when we got there, was no longer in existence. It'd been blitzed. Both of us were annoyed. We went to several sinister-looking restaurants; they wouldn't serve us. 'No meals after three,' they said in foreign accents.

In the end we went to the station restaurant. I said: 'A black coffee.' Wingard wanted cakes. The waitress said: 'You can't have BLACK coffee.' I said why not. She looked helplessly around. Another waitress, seeing my private's uniform, came up and said sternly: 'What's going on here?'

Everybody in the restaurant looked up. They were all civilians; they stared at me as though a nazi in full SS rig-out had strayed in by mistake. We said a black coffee; the second waitress softened finally and said she'd see what she could do. She went off and came back suddenly to tell me not to tilt my chair back.

Wingard said: 'But what is wrong with all these people?'

'It's my uniform,' I explained.

The waitress came back with the coffee; she banged down a plate of pastries. 'I don't want those,' Wingard said. 'I want chocolate cakes.'

'CHOCOLATE cakes?'

'Yes, like those people are eating over there.'

She said: 'I don't think we've any more of those.'

I said: 'You'd better serve him. He's a staff captain you know.'

'What, him?' She looked at Wingard astonished. 'He don't look much like one.'

'Well he is. Come on Wingard, show her your identity discs.'

Wingard said he was damned if he would. The waitress was incredulous but we got chocolate cakes. Wingard pointed at a sign on the counter. It said STRAWBERRIES.

'How much are strawberries?'

'A shilling without cream.'

'I'll have them with cream.'

'There isn't any cream so you can't.'

'All right then, I'll have them without.'

The waitress said he couldn't because there weren't any strawberries either. Not really. Those in baskets on the counter were only dummies. Wingard said: 'Well, I give up.' The waitress, now quite genial, lingered by the table.

'My hubby's in the army too,' she told us. 'He's up in Scotland, miles from anywhere, with two hundred sheep and two women. He says he wouldn't mind if it was two hundred women and two sheep.'

I said we'd private business to discuss, she went off, we ate the cakes. We talked private business. I asked Wingard if he'd like to buy a film. He said what kind of film. I said a script. He said no but he knew a man who might buy it. I wrote the address down. Then I went to a phone box and rang up several people but they were all out or else the numbers were engaged. I'd a train to catch. I collected my kit, said goodbye to Wingard and got on board. There was plenty of room. Later I felt hungry and went to the refreshment car. Businessmen and Home Guard officers were drinking together and saying Old Boy. There were a few blonde WAAFs on the make: a stout Canadian captain was standing them gin.

I said to the woman at the counter: 'Can I have a sandwich, please?'

She said sharply: 'One moment while I serve this gentleman first.'

One moment took about ten minutes. All the businessmen pushed in front of me: one repeat order for the same again all round took up further time. Then the woman said: 'Yes? What do you want?'

I said: 'A sandwich please.'

She said: 'No more sandwiches. All ordered. Only toast.'

'Anything to put on it?'

'Nothing. Just dry toast.'

I went back to my carriage and went to sleep. An hour later I was home.

2. FRIDAY

Breakfast in bed. Sheets and silk pyjamas again; the first decent sleep for three months. Afterwards in civvies once more, sauntering down the high street. The town had changed; barbed wire along the sea-front; my favourite pier closed altogether; my favourite café shut down for the duration. Damn. Canadian soldiers in the streets; empty packets of Winchester and Sweet Caporal in the gutter.

I stood on the street corner watching the officers walk by. They didn't know me; I didn't have to salute. I watched my reflection with pleasure in shop windows: the sports coat, gabardine trousers, no hat. A man again, not just name and number. I kept forgetting I could put my hands in my pockets: I expected an NCO to threaten to sew them up at any moment.

A girl I knew came up to me. She said: 'Fancy seeing you. Why aren't you in the army?'

I said I was but on leave; she said then why wasn't I out in Libya? The spirit of adventure was dead nowadays she said. I'd been rather in love with her once; now I looked at her and felt nothing at all.

'Everything's dead nowadays,' I said. 'We're all dead. You're dead but you don't know it.'

She said the thing she'd always hated about me was I was so depressing.

That evening a party. All the dirt: A. was a prisoner of war; B. had gone bankrupt; the son of C. had got married; the man who handled the pumps at the petrol station was now a captain in the RASC.

They all said I looked well, the army's done you good. I said yes like hell. E. said: 'Tell them about when you were on guard.' I told them; they laughed. It had not been funny for me at the time but of course that made it funnier in the telling. They all laughed; we ate sandwiches and drank Scotch; E. said: 'Now do the CO' I did the CO; it was a success. She said: 'Now do the time when he asked the sentry the time.' I did that too and then the Welshman who had no roof to his mouth and they laughed. The hostess said: 'I'm sure you must have frightful fun in the army. Howling with laughter the whole time.'

I thought oh yeah but I didn't say it. It seemed mean to dispel their illusions. They said do tell us some more. I told them, but on the drive home I was very silent. Being so funny about it all had exhausted me.

In my sleep I heard the siren. What a relief not to get up. I slept.

3. SATURDAY

She said: 'Let's make whoopee. Let's celebrate. We never seem to celebrate when you're home.'

I said: 'All right,' so first we had tea. It cost two-and-six apiece for a pot of tea and a black coffee and two fearfully dull cakes each. As for the coffee: I thought they'd given me Oxo by mistake. I told her about the chocolate cakes and cream doughnuts you could get down where I was stationed. You could eat two cakes and three doughnuts and have a coffee all for elevenpence, *and* in a civilian café. Also there was steak.

She said, 'Oh but everything's more expensive down here.'

I said: 'You're telling me.'

Then the cinema; it was a musical and pretty foul. Coming out E. said there was something good on at C.; we decided to go Monday. We got on a bus and went to see friends. They took us to a night-club, or what passes for a night-club in the country.

Anyway there was a bar and a dance floor and people drinking and it was at night. A parrot hung in a cage in a corner.

There was the hell of a row going on: naval and RAF and army officers and the usual girls: platinum blondes in backless frocks and a sprinkling of grass widows having a good time. One horsey-looking woman in tweeds. A radiogram giving out a rumba.

Suddenly there was a scandal. Dead silence and everyone staring. I looked round and there was a lance-corporal in battle dress, stripes and all. He'd just come in with a party. Well of course the club was officers only; there was another one up the road for other ranks where they sold only beer. One of the officers got up and went over to this lance-corporal, but it turned out he was an OCTU candidate so everything was all right after all and the officer bought him a drink. The music played louder than ever afterwards; they put sixpences in slot machines; they staggered about.

Another officer, a captain with a thick black moustache, had hold of a girl about sixteen: she had a bold enamelled baby face and blue eyes bulging out of her head with booze. He had his arm round her and was reciting a limerick.

> The worthy old Bey of Algiers,
> Said to his wives Now my dears,
> You may think it odd of me...

Luckily the music drowned out the rest, then above it the captain could be heard shouting 'LOUD CHEERS'. He roared with laughter and slapped the girl on the back, so hard he nearly knocked her over. We didn't dance: the floor was too crowded already. Then two officers got up, one stood to attention and the other saluted. They were dramatising some scene that was evidently famous in their battalion. Its meaning was explained to the uninitiated by the black-moustached captain, or rather he started on an explanation then for some reason broke off and began to grope on hands and knees on the floor. An old retired major sitting in the corner said 'Disgusting.' But he was in civvies and you couldn't tell he'd been a major so they paid no attention.

Then the barman began to turn the lights out one by one as a warning that the party was over; it was a night-club but in the country the night ends early and they had to close down. Nobody paid any attention to the lights going off, so at last in desperation the barman turned them all out at the same time and it was dark. At once giggles and slips of protest and the sound of kisses broke out; I seized E. by the arm and we got out by the side door.

Outside by the parked cars two women were squabbling shrilly: something about a fur coat; they seemed on the point of scratching one another's eyes out. A naval officer stood by them saying in a weak voice: 'Here I say, girls, this won't do, damn it, no.'

The last bus back was full of soldiers singing; they'd come from the other ranks club. They had been celebrating too.

4. SUNDAY

Everything was closed on Sunday; the town like a place of the dead. On weekdays the shops closed now at half past five but on Sunday they just didn't open. Even the paper shops didn't open. All cafés were closed too. I said to E.: 'Does anything open?' She said one shop on the front did but as it sold only toys and teddy bears it wasn't much use.

We got on a bus and went to the country: that wasn't closed. We meant to go to a forest but most of it had been chopped down. There were no soldiers in sight but there the tree-trunks were, all chopped and stacked up in order; they had become logs. E. said: 'Of course most of these Canadians were professional woodsmen.'

There had been a camp fire and that part of the forest looked as if it'd been subjected to a scorched earth policy. There were a few bully beef tins and cigarette packets scattered about but not many.

Later we ate sausage rolls and drank gin and ginger ale in a raftered room where there was a card saying: DOGS ARE LIKE DRINK. THEY ARE ALL RIGHT IN MODERATION.

5. MONDAY

We drove over to C.: the film we wanted was not on after all. E. had been deceived by a large poster advertising it on the edge of the town and hadn't noticed the words COMING NEXT WEEK pasted at the bottom.

She said: 'Next week you won't be here.'

I said: 'For god's sake don't let's think about that.'

But then I started to think about it and I was depressed. Only two days more I thought; you couldn't count the last one, it was all taken up travelling.

There weren't any good pictures on so she said let's look over the cathedral. We looked it over and when we came out it was pouring with rain. She said she knew a place where they had some good coffee. We went there; it was very magnificent, like a studio set for a film about the future. Pillars and a double staircase leading to a dance floor above, but there was no dancing on because it wasn't the right day. The rain rattled on the glass roof.

We ordered coffee; the girl said: 'Sorry, no *coffee*.' We asked further questions; she said no, coffee in mornings *only*. She walked away; she wasn't disposed to argue the point. So we drank tea and ate meringues. As we went out there was a sergeant-major from some regiment standing by the door. I said: 'After you'; he said: 'No, after *you*, sir,' and opened the door for both of us.

I wanted to tell him I was only a private in spite of my clothes but E. restrained me. She said: 'Don't be unpleasant.'

It rained all that night and I thought only two days more.

6. TUESDAY

Only one day more.

In the evening I had my fortune told. It was terrible. Black cards everywhere. The death card was there, but luckily the wrong way up. I was to go a journey, abroad it looked like; a fair man would send me there. A dark woman would cause me tears and anguish.

'D'you know any dark women?' they said.

I thought hard; I couldn't think of any. 'No,' I said.

'Perhaps you haven't met her yet,' they said.

Then they said: 'Cut the cards and wish.'

I cut clubs. 'You won't get your wish,' they said.

It was depressing. We listened to the news: that was depressing too. When we came out it was raining again.

7. WEDNESDAY

The last day. In the morning came a letter from the man I'd written to about the film saying he wouldn't.

I got up; there was a lot to do. In the afternoon I had a haircut. As usual I had let my hair grow for a fortnight before going on leave but now I couldn't go back like that or the sergeant'd start talking about hairpins.

Then in the evening there was feverish activity getting my clothes sorted out; I couldn't find my gaiters and socks. Buttons were sewn on and my respirator and steel helmet finally located in a downstairs cupboard. I got my equipment connected up and tried it on to make sure I had everything the right way up.

We kept saying: 'It's only three months before the next.'

'That'll soon pass.'

'It'll be here before you know it.'

'Unless I'm sent abroad.'

'Oh you won't be. Surely you don't believe in that?'

'No, of course not.'

Because it's like the horoscopes: when they are good you believe in them but when they're bad it's a pack of nonsense and you don't believe a word.

I had a bath and went to bed early because I'd a train to catch next day.

8. THURSDAY

In the morning a packet arrived by post marked URGENT. IMME-DIATE. AT ONCE. I thought it was orders for me to go abroad. But it wasn't: only proofs for me to correct. I dressed; khaki chafing the skin again; they said how nice I looked in my uniform. I said oh yeah and goodbye, and made a dash for the bus. I kept thinking I'd forgotten some article of equipment but for a miracle they were all there.

At the station they said: 'It's only three more months.'

'Oh yes. It soon goes.'

A whistle blew; they got quickly off the train but it was a false alarm. Then quite suddenly the train started to move silently; I was caught unprepared and nearly fell out of the window. They waved and I waved and the platform moved backwards with all the people on it waving until at last it seemed they were all waving to me and then the station was out of sight and I drew my head in again.

At Victoria there was no time to eat; I had to get from one station to another. I injudiciously went by tube; changed at the wrong station; went up the wrong staircase; became lost in a labyrinth of tunnels and arrows pointing in all directions at once.

When I at last reached the terminus the departures platform was empty. A railway official said: '3.15 next one,' and I slammed a gate. 'What time does that get in?' I called after him.

'6.10. It's a slow one,' he shouted back over his shoulder.

So there I was. I had to be back by five. 1700 hours it said distinctly on my pass. It'd be 1830 hours by the time I got to the Company Office. That meant CB for sure. Why a full corporal had got court-martialled and stripped for being ten minutes late back from leave. True, he'd done it three times before but still.

I went and had some lunch. I corrected my proofs at an ABC. I thought will it be scrubbing they'll give me. If so not the latrines. Oh my god not the latrines. I found I'd made the wrong mark on my proof and corrected that. But perhaps it wouldn't be scrubbing. And for how long. Three days? Seven?

I looked at the clock and it said three. I dropped my proofs in a post box and ran for the train. I got a seat but I was gloomy. The train stopped at every station. Cows, hoardings, parallel rails, Craven A.

At last I got out and walked downhill towards the billets. I came to the hotel where the Company Office was and started up the stairs. I thought they can't give me more than seven, anyway.

The orderly corporal was just coming out of the bathroom; he'd a bottle of Brylcreem in his hand.

'Hullo,' he said. 'Have a good leave?'

'Yes thanks Corporal,' I said.

'That's good. Just stick your pass on my desk will you?' He passed on whistling. I dropped my pass on the desk and turned to run. From behind me his voice called out: 'Hi, hang on. Half a mo!'

I turned back; my heart sank. 'Yes Corporal,' I said.

'You can stay out till twelve tonight you know,' he said. 'There's a big dance on. Down the Pier. They got the band down special. Smashing band too.'

'You going, Corp?' I said.

'Not half. Aren't you?'

'Yes,' I said.

But I didn't: I was too exhausted with relief. Suddenly I felt tired out. I drew my kit from the stores, laid out my palliasse and went to sleep on it. I needed a rest; first period next morning was PT for all ranks. At seven o'clock: in boots.

I'm Too Old to
Play the Violin

*   *   *

THE OTHER DAY PEOPLE STARTED TELLING ME TO BUY A FIDDLE.
Others addressed me as Maestro. From those observations I deduced I
should have my hair cut. I looked in the mirror and decided that the
time had not really come for this extreme measure. But the RSM,
encountered soon after in the hospital corridor, persuaded me in his
usual kindly way to alter my decision.

'And if you don't have it cut, so help me God, I'll cut it for you,' he
shouted after me.

The need for a haircut, viewed in the light of this new development,
now became imperative.

I went in search of the hospital barber. But he was elusive. Not easily
found. He wasn't in his den, nor in his ward. I went to the Naffy. They
said, 'He's just gone. Just this minute.'

'Half-past ten's the time to catch him,' they said.

'No good,' I said. 'I'm on parade half-past ten.'

'Two o'clock, then,' they said. 'Bound to catch him at two.'

But at two he still wasn't in his den. I went to his ward. He was there,
asleep in a chair.

'How about it, mate?' I said, shaking him.

'How about what?' he said. He didn't even open his eyes. 'Haircut?'
he said. 'No haircuts today. Clippers under repair. Come tomorrow.'

'What time?' I said.

'Any time,' he said, and began to snore.

So I went again in the morning. I sat for a time in the chair, and
presently he came in yawning. He picked up the clippers and came
towards me. But at sight of my hair he faltered. He dropped the
clippers and picked them up again. A look of indecision came over his

face. He wavered about, pushed moodily at the scissors; things were in the balance. Then he said, 'No dammit. Don't feel like work today. Tomorrow morning,' and walked out. I followed him – and ran bang into the RSM.

'Not got that haircut, I see,' he said.

'Tomorrow, sir,' I said. 'I have an appointment.'

But next day was no good either; and the barber'd gone sick. Something wrong with his guts, someone said.

And there was – appendicitis. They're operating tomorrow.

So how did I get my hair cut? I'll tell you. I went and had one down town. It was as simple as that. Life's not nearly so complicated as we try to make it. The only snag was it cost me one and a tanner. One has to pay for these simple pleasures.

Still, it was cheaper than buying a fiddle.

UNFINISHED LONGER FICTION

AUTHOR'S NOTE

18,000 words (approx.) of Original MS of the provisional (uncompleted) novel, based on the Eugen Weidmann mass-murderer case in Paris, 1939, commissioned by Graham Greene when he was Managing Director of Eyre & Spottiswoode Ltd in Summer 1947.

The novel, in this form, at any rate, will never be completed.

J. Maclaren-Ross
26 January 1961

The Dark Diceman:
A Novel

*   *   *

…it will be a gamble and the strange thing is that man who is
conceived by accident and whose every breath is a fresh cast
with dice already loaded against him will not face that final
main which he knows beforehand he has assuredly to face
without essaying expedients ranging all the way from violence
to petty chicanery that would not deceive a child until some
day in very disgust he risks everything on a single blind turn
of a card no man ever does that under the first fury of despair
or remorse or bereavement he does it only when he has realised
that even the despair or remorse or bereavement is not particularly important to the dark diceman.

William Faulkner
(*The Sound and the Fury*)

PART 1

'And do you, then, suppose me such a creature?…Do you
think I have no more generous aspiration than to sin, and sin,
and sin, and, at last, sneak into heaven? My heart rises at the
thought. Is this, then, your experience of mankind? or is it
because you find me with red hands that you presume such
baseness? and is this crime of murder indeed so impious as to
dry up the very springs of good?'
'Murder to me is no special category,' replied the other. 'All
sins are murder, even as all life is war.'

Robert Louis Stevenson
(*Markheim*)

One

THE TYPES WERE SPOOFING MADLY WHEN MR YARROW JOINED them in the pub. Three matches each and you had to guess the total; they greeted him with clenched fists raised like a party salute: 'Come on Yarrow, get them up,' 'Room for you in the next round,' but Mr Yarrow as a rule guessed wrong, and he disliked losing.

'Be with you in a moment boys.' He forced his way through to the bar; behind him the fists were flourished again in the air and a stranger, entering at that moment, stopped in astonishment, believing he had blundered into the beginning of a fight.

Mr Yarrow in his pink plusfours bought himself a preliminary pint. Perspiration crawled stickily like a fly down his face and he slapped at it irritably, damn this heat: even the tankard he drank from seemed, as he clutched it, to break into a cold sweat on the outside.

Beyond the pub door, the lane lay deep in white dust, ridged underneath into hard uneven ruts where in winter was a lake of liquid mud. Sun flashed green off broken shards of bottle-glass embedded in a wall, a cart rocked creaking past with a load of hay. This was the country, but from the main road round the corner came the rumble of a bus; there was a ten-minute service to the nearest town: as Mr Yarrow always explained to clients when showing them over a house, one got the best out of both worlds.

The pub was country too. Long and smoky and raftered, a barrel of cider on the counter: Captain Barrett always referred to the beer as ale. He wore corduroy breeches and he looked a bit like a riding-master, but he didn't come from that part of the world, neither did his strident smiling wife, who called the customers Darling and had been on the stage.

Now she served the stranger without a second glance; bangles rattled on her bare arms as she drew the bitter and plonked down the change. She liked to think of the place as a kind of club, and only members were really encouraged: the spoofers, the regular lunchtime clientele: the optician, the architect, the retired naval captain they all called Skipper, Mr Yarrow the estate agent, fumbling in his pockets for matches to join in the spoof.

'Your call,' the Skipper said, 'Frank lost': five of them, Mr Yarrow noted, and all drinking double-scotch; the bottle was kept under the counter for the regulars, other people had to put up with beer. He drew out his team: they were grey with age, the sticks worn thin from constant clutching in a sweaty palm, but it spoilt the luck if you didn't always use the same three.

He made a quick calculation and called eighteen. If he got in too many rounds, rigid economies were practised at home, but here he'd a reputation to uphold; the spoofers never suspected that he wasn't really a good loser. 'Seventeen,' 'Nineteen,' 'Twenty-one,' the calls went round; a seventh man had come in at the last moment and Captain Barrett wrote each number down, keeping the score; he said: 'Someday I'll make a book on this,' while his wife leaned close to him laughing: a devoted couple.

A shaft of yellow sunlight streamed down from a window high up near the rafters. Smoke and dust-motes floated in its path, a sort of nimbus: reminded the stranger somehow of a church; but here another kind of ritual was being enacted: the incomprehensible game with its esoteric slang: 'One leg up,' 'Best of three,' 'Two to you in the final.'

It was plain, however, that Mr Yarrow had lost; the others were clapping him on the back, he was calling for the drinks. 'Same again, Gwen me dear,' he laughed louder than any, he slapped down two quid: the sight of his bulging wallet reassured him, he remembered the deal pulled off over luncheon: sixty smackers to start with and more where that came from. He called cheerily out to Mr Barnes the bank manager, who'd popped across for a quickie: 'I'll be over your way Barney me boy: stick this lot in before they skin me out,' and the spoofers gathered round making grabs at his wallet.

None of them noticed the stranger: why should they? Young man sitting up at the bar, dark suit, in a corner, very quiet. Yellow gloves, paper unfolded in front of his face. But he wasn't reading: behind the paper he was whistling softly, his gloved fingers tapping out a tune along the counter's edge. He could hear the game going on and on; it ended temporarily in a shattering roar: now they were all drinking to the 'gallant loser'.

It was Mr Yarrow again, his unlucky day; once more he bought a round, changed another quid: his wife'd have to go without a new hat. He said: 'It's nearly two, I ought to be getting back,' but the spoofers had their hands up already, Captain Barrett poised his pencil above the score, there was no escape.

'Mac's call,' 'Loser shouts last,' 'Off we go,' the players dropped out one by one, smoke wreathed greyly up from their cigarettes through the shaft of sun, and the stranger whistled softly behind *The Times*; Mr Yarrow was in the final again, facing the architect.

'Best of three?'

'No,' Mr Yarrow said, to get it over: 'Sudden death.'

'Righto. Your call,' and: 'Come on Stephen darling,' Mrs Barrett encouraged him shrilly from behind the bar; he drew a deep breath and called 'Four' with one in his hand. 'Three' the answer came back, 'Open up,' and three it was: Mrs Yarrow's hat had gone definitely down the drain. He coughed up amid a chorus of commiseration: 'To the loser!' 'Hard cheese, old boy!': so much noise was being made that no one saw the young man in the dark suit go.

'You ought to've held nothing,' a spoofer was explaining; 'Hold nothing and call, three, that's what I always do.'

Mr Yarrow drained his glass: 'I don't like to go empty-handed,' wishing privately he'd made it best of three instead of sudden death. Still, he thought, things could be worse, and the thick pad of notes pressed against his side as he left the pub, waving to the chaps, blowing a kiss to Mrs B: I better get this in the bank quick.

Sun beating down outside, bloody hot; he stumbled a little on the ruts in the road, slapping at his face down which sweat trickled: three doubles and a pint of bitter had gone slightly to his head. The voice at his elbow made him start, he jumped around; it was almost as if the stranger had stepped out from ambush.

'Excuse me, aren't you Mr Yarrow? The estate agent?' The young man spoke softly, his voice was deep, flat and rather precise; there was something faintly foreign about his politeness, the way he stood with head slightly bent, hands hanging deferentially down at his sides. And he still hadn't taken off his gloves: odd thing, that, in this heat. Handsome fellow, though. White teeth, dark wavy hair: sort of young man Mrs Yarrow might easily have married, given the chance.

He said: 'I wondered whether – I have a train to catch at three-fifteen – I wondered if you could show me a house before I go back. There's not much time, I know,' but Mr Yarrow waved apologies aside.

'Say no more, I'm always ready to oblige.' He forgot the bank, he became almost sober, this was business. 'My car's parked just here. Jump in, and afterwards,' with an expansive gesture, 'I'll run you straight down to the station. How's that?'

'Very kind of you,' the young man murmured; he glanced quickly back down the lane before climbing into the car, but it wasn't closing time yet, no one about. He said: 'Preferably not on an estate. Some-where more secluded. Away from the town.'

'I've the very thing for you,' Mr Yarrow assured him. 'I take it you're a bachelor, Mr…'

'Deckert. Walter Deckert.'

'Mr Dekker,' and he felt in his pocket, among the spoofing matches, for the keys of Mon Plaisir, his white elephant, which he always carried just in case: nobody would stay in it for more than a month because of the rats in the thatch. 'Were you thinking of settling down here? Or only for the summer?'

'A year at the least.'

'Couldn't do better,' and a bus bore down on them in a blue cloud of petrol fumes as they swung left into the main road: 'Town and country, the best of both worlds.'

SLOW loomed up ahead, painted in large yellow letters on the macadam, then a sign saying SCHOOL; the village high-street came in sight: a bank, a post office, petrol pumps, a row of small essential shops. Deckert craned out of the car window at a newsagents' on a corner, with posters leaning up outside and enamelled advertisements for cigarettes across the front. He sank back into his seat with a sort of sigh: 'It hasn't changed much since my time.'

'You lived here before, then?'

'As a boy.'

They drove fast along a bypass between open country either side. Big boards advertising estate agents flashed past right and left; they all had names like actors: Stephen Yarrow, Howard Bond, Peter Raine: there was one called Ivan something.

'Didn't I see you in the Swan just now?' Mr Yarrow asked.

'I was there.'

'You should've joined in the spoof,' Mr Yarrow said, slowing down to let a lorry pass, 'It's a grand game once you get the hang of it. You a gambler, Mr…,' but he'd already forgotten his client's name.

'Yes,' Deckert told him, 'I've always been a gambler,' and began to whistle a tune very softly to himself as the fields flew by.

'Isn't that Loch Lomond?' Mr Yarrow said. 'I thought so, my ear never deceives me,' and he added: 'Good old Scotland,' in case his client was a Scot. He said: 'You must join our Operatic if you're musical'; they jolted down a cart-track bordered by high hedges beyond which cows grazed: 'Last winter we did *The Maid of the Mountains*, Mrs Barrett played Teresa. But this year,' the bumps got worse, 'bit more ambitious,' he belched, '*Traviata.*'

The car swayed and stopped, one wheel in a rut. 'Here we are,' Mr Yarrow waved his hand at weeds and a wall, TO LET planted askew on a board in ankle-deep grass; he pointed to a half-overgrown name on a gate. 'Mon Plaisir. Aptly-named, eh?' and he jingled the keys: 'Means "My Pleasure" in French.'

'I understand French,' Deckert told him, in his deep flat rather precise voice. He followed Mr Yarrow along a flagged path fringed with a tangle of brier rose that tripped you up like lianas in a jungle; he began to whistle again as they approached the cottage door.

'Course the lawn needs cutting rather,' Mr Yarrow said, hoping the rats'd be asleep that time of day, 'but I can recommend a good man to go to. Old Binns. Have it shipshape in no time.' He thought if he got away with this the wife'd have her hat after all, pushing on the warped woodwork of the door.

It opened straight onto a smell of damp, an incredibly dark living-room: even with the blinds up, the windows were too low to let in much light. 'Kitchen through here, fitted gas-cooker, everything to taste ...' Mr Yarrow raised his voice to drown a possible scamper on the roof, but the rats were having a rest: it wasn't until midnight that they really got started.

'This'll be your bedroom, and here's a spare, case you have a friend down. Course if it's a young lady I don't suppose you'll be needing a spare. Love in a cottage, eh: what more can you want?' He laughed loudly and winked: at no one in particular, at his own cleverness perhaps: the hat was as good as on his wife's head.

'But the bathroom. Surely there's a bathroom?' Deckert seemed almost to plead, with such sadness in his eyes that Mr Yarrow was startled, and he thanked his lucky stars for that actress who'd shoved in a decent bath before the rats had got her down.

'Indeed there is.' He threw open a door: 'Hey presto! Constant hot water, no geyser to muck about with, special fittings,' he bent forward to screw at one of the taps and Deckert drew the pistol from under his coat and struck him on the back of the head with the butt.

The bunch of keys clattered from Mr Yarrow's hand onto the tiled floor and he flopped forward over the side of the bath without even a groan.

Deckert reversed the gun in his gloved fingers and held the barrel against the nape of Mr Yarrow's neck. The shot was not loud. It didn't even wake the rats in the thatch.

Deckert stood listening for a moment; a bluebottle had got in and was buzzing and banging against the window-pane: otherwise there was no sound. He unbuttoned the dead man's jacket and drew out his wallet. There was an expensive fountain pen clipped to the breast pocket, a Parker 51, black and gold: he took that also. Then he extracted the notes from the wallet and counted them, drawing off one glove in order to do so. Close on £60: two fives, the rest in ones. He frowned at the fivers: anyone else would have cursed, but Deckert never swore.

He transferred all the notes to his own wallet, clipped the pen to his inside pocket, and walked out without a backward glance, leaving Mr Yarrow along with the smell of cordite and the bluebottle buzzing against the pane. No one saw him come or go. He climbed into Mr Yarrow's car and backed it up the cart-track past the grazing cows; he turned the corner onto the bypass, he was gone: he left behind him no clue.

The car was later found abandoned a few miles away, but it was some time before the body of Mr Yarrow was discovered. He lay slumped over the bathtub, one hand trailing limply in the rusty trickle from the tap, the other extended palm outwards.

Two

But for Arthur Loftus it all began with the bookshop in Bloomsbury, or before that, when Carmichael told him about the girl.

'Tall, about five-ten, athletic type, damn good figure, not a bad face if you take her specs off,' and he'd scribbled down an address. 'Here you are. Go in around three, the chap in charge's generally out for coffee about then, and you'll find her on her lonesome.'

'But what about bed?' Arthur had asked.

'A sound bet. Bloody good. I've had it.'

'I might try that. Thanks for the tip,' and Arthur had thoughtfully stroked his thick fair moustache.

Of course he didn't try it: he hadn't the nerve to go about things that way. Then one day, and quite by chance, he found himself looking into the window of the bookshop itself. Beyond the discreet dust-jackets, the volumes of Faber poetry and the little reviews, he could see his pink-and-white face like a moon reflected. A hot dry dusty wind blew across from the bomb craters in Southampton Row behind him as he pressed closer to the pane. It was three-fifteen, his watch told him, but he could not see the girl inside. He remembered the athletic figure, the height: tall girls attracted him, though he was himself over six feet. He pushed open the door, a bell tinkled, and he stepped through into the shop.

There was a kind of cubicle partitioned off at the back: from behind the thin wood he heard a chair-leg scrape and a girl's cigarette-cough. Then she came out: a red-ribbed sweater outlining the athletic shape, bare brown arms and a lot of muscular leg; she lilted languidly towards him, pushing her back hair up, a blonde.

'Can I help you?' The bird-like voice coming from such a big girl was incongruous; Arthur reddened and looked away from her breasts towards a bad painting propped up between two books.

He said: 'I've a message for you. From a friend of mine called Carmichael.'

'Oh, *Micky*!' She became suddenly animated: 'How is he, the darling? I've not seen him for ages.'

'He's up in Edinburgh. Some special course at a clinic. He sends his love.'

'Is he qualified yet?'

'Last month.'

'Come in here and tell me all about him. And yourself, of course.'

But there wasn't much to tell about himself, at the age of twenty-eight; you could deduce most of it from his appearance: the college blazer and Cambridge scarf, the home-service ribbon pinned to his breast, the copy of *Polemic* peeping out of his pocket; he tugged at his moustache and mumbled something, oppressed by the paucity of his past.

She said: 'I'll make some tea. Don't sit in the swivel-chair because it tips you out'; they were alone behind the partition with the gas-ring, the till and the telephone: when she bent forward to put on the kettle, a lock of her hair brushed across his cheek.

Arthur was breathless, he picked up a book at random and blushed: it was the *Kama Sutra*. She'd evidently just put it down: her place was marked with a hair-grip and there was a fresh smear of lipstick on the page.

She said: 'That belongs to Hakim Ali, he's in charge of the shop, you know. It's very interesting: the technique of sex, treated scientifically.'

She laughed. 'Which brings me back to Bobby. D'you know him well?'

'We share a flat. I'm Arthur Loftus.'

'Any relation to the millionaire?'

'My uncle,' but Arthur's natural caution and the memory of a girl called Rita prompted him to add: 'I'm a poor relation, unfortunately.'

'My name's Frieda Druce.' He saw she was wearing a wedding ring. He said: 'Aren't you Swedish?'

'Originally. But I was born in Toronto.'

'And you study mathematics?'

'Logic. Trust Micky to get everything wrong.'

When she sat down opposite him in the small cramped space their knees were almost touching. He could see the tiny blond hairs on her broad brown arms. The cracked cup of tea trembled in his hand. He said: 'You're awfully brown.'

'I do a lot of swimming. The Serpentine.'

'You must come with me to my club. They've the best pool in town.'

'I'd love to. When?'

'Whenever you like.' He held out his cigarette-case: her hand touched his as he took one. She blew a stream of smoke towards the ceiling, her lips shaping a round red O. She had a beautiful mouth: nose was a bit beaky perhaps, but the mouth made up for that; he didn't mind her spectacles because he wore them too.

He said: 'That's a date then,' and added: 'Why not come now?'

'I have to mind the shop till Hakim gets back. Besides, I'm much too tired. No sleep at all last night.' With that she threw her head sideways and yawned, tapping her mouth: 'Pardon me'; he could see her wet pink tongue. He was on tenterhooks. He stood up, he didn't know why, but she rose too, putting her teacup down.

'You're not off already?'

'Oh no.'

'Do stay. We'll go out later – for a drink if you like.'

'Let's.'

She smiled up at him. 'You're nice and tall. I like fair boys. Funny, because I'm blonde myself,' reaching out to touch his moustache: 'Does it prickle?'

Arthur slipped an arm around her, she leant her beaked face forward; it was awkward because they'd both big noses and were both of them wearing spectacles. Then, before they could actually kiss, the telephone rang; its sudden jangle made them jump apart. Frieda instantly became cool and composed, smoothing back her cockatoo's crest of yellow hair as though a customer had entered the shop. She cooed: 'Yes?' taking off the receiver.

A slow, deep voice rumbled distinctly up from the other end; Arthur couldn't help hearing 'Consignment,' 'Held up,' and 'Customs.' Frieda said: 'Right. I'll tell Hakim.'

She hung up: 'That was Mr Maher. He owns the shop. A whole chain of them. You must meet him sometime, he's such a darling.'

Arthur said: 'So are you.' He tried to put his arm around her again, but this time she pulled away, laughing. 'No don't, it's too hot. Besides, here's Hakim.'

An Indian with melancholy eyes and hair parted down the middle came in from the street. He had a permanent air of bearing up bravely under bad news, Mr Maher's message not excepted. He said sadly: 'I expect you two want to be off now, it's opening time. Probably see you later.'

'In the pub,' Frieda said, making-up her face before the spotted mirror. The Indian raised a limp hand, leaning back against the books; Arthur followed Frieda out, straightening his tie, hoping he hadn't lipstick on where his mouth had just had time to touch hers. He felt frustrated, but Frieda took his arm, pressing close to him in the crowded late-afternoon street.

'Don't be cross, darling. You can kiss me afterwards.'

'After what?'

Office workers, released for the day, surged around on all sides; a determined rush for a bus nearly knocked Arthur off his feet; Frieda said: 'After we've had a drink.'

But at the entrance to the pub she hung back suddenly. 'Let's go somewhere else. I've just seen someone I dislike.'

'Where?'

'Over there. At the counter.'

Down the gloomy perspective of the bar, filled with black-suited businessmen snatching a quick pint before the tube-train home, Arthur saw a tall young man who wore yellow gloves and leaned upon a gold-topped malacca-cane, his face turned away in profile under the brim of a soft grey hat. He didn't look especially alarming, but Frieda dragged at Arthur's arm. 'Please come away.'

'But who is he?'

'A friend of Mr Maher's. I can't stand him. I'm scared.'

'Why? What's he do?'

'I don't know. It's just that I feel he's cold, cold all over. Like a snake.' She shivered. 'Don't let's talk about him, please.'

'As you like.'

They turned into another pub, but even over the drinks Frieda still seemed nervous; she spoke in spasms and kept glancing over her shoulder as though expecting the man in yellow gloves to appear suddenly behind them at any moment. Arthur could see things going wrong if he wasn't careful. He suggested a change of scene: dinner in Soho followed by coffee at his flat.

Frieda said: 'All right, but I mustn't stay long.' She yawned: 'So tired. I must get some sleep in somehow.'

'But the shaded lights in the restaurant, the Greek food, a carafe of wine, altered her mood; she smiled at him across the table and squeezed his hand under the cloth: behind the lenses of her spectacles her eyes were dilated like a cat's with excitement when night comes, only hers were grey instead of green.

Arthur could hardly eat in anticipation of the evening's end.

Coffee and liqueurs; a taxi outside; then at last her mouth open and acquiescent under his as they drove on to Gordon Square in the sultry blue summer dusk. She opened her eyes and murmured: 'Are you very passionate, darling,' leaning, a dead weight, back in his arms.

Arthur was embarrassed: 'I don't know.'

Frieda said: 'I can be passionate, but only when I'm used to people. The first time I'm merely polite.'

She was more than polite. Being tired wasn't mentioned again and Carmichael was right: a sound bet; bloody good; he'd had it. In the morning Arthur cooked breakfast and brought it in on a tray.

Frieda sat up in bed stark naked and said: 'What's the time?'

'Twenty past ten.'

'I'll have to ring Theo. He'll wonder where I've got to.'

'The shop?'

'My husband. I must tell him where I've been.'

'You can't do that!' Arthur stepped back, stroking his moustache in agitation; he imagined jealousy, divorce, the effect on his family.

'Of course I can. Don't be silly, I tell Theo *everything*. You mustn't mind.'

'Doesn't he?'

'Not a damn.'

Arthur still didn't like it; but then, looking at her breasts, remembering last night and the *Kama Sutra*, he swallowed: 'All right.'

'Bless you, darling.' She reached out for the telephone and a newspaper slipped from the tray onto the floor; she said: 'I wonder if they've caught the man who killed that estate agent down in Sussex.'

Three

The film has already begun at the Fleapit as the perfunctory torch flashed Trégi to a seat.

Upon the screen, dark city streets, doorways deep in shadow, and a patrolman on his beat. Slow, doomful music, rather scratchy, as the picture's pretty old and the soundtrack getting a bit worn. The beam from the projector flickers and picks out a figure dodging from door to door, shabby overcoat, collar turned up, avoiding the patrolman, who paces on, tapping the buildings with his nightstick. Beneath the brim of a pulled-down fedora, a worn, sad hunted face, deeply-furrowed, hollow cheeks...by god, it's Bogart!

Been a Big Shot too, in his time, according to the trailer Trégi saw last week; but the judge has threatened him with a lifer if he appears again before the bench. Now he's sitting down, dead skint, disconsolate in a café. The straight and narrow don't seem much cop; but when gangsters enter and offer him the chance of coming in on a caper, he still won't play. So they order up a glass of milk and knock it out of his hand as he's about to drink. Bogart lets 'em get away with all this, but Trégi shifts angrily in his seat: he's damned if he would.

Now Bogart climbs the apples to his apartment, and there's a dame in there, got in somehow, all dolled up posh in frigging furs. Turns out she's been his tart, but while he was Inside she married a rich geezer instead: a girl's got to look after herself, eh? Bogart at first says scarper, but she soon gets round him again, and course in the finish he gives in: still, he's got to get his self some dough if he wants her back, so he shoves his rod down inside his pants and off round to the café.

Trégi, chewing gum in the two and threepennies, grips the arm of his stall: maintenant ça va barder; he wasn't bilingual for nothing, being half-French born in Poland Street, and sometimes he thought in French as well.

Sure enough, Bogart tosses the milk over the gangster this time and slaps him down, but geezer's got no guts, see, he daren't do damn-all, and they bend together over a plan of campaign. Fade out, fade in. The big bust. A bank job: bullion. Only naturally this skirt tries to put Bogart off: judies, dolls, palones, whatever you care to call 'em, always do (no one knows this better than Trégi); but Bogart pipes her down, and everything's under control when along come the coppers, bulls, flics or bogeys, whatever you care to call 'em.

Two bogeys get bumped, one crushed by a lorry, but Bogart makes a getaway, smart work that, and he's sitting pretty when bugger me if some other jane don't identify him, and up he comes for trial. No matter, the gang-boss, who's none other than the former sweetheart's husband and a big-time mouthpiece to boot, says there's nothing to fear, he'll get Bogart off. Now this lawyer's a right sod, goes without saying, and he's fixed a doublecross cause of his wife he's jealous of; and though Bogart socks him a right-hander bang in front of the bench, that don't make things any the easier. Now for the sentence – Trégi sits up straight – and with a wild despairing yell he falls through space, while in super-montage the white-haired beak repeats 'Life, Life, LIFE,' and bars come up all around to break the fall, with Bogart clutching onto them and a sunset in the background, kind of symbolical, if you get what I mean.

A prison-scene follows, with a large courtyard and all the convicts sitting around on sacks plotting to crash out. Trégi's been in the Nick his self, Wandsworth wasn't much like this; but then everything's different in the States, the promised land he's never seen. Bogart's planning like stink, he tweaks at the lobe of his ear like he always does when thinking something up, and Trégi strokes the thin white thread of scar on his left cheek in sympathy: it's quite a problem.

Then a concert gives 'em the break: a screw gets shivved but who cares, and Bogart in a couple of ticks is over the high wall and being driven along by the girl who'd smuggled in all the necessary, irrespective of her better half, whom she now knows to be a basket, notwithstanding all his dough.

Trégi'd call it quits at this point, personally he'd love the girl and leave her (putting it politely), but Bogart's gone proper soft: they're together in a mountain cabin, the simple life, cooking flapjacks just as mother made 'em, when a message comes over the radio saying a stooge who appeared earlier on is being held for the murder of that screw.

Trégi's jaws worked overtime on his gum, it's a tense moment, he knows what he'd do, but – ah ça alors – Bogart's bleeding US: they're going to give their selves up to save the stooge from the chair. Just then police roll up on motorbikes, tipped off by the bastard husband, and ... blast! the film's broken down.

Trégi spat out his spearmint and whistled furiously; scattered over the half-empty echoing cinema, people began to clap and boo; the shadow of the operator himself wavered up across the blank screen: projector-trouble or a bad copy, but never mind, he's got it fixed: ah! A chase – terrific. Mountain roads, hairpin bends, wheeee! Wheels skid with fearful screeches, shots ring out, the coppers drive their cycles over cliffs with abandon. But not before one of their slugs has put paid to the tart, and a bloody good thing too, Trégi thought. Bogart doesn't agree. There's a terrible look on his face, you see it filling the screen, music swells up, a crescendo, and any mug can tell he'll seek revenge, an eye for an eye at the very least.

And lo and behold here's the lawyer kipped down for the night, and Bogart creeping in the open window, gun in hand. Lawyer wakes up, grabs a shooter from under his pillow, and bang bang they've both had it. Bogart hasn't quite, though; dissolve to a hospital ward, the film must've begun there, only Trégi didn't see the start; the released stooge and his girlfriend are weeping beside the bedside, Bogart mutters that it's getting dark, his cigarette drops from his dying fingers, he says in disgust 'Big Shot,' to satisfy the censor, and an orderly's foot stamps on the fag in close-up as he crosses over: THE END.

Trégi, instantly on his feet, made for the aisle; behind him a crash of sound announced next Thursday's trailer: Cert A; he turned his head but it was a western: galloping hooves and campfire songs; all right for kids, he'd outgrown that.

Through swinging doors into the small empty vestibule, sunlit street beyond: but half a mo – what's this on the wall! A mirror's a magnet to Trégi, and he stops abruptly to plunge into the reflection of his sharp sallow face, scarred cheek and narrow eyes, smoothing down slick dark hair with both hands, a gold signet-ring on one of them. His suit's smartly cut, snug-fitting, double-breasted, dark blue with a tiny stripe, nothing flash; it's true the tie has crimson lightnings on it, but even that's expensive: set him back sixteen og. All fixed, fine and dandy, he swaggered out, heels hitting the sidewalk hard: not big maybe, but pretty tough – and come to that Bogart's no giant, say nothing of James Cagney or George Raft.

In the Tottenham Court Road it's sticky hot, petrol blowing acrid from buses and huge hoardings with Bogart again and Bette Davis: a pavement artist squatting beside his sad dog, cap in hand. The Guinness clock has stopped again, but it's about five; below, a paper-man is stationed, *Star News Standard*: a late final full of crime, CAR BANDITS ESCAPE, 200 CASES OF WHISKY STOLEN, SUSSEX BATH MURDER STILL UNSOLVED, but Trégi turns at once to the racing results: Christ almighty, another couple o' nicker down the pan.

The paper crumpled savagely in his hand, printer's ink coming off from it, he shoved his way, shouldering the crowd, down Charing X Road and up round Soho Square: the spivs standing about, corner of Frith and Old Compton, hailed him How you doing Tush, but Trégi didn't reply; he thrust on with thinned lips towards the brass nails on the batter by the static water tank.

And who should be coming out of the phone box, just by the blonde with the big legs, but old Theo: been on the blower, as per usual, on at his bleeding missus again. He managed the Wardour Street branch for Mr Maher, and Trégi stepped bang in his path: 'Why'n't you minding the shop?'

Theo Druce jerked back startled, eyes screwed up behind his specs, blinking like a bloody owl in daylight. He said with relief: 'Oh it's you, Robert,' pronouncing the name Ro-bair. He said: 'Business was slack today. I just thought I'd ring up my wife.'

Trégi snorted '*Dames*,' disgustedly. The fate of Bogart, caused by too great an attachment to a skirt, was still fresh in his mind. He asked: 'How's she getting along with what's-his-name? That bloke of hers.'

'Loftus? They're living together. She's just moved into his flat.'

'And you let 'em?' Trégi shouted, so loud a tart turned round to stare; 'Slap me! I'd bash his teeth in. Hers too,' he added as an afterthought.

'You forget,' Theo told him gently, 'that I'm a pacifist.'

And Trégi, with another snort, tossing his *Standard* in the gutter: 'Well, it's your funeral. What about a cup o' char?'

'The cup that cheers,' Theo said with his Chinese smile, 'but does not inebriate. Why not indeed?'

The café bar was under some scaffolding: no one in there now the pubs were open. The waitress put the two teas down and Trégi said: 'Here, Theo. This geezer Loftus.'

'Yes?'

'Let me do him for you, Theo.' He clenched his fists, he itched to sock someone – anyone: to get his own back on all the bastards everywhere: the screws in civvy nick, the sarmajor in the glasshouse, the horse that came in third. He said: 'It's simple. I lay in wait outside his gaff, see. One night when it's dark. Along he roams, unsuspecting. I grab him sudden,' he gripped Theo by the lapel, 'like this: then in with the old head, up with the old knee, and *click*!' he snapped his fingers. 'Couple of weeks in dock. No one the wiser.'

'No no,' Theo said; he was shocked: 'I couldn't possibly countenance, my principles wouldn't allow me to...' He waved his hand: 'Besides, I've other ideas.'

'Such as?'

'Arthur will be a rich man one day. His uncle's Sir Edwin Loftus.'

'The steel bloke?'

'None other,' and Theo folded his hands: you expected him to put them in his sleeves and bow. He added: 'Arthur has money of his own, too. If he can support Frieda in comfort, who am I – a poor man – to stand in her way?'

'I get it. Pickings.'

'Precisely.'

Trégi shouted with laughter; privately he thought Ponce, but you couldn't deny old Theo was deep; a proper one: he'd got it all worked out.

'I'm seeing them tonight,' Theo told him, 'to discuss settlements.'

'Why not take me along, Theo. I might do a deal with him meself. That car o' mine; it's going cheap.'

'Not a chance, Robert.'

'Ah, come on. Be a sport.'

'Well, it could be arranged – on a commission basis, of course.'

'You bloody old Scrooge.'

'Ten per cent,' Theo blandly smiled, 'I'm a businessman, Robert.'

'All right, and may it choke you. Where do we meet?'

'The French House, seven-thirty.'

Trégi threw down a tanner and stood up. 'I'll be there.'

'One moment,' Theo was very earnest: 'not a word about this to your friend Deckert, mind. I don't want him cutting in.'

Trégi ran a finger round his throat: 'Trust me, Theo.'

'I wish I could,' Theo told him.

Trégi, already on his way out, turned at the door and made a rude sign with fingers forked. Then he made straight for the phone box lately vacated by Theo. He dialled a Paddington number, and: 'Hullo. Walter? This is Robert. Look I think I got someone hooked for that beauty parlour scheme: a steamer, a mug, see? Sure, he's got bags of dough, but I've not seen him yet, just reckoned I'd let you know. We're meeting tonight, seven-thirty, I'll sound him then. Okay.'

He rang off and walked on, whistling, to his father's hotel in Dean Street, where he'd a room on the top floor and didn't have to pay rent.

Four

Alec Foley, ex-Aircraftman Foley, long since discharged (unlikely to become efficient in any form of military service), present age 29, height 5'7", minor public-school education (expelled), ex-member BUF (expelled), bi-sexual, deported from France as undesirable British subject, two prison convictions in this country, no visible means of support, sat in the Viennese Café one Sunday morning over a black coffee, waiting for someone who might lend him a quid.

On the crimson plush settee opposite, a bald man of indeterminate origin was scooping bacon and dehydrated eggs out of a dish voraciously; Foley's stomach rumbled: he hadn't even the bob necessary to buy a breakfast.

If only Peter'd come, or Teddy: they usually did on Sundays. But the double doors swung open and shut on the empty sunshine of the street outside, the prismatic chandeliers tinkled to-and-fro in the draught, a girl with a proud contemptuous face wheeled a trolley of cakes up and down, and still no one came in that Foley knew. The clock had crept on: past eleven already; it looked as though nothing could save Alec from the dreary Sunday dinner with Uncle Simon over the chemist's shop in Canonbury: his only chance of a free meal – if he managed to rake up the fare.

The bald man called for another roll in a tone of command, snapping his fingers at the waiter; Foley shifted his neck free of his frayed collar, which was fretting a boil; he finicked at his tie, glancing desperately round the café at the plump jowled Central European faces: a few London University students, rather boisterous: an Indian reading *Reynold's News*. No possible hope there, unless... and his eyes suddenly narrowed.

Surely that face was familiar: there, at a side-table, half hidden by an *Observer* on a wicker frame. Foley craned forward to see better; at that moment the newspaper rustled down and the young man laid it aside, reaching for his coffee cup. Foley had excellent sight: when he saw the hands he was certain. It had been eight years ago, the other had worn a moustache then, but Foley had a memory for faces, and he'd good reason to remember this one. *Johnson*: after all this time. Looked prosperous, too: elegant grey suit, gold-topped malacca cane leaning against the table: the yellow gloves he was pulling on seemed to be hand sewn.

Foley could hardly believe his good fortune; Peter and Teddy were forgotten: if he played his cards right, it was no longer a question of a quid, but a fiver; perhaps even a tenner – beyond the dreams of avarice. Johnson had not noticed him, either; he leant back wiping his lips with a silk handkerchief which he pulled from his sleeve – another mannerism Foley remembered; now he was screwing a cigarette into a short amber holder. Then suddenly a small queue formed out of nowhere, headed by the manager, in evening-dress, who walked backwards in front beckoning the people forward like a drum-major on ceremonial parade. The queue hid Johnson from sight; but suddenly Foley saw him standing up to pay his bill, the waiter was counting change from a ten-shilling note into his gloved palm.

Foley gulped the contents of his cup and stood up also; the chicory in the coffee made his head swim, he caught hold of the settee for support and muttered 'Sorry': the bald man glared balefully up over his raspberry jam. Alec flung sixpence on the table – his all – and swung round, slipping on the tiled floor, to follow Johnson, who was striding swiftly, with his gloves and cane, towards the stairs that led down to the telephones and the gents lav.

He turned right at the bottom and Foley sidled in his wake; a solitary man in shirtsleeves combed his hair before a row of black marble basins, an attendant stood rigid by a sort of throne. The urinals lay beyond, and Alec stepped confidently up beside Johnson: it was not the first time he had accosted a stranger in such surroundings.

He said: 'Haven't we met before?' turning his head sideways as he sprang a leak.

'I don't think so,' the other said, but his voice was right too, as Alec remembered it: deep and flat and rather precise, and Foley said: 'But surely. The South of France, the dear old Côte. I'm Alec Foley. Didn't you know Jeanne Lombard?'

The other didn't move; his face remained still: smoke curled across it from the holder between his teeth: no emotion, no expression, not even a flicker. From behind the closed door of one of the toilets came the sound of a man whistling and the rustle of paper; then Johnson's voice, quite cool: 'Jeanne Lombard. I'd forgotten her.'

'Course the moustache made a difference,' Alec said, adjusting his dress, 'but I'd have known you anywhere. Couldn't we have a coffee upstairs – for old times' sake?' and the flat deep voice replied: 'With pleasure.'

'Poor old Johnny,' Foley said as they climbed the stairs together, Johnson towering six inches above him; 'Remember how she always used to call herself Johnny?'

'Used to?' the other said, and Alec envied him his nerve; 'Doesn't she still?'

'She's dead,' Foley told him. 'Heart failure. Eight years ago. Didn't you know?' and they sat down at a table, nobody near: they were all up the other end eating salads. Foley said: 'I'm surprised you didn't read about it in the papers. Made quite a stir at the time.'

'But what happened?' A waiter hurried up, and Johnson changed his question to: 'What are you having?'

'Twelve o'clock,' Foley said; 'It's time for a drink. I think I'd like,' he smiled with sharp snaggly teeth, 'a café cognac. Remind me of the good old days,' and he saw his grimace repeated in a gilt-framed mirror, flanked by two electric candles in cut-glass brackets, behind Johnson's head.

'Two café cognacs,' Johnson told the waiter, and to Alec: 'You were telling me about Jeanne Lombard.'

Foley said: 'Some of her jewels were stolen. Valuable stuff too, a rope of pearls, apart from ready cash. The French police had a theory one of her lovers was responsible.'

'For the robbery?' Johnson said.

'And her death.'

'But I thought you said heart failure,' as the waiter came hurrying back: 'Deux café cognacs, msieu.'

Foley raised his cup; his hand trembled slightly, the blunt nails were bitten to the quick. 'Salut, as we used to say on the Côte,' and lowering his voice: 'It was a sudden shock did it. There were some marks too, which make it technically murder.'

'I see,' Johnson said. 'Cigarette?' and out came a case, gold by the looks of it, and filled with expensive fags. Foley said: 'You seem pretty well fixed these days,' inhaling the smoke: 'Unlike me,' he added.

'But was the thief never caught?' Johnson asked.

'No. I suppose he left the country.'

'I suppose so.' Johnson took a sip of coffee: 'I hope you yourself didn't come under suspicion? I seem to remember, there was a rumour that you and she were fairly intimate. Of course I'm not suggesting…'

Foley said: 'Oh they questioned me all right. But so happened I'd a perfect alibi.'

'That was very lucky for you.'

'Very. Besides, the police thought another Englishman was the chap they wanted. Fellow called Johnson. Matter of fact he was amazingly like you to look at. An extraordinary resemblance.'

'My name's not Johnson,' Johnson said, and Foley grinned: 'I'm sure it isn't; he took a deep drag at his cigarette, the loaded coffee was like a fire in his empty tum.

'Will you have another?'

'Thanks. No coffee this time, just cognac. Make it a double,' he told the waiter, and to Johnson: 'It ought to be my round, but…'

A voice interrupted him: 'Alec,' and damned if it wasn't Teddy, standing there with one hand on his hip, his prim face powdered white, and his hair done up a new colour, russet.

'My dear,' he said, 'why haven't you been along to the studio. I expected,' but Alec waved him impatiently away.

'Not now Teddy, for Pete's sake. I'm talking business.'

Teddy said: '*I'm* sorry,' going all upstage and putting a hand to his hair, 'I beg you pardon, I wouldn't interfere for the world. Only I thought…'

'Later, Teddy,' Foley told him, 'I'll see you later.'

'Oh don't put yourself out for me. I can tell when I'm *de trop*,' and he flounced off in a huff, almost colliding with the waiter and Alec's large cognac; his parting shot came back to them with a faint whiff of perfume: 'Two's company, three's none, I know.'

'Bloody fool,' Foley said, and: 'These ought to be my drinks, but I'm dead broke.'

'Out of a job?' Johnson asked.

'Worse than that, just out of jail.' He added: 'A political offence,' thinking of when they kicked him out of the Party for pinching the funds, only he didn't go to jug for that: they'd another name for it.

He said: 'I saw my cousin on Saturday. He's a publisher you know. They're going to do my novel about prison life,' and he fished out the card Cousin Harold had given him, with GROSSMAN AND MOFFAT (PUBLISHERS) LTD on it: 'He'll probably give me a job as well, later on.'

Course none of this was true: Harold only travelled for the firm and Alec had no intention of writing a novel, but this was the tale he'd cooked up for Peter and Teddy to raise the wind, so why not try it out on bigger game.

'I didn't know you were an author,' Johnson said.

'Oh I've written a few things here and there,' Foley told him airily, 'but the literary game's not a paying one, as I daresay you've heard. In fact, until I draw the advance, I'm absolutely flat – not a sausage.'

He suddenly began to speak very rapidly: 'I've had a terrible time since I last saw you… Deported from France finally… some silly balls about a cheque… and then the Raff ground-staff, no commission because I wasn't A-1 – two years of it, never even got a stripe… kicked about the Square, shouted-at… jankers, cookhouse… so I worked my ticket but civvy street wasn't much better… selling blackmarket toys in pubs, and clothing coupons… ration books… a few measly quid… people like Teddy, you saw him just now… then prison, the Scrubs… police had a down on me… six months… and now if I don't look out – direction: the mines.'

The recital of his own woes had, as always, a tonic effect on Foley; it heartened him for what he was about to do: blackmail's such an ugly word. He grinned over the glass of brandy: 'I wondered if you could possibly help,' and added: 'Both being friends of Jeanne Lombard I feel I can ask you. Gives us something in common.'

'I never knew her well, actually,' Johnson said, 'but if I could be of any assistance,' and Foley watched greedily as he drew out his wallet: a fiver.

'That's damned decent of you,' Foley told him, tucking it away; 'Now we must have a drink on that.'

'No, I have to go,' Johnson said. 'A luncheon engagement. But we'll meet again.'

'We certainly will,' and Alec meant it: 'Very soon.'

'D'you often come up this way?'

'Seldom. I usually stay round Chelsea. Soho's so sordid, don't you agree?'

Johnson said: 'I might be able to put you on to something good if you could meet me tomorrow afternoon…'

'Yes, where?'

'Cambridge Circus, three-thirty. I'll pick you up outside the Palace.'

'That's a date,' and Foley thought: don't imagine you'll give me the slip. He said: 'Better give me your address in case you aren't able to turn up; I might want to get in touch with you,' and he added: 'Write it down, because I've such a bad memory.'

'I thought you had a very good one,' Johnson said.

'Only for faces,' Foley told him. 'Addresses I always forget. Besides,' he went on, as the other drew off one glove and took out a black and gold fountain pen shaped like a stylo, 'it was your hands that gave you away really. I recognised them right off,' and, proud of his perspicacity, he leaned back and looked round the café as Johnson started to write on a leaf torn from a notebook, but Teddy had gone: good riddance to him.

'Here you are,' Johnson said: no name, just an address: written in a beautiful slanting hand like a calligrapher's exercise, with something slightly foreign about the formation of the letters.

'Thanks,' and Foley tucked it away in his pocket with Cousin Harold's card, while Johnson waved his cigarette-holder at the waiter.

'Tomorrow, then,' he said, standing up, 'at three-thirty.'

Foley said: 'So long,' and with a grin: 'A vous revoir.'

He watched Johnson pay with a pound and disappear through the double doors into the street outside. Foley drank up his brandy and followed, thinking of food: no question now of dinner with Uncle Simon, though he ought to give the old boy a tinkle, as he'd probably a bit put by and it was as well to keep on the right side. The scarlet buses and the people in their Sunday best passed to and fro, the sun struck at the boil on the back of his neck: the day promised once again to be a real scorcher.

Alec Foley stood waiting to cross the road, three brandies under his belt, a fiver in hand, his luck, as he thought, turned at last – a seedy young man in a frayed collar and a shiny demob suit, who had only one more day to live.

Five

(1)

Still the same Sunday, and a slight breeze has sprung up, now that it's getting on for seven. The air for some reason's full of floating thistle-down, and a piece of it takes off for a solo flight along the gutter of Charlotte Street, Soho, skimming over a pair of pigeons pecking desultorily at some crumbs of bread. The street's practically deserted and at peace; most of the restaurants round about – especially those with licenses – are still closed, with little gates up in front, and the spire of a church can be seen in the distance.

Another piece of thistledown becomes airborne and joins the first for a dance or aerial combat, and a little dark girl with a red ribbon in her hair runs out of a doorway laughing and tries to catch them; but they sail away triumphantly together above a sheet of newspaper lying on the pavement, with a HEAT WAVE headline and a picture of sunbathing beauties on a roof. It's yesterday's paper but the heat wave's still on, despite the breeze which doesn't really make such a difference.

Now a drunken soldier staggers along – God knows where they get the stuff, when everything's shut – and he pushes the door of a pub but it doesn't give: solid wood under his hand. So he stands for a moment swearing and then reels off up towards Tottenham Court Road. At once, as though his disappearance were a signal, there's the sound of a bolt being drawn, the door swings back, letting out a smell of stale beer; lights spring up in the rival pub opposite, and – it's seven o'clock: they're open! Life begins again.

(2)

The little Indian doctor seemed very annoyed about something. Froth bubbled out from his lips: it may have been from his bitter, or actual foam. He shook spittle from the stem of his pipe and said in a high warbling voice: 'Certificates! Certificates! All the time certificates! I sign 'em all day long. For a birth, for a death – that's different, I don't mind. But now for every trumpery damn little thing...' he spun round on Deckert, who sat on a stool up at the counter: 'I tell you this, sir – and no word of a lie – my signature's getting more legible every day. Practice – from signing certificates. My handwriting, no! Naturally – I'm a doctor, you can't read it. But the signature – clear as daylight. That's a fact.'

Deckert smiled and nodded. His gloves were on his hands and his gold-topped cane was propped in the corner behind him.

The doctor came closer; he could have passed easily for an Italian: an ascetic face, clever, the colour of coffee; a nose like a scalpel and lips thin as a knife-blade; on top of all that, a bowler, coming down over his ears. He said: 'Listen. You want a certificate: say you're sick, don't want to go to the office, a day off, or get some clothing coupons maybe: listen, if you want one,' he raised a warning finger, 'don't come to me.

Don't come to Chatterji, that's all. I've had enough. I'm fed up,' and he lifted his glass: 'Cheerio!'

Behind the bar the enormously fat landlord, in an apron, shirt-sleeves rolled up on beefy forearms, was laughing; behind him again were bottles and long mirrors advertising someone's celebrated wines and spirits: a blue naval arm, decorated with gold rings of rank, invited you, above his head, to have a Pimm's.

'You can laugh,' the doctor said, teeth clamped on his pipe: 'You can laugh, yes. But I tell you a certificate I'll sign, and date – a real certificate. Look at this,' he pushed a visiting card across the counter in front of Deckert: 'Look here.' His pink fingernail, very clean, under-lined some letters after his name: 'See – brain surgeon, that's what it means. I tell you this – I'm one of the few – the only – doctors in London who can certify you myself – on my own. No two doctors, nobody else – I don't need anybody else. Just me, just Chatterji, and you're inside: a padded cell! That's the sort of certificate I'll sign!'

'You're a psychiatrist, then?' Deckert said, leaning forward with interest from his high stool.

'Psychiatrist. Psychiatrist,' the doctor said, in even deeper disgust: 'Listen, my boy – I'm a surgeon: I look after the body first. The body and the brain. Mens sana!' he shouted; 'A sound mind,' he seemed about to fall, himself, in a fit, 'in a healthy body! Cure disease, physical ills, see to the heart, the lungs, the liver; and the mind,' he made a sweeping gesture, 'will take care of itself,' and wiping the foam away from his knife-like lips, quite soberly: 'Service please, landlord,' he said.

Deckert also pushed across his glass: 'Another lager. Iced,' he added: it was stuffy in there, despite the open door and the electric fan spinning high up in the ceiling. Not many people yet: a twitching seedy youth with a beard and a pair of lesbians: one very prim, grey-haired and tailor-made, who look disapprovingly at the doctor. And the drunk soldier staggered in and stood swaying at the counter, but he wasn't served.

Deckert said in his slow voice: 'But I suppose every doctor must be something of a psychologist? Like a priest.'

'Priests, priests!' The doctor's voice rose higher and higher; he almost screamed: 'Don't talk to me about priests!' hitting the counter a whack with his pipe: 'Those dirty black crows! You a Catholic?'

'No.'

'No,' the doctor said, 'you're too intelligent, that's why – I'm a physiognomist, I can see it in your face. You're no fool to be taken in by...' swallowing his spit and clamping the pipe back: 'priests. They're parasites, look what they did in Spain. You a Marxist?'

'I have no politics,' Deckert told him, 'and no religion.'

'But you must have read Marx? I am a Marxist; I can show you my Party card! Listen: dialectical materialism, it's the only thing. Do you know Mulk Raj Anand?'

'His books, of course.'

'Books!' the doctor brushed them away; 'Mulk and me – I tell you the truth – we were like that,' holding up his fingers crossed. 'Both dialectical – he's in India now. A doctor must know something of politics – the social system: that's indispensable. As for priests,' he snatched off his hat: on top he was bald, like a tonsure: 'I'll tell you. The other day I operated on a man – successfully. Saved his life, pulled him through. But – absolute quiet afterwards: essential. And the priest comes, this black crow, because he's a Catholic, to disturb him. "No!" I said, "¡No pasaran! Thou shalt not pass! Do you want my patient to die? If he does," I said, "all right, you can bury him. But I'm a physician: my business is to keep men alive – to serve mankind. Go away, get out," I told him, "Witch-doctor with your mumbo-jumbo. Your business is with the dead!" Was I right or wrong? What do you say?'

'It's a difficult problem.'

'Bah!' and the doctor crammed down his bowler again: 'I was right! The man lived. He's alive today. But if that priest...listen, I ask you: what use are they? What they for?'

'I suppose,' Deckert said slowly, 'to be intermediary between God and man.'

The doctor's eyes rolled, his lips were red; he screeched: 'That's it – intermediary! Man needs no intermediary: he's made in the Image. God is there,' he pointed upwards to the ceiling; the bearded youth twitched nervously again. 'Man can make his own peace with Him. No intermediaries – we don't want 'em!'

Deckert bowed his head: 'I'm inclined to agree.'

'Of course, of course you do. You're – I can see it – an intellectual. A serious young man. I'm serious too. I joke – yes, Chatterji jokes, but he's serious underneath,' and picking up a black bag from the bar stool beside him, with a glance at the clock: 'Half past. I must hurry off.'

Deckert bowed again: 'It's been an interesting discussion,' seeing, over the doctor's shoulder, Trégi with his scarred cheek, slick hair and Cecil Gee tie, threading his way past the tables by the pub door. 'Goodnight, doctor.'

'Goodnight – and remember what I tell you. We must be dialectical: socially, morally, and,' raising his emphatic forefinger, 'metaphysically! Bye-bye, cheerio – and keep away from those black priests!'

He made a bolt for the door, sudden and with his head down, almost bumping into Trégi as he joined Deckert at the counter.

'What's that wog yapping about, Walter?'

'Just a friendly argument,' Deckert told him. 'Politics – and religion.'

'You religious, Walter?' and without waiting for Deckert to reply Trégi went off into a shout of laughter: 'Here,' sobering up suddenly: 'we got to meet Loftus. He's over the road, with his tart. Some reason, she won't come in here.'

'The Druce woman?' Deckert said, sliding off his stool and standing up; 'I don't care for her.'

'Nor me,' as they reached the door, 'but ...' and he broke off. 'Here she comes,' as Frieda Druce, plainly furious, burst out of the pub opposite and set off rapidly down the street without seeing either of them.

'Another bleeding row,' Trégi said, 'I reckon. They been at it off and on all evening.'

Deckert asked: 'Did you sound him about the scheme?'

'Trust me, Walter. I got him eating outta my palm. But there's a snag,' they crossed the road, thistledown drifting gently towards them, 'he wants to cut the wench in too. Seems she worked in a beauty parlour once and knows all the stuff.'

'That won't do, Robert,' Deckert told him softly. 'I don't like girls mixed up with business.'

'Couldn't agree with you more. Nemmind, let's hope she's upped and quit him for keeps.'

And they disappeared through the door marked COOLED DRAUGHT BEER, an advertisement, on the outside.

(3)

Time marches on. Twenty to nine already, and don't forget they close at ten.

This particular pub has a faintly literary and artistic flavour; even the landlord's infected: when complimented on his pink shirt he cracks back: 'You mean my Secker and Warburg.' Pints of cooled draught flow freely as he pulls the black beer handles; a woman in a red coat, who'd once been beautiful – but it was a long time ago – calls peremptorily for a foxy gin.

Look around. That's the editor of *Hocus*, the Left magazine – up by the bar, waiting to insult anyone who approaches him. Those chaps in kilts, sucking sagely at their curved pipes, are painters, but they're discussing poetry; while the girls with them sit about wearing fringes: ever so arty-crafty. A few trippers – black-hatted superior civil-servants and their would-be modish wives – have come slumming, as it's Sunday, to see the sights: London's Bohemia and so forth; and two tall guardsmen, their flattened cap-peaks making them look broken-nosed, frown grimly down on all that.

Trégi's telling for the umpteenth time how he got that scar on his cheek. There are several versions, including a negro with a razor, the Sabini Boys, whom he tackled singlehanded, and desert warfare. Now the latter's served up for Loftus, while Deckert orders another round: sticking, himself, to Pilsener; the others are on shorts. He listens, smiling, as Trégi irons out all the eyeties within sight and slaps Arthur on the back: 'Cheers Walter,' 'Best o' luck,' 'God bless.'

A drop of mother's ruin to lubricate the larynx, and Trégi's off on the story of his first spell in stir, GBH: a right sod had done his Dad for fifty nick, and Robert – who could blame him? – had fixed the cowson bastard. 'Wouldn't you, Arthur? Put yourself in my place,' and Arthur, in an open-necked shirt, been sun-bathing, face and throat burnt brick-red: 'By God I would,' plainly he's lapping it up – Life with a capital L.

'Drink up, fellows, my turn!' Because of the row with Frieda, he feels a hard lump of unhappiness inside him, which he hopes drink will melt. He sways slightly, waving half-a-bar at the Secker-and-Warburg shirt: he draws all his money in ten bobs from the bank, as it seems to last longer that way and he's not made of the stuff after all. 'A gin, a rum and orange, and a Pilsener, please,' and he leaves incontinently for upstairs, feeling nature's call.

'See?' Trégi says triumphantly, 'What'd I tell you?' to Deckert. 'Out of my bleeding hand. He's taken to you too, I can tell that.'

'But has he got the money?'

'There's some in trust that he can't touch till he's thirty. Lawyers let him have a bit now and again, though, besides his allowance. He can raise it when he likes. Look how he bought my car,' and Trégi went off into another loud shout of laughter, rocking his self to and fro. 'Cripes, when I think of old Theo. He won't half be wild.'

'Druce? Why?'

''Cause he's poncing on his missus, that's why, and it's Arthur does the paying. Only now he's got browned off with it, he don't want to do no more, see, that's why they had the to-do about tonight, and Theo...'

'Careful,' Deckert said, 'here he comes,' as Arthur, much relieved, rejoined them at the bar.

Drink up again, another round – Trégi's this time – and some street-musicians start creaking out on accordions, outside the open door, a tango: appropriate, as it's Soho and, they think, the pub's probably full of foreigners. Trégi, who doesn't care for music, complains he can't hear his self speak, and he's all for giving them a sock on the kisser to shut them up; but luckily a shady-looking geezer, not to say spiv, just come in, taps him on the shoulder and they go into a huddle apart: 'Kewpons' crop up inevitably, and – oddly enough – 'Rice'.

That leaves Loftus alone with Deckert, and Arthur says, all that rum and orange making him sentimental: 'Grand bloke, old Robert, one of the best,' and he adds: 'You're a grand bloke too, Deckert, I'm damn glad we met.'

Deckert, raising a glass in his gloved hand, bows and smiles, to show it's mutual, and Arthur goes on: 'Yet you know, Walter – I'm going to call you Walter – it's a damn funny thing: I know somebody who's scared of you. Absolute fact,' slurring his words. 'She's scared stiff.'

'How extraordinary. Why,' Deckert asks him softly, 'should anyone be scared of me?'

And Arthur agrees: 'Exactly. But that's what she's like. Unreasonable,' he sighs, 'Quite unreasonable.'

'Women tend to be that way.'

'I expect,' Arthur says enviously, 'that you know a lot about women?' Seeing one of the painters' girls flash an admiring glance at Deckert, but not because he's handsome: no sex involved, naturally: just Art; she likes the way his face is built up – good bone-structure and all that balls. Arthur takes another pull at his rum and says: 'Perhaps you could give me some advice – as a man of the world. What am I to do? You see,' and he leans forward, eyes swimming behind his spectacles, 'I'm in love with her.'

'With the girl who's scared of me?'

'Frieda Druce.' He nods. 'Hopelessly,' with a hiccup: 'Can't get her out of my system.'

'Adios Muchachos' comes to an abrupt halt and an accordion-man, his instrument strapped to his chest, appears shaking a bag in front of the customers: 'Coppers please, gentlemen.'

Deckert drops in sixpence and says to Arthur: 'What advice can I possibly give?'

'Well, surely you've been in love yourself?'

'No,' Deckert says with an odd nostalgia: 'Never.'

'But you must have had girls.'

'Oh yes. But,' with a faint regretful smile, 'perhaps I'm too wordly to fall in love with them.' He adds: 'I suppose the problem in this case is the husband – Druce.'

'He wants me to pay him six hundred pounds for a divorce.'

'It's an abominable suggestion.'

'That's what I think. Yet there's the funny part – Frieda's in favour of it. You see, she's still fond of him in a way – they read these books on logic together. So what can I do. We had another row tonight and she walked out on me.'

'Difficult,' Deckert screws a cigarette into his holder, striking a match. 'Very difficult.'

'But I'm damned if I'll be made a stooge of,' Arthur squares his jaw, quite pugnacious: the stubborn streak. 'Nothing'll persuade me to pay up,' banging down his empty glass: 'They can both go to hell,' and Deckert's glad to hear it.

'A refill?'

'Thanks, o' boy. Where's Robert?'

'Busy.' Trégi and the spiv are still hard at it: natter, natter, now they're on about racing, and the bookies'll drop a packet, that's dead certain.

'Reminds me,' Arthur says over his rum. 'Business,' and his speech becomes more and more blurred. 'Robert told me about this scheme of yours, the beauty parlour. Sounds bloody good, I'm very interested. Couldn't we get together one day next week? Discuss the details?'

'With pleasure. I'll give you my address,' and for the second time Deckert writes this down; Arthur exclaims: 'I say, what a wizard pen!' as a tripper thrusts his way between them with three empty pints.

'I won it,' Deckert smiles, 'at Spoof. It's a game,' he adds, 'played with matches,' and Arthur, pocketing his card: 'I've always wanted to go into business, y'know, Walter. I was going to be a publisher once, but the other chap turned out to be a crook.'

'Who's a crook?' Trégi's back, Arthur calls for a gin; the cooled draught foams up like yeast in the stuffy heat; mopping it off the counter with a beer-cloth, the landlord glances round at the clock: three quarters of a bloody hour to go: his feet are aching like hell, the Secker and Warburg stuck to his back with sweat.

And now it's near time, customers absolutely pour in: they can't all get served; damned if the drunk soldier hasn't rolled in, and he certainly won't be. The civil servants are elbowed aside; somebody knocks over the *Hocus* man's drink: it's the kilted painter, too; a row

[manuscript ends]

Astrid: A Long Story

*　　　*　　　*

THESE ARE SOME OF THE THINGS I KNOW ABOUT ASTRID:

She had been married three times.

She was illegitimate by birth.

She had been educated at a Catholic convent school.

She was half Jewish by parentage.

She had, at the age of thirteen, been a waitress at a coffee shop in Baker Street.

She had started her adult life as a sort of personal assistant to the late Norman Douglas.

She was deficient in calcium.

She was a Cordon Bleu chef.

She was known at one time as the strongest woman in Oxford.

She was also known as the most attractive woman in Oxford.

Her favourite novel was *Middlemarch* by George Eliot.

When I met her first, in 1954, she'd been blonde. It was in Oxford. At a party given in her house. An opaque autumn mist encroached upon the drawing-room windows; doctors of philosophy and lit. single-mindedly plugged their subjects on every side. Rufus Ives, her husband at the time, was some kind of university don, said to be extreme left politically and very jealous of his wife. I'd therefore been anxious and alarmed when Astrid, more than a little high, spent part of the evening sitting on a cushion at my feet.

She said: 'I sometimes long to escape from all this. Back to the Bohemian life.' She stroked the red velvet jacket I was wearing and smiled up into my face. 'When I think of the times we had in London during the war.'

She herself had on a shimmering white frock with long tight sleeves ending in triangular points on the backs of her hands. I could see down the low bodice into the valley between her breasts. I glanced uneasily towards her husband, a big scowling sullen man, dressed in dung-coloured corduroys, by the bottles on a trolley up the other end. He had muttered a few words of welcome when we were introduced, and surprised me by shaking hands when I approached him circumspectly to say goodbye. His grip was powerful enough to crack the bones of my hand, and I felt glad to get away without my neck being broken instead, especially as Astrid had hold of my other arm.

'Lucky bastard,' Matt McCarthy, who was putting me up, said in the taxi going back to his house; 'You made a hit there. Astrid's the most attractive woman in Oxford.'

'Not my type. And anyway she was pissed as a newt.'

'Just because she hasn't hair hanging halfway down her back.'

'What's her hair got to do with it?'

'Your last girl had long hair,' Matt McCarthy said. 'So had the one before. That ghastly gangster woman who robbed your gas-meter also had long hair. Astrid hasn't had long hair, so Astrid isn't your type.'

'If she had hair down to her knees,' I told him, 'I still wouldn't risk having my head knocked off by her husband.'

Peals of Sunday bells pursued us all over the city as we set off shakily for the pub the next morning. Astrid was there, without Ives, wearing green and hungover to an extent that made her seem withdrawn and remote although the centre of the crowd. A different person from the forthcoming woman of the night before. I gave her one of the capsules, called Green Bombs by McCarthy, which I was taking at the time and which almost matched the colour of her current frock. The effect on Astrid was indeed explosive; within seconds she had started on a violent flirtation with a lecturer in science named Lionel Hope-Friend, who responded by flashing his spectacles archly at her and ruffling up, as a cock-bird might its feathers, what little hair he had.

At this, Pamela, his wife, an expert on folklore and basket-weaving, began to thrust her long neck out aggressively and to rattle the beads encircling it; and Matt, to avoid a possible clash between the women, proposed that her husband and he should Try Hands: being a New Zealand Irishman, Matt is prone after a few pints to indulge in his trial of strength kick, which I deplore.

The bitters were pushed aside for safety and the contestants clasped hands in mid-air, each endeavouring to force the other's down without lifting elbows from the table-top. Hope-Friend strained with set teeth, determined to put up a good show with Astrid looking on; but his defeat coincided with the arrival on her bike of the McCarthy daughter, bearing a message from Mummy that the lamb would be burnt to a cinder if we didn't come to Sunday dinner soon.

'Lionel's tougher than you'd think,' Matt said, walking elatedly home up Walton Street. 'D'you know he almost had me beat back there.'

'Perhaps he's in training to try it with Rufus Ives. Or d'you suppose the girls should maybe have a go?'

'Astrid would win hands down,' Matt told me. 'I mean that literally. She's the strongest woman in Oxford.'

'I always understood your wife was.'

'So did I,' Matt said, 'until she Tried Hands with Astrid one day. And would you believe it, Astrid bloody well beat her.'

I didn't believe anything of the sort; but later, over the New Zealand lamb, Maggie McCarthy to my astonishment confirmed it.

'Astrid had my arm flat down on the table-top.'

'Really?' I said. 'So now we know why Ives has not yet strangled her. He simply isn't strong enough.'

Maggie said: 'You think Rufus should keep a tighter rein?'

'Unless he wants to lose her.'

'They've been married eight years and he hasn't lost her yet.'

'And if he did,' Matt said, rising to carve us all another plate, 'it wouldn't be to Lionel Hope-Friend.'

He was mistaken. A month later the scandal broke. Astrid had bolted with Hope-Friend, who'd left the basket-weaving wife in turn; and the happy couple went to live together on a houseboat hard by the old Perch Inn.

'Which young lady d'you mean?' I asked.

This was a year later, on a train travelling up to London from Oxford, where I'd been staying the weekend.

'Over there in yellow, sir,' the dining-car attendant said. 'Left-hand side, three tables down. Said would you like to go over and take a drink with her.'

'Never seen her before in my life,' I told him, but another look along the aisle proved me wrong.

The young lady in yellow sat alone, with her neat brown head bent over a book. Brand-new luggage was piled on the adjoining seat and in the rack above; a brand-new hair-do rendered her at first sight unrecognisable.

'Isn't it Astrid?' I said. 'Miss Ives.'

She looked up, smiling, from Norman Douglas's autobiography. 'Astrid still, Mrs Ives no longer, Mrs Hope-Friend soon to be.'

'Congratulations.'

'It's tomorrow, as a matter of fact.'

I signalled the attendant: 'We'll have a drink to celebrate.'

But Astrid said: 'Then it must be on me. I asked you over, after all.' She shifted a suitcase so I could sit beside her; the initials 'A.H.F.' were stamped already on the leather.

She said: 'When I'd sent that message I was afraid you wouldn't want to come, so I pretended to go on reading my book regardless. A lot of that stuffy Oxford crowd would have cut me dead, of course.'

'I don't want to belong to the Oxford crowd. And why the devil should they cut you dead?'

'Well it was the double divorce upset them all, you see. They gave Lionel the heave soon after. Then he got a red-brick appointment at Reading, where we've been living for a bit, but even there people didn't seem to care for it an awful lot. Still, now he's landed another much better job in London, so we're moving up forthwith.'

She paid for the drinks from a handbag stuffed with notes and added: 'Not that it matters about jobs anyway, because Lionel's madly rich, you know.'

'I didn't know.'

'Oh yes. An uncle died last year and left it him.'

I reflected that Ives had also been well-fixed, despite the left-wing politics attributed to him. Astrid was meanwhile asking me to the reception in Albany next day. Practically everyone in Oxford, no matter how stuffy, seemed to be going, except the McCarthys, now in America: Rufus Ives and Pamela Hope-Friend were other possible exceptions. I too accepted, though I rang up next day and made excuses for not attending.

Astrid said, glancing down at her copy of *Looking Back*: 'I'd ask Uncle Norman if he wasn't dead. He always thought I'd never settle down.'

She added: 'I'd a job looking after the old boy in London during the war.' (London during the war had evidently been her finest hour.) 'Mind you, he could be jolly awkward at times. Always wanting a fire lit at inconvenient moments because he felt the cold. D'you ever come across him at all?'

'I once hijacked him from a party given in his honour and took him instead to drink strong Scotch ale at the Wheatsheaf in Rathbone Place.'

Astrid said nostalgically: 'I used to go to that pub too. Funny to think we might have met in those days.' And she went on to talk about the Love of Her Life, in some way connected with Douglas, and how she'd married her first husband by mistake instead. And Hope-Friend tomorrow makes three, I remember thinking as we parted outside Paddington Station; and I forgot Astrid again for several years.

[manuscript ends]

Business and Desire

*　　　*　　　*

1. HER

I WAS CALLING MYSELF MR JONES AT THE TIME. IT WAS SPRING 1956, at a club mis-named the Clair-de-Lune. Nevertheless I noticed her at once, despite the perpetual twilight that reigned at any time of day inside and the dark glasses which I always wore.

The first thing that struck me was her hair. At a period when most girls had given themselves, apparently, a short trim with the garden shears, this one wore hers more than shoulder-length, curling to a point well below her nape. In colour it seemed, so far as I could tell through smoked lenses and in that aquarium gloom, a smooth and shining chestnut brown. I'd been ten years a member, but I'd never seen her in the club before.

She sat looking straight ahead on a corner stool at the counter; the immediate effect was of enormous repose. My reflection was visible in the mirror behind the bar, but she neither moved nor turned when I leant on the brass rail beside her. Reflected also was the piano on a wooden platform where at night a three-piece combo performed and, beyond sad-eyed Colum the Irish doorman at his desk, the door itself: standing open on the Soho street across which late April sunlight slanted. She had on a dark red dress.

I said: 'Would you care to join me in a drink?'

She shook her hair back and for the first time turned towards me: her brief but pleasant smile did not lessen the impression of aloofness that she gave. 'I've got one, thanks.' One long hand pointed a cigarette in a short holder at the glass of white wine that stood before her.

I said: 'You've drunk half of that already. Medium, sweet, or dry?'

Down from the counter's end, with a chink of jewelled chains hung on black and trailing silk, came Queenie, who owned the club. 'A brandy, is it, dear?'

I nodded. 'And this lady's, please?'

Queenie said: 'A dry white wine, wasn't it, Mrs Walker?' And I saw too late the wedding-ring on the girl's left hand. Young woman, rather: in her late twenties would have been my guess. She smiled again and said: 'So now you know my name.'

I said: 'Mine is Jones. Plain Mr Jones.'

'How d'you do Mr Jones.' Her eyes flickered at an elusive memory when I gave the name like that; but she did not pick up the reference right away, or perhaps it had passed her by. Her eyes were, incidentally, blue.

She added: 'And now we're introduced,' as Queenie set down the drinks.

'That'll be five and sixpence, Mr Jones.' You were 'dear' to Queenie no longer when it came to paying up; the passage of money over the counter required the rigid formality of any serious rite.

The cash-register pinged under the chain of coloured lights looped above the bar. Facing me from the wall beside the mirror was an attenuated clown, obscurely menaced or perhaps tempted by a thin bare female arm projected into the picture by some person standing outside its frame. I had resolutely turned my back to the headless white horse rising from a pyramid of pink sand which hung above the piano platform and which I believed brought me bad luck if squarely confronted. Other paintings plainly executed by the same anonymous artist, the unsold relics of some exhibition held in the club at a date long past and abandoned even by their creator, were hung along the right-hand wall. Below these, a few beatniks, at this time known simply as bums, sat at tables arguing over who should buy the next round of bitter.

Mrs Walker did not seem at all to fit this setting, and I asked her: 'Do you come here much?'

'I haven't been back in England long,' she said. 'I lived abroad for years.' At the foot of her stool stood a shopping bag from which a long loaf of French bread protruded. 'France?' I said.

'Africa. East Africa. My husband's in the political service, you see.'

'Well,' I said, picking up my glass and preparing to move, 'I really mustn't embarrass you any longer.'

'Embarrass?'

'I mean, your husband might be joining you here.'

She laughed.

'That's not very likely. Eric's still in Tanganyika. Besides, we divorced last summer.'

I said: 'I'm sorry to hear that.' I wasn't at all.

'Are you married, Mr Jones?' she asked.

'Once upon a time. I haven't seen my wife for twenty years.'

'Any children?'

'None.'

'I have a small daughter,' Mrs Walker said. 'Eight years old. She's at school in Sutton.'

'You don't look old enough to have a child that age.'

'I married young. Lucy's my daughter by my first husband.' The information came out quite unselfconsciously; she didn't add, as I expected, 'I don't know why I'm telling you all this.' Instead she asked: 'Are you Welsh?'

'Scottish,' I said, forgetting for the moment that my name was Jones. She looked surprised, but said: 'My first husband was Welsh.'

'And you?'

'My maiden name was Lamprey.'

'That's unusual.'

'Nadine Lamprey.'

'And now you're Mrs Walker?'

[manuscript ends]

A House of Cards

*　　　　*　　　　*

PARTNERSHIP DAY

1

'AND THEN OF COURSE SHE'S A CHASER.'

The colonel sat forward in his chair over the clubroom fire, while outside a high wind whirled round the hotel and the December sunshine shone down without warmth on the Sussex Riviera.

'Anything in trousers,' the colonel said. 'During the summer it was perfectly disgusting. She was staying in the house then.'

'Has she ever chased you?' Gerard St John asked him.

'No bloody fear! I think she's rather frightened of me, you know.'

The colonel, who was the secretary of the club, spoke in a voice which made credulous people believe that he had been to Oxford. When addressing any of the bridge-members, his accent became especially exaggerated. He modulated his manner and opinions upon the traditional retired colonel of fiction and the stage.

He had a lean, dark, leathery face and iron-grey hair, cropped close at the sides and back of a square, narrow skull. The tough, fever-parched skin, tight drawn across his cheeks, sagged in deep bags below the eyes. This characteristic, in conjunction with the parrot nose and small pursed mouth, lent to his aquiline features a permanent expression of constipated contempt. He wore tweeds: in the afternoon, before bridge began, he would escape into dark-blue serge.

He was taciturn and talkative by turns, and only the subject of Miss Lorraine Archer would have persuaded him to enter into conversation with Gerard St John, for whom he had not the slightest possible use. But opportunities for running down Lorraine were not to be neglected.

'What defeats me completely of course is what anyone can possibly see in her, because I mean to say she hasn't a single idea of her own and she's the most awful poseuse, although I must admit she's distinctly attractive in appearance,' he amended.

'I'm having her to tea tomorrow afternoon,' Gerard St John told him.

'God almighty,' the colonel said. 'Some people take their pleasures sadly.'

'Don't you like Lorraine, Colonel?'

'Like her? But good God there isn't anything to like about her.' The colonel drew a gold flake from his double-sided gun-metal cigarette-case, which he closed then with a determined click. 'No. There's only one use for Lorraine so far as I can see, and that's to go to bed with.'

'Why? D'you want to go to bed with her?'

'I don't myself, no. Wouldn't you like to?'

'Not particularly.'

'Matter of fact it'd do Lorraine good if she did go to bed with a man. It'd make her more human.'

'I rather like Lorraine,' Gerard St John said.

He was a handsome young man who sometimes described himself as a film star because he had been employed on three occasions as a studio-extra at Denham, and once by Raymond Royal, the producer, in Paris. At present, owing to an illness that enforced his temporary retirement from the screen, he was engaged in writing a book called *Women I Have Proposed To*, which, although he described it as a fictional treatise, was based largely on personal experience.

His mother's maiden name had been Isaacstein but she had Spanish blood and on the whole, with his smooth sallow skin and kinky hair like black crepe, looked more Spanish than Jewish: except for his nose, which was aristocratically but undoubtedly curved, and his bold dark oriental eyes. He sat opposite the colonel on the other side of the fireplace, above which hung a glass case containing medals.

Despite its name, the clubroom was reserved for residential members and guests staying at the hotel. It was a bright, pleasant room with a red carpet and hunting prints framed upon the walls. A shaft of sun struck through the window-pane, drawing the heat from the fire; and the colonel, abandoning the subject of Lorraine, said: 'If something isn't done soon this damn thing'll go out.'

'Why not put some coal on?'

'The scuttle's empty.'

'Ring for Beauchamp then.'

'Bloody bell's out of order.'

It always is.'

'Call this a bridge club,' the colonel said. 'My Christ. How the hell Ethelred expects me to run it for him I don't know. God only knows. By the way, have you seen him this morning?'

'Ethelred?'

'Who the devil'd you suppose I meant?'

'He's not up yet.'

'Not up?'

'Still in bed.'

The colonel cleared his throat with an angry snorting chuckle. 'I can't understand the mentality of people like that. A boy of nineteen who can lie in bed till after eleven. He must be diseased, that's all: it's the only reasonable explanation.'

'He seems perfectly healthy to me.'

'What the young slacker wants is a bloody good hiding. Why at his age I was on parade every morning by half-past six. But that's the trouble with contemporary youth: no discipline.' He eyed with distaste Gerard St John's pale grey suit with the thin purple stripe and his grey suede shoes. 'Yes, that's what they need: discipline!' he repeated dourly.

'They definitely do,' Gerard agreed with a grin.

The door opened to admit Beauchamp, the butler, bringing a shovelful of coal for the fire.

'Is Ethelred down yet, Beauchamp? The colonel asked him.

'No sir. But the doctor is.'

'Ah yes. The doctor. Where is he now?'

'Gone out again, sir.'

'Did he eat any breakfast?'

'No, sir.'

'Humph.'

Beauchamp left the room.

Gerard St John said: 'The doctor's gone on the booze again.'

'I'm afraid so. God, I'll bet he has a head this morning – what!'

'I'll bet he has.'

'Still, it'll be awkward if he comes in oiled again today.'

'Who is his partner?'

'Mrs Emmanuel.'

'How amusing for her.'

'He may not get tight of course.'

'No he may not.'

The colonel lit another cigarette and tossed the match irritably into the fire. 'I wish Ethelred'd come down, damn him.'

'He has no discipline,' Gerard St John said.

'I suppose he'll be going off to golf with Lorraine when he does get up.'

'Yes.'

'Gives me no bloody help at all.'

Picking up the *Daily Telegraph*, the colonel threw himself back in his chair and began to read. The conversational interlude was over.

Gerard St John got up and crossed to a table in the window, on which stood his Imperial portable. He unlocked the case and inserted a sheet of notepaper into the machine.

'Do you mind me typing, Colonel?'

'Not in the least.'

'You're quite sure?'

'My dear chap, if it disturbed me, I should tell you.'

Gerard sat down and started to click the typewriter keys, which tapped out a letter to his literary agent in London.

'... may be necessary to collect further copy before the book can be finished, as I am not certain whether I have quite enough material at my disposal just at present, but the complete MS should be in your hands at any rate after the New Year.'

Two

A persistent whining and scratching sounded outside the closed door, and the colonel without looking up from his paper growled: 'That blasted dog again.'

Gerard got up angrily and went over to open the door. 'Come in curse you,' he said.

A large golden spaniel slunk past him into the room. He had a lovely coat but no waistline whatever. His name was Tabasco. He immediately commenced to clamber into a vacant armchair, but Gerard pulled him off by the collar.

'Another one who needs discipline, colonel.'

'Yes I know, he's thoroughly spoilt. Lie down, sir!'

With an affronted expression Tabasco settled himself sulkily in front of the fire. Gerard St John revolved the platen knob of his typewriter, releasing the letter. Somewhere close by, a door slammed. Heavy footsteps bounded along the corridor outside, the carpet muting their sound to a series of thick thuds such as a kangaroo might have made. The clubroom door burst open and Tabasco started nervously up.

Ethelred Archer appeared on the threshold, halting dramatically to exclaim 'Aha!' as though he had at last run to earth some quarry, for which he had been seeking.

'Good morning Colonel! Good morning Gerard!' he greeted them with great heartiness.

Impeded by Tabasco, who had leapt forward to welcome him and was now attempting to chew his arm, he advanced into the room.

Ethelred Archer was very tall and thin, with sloping shoulders and a faintly soppy face; fair hair slicked back from a receding forehead. Elderly women admired him and said he was so sweet, such a nice boy. He wore a check sports jacket and beige flannel trousers, with a yellow pullover and a yellow tie: when he sat down, yellow socks could be seen.

'Got any more work for me today, Colonel?'

'Yes. Since you've at last deigned to get out bed, I should like to go over the books with you.'

'Certainly, sir.'

Crossing to the colonel's desk, which was placed in the other window, they bent over the books. Tabasco, exhausted by his recent display of activity, flopped down again by the fire. Gerard St John produced a fountain pen and flourished his signature across the sheet of newspaper, that had the name of the hotel and bridge club stamped at the top.

Ethelred Archer said: 'Gosh! Five bob for lights last night, on this side of the house alone. It's simply terrific.'

'I am convinced,' the colonel said slowly, writing in a ledger, 'I am convinced there is something wrong with the meters.'

'Mrs Trick on the phone for you, sir,' Beauchamp said, entering.

'Curse the woman. I suppose she wants a partner for this afternoon. How about you Ethelred? Are you free?'

'I'm fixed up. With Miss Stott.'

'Blast!' The colonel went out, letting the door bang to behind him.

Ethelred said to Gerard: 'How's things old fellow? Working on your book?'

'Not at the moment.'

'Could you type out the new membership list sometime?'

'Alright.'

'Here it is.'

'I'll get it done.'

'Thanks, old fellow, thanks.'

The colonel stamped back into the room, slamming the door and making Tabasco start from the hearth. 'Damned unpleasant woman, Mrs Trick!'

'Darling,' Ethelred said to the dog. 'Did he make you jump then, darling? Lie down again, my pet, no one's going to hurt you.' And to the colonel: 'Did Mrs Trick want a partner?'

'Yes. Can't think of anyone fool enough to play with her though.'

'Mrs Cowle might.'

'D'you think so?'

'I'll ring up and see.'

Ethelred went away, followed by Tabasco. The colonel stood by the window biting his nails and looking out at the high privet hedge shaken in the gale. Gerard St John glanced down at the membership list, chuckling every now and then at some particularly absurd name.

Ethelred, returning, called out: 'Okay, Colonel. It's all arranged.'

The colonel said: 'I always thought Mrs Cowle was mental. Now I am certain of it. No one who's willing to partner Mrs Trick can possibly be in their right senses.'

'D'you think she's the worst player in the club?'

'Without exception.'

Ethelred giggled. He said: 'D'you want me for anything else, Colonel?'

'No, that's all for today. Going to golf?'

Not this morning. I've some things to do for mother.'

They heard him burst into song as he hurried down the corridor.

Three

Ethelred's mother, Mrs Mandrake-Archer, had been married twice. The first husband was called Mandrake and the second was called Archer. Both of them were now dead.

Although in her twice-widowed state she had retained both their names, Mrs Mandrake-Archer seldom spoke of her first husband, who had been a mistake and had died of drink; but she frequently mentioned her second, who had been a brigadier-general and Ethelred's father. At his death he had left her the house, which she promptly and sensibly converted into a hotel. The bridge club was Ethelred's idea and came into being much later.

Mrs Mandrake-Archer sat before the small square stove that heated the lounge-hall, reading her morning correspondence. Rose, the chambermaid, sat beside her chair on the wooden bench which ran along the wall, reading the letters over her shoulder and giggling.

Both of them looked up as Ethelred plunged headlong into the hall with a shattering roar of laughter.

Mrs Mandrake-Archer said: 'Hullo, darling,' and smiled at her son. She was of an equable temperament and not easily startled.

Ethelred continued to roar with laughter. Carefully controlled while in the colonel's presence, he now felt that he could let himself go. Rushing over to the wall he switched on the radio, which answered obediently with a burst of swing. Ethelred, shuffling his feet to the tune, returned to his mother's chair and sat on the arm of it, hugging her against him.

'What's the news, mother dear?'

'The Macdougals want to know our terms for Christmas. You remember the Macdougals, don't you darling?'

'Never heard of them.'

'Last Easter. That man who kept making Scotch jokes.'

'Oh yes.'

'We could shove them in No 5. Or No 6 when the doctor goes.'

Tabasco came shambling out through the passage that led from the hall to the kitchen and the servants' quarters. Wagging his tail, he climbed up on the bench beside Rose and completed the family circle.

Mrs Mandrake-Archer said: 'We could charge them four-and-a-half for No 6.'

'Five-and-a-half. They've bags of dough.'

'They'd never pay that.'

'There's no harm in asking.'

Tabasco thrust his head forward and tried to lick his mistress's face, at the same time endeavouring to climb into the chair and onto her lap.

'No darling.' Mrs Mandrake-Archer pushed him away. 'You're too heavy. Also you stink.'

'Not half,' Rose tittered in her squeaky voice. 'He don't half stink.'

What are they saying to you, darling?' Ethelred asked Tabasco, who wagged his tail in rueful response.

'Well it is time he had a bath, dearest.'

'No I like him to stink. Besides, who the hell is going to give him a bath?'

'We might get Corke to do it.'

'Yes Madam, Corke'll do it.' Rose giggled. 'Not half.'

'Why aren't you doing the bedrooms, Rose?' Ethelred asked her severely.

'She's done the bedrooms,' his mother told him.

'Humph,' Ethelred said, imitating the colonel's snort. 'Any more enquiries for Christmas?'

'A woman from Yorkshire with five kiddies.'

'Oh God. No children.'

'But darling, why not?'

'We don't want the place cluttered up with a pack of howling kids.'

'How d'you know they'd howl?'

'Well they did last year.'

'But these are not the same kids.'

'All kids howl,' Ethelred answered obstinately.

'You didn't howl much as a kid,' Mrs Mandrake-Archer told him.

'That's because you were such a good mother, darling,' and Ethelred hugged her again.

Beauchamp began to lay the tables noisily in the restaurant, which was on the other side of the hall. He passed to and fro putting down plates and whistling the dance-tune that was being played on the radio.

Mrs Mandrake-Archer said: 'Damn. I've just remembered. The menus.'

'Aren't they done yet?'

'No I clean forgot. Be an angel and do them for me.'

'Oh mother must I? You spell much better than I do.'

'There's a dear.'

'All right then. Where's the dictionary?'

Armed with Nuthall's, Ethelred went out through the passage to the kitchen. Tabasco jumped down off the bench and followed his master.

Mrs Mandrake-Archer commenced laboriously to compose a letter to the Macdougals. She found concentration difficult because Ethelred had begun to sing discordantly in the kitchen the same tune that Beauchamp was still whistling, regardless of the fact that the radio was now playing something entirely different.

She had just written the opening sentences when the colonel clumped into the hall carrying a walking-stick and wearing a very raffish tweed cap on the side of his head. This he removed on seeing Mrs Mandrake-Archer. He bid her good morning in his best drawl, smiling fiercely at the same time, but with a baleful glance at Rose, who had forgotten his shaving-water that morning. Rose returned the look unmoved.

'Going for your usual walk, Colonel?'

'Yes. Got to get up an appetite for lunch, you know!'

The colonel flourished his stick and the front door banged behind him. Watched closely by Rose, Mrs Mandrake-Archer wrote on a fresh sheet of notepaper: 'Dear Mr Macdougal, In reply to yours of December 14th...' but the singing in the kitchen had now grown so loud that even her iron nerves were affected.

'Stop it, Ethelred! For heaven's sake, stop it!' she shouted in exasperation.

'Did you call me, mother dear?' her son said, appearing from the kitchen.

'Yes. How on earth can I write a letter while you're making that awful din out there?'

'You want me to stop singing?'

'Yes.'

'Alright then. No need to get in a state about it.'

'I'm not in a state about anything, my own, but I've got to get through with this letter.'

'Right-ho, darling.'

Ethelred returned to the kitchen. The music on the radio stopped and a voice announced that they had been listening to both sides of Mecca Record DB581.

'Next on our programme is a record by Boy Cox and His Band playing that popular number 'I'll String Along With You'.

Four

Left alone in the clubroom, Gerard St John decided it was time for his midday snort. He therefore went in search of Corke, the barman and club steward.

Corke was in the bar polishing brass: an uncongenial occupation. His sad face and hollow eyes brightened however on seeing Gerard – a good customer.

He said: 'The usual, sir?' reaching behind him for the brandy bottle.

Gerard said: 'That's right, Corke,' and settled himself on a high stool at the counter. Corke poured out the brandy and squirted soda. Gerard said when. 'Have something yourself, Corke.'

Corke thanked him gravely, opening a bottle of Bass. He said: 'It's a hard life, sir,' and drank his down as if it were a toast.

Gerard said: 'Why? What's the matter, Corke?'

'Well sir, I'll give you an instance.' Corke leant confidentially across the counter. 'This morning I had difficulty in obtaining any cakes for the bridge tea today.'

'How was that? Baker's sold out?'

'No sir. They didn't wish to serve me because there was a sum of money owing to them from last month.'

'Well couldn't you go to another baker?'

'No sir. Mr Ethelred owes money to all of them.'

'I see. That makes it awkward.'

'Indubitably, sir.'

'Doesn't Ethelred ever pay his bills?'

'Very seldom, sir.'

'Well I'm damned.'

'Seen the doctor today, sir?'

'Not yet. He's probably in the pub.'

'He can certainly put it away.'

'He certainly can.'

'Well sir, I reckon he deserves a holiday don't you?'

'Undoubtedly.'

'A mental doctor isn't he, sir?'

''He runs a private clinic for nerve cases. Breakdowns and so on.'

'Well, we all know what that means, don't we sir?'

'We do indeed.'

'Being cooped up with a pack of loonies all day is enough to make anyone drink.'

'Quite.'

'Enough to drive the bloke barmy himself, isn't it sir?'

'It certainly is.'

The door opened and Mrs Mandrake-Archer poked her head in. 'Drinking again, Gerard?'

'Come and join me.'

'That's very kind of you.'

Gerard respected Mrs Mandrake-Archer for displaying in her contacts with other people a suave lack of scruple akin to his own, though applied to a different aim. She in turn admired his good looks and considered him singularly unspoilt in spite of his romantic profession.

'What're you having?' he asked her.

'A small sherry, please.'

The door opened again and Ethelred appeared suddenly behind him.

'Caught in the act,' he said. 'I'm surprised at you, mother dear.'

'Darling I need something after writing that letter.'

'Have one yourself and shut up,' Gerard told Ethelred.

'Thanks old fellow,' Ethelred replied to the first half of this injunction. 'Make it a gin and lime, Corke.'

'And give me another brandy.'

'Very good, sir.'

'Cheerio!'

'Here's to your book, Gerard.'

'Yes, how's the book going, old fellow?'

'It's stuck.'

'Done much proposing lately?'

'Not a lot.'

'You're losing your grip, old boy,' Ethelred said.

Mrs Mandrake-Archer said: 'I expect the girls propose to him instead, don't they Gerard?'

Gerard said: 'That hasn't happened either – yet.'

They all laughed, including Corke, who now seemed to be in high spirits. Gerard got down off his stool and stood up beside Ethelred, who was two inches taller, though both of them were over six foot.

'Twelve o'clock. I must be going down town.'

'Shall I put the drinks on your account, sir?'

'By all means.'

Ethelred said: 'Give my love to Lorraine, old fellow.'

Gerard said: 'But I shan't be seeing Lorraine.'

'Well give her my love anyway,' Ethelred said with a wink.

[manuscript ends]

ESSAYS ON THE CINEMA

A Mirror to Darkness:
Symbolism and Melodrama
in the New American Films

*　　　*　　　*

ONCE, WHILE WORKING FOR A BRITISH FILM COMPANY, I WAS ASKED
to write a specimen script of Graham Greene's novel *The Confidential
Agent*. All reference to the Spanish Civil War would have to be deleted,
however, I was told: presumably for fear of offending Franco. I pointed
out that no such reference is made in the novel; certainly a civil war is
taking place, but in an unnamed country, and the rival agents are
known only by their initials.

But the producer was still not satisfied: 'Tell you what,' he said, 'how
about shifting the action to *this* war, and have it all happen in Lisbon...
or Dublin.'

I said: 'Then why base the film on Greene's book at all? Let me do
an original script about Nazi agents in Lisbon *and* Dublin.'

'You've got something there,' said the producer.

In the end the film was never made.

I am reminded of this incident by the fact that the most significant
films which have appeared during the past two years have all been (a)
American, (b) that they have been based (with one exception, *Double
Indemnity*) on novels with ideas behind them, written by authors
in complete control of their own medium. In most cases, also, the
scripts adhered faithfully to the books from which they were adapted:
consequently some view of life does emerge beyond the intrigue and
the action.

The films to which I refer are: *The Maltese Falcon* and *The Glass Key*
(Dashiell Hammett), *The Mask of Dimitrios* (Eric Ambler), *Double
Indemnity* and *Laura* (Vera Caspary).

That they should all of them be concerned with crimes of violence
makes them, to my mind, all the more significant: like the books on

which four of them were based, an apt comment on our melodramatic violent age.

The first of them to appear was John Huston's production of *The Maltese Falcon*. This novel had been screened several times before, once with Bebé Daniels and Ricardo Cortez; I saw only a version starring Bette Davis and Warren William. It was a most astonishing piece of work. Almost nothing remained of the original story; not even the title: it was called *Satan Met a Lady*.

The Maltese Falcon itself, 'the stuff that dreams are made of', turned into something called the French Horn, which Charlemagne was claimed to have blown through; later on it was filled with jewels; on its track came Arthur Treacher as an Englishman with a rolled umbrella and a bowler hat; he packed a gun and a whisky-flask on his hip; everyone got enormously drunk and made wisecracks over the corpses scattered about; the Fat Man became a dear old lady called Madame Barrabas, who when the characters got out of hand called them to order by firing off a pistol at the ceiling; instead of the boy Wilmer she had as a bodyguard a psychopathic nephew in a beret basque, who was constantly being fobbed off with promises of having Warren William to 'play with'.

As comedy-drama this was brilliant, but it was difficult to understand why the script-writer, whose imagination had conjured up these completely new characters, bothered to acknowledge a debt to Dashiell Hammett at all.

Then, some years later, Huston – a young man in his late twenties – hit on the original idea of making a film which would follow, scene for scene, the book exactly as Hammett wrote it. Huston did the script himself; it contained the original dialogue and situations; here in fact was the story one read in 1930 and the characters as one might have imagined them: Joel Cairo with his scented visiting-cards and his high-pitched hysterical menace; Brigid O'Shaugnessy enmeshed in a tangle of her own lies; Gutman with his jouncing jowls and his treacherous joviality; the gunsel kicking Sam Spade's head with tears of anger and humiliation in his eyes.

Humphrey Bogart put up a fine performance as Spade: the sudden savage sugary laugh, the shamefaced grin after a neurotic outburst of glass-throwing and door-slamming. Here was all the pride and arrogance; the curious code of loyalty and the sense of justice ('Don't be so sure that I'm as crooked as I'm supposed to be') carefully concealed beneath the bad reputation and the taut cynical mask. Here, too, Sidney Greenstreet appeared for the first time in a star part: the huge stomach and the too-short sleeves, the fruity Claridges voice and the waddling nimble walk: always ready with the levelled pistol or the doped drink: always ready to forgive, and to make a deal with, the man he has caused to be drugged and beaten up.

Next came another Dashiell Hammett: *The Glass Key*. This time the script, done by Jonathan Latimer, was a little less faithful to its original; Latimer, in his own right a brilliant detective-story writer, introduced a touch of comedy into the final scene, and by converting Paul Madvig into a clown removed the stain of guilt and betrayal from the lovers; and the dream which gives the title to the book and foretells an unhappy ending to the love affair, was left out altogether. Corruption and brutality were there in plenty – one wonders how Beaumont survived the beating up and the headlong dive through the glass awning – but the sombre sense of hopelessness which pervades the book is somehow lacking.

Alan Ladd, Brian Donlevy, Veronica Lake and Joseph Calleia were in the cast; but it was a new actor, William Bendix, who stole the picture as a sadistic snivelling thug: choking his boss with maudlin sobs of self-pity, wiping his nose with his sleeve, and pulling the backs off chairs as in childhood he might have pulled the wings off flies.

The underlying theme in both these films is betrayal. Sam Spade in *The Falcon* betrays his partner with the partner's wife, then betrays the murderess of the partner to the police, although she has been his mistress in the meantime; Beaumont in *The Glass Key* betrays his best friend by stealing from him the senator's daughter; the gangster-bosses and their hirelings betray one another endlessly; the detectives and the district-attorneys cast around for fall-guys, irrespective of innocence or guilt, to preserve their professional reputation: anyone may be sold up at a moment's notice, as a matter of expediency.

Hammett wrote these novels in the 1930s: they were set in the lawless machine-gun-swept streets of American cities, where policemen and politicians were openly corrupt. But the atmosphere of distrust and terror engendered by such conditions was not confined to the USA; the glass key had indeed snapped in the lock and the door could no longer be closed against the snakes – although immense publicity given to American gang-warfare contrived to draw attention from more sinister trends elsewhere. (The film *Scarface* was billed in 1932 as 'The Shame of a Nation.')

Now, caught in close-up on the screen, the murderous activities of these power-intoxicated puppets begin to acquire a symbolical value that reaches far beyond their ostensible purpose and setting; in five years of war we have become accustomed to the constant double-shuffle, the ready change of front and the trumped-up charge; we have seen without surprise the machine-gun turned upon the liberated ally: treachery is part of our daily times.

At roughly the same period as *The Glass Key*, an attempt was made to adapt Graham Greene's *A Gun for Sale*, filmed as *This Gun For Hire*. Although technically competent, the adaptation, by omitting every significant item of the book on which it was based, reduced it to ordinary thriller level; one can see that the original story, a plot by industrialists to promote war in the interests of their own combine, would not readily recommend itself to the film magnates; but worse still the scene was switched from England to the United States, Los Angeles substituted for Nottingham, a Hollywood mansion for the horrible furnished room with the double bed and the wireless blaring away; the gunman, goodlooking Alan Ladd again, had a smashed wrist instead of a hare-lip and died, smiling, for his country with the heroine's approval.

It seems extraordinary that no attempt has been made to do for Graham Greene what John Huston did for Hammett: why not a British film of *The Confidential Agent*, *not* set in Lisbon or Dublin, but in its original background of Bloomsbury hotels and the Dover Road? But Greene's novels continue to be filmed in America; *This Gun for Hire* was followed by a fantastic Fritz Lang version of *The Ministry of Fear*: all the tatty terror of the book tidied away and taking place in an odd city, supposed to be London, full of Dickensian characters in wing-collars, second-hand bookshops twice the size of Foyles, and tube-shelters to which the sound of All Clear can penetrate.

Eric Ambler next engaged the attention of the film companies. We had in quick succession an outrageously bad production of *Background to Danger* and a near-miss in *Journey into Fear*. Then came Jean Negulesco, a Roumanian caricaturist turned film-director, with *The Mask of Dimitrios*. This was eminently satisfactory: Greenstreet at the top of his form; Peter Lorre in a sympathetic part for once; and a talented newcomer, Zachary Scott, as Dimitrios, the elusive, the pimp turned master-spy.

The background and the minor characters were meticulously observed (though one is saddened to see Eduardo Cianelli wasted as a profile with only one sardonic crack allotted him): Faye Emerson as the night-club queen with sequins and a bedraggled fan and a shiny sensual face; Bulic's wife licking turkish delight from her fingers and wiping them on her skirt; the archives-official so proud of his simple filing system. But quite apart from its excellence as cinema, the film had enormous social significance: all the more since politics are not directly mentioned in it. One again becomes aware of the shadow-play in the darkness beyond the lighted pane; the shabby killer with his wolfish face skulking outside the Underground; the endless struggle for power going on out of sight, out of the newspaper headlines: sometimes flourishing openly at peace conferences and diplomatic receptions.[1]

The violent dupes serve their purpose and are done away with: Bulic shoots himself – poor misguided uxorious fool – even Dimitrios dies in the end and Mr Peters is led away by the *agents de police*; but Grodek, the man behind, the employer of spy labour, keeps cleverly out of trouble: retires airily to write a life of St Francis with Siamese cats and Scotch whisky as his chosen companions; straddling over the log-fire in his comfortable brocaded dressing-gown, he says of Bulic's suicide: 'After all, he was a traitor, and one cannot sentimentalise over traitors.' How many heroic and helpless rebellions against corrupt powers have received just such an epitaph in our day. Dimitrios may be despicable, but the Grodeks are the real danger, because they remain unsuspected and influential. Not for them the bullet in the dark or the bayonet in the guts, but the safe sick-bed in the private ward and the epitaph in *The Times*.

Double Indemnity and *Laura* are in a different category of violence altogether. Away from the shadow-world of intrigue into the personal world of sexual passion, and in both cases sexual passion leads to killing.

Many people with whom I have discussed these two pictures prefer *Double Indemnity*. They are those who are seduced by the glamour of the sordid: the floosie with the bangle round her ankle, the scenes in which the characters are striped like convicts by the shadows of the latticed blinds, the middle-class setting of shirt-sleeves and insurance-policies.

It is a first-person film, the cinematic equivalent of those tough American short novels current in 1936: *They Shoot Horses, So I Killed Her*, and so on. James M. Cain wrote the story, the script was by Raymond Chandler, considered by many critics to be the equal of Hammett

---

1 A similar symbolism is inherent in the spy-melodrama of Alfred Hitchcock, which I am examining in a separate essay (see p.251).

himself. The theme is a new perversion of *The Postman*; violent yen at first sight leads to murder-plot against husband of Tiger Woman: told in flashbacks by a tough insurance salesman who confuses murder with honeysuckle and honeysuckle with murder – dying of a bullet-wound given him by his girlfriend before the film opens. It compared unfavourably with the French version of *The Postman* called *Le Dernier Tournant*; the characters kept on turning out good *au fond*, beneath the fashionable sordid surface: the daughter of the murderee, who started off well as an insolent shrew with an eye for men and ended up oddly as the embodiment of innocence; the hectoring lawyer with a heart of gold; everyone fundamentally good except for the husband (because the Hays Office doesn't allow nice people to have their heads bashed in) and the Tiger Woman herself – and even *she* faltered a bit at the finish.

Personally I preferred *Laura* by far. The dialogue was the most subtle and scintillating I have heard on a soundtrack for years; for once the script-writers had improved considerably on the novelist's conception; from the first fade-in – the darkened screen and the sad impressive interior monologue – to the last scenes full of terrific suspense – Laura turning out light after light, locking herself in with the murderer when she believes she is alone in the flat; the murderer screwing his face up with a shudder of revulsion as he loads the shotgun and his recorded voice on the radio recites Ernest Dowson.

Sex is again the motivating factor: an egotistical New York columnist with a Pygmalion complex, probably impotent, plans to kill his own creation, 'the best part of myself', so that no one else shall possess her. Having shot the wrong girl by mistake, he sets out to rectify his error and would have succeeded – but for the fact that he closes his eyes when about to squeeze the trigger.

Clifton Webb as Waldo Lydecker, the columnist, gives us for once on the screen a complete portrait: the bitter pride and the waspish wise-crack, the affectation covering up the sense of inadequacy: a character pitiable and repellent, capable of murder for humanly comprehensible, though warped, motives. Here is an example of the dialogue from the opening sequence; Dana Andrews, as Macpherson the detective, questions Lydecker as to his relations with Laura:

> 'Laura considered me the wisest, the wittiest, the most interesting man she had ever met. I was in complete agreement with her on that point. She also considered me the kindest, the gentlest, the most sympathetic man in the world.'

'D'you agree with her there, too?'

'You won't understand this, Macpherson. But for her sake I tried to become...the kindest, the gentlest, the most sympathetic man in the world.'

'Have any luck?'

'Let me put it this way. I should be sincerely sorry to see my neighbour's child devoured by wolves...shall we go?'

Dialogue of this sort, on a level with that of the best modern American novels, is extremely rare in films: for that reason alone *Laura* would be remarkable. But there are many other outstanding features: the uncompromising presentation of detestable traits in the minor characters: the sloppily handsome young fake with the southern accent whom Laura is engaged to until she finds out he lives on women; the older woman who wants him at all cost; even the detective-hero is a pervert who falls in love with the heroine's corpse. There is one magnificent necrophilious scene: Dana Andrews sweating and swilling whisky from a tumbler, wandering from room to room in the huge tasteless apartment full of clocks and lampshades, counting the dead girl's frocks, smelling her scent, finally passing out in the armchair under her portrait while the rain pours down outside window-panes. The use of music, too, is admirable: the one beautiful nostalgic tune used as a theme throughout; distorted, when necessary, to convey a terrible message – as, for instance, in the sequence outlined above.

All the films I have examined at length hint at elements implicit only, until now, in the foreign cinema: homosexuality in *The Maltese Falcon*; sadism in *The Glass Key*; individual greed exploited for political aims in *The Mask of Dimitrios*; physical passion run riot in *Double Indemnity*; necrophily and sexual impotence in *Laura*. Sophistication seems to be creeping, under the cloak of melodrama, into American films: it might even spread – one hopes – to this country. There are no signs, however, that this will be the case: the usual dreary spate of photographed plays and escapist musicals continues to pour *ad nauseam* from our studios. British film companies had the chance of screening Patrick Hamilton's *Hangover Square*, a scathing exposure of petty drinking and whoring in Earl's Court pubs and Brighton hotels on the eve of war, which, if faithfully filmed, would have offered a topical commentary on a disintegrating society at a time when its nauseous fascist types are being enrolled as officers in the international police forces of the future. Instead we allowed the story to be sold to Hollywood, where it has been filleted into a period-piece with the late Laird Cregar as a composer with homicidal instincts and chambers in Chelsea.

From America we are promised a screen adaptation, by the director of *Double Indemnity*, of Charles Jackson's *The Lost Weekend*, a vertiginous nightmare describing four days in the life of a dipsomaniac. From this it would appear indeed a period or renaissance is under way in the States; I look forward still to seeing Sidney Greenstreet in the title role of Christopher Isherwood's *Mr Norris Changes Trains*: perhaps even Faye Emerson as Sally Bowles. A film of Nigel Balchin's *Small Black Room* is announced for the forthcoming production by a British company; but given the theme – corruption and personal power-politics in the Civil Service sabotaging the war effort – I have no doubt that authority will intervene against a truthful adaptation.

Summing up the effect of the films I have been discussing, I am left with a consciousness of the mirror held up by them to the darkness of our times: whether intentional or not, the symbolism is there: *The Maltese Falcon* and *The Mask of Dimitrios*, especially, present a picture of greed and disintegration which might well be the world of modern diplomacy in microcosm; the same impression, to a lesser degree, emanates from *The Glass Key*, though its politics are intended to be purely local. Even *Double Indemnity* and *Laura* make their point – in an age of so much licensed slaughter in equivocal causes, why not settle one's sexual problems with bullets instead of flowers?

A quotation from the last page of the novel *The Mask of Dimitrios* seems to sum up the situation adequately: 'All I do know is that while might is right, while chaos and anarchy masquerade as order and enlightenment, these conditions will obtain.'

The World of Alfred Hitchcock

*   *   *

BY THE TIME THIS ARTICLE IS PRINTED, ALFRED HITCHCOCK'S latest film, *Spellbound*, may have been released in England. Up to the time of writing I have only heard rumours about it – that the script has been written by a famous female psychoanalyst, that the dream-sequences are by Salvador Dali, and so on and so forth. I do, however, remember reading the original story – a novel by Francis Beeding, about a mental home taken over by a psychopathic patient who impersonates the senior psychiatrist in charge.

This choice of theme seems particularly significant to one who has admiringly followed Mr Hitchcock's progress as a film director since the days when *The Lodger*, wearing a white silk scarf and the face of Mr Ivor Novello, climbed from carpet to linoleum up the decaying but still respectable stairs of the apartment house to the attic, where he disposed of the remains of his victims. Or did a twin-brother commit the murders, was Mr Novello wrongly suspected in that early version of Jack the Ripper? I don't remember it; it's some time ago since I was fifteen; at the time I didn't even know that the director's name was Alfred Hitchcock: the film when I saw it in France was called *Les Cheveux d'Or*: apparently, this particular Jack shared the average American soldier's obsession for blondes.

The details are unimportant; here, for the first time, is the stated theme: the impact of the abnormal on the normal – the figure of the psychopath stepping from out of the fog into the world of kippers and aspidistras – as many years later the murderous uncle in *Shadow of a Doubt* was to step back into the bosom of his horribly smug provincial family, looking for peace but unable to accept it in the sleepy, narrow, small-town atmosphere, with the big-hearted dicks disguised as mass-observers on his tail.

In between these two films comes the great Hitchcockian cycle of spy dramas, in which melodrama is used symbolically, the basic pattern in each case identical, and out of which a new theme begins to emerge: the man hunted by society for a crime that he has not committed. Society must have a scapegoat, and with Hitchcock it is always the innocent, the bewildered, frightened man, shouting out the truth of the conspiracy which no one will believe.

In *The Thirty-nine Steps*, the milkman, with sound British common sense, refuses to credit the hero's story of foreign spies and only agrees to help him escape from a tight corner when he is told a lie about seduction and jealous husbands.

In *The Lady Vanishes*, who will listen to the distraught tales of Margaret Lockwood on board the rushing, roaring express? Least of all the two tweeded Englishmen, obsessed with a desire to get home for the cricket: it's true that they do at last join in on the right side, but only when they are actually shot at. (Surely this piece of symbolism could not have been unintentional.)

In *Foreign Correspondent*, the only person who listens sympathetically to the hero's fantastic tale is the chief fifth-columnist himself; a similar situation occurs during the nightmare ballroom-scene in *Saboteur,* when the British general with his medals and the American tap-dancer with his attendant floozies have turned their backs on the truth, exclaiming, respectively, 'Drunk' and 'Screwy'.

In every instance, the 'normal' everyday citizen is shown as a bar to progress, impeding the happy ending through solid stupidity and ignorance – or, truest of all, through misplaced kindness of heart (the fatherly patrolman holding up Teresa Wright in *Shadow of a Doubt,* with a homily on how late little girls should be out, until the sinister uncle, from whom she is fleeing, can grasp her arm). Sometimes, certainly, as in *Saboteur,* the lorry-driver with his bitter, humorous monologue about wives and new hats, does connive at an escape – but only because he is unaware that the hero is a fugitive.

Sometimes, too, the atmosphere of terror and distrust is so diffused that the genuinely normal character appears sinister, like the commercial travellers swapping smutty yarns and showing samples of silk stockings in *The Thirty-nine Steps.* Anyone may be an enemy agent; the proffered cup of tea may be poisoned; the housekeeper's black, sensible reticule may contain a revolver; an opposite twist makes the dear old vanishing lady a spy, though on the British side.

As a director, Hitchcock employs few startling, technical tricks,[1] and the smooth, easy surface of his films should not be mistaken for slickness: a word, in any case, far too often employed by literary and cinema critics both here and in the States. It is the atmosphere, the ironic juxtaposition of background and situation, that counts: the brilliant succession of minor characters – the disagreeable lady-librarian in *Shadow of a Doubt*; the malevolent dentist in *The Man Who Knew Too Much*; the horrible little Dickensian pseudo-detective with a passion for pushing people off high places in *Foreign Correspondent*; the young plain-clothes man examining a surrealist painting during the domiciliary visit in *Suspicion*; the polite, broken-nosed butler with the blackjack in *Saboteur*: Hitchcock's most complete portrait-gallery to date.

In Hitchcock's films, one remembers whole scenes, not individual shots: although when he does use the camera to startle, the effect is unforgettable (the diplomat's double with his face blown away in *Foreign Correspondent*). Applying the test of memory, I recall the saboteur talking nostalgically about his childhood, about his small son's toys ('when he smashes them he seems almost sorry'), with a side-glance at the enormous bridge he would like to blow up – as the car gathers speed and the thugs with their arms around each other sleepily croon 'A Rhapsody for Two'.

In the same picture – which is a sort of summing-up and compendium of all Hitchcock's spy-dramas – I can recall the blind musician with his intuition and his blank, benign face, watching Robert Cummings lift logs awkwardly for the fire, because of the handcuffs on his wrists; the astonishing scene with the freaks in the travelling circus-truck – with the malignant fascist midget (symbolically known as the Major) and the fat, sentimental, bearded lady; the stout society-woman worried about the servant problem and the ice cream that hasn't arrived, wringing her jewelled hands, accusing her fellow fifth-columnists of inefficiency; the crowded ballroom with the young couple dancing desperately, the auction of the hostess's jewels while the sinister footman

---

1 In an essay on Direction by Mr Hitchcock himself, printed in *Footnotes to the Film* (Lovat Dickson, 1938), he states that nowadays he always tries to tell the story in the simplest possible way, in order to avoid puzzling the audience. He closes this essay with a plea for more freedom – if audiences will give it to him. Let us hope they will.

whispers politely in the hero's ear, drawing his attention to the gun pointing from behind the curtain.

To my mind *Saboteur* is the best of all Hitchcock's melodramas, the most full of excitement and suspense: the girl signalling forlornly from the skyscraper window while the taxi-drivers gossip below and the doomed ship awaits its launching; and, of course, the climactic scenes on the Statue of Liberty – Alan Baxter's hoarse, despairing whisper as he clings by his hands over the unnerving drop and his sleeve rips at the seams.

But if, in my opinion, these scenes are as yet unequalled, the earlier films contain moments not easily forgotten – the terrifying 'Knife' sequence in *Blackmail*, where the fateful word drums in the girl's mind out of the mutter of everyday conversation whichever way she turns; the assassin in *Foreign Correspondent* making his escape under cover of a forest of umbrellas: the arc-lamps and the screeching gramophone needle used to torture the old peace-loving diplomat into submission while Eduardo Cianelli's sad, lined, terrible face looks down at him; the aquarium and the bird-shop in *Sabotage* (an adaptation of Joseph Conrad's *Secret Agent* and in many ways one of Hitchcock's few failures); Godfrey Tearle firing point-blank at Robert Donat in *The Thirty-nine Steps* and the quick subsequent cut to the Bible with a bullet embedded in it, the shadow of the strangler's hands intruding on a moonlight serenade in *The Lady Vanishes*; assassination at the opera-house in *Man Who Knew Too Much*.

Then, with the production of *Rebecca* and *Suspicion*, we come to Hitchcock's logical progression from the crowded melodramatic scene to psychological drama with a restricted setting and cast: a mode which culminated in the superb achievement of *Shadow of a Doubt*.

Each of these films derives from its predecessor, with an improvement every time; *Suspicion* derives from *Rebecca* and probably in turn from *Love from a Stranger*: an earlier film which, unfortunately, I have not seen.[1]

Rebecca was adapted faithfully from the best-selling novel by Daphne du Maurier: the story of a vicious, unquiet spirit whose evil influence dominates, even after death, the corridors of a doomed family mansion, almost ruining the lives of her former husband and

---

1 I regret also that I have not seen *Rich and Strange*, an experimental film in which, I am told, Hitchcock was given a completely free hand.

his new bride. There was really little that Hitchcock could do with this modern-gothic tale: the film is oppressive rather than impressive, although the more realistic scenes are handled with the director's usual brilliance – George Sanders imposing his blackmail terms genially over the gnawed carcass of chicken at the picnic-lunch in the car after the inquest, the half-wit muttering over the cigarette-butts in the seductively furnished beach-hut, the fat, vain social-climber tittering coquettishly at Laurence Olivier in the Riviera hotel.

With *Suspicion*, however, the director is once more at home with his story: a reversal of the *Love From a Stranger* theme – the young bride's suspicions of her husband prove, in the end, to be unfounded.

Some critics at the time the film was first shown were disappointed with the final twist: I personally found it satisfying after the suspense of the crazy car-ride towards the fatal cliff: Hitchcock is the only film director who can make one hope for a happy ending. Also, the revelation of the husband's innocence makes the film a complete study of persecution-mania, showing its gradual growth in the girl's mind until it becomes a gigantic shadow, eclipsing all else. A malicious phrase from another woman, a paragraph in the paper, a visit from two detectives, a lady novelist discussing poisons at the dinner-table, an AA map, the kindly, blundering friend subject to heart attacks who dies of too much brandy in a French hotel, an accident which might have been arranged: once the seed is planted, each of these incidents becomes a significant fact that seems to lead to only one conclusion – murder. True, the cloud finally lifts; the husband is an embezzler and a potential suicide, not a murderer, and a reunion is promised for the young couple in the future, outside the prison gates.

So, with *Saboteur* in between, we come to *Shadow of a Doubt*. Here, there is hardly any melodrama; the murders happen off the screen; there is little action and only one death – the murderer's fall from a train while attempting to silence the niece who knew too much.

The scene is laid in a small American town, in a 'typical American home', complete with horrible, precocious children and a detective-story fan for a father. Even the dominant sinister figure itself assumes this time the appearance of outward normality: the saboteur, with the animal speed of movement and the frightening, fish-like face of Alan Baxter, gives way to Uncle Charlie, the charming young psychopath with curly, blond hair and a gleaming smile, actuated by a secret urge to iron out rich, elderly widows and make off with their money.

(Charlie has had many parallels in real life: the most startling is perhaps Hendrik de Jong, known as the 'Top Hatted Slayer' owing to his predilection for morning dress, who married his victims and then bashed their faces in with his bare fists. De Jong operated in the States and was never caught: disappeared without a trace while all the ports were watched and the police patrolled the streets: he was never seen again.)

In Charlie's case it is implied that an accident in childhood (fall from a bicycle and injury to the head) is the cause of his insanity. It is doubtful, however, that he is a certifiable case, and he himself has another explanation for his activities – the pressure of life itself – as he pleads for sympathy, for understanding, in an impassioned, tortured speech to Teresa Wright over the uneaten plates of ice cream in the horrible tatty restaurant he has dragged her into. But the weight of hatred and bitterness inside him are too much for her to bear – the adolescent without experience, who has suffered from no more than the boredom of small-town Sunday afternoons, enormous family meals and too much candy: she can neither sympathise nor understand, and so the poor, disordered, unhappy mind starts to plan her murder – carbon monoxide, a broken tread on the stairs; even when the death of another suspect ensures his safety, he cannot stop, must make completely sure: he has no confidence in human loyalty any more.

So to his death on the railway line and the magnificent, ironical closing scene, with the memorial to his memory being unveiled and the clergyman's solemn epitaph: 'The kindest, finest, most unselfish man we have ever known': while the niece weeps beside her new boyfriend on the steps and THE END flickers up across the screen.

Does the small town return now to its sleepy, everyday round in smug triumph, and do the members of the audience return, too, to their safe, 'normal', humdrum homes, as oblivious as their prototypes in the film, to the menace underlying the surface of life, the stealthy terror which Alfred Hitchcock has surely attempted to show, under the guise of melodrama, so many times? In *Shadow of a Doubt* he seems to have despaired a little: the 'decent, ordinary, everyday folk' are spared the final knowledge of what has been in their midst; perhaps it's better that they shouldn't know, because they would not, in any case, understand. But Hitchcock's sojourn in the States – in the land of cookies and mothers, of enormous sentimental gestures across floodlit hoardings, of the American dream and the muddled, democratic ideal

– has sharpened his sense of satire, and it cannot be an accident that the members of his representative normal family are individually so obtuse and boring.

Mention of democracy brings me to an examination of *Lifeboat*, Hitchcock's only real war-film – although in *Saboteur*, in a speech by Otto Kruger, he gave us the specious fascist philosophy of a fifth-columnist.

Lifeboat is not outwardly a political film, though there is a Communist among the characters and the story is by John Steinbeck. Several survivors from a torpedoed liner are brought together in a lifeboat on the open sea and suddenly the captain of the Nazi submarine that has torpedoed them is hauled on board. His advent starts an argument: should he be thrown back into the sea or not? Those in favour of this step are overruled, because to do so would be not only inhuman but undemocratic.

The Nazi is therefore allowed to live, despite the vehement protests of the Communist stoker: dark-faced, scowling he-man John Hodiak. For a time he shares their trials in perfect harmony, and even comes in useful (having been in civilian life a surgeon) for cutting off William Bendix's leg, which had become gangrened as the result of an injury. From this to persuading Bendix, when delirious, to throw himself overboard (and helping him do so with a slight push) was only a step.

The Nazi now proceeds methodically with a plan to murder the other survivors one by one. He has concealed his perfect knowledge of English and the presence of extra food and water on his person; he has also a hidden compass: the others were apparently too democratic to search him thoroughly. A sudden storm springing up gives him complete command of the boat: owing to his extra nourishment, he is the only one with strength enough to row for hours on end without stopping. The democrats are by now so much under his spell that some of them are even prepared to play German songs to him on the mouth-organ.

But the discovery of the concealed rations, the fact that he is rowing them steadily into enemy waters, and his blatant admission of Bendix's murder, makes them rise against him at last: he is battered to death with an oar and flung over the side.

Yet at the close of the film another Nazi is hauled aboard and the same process seems about to start all over again, despite the lesson just learned: 'Why, he's only a child!' a woman exclaims sympathetically, and even the appearance of a pistol in the 'child's' hand only leads to its being harmlessly knocked aside. 'Decency', 'democracy', 'humanity' triumph once more, and this new Nazi is still alive as the film ends.

Such an ending – like that of *Shadow of a Doubt* – is of necessity equivocal: each cinema-goer may read into it what he likes – an indictment, a plea for total war, a fundamental faith in humane man's inevitable triumph despite the callousness and cunning of his enemy.

I believe the film, when first shown, almost caused a diplomatic incident. The Americans complained that the democrats were made to look completely silly. There seemed, also, to be an opinion that the Nazi was portrayed as a superman: far superior in strength and intelligence to his opponents.

I don't agree at all. The Nazi was portrayed as a completely despicable character, lying, treacherous, brutal and servile by turns. Plausible, certainly, very plausible: the puzzled, ingratiating smile, the big, brutal body deferentially bent, while the cunning, tortuous brain schemed on behind the façade of acceptance and comradeship in a tight corner.

Nor were the democrats made to look especially idiotic: no more so than the citizens of those democratic countries who allowed 'Herr' Hitler to commit his barbarities in peacetime with no more than a mild, reproachful protest.

But after such a reception of a fine and sincere film, containing so many brilliant oblique truths, one can well understand that Alfred Hitchcock turns to making a picture in which the mad pass themselves off as the sane.

Is the subject symbolical? I leave that to film-goers to decide when *Spellbound* is shown. It may be that I have read a meaning of my own into the work of Alfred Hitchcock; if so, I am sorry, and I am prepared to apologise to Mr Hitchcock immediately.

A Brief Survey of
British Feature Films

*   *   *

1. YESTERDAY

LOOKING BACK ON THE BRITISH FILMS PRODUCED DURING AND after the 1914 war, one supposes them to have been more advanced in their choice of background and subject-matter, more in the modern tradition, than the majority of American films then being shown in this country. The characters were frequently proletarian and their surroundings sordid; I remember a serial of several episodes which took place entirely on a barge: although this culminated in a murder of unexampled ferocity, there was little other action throughout; the drama seems, at a remove of memory, to have been purely psychological. My parents enjoyed it and went every week; I, being at the time a child of eight or nine years old, naturally preferred *The Phantom Rider* or *The Clutching Hand*: life on the barge bored me.

These were the days of the Bad Man and the Wild West; the Artcraft Tiger and William S. Hart, Tom Mix and his horse Tony; Ruth Roland, Pearl White, Juanita Hansen were being pursued through eighteen episodes by a variety of sinister figures, masked, hooded, cloaked, and in one case dressed from head to foot in furs; there was a mystery man got up in a diving-suit and one disguised as a mummy, who emerged nightly from a sarcophagus and was described on the subtitles as a Strange Soulless Thing.

These were the figures that gripped one's imagination at that age; I cannot remember the name of the actor who played the bargee, Trask, and ended by cutting someone's throat with a clasp-knife, but I remember the names of Henry Edwards, Chrissie White, Alma Taylor, who were produced by Cecil Hepworth in scenes of unredeemed

259

squalor, in films which would doubtless have seemed to me now above the average. At the same time, of course, there were other British films more spectacular in setting and treatment: Matheson Lang as *Mr Wu*, Gerald Ames in *The Prisoner of Zenda* and *Rupert of Hentzau*, *The City of Beautiful Nonsense* with, was it Stewart Rome, *Carnival* by Compton Mackenzie. Eille Norwood was appearing as Sherlock Holmes in a series of two-reel shorts adapted from the stories; Henry Edwards in a serial of *The Amazing Quest of Mr Ernest Bliss*.

Then my parents took me to live with them in France, where I saw no British films, but some of the French serials seemed to me the same type; *L'Assommoir* and *La Pocharde* were being shown, attended assiduously by my father and unwillingly by me: working-class characters staggered about drunk and a workman with a bottle in his pocket fell from a ladder; I preferred *Michel Strogoff* and *Les Trois Mousquetaires*.

It was not until about 1928 that I happened to see two British pictures, *The Sinister Man* and *The Crimson Circle*; both were adapted from Edgar Wallace; one featured Paul Cavanagh, the other Stewart Rome: Henry Edwards, Chrissie White, Gerald Ames were apparently no more, and the realistic mood, which I would now have welcomed, had died with Cecil Hepworth. No barges or proletarians here, with the exception, possibly, of a pickpocket: these were detective dramas unimaginatively filmed, inferior in fact to their French equivalents featuring René Navarre.

Very different, however, in approach and technique, was Alfred Hitchcock's *The Lodger*, which I must have seen roughly at the same time; later came the talkies and *Blackmail*; later still, in a London suburb plastered with posters advertising *M*, *Scarface* and *Frankenstein*, I saw an outstanding film, *The Old Dark House*.

I saw it again recently, and except for the clothes of the characters it doesn't date; on the contrary, in its realistic overlapping dialogue, its large close-ups, its beautiful grouping and its fine disdain for the accusation of melodrama, it reminded me at times of films like *The Magnificent Ambersons* and *The Lost Weekend*.

There was the same selection of significant detail, by which an indifferent story became transformed into a work of art; one remembers particularly the long, almost interminable meal after the muttered grace, the endless carving of the cold joint, the old envious woman piling her plate with food while the dumb dangerous servant prowls round the table and the maniac waits in the attic. The most creaking conventions of the gothic novel are given, by means of brilliant direction and acting, a new lease of life; banging shutters, a storm outside, sinister footsteps, a barred door concealing an abominable family secret: all these become once again authentically terrifying, and the oldest trick of all, the hairy knuckled hand from the film serials of one's youth, gripping the stair-rail as the madman is expected at last to descend, produces a moment of horrible suspense, unequalled in more recent thrillers such as *The Spiral Staircase*.

This is a genre in which the British cinema could excel. Another example is the film of *The Frightened Lady* with Marius Goring, a young actor who seems, regrettably, to be no longer in the lists nowadays: one would welcome his return – the twitching boyish face and the bubbling laugh – in place of the solidity of Mr Stewart Granger.

The Frightened Lady is another tale of madness running in the family, and this particular version, directed by George King, exhibited some of the same qualities present in *The Old Dark House*; a similar grouping of the characters, few exteriors, no time lost in transitions or in the delivery of the dialogue, no boring slow fade-in: the film opens directly with the terrified girl running down the stairs, screaming at sight of a shadow which is merely the footman's: the sense of mounting tension is conveyed with admirable economy from the very start.

But let us return to the earlier talkies: to the days of Elstree and London Films, when Laughton was still in England and also Alfred Hitchcock: when Sir Alexander Korda made *Henry VIII*, prior to his excursions into jingoism and Technicolor jungles. It was a peak period: *The Thirty-nine Steps*, *Pygmalion*, *Things to Come*, *Henry VIII* itself: these four films alone compared favourably with the best American talkies then being issued, with *Mr Deeds* and *The Thin Man* and *The Petrified Forest*: perhaps, even, with the French. (De Montherlant, in *Les Lepreuses*, makes his mouthpiece, Costals, issue a pæan of praise in favour of British films about this time, and Solange is dragged from cinema to cinema in search of a British picture: the reverse process to that in force among intellectuals over here.)

Another title, too, comes vividly to mind: *On the Night of the Fire*, a fine sombre film directed by Brian Desmond Hurst from F.L. Green's novel about a murderous megalomaniac barber: this was reminiscent, occasionally, of John Ford's magnificent *Informer*. But the shadow of Sabu, swaying high up in his howdah, soon fell across the scene: glorious Technicolor was on its way and the critics lost their heads over trivial comedy-thrillers like *Q Planes* and *This Man is News* – two attempts to do a Thin Man on us. *The Four Feathers* exploded with such a blare of sound, such a blaze of bright colour, that the eyes of audiences could hardly accustom themselves to the gloom of Carol Reed's *The Stars Look Down*, and *They Drive by Night*, in its way a minor classic worthy of a place beside any French drama of the Lost, received little attention save in the columns of the highbrow weeklies.

They Drive by Night, adapted from James Curtis's story of an ex-convict suspected of murder, who lorry-hops across England in order to escape the police, had the authentic flavour of life among the small-time spivs, of caffs and gaffs, grafter and palone; words had crept into the dialogue not usually heard on a British soundtrack; Emlyn Williams played the tough scared suspect, but the film was almost stolen by Ernest Thesiger, memorable as the prim cowardly toper in *The Old Dark House*, this time the real murderer: a sex-maniac with a passion for stroking stray cats and seeing fear reflected on the faces of stray women before the silk stocking is finally wound tight around the tawdry throat. Who, having seen his performance, is likely to forget the mincing delicate walk, the fussy gallantry in the Palais de Danse among the professional partners, the sunken starved eyes and the long pointed mobile nose pressed against the pane?

But *They Drive by Night*, with its sympathetic treatment of dispossessed people, was not followed up by the British film industry; *The Puritan*, by Liam O'Flaherty, was filmed in France with Jean-Louis Barrault instead of in England with Marius Goring; Emlyn Williams made a good thriller in *Dead Men Tell No Tales*, with himself in a double part and an impenetrable disguise; the picture was worth ten of *This Man is News*, yet passed almost unnoticed. Then war broke out: the *Athenia* sank and Warsaw burned; Hitchcock's one horrible failure, *Jamaica Inn*, was playing to packed houses before the cinemas were temporarily closed.

2. TODAY

It is not my business to discuss documentary films here; yet it is in this genre, on the whole, that British films held their own during the 1939 war. Before this broke out, it was to the documentary that one turned for technical beauty and experimental accomplishment, to

John Grierson, Basil Wright, Paul Rotha, Donald Taylor and the rest; not only for these qualities, but for understanding of common problems and a political content that was lacking for the most part in our feature-films. These were the inheritors of Hepworth, and it remains a fact that our most successful war-films had a documentary interest: *In Which We Serve*, *San Demetrio*, *London* (naval), *The Way Ahead* (army), *The Way to the Stars* (RAF): the list is too long to continue, and in any case these films have been fully gone over elsewhere. There were two good melodramas, *Next of Kin* and *The 49th Parallel* (this latter narrowly missed being on a Hitchcockian level); on a lighter plane we had *Night Train to Munich* and *The Four Just Men* (brought up to date to include a sequence of marching soldiers at the finish). Yes, during the war the standard was undeniably high, with the exception of a few frank stinkers such as *Half Way House*. And, of course, one can discount the mad outpouring of Old Mother Rileys and Sexton Blakes: this sort of commercial tripe exists in almost any country where films are made.

But what of the aftermath? 'The British cinema, with the achievements of Noel Coward, Anthony Asquith, Carol Reed, Powell and Pressburger, Launder and Gilliat behind it, is ready to challenge the world.' These words, twice repeated in different forms, are part of the editorial of a recently started film magazine which lies open in front of me as I write. Judging from their weekly effusions when any new British feature appears, most film critics seem to be in agreement with this opinion. I myself am extremely doubtful, on the evidence of, say, *The Rake's Progress*, *Dead of Night*, *I Know Where I'm Going* and *The Seventh Veil*, to mention four of the best British pictures which have appeared since hostilities ceased. None of these appear to me on a level with the French cinema, and not even with the best of the newer American films. (For example, compare *The Seventh Veil* with *Laura* and *The Rake's Progress* with *The Lost Weekend*.)

One can, I suppose, comfortably ignore vulgar nonsense like *The Wicked Lady*, *Caravan* or *The Madonna of the Seven Moons*, but one cannot really ignore the way in which *Night Boat to Dublin*, a secret-service thriller inferior even to one of the Sherlock Holmes films both in direction and acting, was foisted upon West End audiences instead of being relegated to the suburbs as a second feature. One is also forced, reluctantly, to mention *Caesar and Cleopatra*; let us not, however, go into a discussion of this colossal fiasco: the story has already been sufficiently publicised, the enormous sums expended, the sphinx and sand transported to the desert, the nauseating exchange of letters between director and dramatist: 'You are my greatest inspiration in this or any other life.' It is sad that the achievement of *Pygmalion* and *Major Barbara* should culminate in such a spectacular failure but it was perhaps to be expected; one has had enough, in any event, of Messrs Shaw and Pascal being geniuses together.

In talking of current British films, mention of Mr J. Arthur Rank also seems unavoidable. His determination to conquer the American market cannot fail to have a detrimental effect on film-making in this country: one visualises valuable studio space being taken up with more and more 'naughty' costume-pieces and perhaps even gigantic musicals. *Henry V* was a magnificent pageant, and, moreover, good cinema; but one fears that its success in the States will lead to the production of huge Technicolor sagas on a De Mille scale, in an effort to outdo Hollywood, and even without this menace, the outlook is already fairly bleak when one compares a list of coming British films with those to come from France.

Marcel Carné's *Les Enfants du Paradis* and *Les Portes de la Nuit*, Duvivier's *Panique*, Delannoy's *Sortilèges*, Cocteau's *La Belle et la Bête*, or Gilliat's *Green for Danger*, Lance Comfort's *Bedalia*, Peter Ustinov's *Top Secret*, *Hungry Hill* by Daphne du Maurier, *The Magic Bow*, about Paganini: which, given the choice, would one rather see? We are told that during the Nazi occupation French film-makers were forced to turn to the period-piece and the fairy-tale: we have had no occupation here, but fairy-tales in plenty; now that the war is over, the fusion of the documentary and the imaginative which was so effective in, for instance, *San Demetrio London*, is gradually giving place to a quality of showy escapism in the worst Hollywood tradition: the new stars are being photographed in cloak and sword costume: Sir Alexander Korda has just paid £100,000 for the film-rights of Daphne du Maurier's *King's General*, twice the price paid for *Gone With the Wind*.

True, Sydney Box is to make Graham Greene's *The Man Within*, a psychological study of a coward which promises something out of the ordinary providing the original story is adhered to; but on the other hand he has also made another Daphne du Maurier, *The Years Between*, in which we are threatened, according to the advertisements, with a 'topical' examination of the problems of returning soldiers whose marriages, in the meantime, have gone wrong.

The problems of returning soldiers, this time POWs, were also dealt with in *The Captive Heart*, and had the scene been limited to the prison camp itself, this would have been a sincere and moving film; but once the soldiers were released and set foot on British soil, sentimentality and bathos inevitably crept in: artificially created 'situations' which helped to destroy the reality of the earlier sequences. A sort of cheapening sentiment reminiscent of the penny novelette: that has always been the threat to good British films; it is, however, entirely absent from the story and treatment of Noel Coward's *Brief Encounter*, a beautiful poignant picture conceived throughout in cinematic terms which has every right to be considered as a classic. What a joy to see Mr Coward turning from the glorification of poker-faced naval captains and middle-class stolidity to this delicate poetic tale of meeting and parting, haunted by the sad hoot of railway trains sounding a call to departure. I have only one criticism to make: whenever a working-class character appears, he or she is treated as *comic*, light relief. And this fault is not confined to Mr Coward: it exists also in so many of our best recent productions. Not, it is true, in *Waterloo Road*, perhaps our nearest approach nowadays to the mood of *They Drive by Night*; but this is merely the exception that proves the rule. It is an attitude never present in French films, one more reason for their superiority: only in documentaries over here are proletarian people taken for granted, and not exploited as objects of mirth. One can only hope for a more enlightened approach, when the cockney 'character' will die out altogether and working-class themes be seriously treated, not necessarily as socialist propaganda, but in terms of the human heart. If we must start with the underworld, the spiv, as being, of course, more colourful material, why not have scripts written by Bill Naughton and James Curtis, who adapted, himself, *They Drive by Night*? Then perhaps we might progress, say, to a film of Welsh life written by Rhys Davies or Dylan Thomas: such a story, properly handled, might prove equal to *La Femme du Boulanger*. These are vain hopes: a plea for better and more imaginative script-writers must prove futile when our best contemporary novelists are steadily selling their rights to Hollywood owing to lack of response in the British feature-film industry.

There is news that Georges Simenon is to be filmed by a British company: why not Gerald Kersh's *Night and the City* or Patrick Hamilton's *The Midnight Bell*? And if we must have psychopathic cases pounding the piano, then why not G.S. Marlowe's novel about a schizophrenic composer, *I am Your Brother*, or on a lower level, Margery Allingham's *Dancers in Mourning*. But let us have less Miss du Maurier in the future, less photographed plays like *Pink String and Sealing Wax* and fewer dull semi-documentaries like *Painted Boats*: the only recommendation for which is that the posters are designed by John Piper. Then, perhaps, the optimism of the editor whose words I have quoted earlier on might one day prove justified.

Parade of Violence

*　　　*　　　*

WE CAME OUT OF *THE BLUE DAHLIA*, TWO OF US, BOTH disappointed and angry, and my friend, a big man, shouted at the top of his voice: 'More and more murders! Bigger and better beatings-up! By all means break your toe kicking the hero in the head. Corpses littered all over the place, never mind who does the shooting so long as they're dead!'

The speaker was taken by passers-by for a Fascist advocating his creed; his qualifying remark: 'That's what the Hollywood producers seem to be saying nowadays,' was lost in the general outcry.

How right he was, however. Gone completely the sophisticated and adult attitude of American film-melodramas such as *Laura*, *The Maltese Falcon*, *Mask of Dimitrios*, etc; instead we have the purposeless parade of violence for its own sake: physical violence unrelated to any known form of life and apparently catering for a supposed audience of sadistic schoolchildren.

Start off with *The Blue Dahlia* itself, a film which has been praised by critics who should certainly know better, unless they have themselves become punch-drunk with watching the hallucinated antics of the slap-happy puppets on the screen.

Here was an opportunity missed: a good cast, Alan Ladd, Veronica Lake, William Bendix, Howard da Silva, Doris Dowling; Raymond Chandler was apparently given a free hand to do the script and dialogue. One expected something outstanding, and what does one get? Conventional characters and story, conventional neurotic war-torn hero (Ladd), conventional psychopathic pal (Bendix), conventional night-club racketeer (da Silva), conventional wise-cracking dreary lost-girl wife of racketeer (Lake), bound for conventional happy ending with Ladd after racketeer has been ironed out in conventional gun-battle during which his henchmen are also accidentally shot to death. This high rate of mortality continues throughout the film and nobody could care less: the whole picture is made incomprehensible for much of its length by bad cutting and, I am sorry to say, by bad scripting; the director seems determined to equal in savagery the beatings-up in *The Glass Key*: a gangster does indeed break his toe by kicking Alan Ladd too hard, and Ladd afterwards stamps on the broken toe of his aggressor when this has just been withdrawn from a mustard bath.

In another picture of the same kind, *The Dark Corner*, there is more stamping: this time on thumbs; Mark Stevens, a new star attempting unsuccessfully to emulate Bogart, smashes William Bendix's thumb with a paperweight; later his own thumb is stamped on by Bendix when he is laid out in turn. Even bigger and better beatings-up, but one of the features of this type of film is that everyone recovers from the most savage pasting with incredible speed and few ill effects: it is true that in *The Dark Corner* Bendix fails to recover after being thrown from the thirty-third floor of a skyscraper by Clifton Webb.

Yes, Clifton Webb, so admirable in *Laura*, is on the scene again: typed, alas, as an art dealer with a fund of malicious epigrams and a cuckolded devotion to a young wife with a Laura hair-do; this time it takes six bullets, fired by the wife, to dispatch him, after which the wife, for whose lover's death he has been responsible, throws the empty gun in his dead face.

Tough, what? Never mind: we're tough too. Tough enough to take, also, Dick Powell bashing his enemy's face to a pulp in *Cornered*: this, in my opinion, a much better show despite its slowness in getting to the point: the direction more lively than the dull long-shot-to-medium-shot-to-close-up technique of the two films previously discussed.

In *Cornered* too, we have Walter Slezak, plump, obsequious and untrustworthy, in soiled white ducks and a character part; it is uncertain up to the date of writing whether he or Vincent Price will finally occupy the place left vacant by the death of Laird Cregar: Slezak is fatter of course, but Vincent Price has a good, deep, soft toneless voice, almost equal to that of the master himself (Cregar was once billed as Hollywood's super-soft-silky-voiced slaughter-man).

Cornered takes place, if I remember rightly, in the Argentine; Lisbon is the scene of *The Conspirators*, in which the complete cast of *The Mask of Dimitrios*, with the exception of Faye Emerson and the addition of

Paul Henreid, assembled under the direction of Jean Negulesco in an attempt to repeat the success of his former fine melodrama; a resounding failure resulted instead, despite the presence of Sidney Greenstreet, Peter Lorre, Victor Francen, Joseph Calleia and Eduardo Cianelli: these last two, curiously enough, cast as chiefs of police, instead of as gangsters or spies. The story was completely altered from Frederic Prokosch's novel; this in fact resembled the plot of *Cornered*: a man hunting down his enemy, a traitor and murderer, in the labyrinths of a neutral city.

After *The Conspirators*, Jean Negulesco had another go with *Three Strangers*, which had a good story by John Huston, director of *The Maltese Falcon*; the film, with Greenstreet and Lorre to act in it, suffered a little from its scene being laid in London and the usual irritating errors entailed thereby; but here at least violence was cut to a minimum: a copper (designated in the dialogue as a bobby, to make it more English) murdered off-stage, an informer knifed in a train, a woman's head bashed in by Greenstreet with the Chinese idol that has caused all the trouble.

Not in any way an outstanding film, but there *is* at any rate an attempt at characterisation – the drunkard, the embezzling solicitor, the horrible nymphomaniac spider-woman (excellently played by Geraldine Fitzgerald); the characters are a cut above the conventional marionettes of *The Blue Dahlia* and *The Dark Corner*.

Film critics also went crazy over *The Spiral Staircase*, a film directed by Robert Siodmak from the novel by Ethel Lina White. I attended the performance of this with a pleasant feeling of expectation, remembering the director's splendid piece of work in his first American picture, *Phantom Lady*; also it seemed that I was to be transported back to the film-world of my childhood, the atmosphere of Pearl White and the silent serials: lonely girl terrorised by mysterious killer in dark house miles from anywhere, a crippled malignant woman upstairs, night pressing closer to the windows, shots of gloved hands and glaring eyes: the whole *Cat and the Canary* set brought up to date in fact, with additions from Freud.

I was disappointed. *The Spiral Staircase* had the distinction of being one of the few thrillers in the middle of which I almost went to sleep. The heroine was dumb, and played by an actress whose name I cannot even remember, but whom the critics raved over: I found her dumb in more senses than one, and her acting negligible. Of course the murderer is a maniac (there is a maniac concealed in every Siodmak film); he finally corners the dumb girl on the landing and prepares to do her in, but unfortunately his preparations take too long and there is time for his paralysed stepmother, who has suddenly recovered the use of her legs, to shoot him from the top of the stairs. Whereupon the heroine, in turn, miraculously recovers the power of speech and is able to telephone the police.

The moral of the film seems to be, get yourself assaulted by a madman and, if you're afflicted in any way, you're bound to snap out of it on the dot: a curious theory vaguely reminiscent of the conditions obtaining in certain army psychiatric hospitals, where sergeant-majors themselves on the borders of lunacy are allowed to shout at the patients, presumably with the idea that neurosis can be cured on the word of command.

The critics, oddly enough, gave bad notices to *The Unseen*, another Ethel Lina White adaptation, which I found, personally, far superior to *The Spiral Staircase*. Here again a lonely girl is trapped in a house where a murderous maniac prowls by night; but a new turn of the screw is given (for by no means the first time, it is true, *vide* James) by the fact that the children of the household are being corrupted into co-operation with the murderer. The little boy of seven is in love with the former governess, who bribes him with silver dollars to let the killer into the house at night, and also to lure her successor to the dark alley where he lies in wait.

Finally the maniac is unmasked and, about to draw his gun and iron everybody out, is forestalled by the little boy who says: 'Here, take your money back. You're a bad man, you kill people,' and shoves the dollars into the pocket containing the pistol. The murderer then gives himself meekly up to the waiting detectives: a conclusion, I think, much more original and satisfying than the penultimate scenes of *The Spiral Staircase*.

The script, by the way, was by Raymond Chandler, who did a much better job on it than he did on his own film, *The Blue Dahlia*.

Such films as *The Unseen* and *The Spiral Staircase* are, of course, not to be taken seriously, even with the present literary trend in England and France (Mervyn Peake and Julien Gracq) to read symbolical meanings into books which derive directly from *The House of Usher* and *The Castle of Otranto*.

Let us return from the modern horror-fairy-tale to a realistic vision of the world with two films by Fritz Lang: *The Woman in the Window* and *Scarlet Street*: both featuring the same team, Edward G. Robinson, Joan Bennett and Dan Duryea, in practically the same parts; in both Edward G. starts off as a typical stuffy American citizen coming home a bit tight from a bachelor reunion; Joan Bennett crosses his path and trouble starts immediately; the stage is set for Dan Duryea to stroll on in his straw hat, as a pimp or blackmailer.

The Woman in the Window contains a stabbing with scissors and turns out to be a dream; *Scarlet Street* has a stabbing too, but done with a palette-knife and through Joan Bennett's bedclothes: this time it isn't a dream, though the wrong man is hanged and Robinson remains haunted for the rest of his life by the whispering voices of the dead sordid couple; therefore the film caused a scandal in America and was considered by critics over here as highly adult, despite the fact that it bears the same relation to, say, *Destiny* that *No Orchids for Miss Blandish* does to *Sanctuary* by William Faulkner.

Fritz Lang, however, always brings with him some of his cold German-intellectual quality: a feeling for the squalor and menace of a great city which has a parallel in novels like *Auto da Fé* by Elias Canetti. The city with its dark streets is a trap for the unwary (he is usually middle-aged and a professor); stark horror lies in wait round its corners, ready to pounce out at any moment; repression from within and circumstance from without combine to drive the scissors home and the victim out of his mind. I must say, though, that I consider Robinson miscast in these roles as Little Man; I prefer to see him as Little Caesar.

Otto Preminger, director of *Laura*, is also, one supposes, of German or Austrian origin; his film, *Fallen Angel*, has much of Lang's quality: this time the dark streets are those of a small town whose English equivalent would be perhaps Littlehampton, and the trap closes round Dana Andrews as a bird of passage who lives on his wits. The bait is Linda Darnell, a waitress on the make and with her hair down; soon she and Dana Andrews are seen kissing in huge close-ups. But Darnell wants money and marriage: Andrews, in order to raise the ready, is obliged to make love to a rich girl who plays the organ in the Methodist church and regularly attends the congregation. Naturally it's not long before Darnell gets bumped off and Andrews is accused of the murder and forced to flee. The rich girl follows him into exile: all comes right in the end and a sadistic detective, who draws on a glove over his knuckle-duster, proves to be finally responsible for the crime.

I preferred *Fallen Angel*, both for direction, acting and story, to *Scarlet Street*, because in it a moral problem has been posed: not a problem of sexual morals (those in *Fallen Angel* are on the whole far looser and the scenes of love-making genuinely erotic), but a problem in which sin and the sense of sin is considered important; the rich church-going girl throws over her principles to stand by her dubious husband, who has married her in the first place in order to give her money to another girl; but her devotion does bring him to heel and back into the fold, in the sort of happy ending unknown to the world of *The Blue Dahlia* and *The Dark Corner*, where sexual morals are far stricter and a genuine moral code is simply non-existent.

That, I think, is the secret of success and failure in all these thrillers: the absence of any moral standard by which the characters can be judged, other than a sexual one: and this is always rigidly enforced; though violence is *de rigueur* in *The Dark Corner* and the wife of the villain may be allowed a lover, dreary Lucille Ball, as the heroine, is consistently hard to get outside of marriage, and her teasing technique is regarded as admirable; whereas when Linda Darnell tries the same tactics in *Fallen Angel* she is represented as evil and self-seeking. The rich organ-playing girl doesn't act hard to get; she is only too ready to give herself to Dana Andrews, to take the chance of securing his love that way; yet this is not shown as reprehensible either; in *The Dark Corner* it would, however, be extremely reprehensible if Lucille Ball were to succumb to the advances of her neurotic private-detective employer; the theme of secretary eventually marrying boss is glamourised and made savoury to satisfy the tawdry suburban typists who only a year ago were determinedly pursuing GI Joe up and down London Town.

Scarlet Street is naturally more sophisticated, but here again there is no contrast between good and evil; the victimised hen-pecked cashier, who does a spot of painting in his spare time, is not 'good', but merely a crashing bore; and a picture of pure evil, as represented by Bennett and Duryea, fails to convince, as pure evil always does; even Hitler had ideals, even if they were perverted, and Lucifer himself was once an angel of the Host.

Nor am I particularly enthralled by a blackmailer feeling a sudden lech for a woman when she has just attempted to poison him (*Woman in the Window*); although I am sure that to a Central European mind it would seem the acme of sophistication: I am reminded of the Viennese girl saying of the scene in *Laura* when Waldo Lydecker was about to shoot his protégé to prevent her from belonging to anyone else: 'Now he should drop the gun and they should make love,' and all the Café Royal film-people acclaiming her acumen.

No, it is time that film directors, script-writers and critics grew up and realised that a cinematic world of violence and corruption without contrast or code of moral values does not make for distinction and certainly not for art; such a world may well be considered existentialist, but existentialism is at least based on a philosophy and I would sooner read Albert Camus than see Alan Ladd booted once more in the boko.

The two best films I have left to the last: they are too well known (I hope) to be discussed at length; I refer to *The Lost Weekend* and *The Southerner*. These, too, are films of violence, but in one the violence is spiritual and in the other political and social: these qualities at once place them on a different plane. Don Birnam in *The Weekend* is driving himself mad with drink; the family in *The Southerner* are being driven mad by their environment and by catastrophes of nature which they attribute, humbly, to God's will.

Birnam has no talent; no amount of persuasion on the part of the director or his girlfriend in the film will persuade me that he has any; he can't write, so he seeks illusion in soaking it up instead: his proposed regeneration at the end doesn't convince me either, any more than I believe that the Southern family will build up their life again after the flood and the final disaster; but at any rate a ray of hope has been shown and the optimism of man asserted itself: an optimism surely less foolish than that which presupposes that the possession of Lucille Ball or Veronica Lake will make the world we live in any less violent, treacherous and cruel.

Griffith, Stroheim and
the Decline of Realism

*　　　　*　　　　*

IT CANNOT BE STATED TOO OFTEN THAT WE OWE THE WHOLE concept of the modern cinema to one man alone: David Wark Griffith, as no maker, critic or student of motion pictures would deny. With the possible exception of the mobile camera (said by Professor Siegfried Kracauer to have been conceived, originally, by the script-writer Carl Mayer), all technical innovations can be traced back to him: the close-up; the fade and the dissolve as means of visual transition from scene to scene; and, perhaps even more important, the art of constructive editing (later known as montage): the swift juxtaposition of one shot to another contrasted or associated image, for the purpose of arousing an appropriate emotional reaction from the audience.

It is true – as Sergei Eisenstein pointed out in a magnificent essay – that this latter technique had already been used in a literary form by Charles Dickens (possibly the most 'cinematic' of stylists, though – apart from David Lean's versions of *Great Expectations* and *Oliver Twist* – this quality is conspicuously lacking in screen adaptations of his work). Not only was Griffith a great admirer of Dickens, but he began directing films at a period on which the new school of American naturalistic writers had left an indelible mark; one of these, Frank Norris, had also employed the method of ironic contrast, intercutting the death of a destitute widow from starvation with descriptions of the sumptuous dinner given by a railroad king obliquely responsible for her condition, and a strikingly similar comparison occurs – between unemployed workers unable to afford bread and a rich speculator's banquet – in one of Griffith's earliest films, *A Corner in Wheat* (1909), which must have originated from a short story by Norris bearing an almost identical title.

So the tradition of realism in films was born; and though Griffith is better known for his spectacular masterpieces *The Birth of a Nation* and *Intolerance* (which set a standard of screen narrative by cross-cutting and contrapuntal action never since surpassed), he was to return again and again to the examination of those social, moral and industrial problems that continued to preoccupy him long after Hollywood escapism had condemned such themes as certain of failure at the box-office: one of his last pictures, *The Struggle*, made in 1931, was based on a play of Émile Zola's about alcoholism.

But if Griffith's ideas were derived primarily from literary sources, he translated them entirely into visual terms. By introducing the flashback as a fluid link between past and present, close-ups of various sizes to illustrate his characters' thoughts and emotions, and adopting a two-camera and quadruple-set technique not dissimilar from that used in television today, he broke boldly away from the theatrical conventions in which he had been trained: unlike those contemporary producers and directors who are content to interpret the events in some dull bestseller without imaginative alteration or to film a successful stage-play exactly as it stands.

Erich von Stroheim, Griffith's pupil, continued in the naturalistic mode (indeed, his passion for authenticity of background detail finally came to border on the fanatical), but his psychological approach to the screen medium was markedly different and individualist to a degree. In many ways he is perhaps the purer artist of the two: lacking Griffith's lyrical sense, and the tenderness that occasionally degenerated into bathos, sentimentality and melodrama, his own brand of poetry was at once more sensual and more severely classical – his pity, like a surgeon's, subjected to such iron control that it was often mistaken for mere clinical curiosity by those too fastidious spirits who were repelled by his flat refusal to show disgust or anger, shed glycerine tears for the suffering, or diverge in any way from the rigid objectivity imposed upon him by the tenets of his artistic creed. (When he permits himself to do so, the result is regrettable; the one flaw in an otherwise impeccably balanced production, *Foolish Wives*, is the scene where the frustrated chambermaid throws herself, after much indecisive posturing, from the cliff-top into the moonlit sea. Her abject jealous misery has been previously, and poignantly, conveyed by the camera's slow track in to close-up of her anguished face framed by an iron bedstead, whose bars symbolise the prison of self from which there is no escape: since, after this, her last desperate act is unnecessary and out of keeping with the general mood of the picture, it arouses only an embarrassed snigger which has nothing to do with the acting conventions of the time.)

Griffith had a strong puritan streak and a burning desire for reform; Stroheim (certainly not devoid of moral values, since his first two films could be described as parables of original sin) was not directly inspired by the wish to expose any particular social evil, but rather to present an overall prospect of human corruption: his protagonists are either beyond redemption when we come upon them or the dry rot has already set in below the surface, the decay is spreading out of sight. Criticism of the established order was implied, never explicit, in his work: the camera-lens supplied the only comment, reflecting not only the tarnished outer shell of life but, like an X-ray photograph, the corrosion within: it was up to the audience to voice an indignant protest against the system that allowed such insanitary conditions to prevail.

It was in their respective attitudes towards sex, however, that Stroheim, as a director, differed most from his master: the love-interest in Griffith's films, usually tormented and tragic, was spiritually pure; though the heroines might err, it was always through an excess of their innocent trust in mankind: there was more than a touch of Drury Lane in his apotheosis of the Dickensian ideal, for ever epitomised by the appealing fragility and wistful vacant loveliness of Lillian Gish. Stroheim, in direct contrast, treated sex as a powerful motivating force; he pictured women as frail in the Shakespearian sense: lunar creatures whose secret inner ferment mounted with the fluxional tides (hence, perhaps, the symbolic moonlight flooding of so many of his 'romantic' scenes); avid for carnal pleasure beneath a superficial coolness and decorum; the natural prey of any specious seducer willing to provide release from their repressions.

Woman, then, became the eternal Eve in a paradise already lost, where the serpent's iridescent scales were replaced by immaculate uniform and the tempter wore the arrogant Prussian mask (schooled to a cold impassivity matching his style of direction) that Stroheim as a former officer of the Palace Guard could assume at will: only by an occasional sardonic twitch of the muscles round the mouth, a derisive gleam faintly perceptible behind the vitreous stare of his monocled eye, did he betray his delight in these uninhibited exposés of a type which he, the aristocratic Viennese evidently looked upon with fascinated loathing. To his series of roles in this genre, he added a psychological depth of impudent depravity which no actor impersonating a member of the German military caste during the 1914 war has ever achieved, and which countless imitators have not yet equalled: it was the measure of his histrionic skill that, as the Man You Love to Hate, he came to be identified in the public mind with the parts he acted rather than the films he made.

The culmination of Stroheim's first period was foreshadowed in his two previous pictures, *Blind Husbands* and *The Devil's Pass-key* (1918 and 1919 respectively). These were films of moderate length, made within a reasonable budget, and their resounding commercial success resulted in the director being given the latitude to embark upon a vaster and more ambitious project: a restatement and summing up of the paradisiacal theme in which the 'garden eastward of Eden' was represented by Monte Carlo during the post-war inflationary years and the snake in the grass was not this time a Teuton but an international spiv of Slavonic origin posing as a Russian prince.

Foolish Wives (1920–21) was originally intended to run for twenty-one reels (eight reels longer than *Intolerance* itself) and to be shown in two parts: though, owing to the unwarranted interference of Universal Pictures' executives, the released version was eventually cut to almost half its initial length. Stroheim, who not only wrote the story and screenplay, directed the picture and enacted the principal role, but also designed the sets in conjunction with Richard Day, spent nearly a year in production; meanwhile the rising cost, which the Publicity Department proudly assessed as totalling a million dollars, was proclaimed on the Great White Way by an enormous electric sign that spelt the director's name $troheim.[1] His insistence on absolute verisimilitude – triumphantly justified in the outcome, since we seem at times to be watching a documentary of Monte Carlo rather than a studio-reconstruction of the city – caused him to erect an exact facsimile of part of the Casino's façade; and in doing so he might have been building his own memorial:

---

1 The author is indebted to Lotte Eisner's informative and carefully documented essays for these and other details of this director's early career, and also to the British Film Institute for supplying copies of programme notes to the recent season of Stroheim films shown at the National Film Theatre, in which Mme Eisner's essays were reprinted.

for the legend of his extravagance – fostered at first, for advertisement's sake, by those who were later to turn it against him – threw a long shadow which came to eclipse, in the eyes of parsimonious producers, the stature of his achievement. (By a stroke of irony which he must appreciate, the prodigal expenditure that earned him such disapprobation was perpetuated, and even exceeded, by Hollywood mediocrities of the same type from which his detractors were drawn; today, far more lavish sums are squandered on so-called 'epics' which, once seen, are forthwith forgotten.)

Despite its popularity in Europe, the transatlantic reception of *Foolish Wives* could have done little to diminish Stroheim's growing unpopularity with his financial backers: a flanking attack by a female federation, outraged protests from puritanical critics, demands for drastic censorship, and severe moral strictures were now added to the accusations of heedless improvidence, and a break with Universal Pictures duly followed. None the less, it must be said in all fairness that no policy of retrenchment seems to have been insisted upon by Metro-Goldwyn-Mayer, the producers of *Greed* (1923): though here again the finished product (almost five hours of screen-time and longer than *Birth of a Nation*) was whittled down by more than half for public release.

Here the sophisticated continental backgrounds and sumptuous interiors were abandoned for the unremitting squalor of the San Francisco slums and the arid immensity of the Californian wastes, where the protagonist (a moronic dentist of massive build and dubious qualifications, who has become infected, through extreme economic pressure, with the avarice to which his wife has already succumbed) eventually dies, handcuffed to his enemy under the implacable sun; the actual cost of production must have been enormous, for none of the scenes – not even the closing sequences in Death Valley itself – were shot in the studio, and the difficulties attendant as a result (the problem of adequate interior lighting, for one) may readily be imagined.

Frank Norris's novel, *McTeague*, from which Stroheim's script is adapted, was published in 1898; and the director, with almost obsessional care and patience, recreated scrupulously both the period atmosphere and the appropriate décor, running the complete gamut of poverty, from the stuffily overcrowded, shabby-genteel apartment shared by the couple during their early married life, to the cumulatively sordid dilapidation of later years: the soiled, tumbled sheets, the warped, dusty furniture and broken crockery, the hoarded gold under the bed. (Those who commented recently, in the daily press, on the lack of 'style' in Stroheim's films, should have observed more closely the careful composition of the separate shots, and the use of extraneous detail as a frame against which the inner tension of the characters might be projected in higher relief; just as those who have sometimes censured him for lack of feeling should have listened to his moving tribute to D.W. Griffith, broadcast after the great director's death.)

Seeing these pictures today, even in their truncated form, one is primarily struck by their perennial freshness of subject-matter and psychological approach; secondly, by the intensely visual quality of their presentation. Here, still surviving in an age of redundant dialogue and, worse still, explanatory narratage, are stories really told in pictures; the subtitles are few, employed mainly for the introduction of new characters and to interpret situations arising from the dictates of plot, where a few lines suffice (one is reminded of an early Chaplin comedy, *The Count*, where the entire motivation is conveyed by a single title): yet the most obtuse member of the audience could not fail to catch up, though it is true that much of our ability to understand is due, in *Foolish Wives*, to Stroheim's masterly performance as the spurious prince (the stiff, 'correct' military bow and unsmiling gallantry for public occasions; the sly, insidious smile and the sudden ribald grin, superbly indicative of his true nature as he relaxes in bathrobe on the terrace or contemptuously pockets the savings extorted from the pathetic, deluded chambermaid). One cannot avoid a twinge of admiration for his effrontery and resourceful cunning; yet he is never portrayed as other than entirely contemptible: a pimp, a pervert, and a coward – trapped in a fire, he leaps to safety first, abandoning the pregnant American wife to her fate on the burning balcony; knocked down by her outraged husband, he threatens a duel but sets out, instead, to seduce the beautiful, vacuous daughter of an old Italian artist who supplies him with forged banknotes as a means of support. (The counterfeit *motif* is constantly repeated in this caustic appraisal of a capitalist Eden, where the apples on the tree of knowledge have turned sour and lie, as rotting windfalls, on the ground: even the hair of the 'princes's' female accomplices proves to be false, and they wrench off each others' wigs when arrested by the police.)

The penultimate scenes of *Foolish Wives* suffer most from their mutilation in the studio: the murder of the prince, when surprised in his attempted rape by the counterfeiter, is deleted altogether, and the sight of the old man carefully inserting a shrouded corpse down a manhole comes as a too-abrupt shock in consequence; the film ends at this point, and we are not allowed to see, as Stroheim intended, the body of Karamzin floating out on a tide of scum and refuse accumulated in the bowels of the corrupt city.

The powerful impact of *Greed*, on the other hand, remains unimpaired; much though we deplore the fact that the original is denied us, one cannot help feeling, also, that the deletion of the allegorical subplot, for instance, may have heightened the tempo and allowed a greater concentration on the central situation: perhaps the circumstance that Rex Ingram (who in his own productions showed some sympathy with Stroheim's aims) was part responsible for the invidious labour of cutting explains the basic symmetry of the edited version. In one important instance only is there obvious evidence of something missing: the transformation of McTeague's friend Marcus (admirably played by Jean Hersholt) from a comic but good-hearted vulgarian to a sullen, malicious enemy appears too abrupt, and the apparent motivation (his envy of Mac for marrying Trina after she has won the lottery) seems insufficient, for we are given no previous indication that Marcus has been affected by the prevailing acquisitiveness of the general atmosphere.

Stroheim has declared that he considers *Greed* as his 'one real picture'; certainly it must be acclaimed his masterpiece. He does not appear in the film himself; but, though his direction is at its most impersonal and objective, the controlling force of his personality can be felt throughout: from the timorous courtship in the dental parlour to the egregious embarrassments of the wedding day (the ceremony interrupted by the passing of a funeral cortège outside, to symbolise the doom that lies ahead of the unhappy pair); through the middle sequences of increasing disintegration to the murder of Trina by McTeague and the final tragic irony beneath the incandescent desert sun, he exercises an authority over production and performance that extracts every shade of meaning implicit in the theme.

Since then, his pictures became mainly sardonic variations on the Cophetua legend (*The Merry Widow, The Wedding March*), culminating in the incomplete, ornately expressionist *Queen Kelly* (1928), which was 'swept off the floor,' Lotte Eisner tells us, by the advent of sound and the release of *The Jazz Singer*. Although always remarkable as cinema (*The Wedding March* being particularly notable for Stroheim's interpretation of one of his favourite roles), these later films never attained to the lonely eminence of *Greed*, which remains a solitary landmark in the history of cinematic realism, its influence manifest chiefly on the continent, where Jean Renoir, for one, has admitted his debt to Stroheim as Eisenstein, Pudovkin and René Clair have acknowledged theirs to Griffith.

Who, in America today, are the heirs to the tradition? John Huston (*Treasure of the Sierra Madre*, *The Asphalt Jungle*, *Red Badge of Courage*); or Billy Wilder (*The Lost Weekend*, *Ace in the Hole*, *Sunset Boulevard* – in which Stroheim himself played opposite Gloria Swanson in a situation which might have arisen from the abortive production of *Queen Kelly*)? The nearest candidate, of course, would be Orson Welles, whose *Citizen Kane* and *Magnificent Ambersons* surely owed much, in their grandiose composition and meticulous devotion to detail, to the Stroheim example. Yet it seems unlikely that, owing to circumstances not dissimilar from those responsible for the long silence of his predecessor, Welles will be able to make a realistic film again; there has been a marked abandonment, also, by European directors, of the naturalist genre: Italy, after a succession of splendid pictures, seems about to compromise with the Wardour Street slogan of Breasts and Bullets, with the French (Clouzot apart) appearing to follow suit.

Griffith and Eisenstein are dead; Welles, and Stroheim himself, immobilised; with the encroachment of television, 3D, Cinemascope and similar innovations (entailing inevitably a flood of photographed plays, outdoor and biblical spectacle), it may be that the realistic mode is not only headed for a decline: but is, indeed, already dying.

Story-telling and the Screen

*　　　*　　　*

IS THE DANGER GREATER TODAY THAN IT WAS IN THE PAST THAT direct forms of story-telling – such as realistic fiction, the novel of action and pursuit, the detective or mystery thriller – will eventually be superseded by the cinema?

Before any attempt can be made to answer this question, a number of current trends must first be considered, the connection between modern story-telling and the film itself traced, and the relationship between the film industry and the writer examined, among many other things.

What is now known as 'cinematic' prose – though increasingly developed during the past twenty-five years – is in itself nothing new: novelists with a strong visual sense have always existed. The great Russian director Eisenstein, in his book *Film Form*, has, by 'breaking down' into separate shots a dinner-party from *Dombey and Son*, shown how closely Dickens's technique resembled that of the screen-writer; the opening passages of *Bleak House* are a supreme evocation of atmosphere which no contemporary scenarist could equal: yet – with the exception of David Lean's brilliantly directed *Great Expectations* and *Oliver Twist* – Dickens, largely owing to the multiplicity of characters, the three-volume-novel length, and the complex melodramatic nature of his plots, does not translate successfully to the screen. The same applies to Dostoevsky, as demonstrated by the recent American version of *The Brothers Karamazov*: the story of a film, to be satisfactory, must consist of a single unbroken curve in which sub-plots involving extra characters should have no part.

Paradoxically, however, the medium – consisting as it must of short vivid scenes, each carrying the action a stage farther – is of its nature episodic; and this influence, with its attendant added speed and economy of detail, was strongly apparent in the work of progressive writers everywhere during the 1920s and 1930s, and on their successors ever since. In this country, notable examples of the trend were Graham Greene, Evelyn Waugh and Arthur Calder-Marshall (whose early novel *About Levy* was a perfect example of filmic construction, and might actually be filmed one day soon, now that the evil of anti-Semitism is no longer a theme forbidden by the front office). And it was Graham Greene who first, influenced by John Buchan and the pursuit films of Fritz Lang and Alfred Hitchcock, devised the swift-moving series of 'Entertainments', with realistic characters and seedy everyday settings, from which so much of contemporary fiction derives.

These books were not written with one eye on the studios – indeed the screen-versions of at least two, adapted by Hollywood writers, do them less than justice – but nevertheless they were eagerly bought up by American companies, and thus opened the possibility of a new and profitable vein to novelists unequipped with either Mr Greene's talent or his ability to comment obliquely on the social scene and the human condition through the channels of an ostensible thriller. The similar success, in a different sphere, of Eric Ambler, whose novels of intrigue and espionage, with cosmopolitan backgrounds and a sardonic, disabused approach resembling that of Somerset Maugham in his 'Ashenden' stories, resulted also in a spate of imitations concerned with conscientiously unheroic heroes pursued by obese and perfidious villains through the purlieus of some polyglot city: the international situation helped to uphold this concept of the Hunted Man as a symbol of the times.

A school of writers gradually emerged, the members of which travel assiduously in search of new exotic backgrounds with cinematic possibilities, return after a six months' sojourn with copious documentation on local customs and a mass of descriptive detail; then proceed to graft on to their expanded notes a confected thriller plot, complete with flat celluloid characters whom any competent actor can portray when the completed novel is, inevitably, sold for a vast sum (sometimes before publication) to MGM or RKO. The heroes have become increasingly American or Canadian, since Anglo-American distribution demands the presence of a transatlantic male star, and the United States book market must also be taken into account; the heroine is invariably foreign, with a pretty line in Hemingwayesque pidgin-English, owing to the preponderance of continental starlets whose sex attractions outweigh their ability to act.

No one could possibly grudge these authors the rewards of their beaver-like industry, and their literary style is often an advance on that of their pre-1940 equivalents: the amazing thing is that they are often taken quite seriously by the critics, and advertised with overt reverence by their publishers – though this is more natural, since their sales represent a considerable turnover, plus a comfortable percentage of the film rights and a further profit on cheap paperback reprints when each screen version is exhibited. (The evident popularity of these 'Books of the Film'– often with a changed title to accord with that of the motion picture, and showing a 'still' of the principal stars in some provocative position on the cover – seems to argue that the sales of a novel are actually increased by its translation to the screen, rather than the reverse.)

Writers of this type, whose main concern is to turn out material which can be sold in book form to the films, are occasionally employed by producers to adapt other people's novels, but – unlike Mr Greene and Mr Ambler – have no desire to write directly for the screen; the danger which they represent, with regard to the cinema superseding the novel, is therefore minimal: indeed, they form bulwarks against it, for the public will continue to buy their books or borrow them from lending libraries until they either run out of new backgrounds and stock situations or are replaced by a younger generation of writers specialising in 'adventure stories with a strong love interest'.

Before the recent war, poets and university dons had already turned to writing detective stories as a sideline, but these were rarely, if ever, filmed; for the detective story proper is not ideal screen material: there are too many penultimate explanations to be gone into and, as a film-producer once explained to me, audiences are unwilling to wait ninety minutes for a final elucidation which may cause them to miss the last bus home. The detective story is for the winter fireside, the beach in summer, the railway journey and the tube train, and will continue to flourish and fulfil its function; but since the dons and the poets raised its literary standard, the line of demarcation between crime, fiction and the 'straight' novel became perceptibly fainter, while the war itself was responsible for the rest.

Fear of sudden death, the escaped prisoner, the spy, the saboteur and the secret traitor: all the commonplaces of the pre-Nazi 'shocker' became for a few hectic years the stuff of everyday life. 'The world,' as Graham Greene put it, ' had been re-made by William Le Queux'; the uneasy peace and the Cold War gave us missing diplomats, kidnapped and absconding scientists, the 'agents of a Foreign Power' exchanging passwords outside the British Museum; and in the background one felt the lurking presence of 'great extra-social intelligences': something perilously reminiscent of Buchan's *Power House* had come to pass.

The reflection of all this on fiction was not slow to take effect: sensational elements began to infiltrate like fifth-columnists into the work of serious novelists who otherwise would never have permitted an enemy agent, psychopathic criminal, or death by violence to enter their cosmos; George Orwell, who analysed so brilliantly the appeal of *Raffles* and *No Orchids for Miss Blandish*, himself presented his terrible vision of a totalitarian future in the basic terms of the boys' magazine – the secret-policeman masquerading as a sympathetic figure, the cage of rats which I read about in *Pluck* or *The Rocket* at the age of eleven – and it is significant that *Nineteen Eighty-Four* has proved to be the most popular of all his books.

'Has the pace and excitement of a thriller' soon began to figure as a phrase of commendation in critical weeklies and publishers' advertisements: film-studio executives sat up and took notice of the work of writers whom they had previously dismissed as unfilmable. But the Hunted Man has almost had his run: not Pursuit but Suspense is the current watchword. A magazine of this title – containing 'stories that will astound you by their ingenuity, thrill you by their pace, chill you with their horror' – is about to appear as I write, and an announcement in the autumn *Bookseller* of a first novel is fairly typical of the present situation: 'essentially a novel of suspense but far more than a thriller.'

Another full-page advertisement describes 'a CERTAIN seller...a really *superb* novel of suspense', written in collaboration by the TV playwright Arthur Hailey, who specialises in unexploded bombs, air-crews overcome by food poisoning in mid-flight, and other quasi-natural phenomena ('Ten foreign book-rights under option, six months before publication'). The novel in question is adapted from a recent success of Hailey's on the small screen, and, needless to add, a film version is already being prepared.

The evolution of this particular type of suspense-story – dispensing entirely with villains or any human agency to generate the required tension – may be traced from Nigel Balchin's *The Small Back Room* and Nevil Shute's *No Highway*, and is usually full of scientific or engineering detail: thus satisfying the man-in-the-street's newly awakened interest in such matters. The other most popular type derives from Conrad's *Victory*, through *The Petrified Forest*, to present-day examples like Joseph Hayes's *Desperate Hours* and the film (identical in theme) *The Night Holds Terror*: a gang of bandits and/or escaped convicts – almost always three in number and including a sub-human psychopath – terrorises a family of ordinary citizens, sometimes until dawn, sometimes for several days, after which the male members of the household succeed in defeating and routing the gangsters with or without the assistance of the police. The deeply satisfying appeal of this last theme to a mass audience may readily be seen: it both gratifies the vanity of the average members, who identify themselves with the beleaguered family and imagine how they too would cope successfully with such a situation, and reaffirms the triumph of the normal over the abnormal – the encroaching menace of the dark has once more been shut out, and the audience can safely return home to read about the hydrogen bomb in comfort over a final cup of tea.

Variations of such themes are not, however, inexhaustible; and I would predict a return, shortly, to the gothic tale of terror and *The Exploits of Elaine*: a modern and more sophisticated version of the pure-hearted heroine persecuted by a latter-day adaptation of the Clutching Hand; these trends go in cycles and the wheel must come full circle.

The foregoing tends to show that the cinema will never supersede the direct forms of story-telling so long as the screen derives its material from the novel (an alternative source is, of course, the stage; and any moderately successful play can be sure of being bought up by the films, in spite of the fact that an enclosed setting is intractable to a medium which, by its very essence, relies upon movement). Producers, not unnaturally, are mistrustful of subjects and stories which have not already proved acceptable to large numbers of people; it is simpler to buy a bestseller than to assess the probable value of an original script, and such submissions receive short shrift from the readers employed by film companies; all of whom doubtless feel they could do better themselves, and earn large fees by so doing in their spare time.

Besides, writers prepared to devote themselves to writing specifi-cally for the screen and to risk the terrible setbacks and disappointments attendant upon such a career are extremely rare. Moreover, their efforts are discouraged from the outset unless they come from within the industry itself. They may at best be signed on to adapt a war novel or write additional dialogue for some record-breaking play; or, perhaps, achieve a successful collaboration with a good director, as happened between Graham Greene and Carol Reed: which, to a writer whose real medium is the film, would be as disheartening as if a novelist were to hand the outline of a novel to his publisher and then watch him doing the creative work.

How many genuine screenwriters have achieved any success in this country? T.E.B. Clarke, William Rose, Launder and Gilliat: there is no English equivalent to the German Carl Mayer, part-author of *The Cabinet of Dr Caligari*, who is said to have been responsible for the moving-camera and whose scripts could be put on the screen exactly as they were written. Dylan Thomas's *The Doctor and the Devils* remains unfilmed; Eric Ambler ventured once into independent production and relapsed into adaptations of naval or maritime subjects, following his screenplay of *The Cruel Sea*; since *The Fallen Idol* and *The Third Man*, Graham Greene wrote one original story, *The Stranger's Hand*, which combined elements of both the previous films, followed by adaptations of *Saint Joan* and, it is rumoured, *South Wind*. Until a writer, such as the American Paddy Chayefsky, arises who is permitted – and able – to write and control the production of his own pictures, there is little danger of the novel being superseded by the film.

ESSAYS ON LITERATURE
AND BOOK REVIEWS

A Poet of Fear
(Henry Green)

* * *

LIKE MISS I. COMPTON-BURNETT, ONE OF THE FEW MODERN novelists with whom his work may be compared, Mr Henry Green tells his stories mainly in dialogue, which, though in his case brilliantly colloquial, is yet as formalised as Mr Ronald Firbank's; he uses as a rule a restricted setting: the fog-bound railway station in *Party Going*, the Irish castle in *Loving*, the great estate and its grounds in his latest novel, *Concluding*. His plots also, though lacking the off-stage melo-drama of Miss Compton-Burnett's, usually turn upon a series of misunderstandings worthy of a Victorian novelist: the characters, even in the most casual conversations, are constantly at cross-purposes, and *Concluding* is no exception to this rule.

Here the cross-purposes are aggravated more than ever owing to the fact that old Mr Rock, the principal figure, is deaf and apparently scorns to employ the aid of an ear-trumpet. The action is limited to twenty-four hours of a summer's day and takes place in a nebulous future, when this country is controlled by a State bureaucracy: whether Fascist or Democratic is not specified. Mr Rock, nearing his seventy-sixth birthday, is a State pensioner, living in constant fear of losing the cottage allotted to him, for past services, on the edge of a country estate now used as a training ground for future female civil servants. He is a sort of scientific GBS, referred to from time to time as 'the sage', though his status does not become immediately apparent because of the classless conversational idiom which he employs, in common with most of the other characters. His affections are divided between Ted, his goose, Daisy, his pig, and his granddaughter Elizabeth, who, after a nervous breakdown at work, is at the age of thirty-five carrying on a clandestine and passionate affair with an ineffectual young tutor named Sebastian Birt.

Mr Rock's day is passed fetching swill for his pig, bran for his goose and cadging his breakfast from the cook: meanwhile, at the great house, preparations are being made for the annual Founders' Day Ball, while one of the two principals, Miss Edge, intrigues for the eviction of Mr Rock, in whose cottage she wishes to house a new furnace-man. At the same time no open move can be made in this direction because of the belief that Mr Rock's word carries weight with the Secretary of State. The day begins ominously with an anonymous letter accusing one of the staff – or possibly Mr Rock – of 'furnication'; this is followed by the discovery that two of the girl pupils, Mary and Merode, are missing. Later Merode is found, unharmed but in torn pyjamas, by Elizabeth and Sebastian while they are kissing in the thicket. The absentee faints under questioning and refuses to talk, but a sinister construction is placed upon her absence by the spinster principals; an aunt is summoned and kicks up a row; suspicion is shared between Mr Rock and the forester, Adams; the misunderstandings multiply.

When, during the afternoon, Mary's doll, painted as a crude replica of herself, is found 'embowelled' on a pyre of azaleas, the stage seems set for drama: all the more since the book is divided into three parts, like the acts of a play. But in the end nothing happens: though one of the girls, a minx named Moira, does her best to complicate matters, all the conflicts remain unresolved: the missing Mary is never found, nor are we at any time made aware of her exact whereabouts; the engagement of Elizabeth and Sebastian is not announced at the dance, and Mr Rock's fate remains in doubt, though he triumphs over his enemy Miss Edge during a conversation, while she is drugged by cigarettes, which affect her like opium.[1] Nor, as might be expected, does the old man die; for in the last line, after a long and – to him – satisfactory day, he falls asleep 'almost at once'.

The purpose of the novel, therefore, must remain obscure: it might be intended as a study in anti-climax or a sophisticated fairy-tale; one remembers in this connection the beginning and ending of Mr Green's previous novel *Loving*; here, in *Concluding*, there are touches both of *Cinderella* and of *The Girl's Friend Library*. The main interest of the book, to a student of Mr Green's work, is the meticulous care which the author has expended upon its construction, and the stylistic advance which he has made since the publication, in 1929, of his second novel,

---

1 Henry Green, *Concluding, Living*, Hogarth Press.

Living. For it is principally his qualities as technician and stylist which, in a decade of undistinguished prose, make this writer remarkable.

Living, set in and around a Birmingham factory, was conceived before the proletarian school of writers came into being and such subject-matter became fashionable. Unlike its successors, it never sank to the dead level of documentary; its prose was harsh, clipped and curt, omitting for the most part the definite article, and achieving on occasion an effect of biblical poetry. The complicated plot-mechanism which Mr Green later adopted (incest by accident in *Caught*; resemblance between half-sisters in *Back*) was also absent from his early work, as it was in *Party Going*, which did not appear until ten years afterwards; in this latter book, and in the autobiography *Pack My Bag*, which followed almost immediately, the prose-rhythms owed something, perhaps, to Proust and something, in the sparseness of the punctuation, to Gertrude Stein:

> The court was out at the back by stables which were built round three yards, brick buildings over cobblestones the colour in sunlight of dried seaweed on white marble with the smell so like but not the same as when under a hot sun the small wind blows inland the bite of season a temple grown over and uncovered at low tide.

Doughty too may have been a formative influence; Mr Green's one critical article was in praise of Arabia Deserta, and the following passage describing a mare might almost have been written by him: 'Never combed by her rude master, but all shining beautiful and gentle of herself, she seemed a darling life upon this savage soil not worthy of her gracious pasterns.'

These rhythms have since evolved, in the descriptive passages of *Concluding*, to a style which carries the visual clarity of a beautifully shot film:

> A world through which the young man and his girl had been meandering, in dreaming shade through which sticks of sunlight slanted to spill upon the ground, had at this point been struck to a blaze, and where their way had been dim, on a sea bed past grave trunks, was now this dying, brilliant mass which lay exposed, a hidden world of spiders working on its gold, the webs they made a field of wheels and spokes of wet silver.

If the above excerpt is compared with one from *Living* –

> Water dripped from tap on wall into basin and into water
> there. Sun. Water drops made rings in clear coloured water.
> Sun in there shook on the walls and ceiling. As rings went out
> trembling over the water shadows of light from sun in these
> trembled on walls

– some idea of the distance covered by Mr Green in nineteen years will have been conveyed; yet in both cases style is perfectly adjusted to subject and environment: for with Mr Green, as with Doughty, the style 'is the book', and an examination of his material seems inseparable from a discussion of his technical equipment.

An echo of hangover from *Living* may be detected in the opening sentence of *Party Going*, where the author's preoccupation with pigeons (as, perhaps, a symbol of flight) re-asserts itself. Indeed, the cumulative effect of this novel (dated 1931–38) is oddly symbolical, but here the pigeon is a dead one and the story concerns a party of rich silly young people beleaguered by fog in a railway terminus; the yelling horde which besieges the station hotel from below might be taken, it has been suggested, as an allegory of some proletarian uprising – say, the general strike. The writing, appropriately, sounds a muffled note throughout, which is entirely absent from *Caught*, Mr Green's novel of the AFS, and one of the most convincing descriptions of service life published during the war.

Caught begins with a page of Defoe-like narrative simplicity; the rhythms later become richer, but with no confusing effect: the only occasional confusion arises from the manner in which the story is told, moving arbitrarily backwards and forwards in time. Like *Living*, it is not content to be a documentary masquerading as fiction, but deals primarily with human relationships: between Pye, the fire-station officer, and his mad sister; between Richard Roe, the educated Auxiliary, and his small son Christopher. The title, like most of Mr Green's, means exactly what it says: the characters are inextricably trapped: by their own emotions, by sex, by service regulations, by the war itself. One critic has already described this novel as Kafka in a naturalistic setting: a comment true of nearly all the author's books, for Mr Green is a poet of the persecution complex. His protagonists live in terror: the workers of losing their jobs, the rich of losing their money; Pye is afraid of losing his pension, Charley Summers is afraid of the sack, Mr Rock is afraid for his grand-daughter's sanity: the minor characters are sycophants madly currying favour and intriguing for position (Piper in *Caught*, Tupe in *Living*), while all are mortally afraid of the organisations with initials and the red tape that rings them round.

These fears are combined with a fanatical worship of ritual and power: Raunce, the Butler in *Loving*, is a stickler for the conventions and a despot in his own domain, while Craigan in *Living* is a bigger autocrat at home than Mr Bridges, the manager, at the works. It must not be thought, however, that Mr Green presents an unsympathetic picture of the proletariat: on the contrary, it is the upper-class characters against whom the scales are heavily weighted. These are invariably portrayed as vague, moronic, well-meaning but without purpose: in *Loving* they are reduced to the status of the 'lower orders' in a 'society' novel, cursorily sketched in to provide exasperation and comic relief by their monstrous blunders and aimless attitude to life in general, so completely does the author ally himself with the domestic servants who are in this case his main characters and with whose fate the book is bound up. *Loving* is, in fact, a survey of the servant problem from below stairs; it is also the book which invited most of all the initial comparison with the work of Miss Compton-Burnett, partly because of its high merits as a conversation piece and partly because of the setting of Miss Compton-Burnett's hierarchical households, though the hierarchy here is that of the servants' hall.

Turning to *Pack My Bag* (subtitled 'A self-portrait') in an attempt to discover what motives prompted Mr Green to take up his stance as a novelist in the class struggle, on the other side of the fence a not unfamiliar early background emerges: country house, private school, public school, university etc: later, hunt balls and holidays abroad play their appointed parts. The author cannot resist a typical English temptation to make himself out, modestly, a bit of a muff; nor was he by any means free from the obsessions common to writers of his generation: belief that an outbreak of war meant annihilation for all concerned, and himself in particular; that life at a public school constitutes a microcosm of the world at large; and sense of guilt towards the working class: at the time of the general strike he found himself 'unable to look a labourer in the eye'. But there emerges also one important difference between Mr Green and those of his contemporaries who were tortured by the same guilt-complex: he joined no party of the left as a solution, but went to work in his father's factory instead.

'That is to say that I lived in lodgings, worked a forty-eight-hour week first in the stores, then as a patternmaker, then in the ironfoundry, in the brassfoundry and finally as a coppersmith, and wrote at night.'

It was the first-hand experience gained in this way which made *Living* so authentic in its detail, and it is possibly Mr Green's non-political standpoint that enables him to continue writing when so many others who adopted a partisan attitude have, consequent upon a loss of faith, been led to a scorpion's suicide of their talent. Certainly his work has been refreshingly free of the tormented young intellectual characters who recurred *ad nauseam* in the 'politically conscious' novels of the thirties and are now being resurrected by contemporary French writers such as Jean-Paul Sartre and Simone de Beauvoir. Possible projections of himself are Dick Dupret in *Living* and Richard Roe in *Caught*: but even so they are not figures idealised in a mood of self-pity, and Dick Dupret, the factory-owner's son, while in a way progressive and alive to conditions prevailing among the workers, is presented as being otherwise actively silly, and unable even to conduct a successful love affair.

Nor does the class conflict, as such, figure in any of Mr Green's novels, and for this omission he has, in the past, been censured by some critics of the left. Even these critics, however, could hardly fail to deny that few social questions of the day have been neglected by him as subject-matter: *Back*, for example, deals with the rehabilitation of a returned soldier who has lost a leg in the war. This, incidentally, is the only book of his to be set in specifically lower-middle-class surroundings; and in the portrayal of this most difficult of all *milieux*, he is once again triumphantly successful, though, as we have already stated, the plot is over-complex and might, in the hands of a less skilful author, have conveyed a sense of unreality, however well the setting was depicted.

Again, the liberal use of coincidence employed throughout – for instance, the fact that the woman instrumental in bringing about Mr Grant's initial meeting with Nance's mother should later turn out to be Charley's landlady – does not, oddly enough, detract from the effect of strict realism which the novel makes upon the reader; nor from the evident seriousness of its purpose in describing the impact of an uneasy peace upon a repatriated prisoner. The details of Charley's office routine, the raffish heartiness of Mr Middlewitch, the sententious pronouncements of Mr Grant, the prim indignations of Nance, and the bewilderment of the hero himself: all have the ring of truth; and here Mr Green's skill in rendering dialogue and his accurate ear for idiom are displayed to a high degree.

It is not a matter for regret, however, that the author now shows signs of returning to a simpler story framework, though this leads, in *Concluding*, to a paradoxical inconclusiveness. Nevertheless, though perhaps not his most satisfying book, it is an interesting work from the point of stylistic development alone, and it is to be hoped that its title is not intended to be prophetic, for Mr Green cannot be spared from the present-day literary scene. He may never become widely popular in his own time: it is conceivable that his largest public will exist in that future which, in his latest novel, he so bleakly forecasts.

Story of a Full Life
(Joyce Cary)

*   *   *

MR JOYCE CARY IS AN AUTHOR NOT EASY TO CLASSIFY, FOR THOUGH
few living English novelists could be described as more 'advanced' in
technique and approach to subject-matter, he is not influenced by any
fashionable literary trend: untouched by Kafkan symbolism, existentialism or the cult of the tough: devoid of self-pity, sentimentality, bitterness
or morbidity. His work follows in a peculiarly English tradition, deriving
from Defoe and Fielding, and could, broadly speaking, be catalogued as
picaresque, owing to Mr Cary's predilection for rogues, thieves and
scoundrels (Mister Johnson, Gulley Jimpson, Bonser in his latest novel,
A Fearful Joy); yet he is neither a satirist nor, primarily, a novelist of
manners.

Scenes of the broadest comedy, however, abound, alternating, in most
cases, with the grimmest tragedy; the latter, as a rule, is passed off with a
matter-of-factness unequalled even by Mr Richard Hughes in *High Wind
in Jamaica* or by Mr E.M. Forster in *The Longest Journey*. Here is an
example of his manner in dealing with violent death: the ritual murder of
a child and its mother by witch-doctors, from his first novel, *Aissa Saved*:

> Owule struck off the boy's head with a machete and the blood
> spurted upon the Oke mound. Afterwards Ishe was thrown
> into the river. Owule had not wished to kill Ishe. It was
> necessary to do so only because she had tried to complain to
> the white man and might do so again, and thus bring further
> trouble to the Church of Ifa and Oke. But all who took part in
> the murder of the poor woman felt guilty and ashamed, and
> hated the white man for it.

This extract is typical of his method: death and violence are never
used for sensational or dramatic purposes, though *Aissa Saved* culminates

in a massacre and the book ends with a native girl being eaten alive by ants. Mr Cary's approach is saved, nevertheless, from an accusation of deliberate bareness by his original sense of humour and by the fact that his style is always exactly adapted to scene and subject: the ritual murder is, after all, a recognised local custom in the part of Nigeria which forms the setting of his book, first published in 1932, when the author was already over forty.

Aissa Saved, though short, is like all Mr Cary's novels, packed with incident, crowded with characters and difficult to summarise, since the action springs from psychology rather than from a mechanically contrived plot: local politics and remote official intrigues also play their parts in promoting the final catastrophe, in which most of the characters are killed. Briefly, it could be termed the story of a religious crusade, and Aissa herself, the native girl converted to Christianity, has points of resemblance with Tabitha, the heroine of *A Fearful Joy*: both, for instance, are fanatically devoted to their illegitimate children, and in both cases the father is a blackguard whose frequent and unexpected reappearances on the scene lead to complications and disruption.

Gajere, the father in *Aissa*, rolls his eyes, bares his teeth, beats his breast and gets drunk on beer; he is a primitive version of Bonser, the forerunner of Mister Johnson, just as Mister Johnson was in a sense the forerunner of Gulley Jimpson. He is, moreover, just out of gaol; and when Aissa hears the news of his release she abandons the mission where she had been singing hymns in order to join him, giving as an excuse to herself the forthcoming religious festival in Kolu, her home district, where the pagans are in urgent need of conversion. Most of her fellow Christians follow; the missionaries, Mr and Mrs Carter, follow in turn, to protect their flock from the consequences of this folly. They arrive at an unsuitable moment, when the pagan priests, who have been praying for rain, are looking round for a sacrifice with which to propitiate their gods. Aissa at first defies the witch-doctors, calling upon the people to come to Jesus; but, suddenly catching sight of the grinning Gajere in the crowd, she immediately surrenders once again to the potent spells of sex and strong drink, and deserts her following. Things are beginning to look black for the Christians, and a native child, Tanawe, is dispatched to get help. But the Resident, Bradgate, is intent on building a bridge over the well-nigh impassable Akoko River; when Tanawe reaches him he is knee-deep in its bed, demonstrating to the Emir how the bridge should be constructed ('I want to see the judge.' 'There he is, in the mud.') Meanwhile Aissa, denounced as a Christian witch and changeling, has been torn from her lover's arms and her leg broken by a blow from a cudgel; the ambitious son of the Emir's Waziri, Ali, arrives to save her from being killed, but orders her to be flung into prison. There she lapses into delirium and has visions; later her leg is amputated and she escapes into the bush, but her sufferings and the loss of her baby, who has been kidnapped by the pagans, cause her to renounce Christianity and relapse into mutism and the death-wish. One of the mission boys brings her back, secretly, to the Carters' bungalow; there the missionaries nurse her round to health and she experiences a second conversion. This takes the form of leading another, and more successful, attack on the pagan stronghold; she finds her baby again and slays a witch-doctor with her own hands during a pitched battle; Gajere is also killed trying to defend her after she has renounced him in favour of Jesus. Unfortunately the Christians have by this time, and without guidance from the Carters (Mrs Carter having died as a result of the riots), become confused, and demand that she shall sacrifice her baby to God. Aissa, delirious again and in ecstasy, agrees, and the child is duly murdered – the Christians in turn being butchered by pagan rein-forcements, who leave Aissa to die upon an ant-heap. At the last moment, however, she is comforted by a vision of her child safe in Heaven, and we leave her overjoyed: 'she was helpless with laughter'.

As has been said before, it is impossible to convey the quality of this novel by synopsis: its originality and high spirits; its wisdom and profundity (the doubts, for instance, of the missionary, Mr Carter: 'How could you fight against ambition taking itself for public spirit and egotism pretending to be dependence on God's will? Or even come to grips with greed, lust and selfishness, which could change their very being and appear as industry, love, chastity and thoughtfulness?'); its economical evocation of an unfamiliar scene; its mastery of terse dialogue and narrative pace. Some critics have seemed surprised that this book, on its first publication, should have been almost ignored; but it should be remembered that *Aissa Saved* saw the light during the party-novel period, the days of brittle wit and cynical wisecracks, before the cynics had a change of heart and began themselves to write on religious themes: it was therefore completely out of fashion, and likely to pass unnoticed at a time when the average first novel was devoted to the agonies of undergraduates being sick after Bump Suppers.

Mr Cary's second book, *An American Visitor*, again dealt with the Nigerian scene; but, though considerably longer and more ambitious, it was much less successful in execution; here, however, in the person of Hasluck, the American woman journalist, the dogged, courageous, devoted Cary heroine made her first real appearance ('Her face was broad, her nose small, her chin short and round, her mouth rather big'); these women are seldom beautiful, though they usually possess sex-appeal: Tabitha Baskett is monkey-faced, Judith Coote short-sighted and lame; they rarely escape without being disfigured by protracted pregnancies (Mrs Carter, Amanda in *The Moonlight*), or ravaging fevers (Aissa, Hasluck, Judy in Mr Cary's first three novels). Nor are the men much more glamorised; Gulley Jimpson small and bald and pigeon-breasted, Rackham bow-legged, with a jockey's stoop, Mr Wilcher hopping like a grasshopper, with a 'face like a bad orange'; only the cad, Dick Bonser, is allowed to retain his meretricious good looks until dying of dropsy at an advanced age. It is also part of Mr Cary's austerity campaign to give all his characters, irrespective of their sex, the most outlandish and ugly surnames: Brewsher, Burwash, Coker (twice), besides those already mentioned: Manklow, Dobey, Boole, Sturge, in *A Fearful Joy*.

The third Nigerian novel, *The African Witch*, was Mr Cary's first popular success; it is long, exciting and uneven, with a central theme vaguely reminiscent of *A Passage to India*, but lacking the objectivity and compactness of *Aissa*: the interest is too diffused, the threads too loosely tied. It can be used, however, as a key to the author's later work; almost as a sort of compendium, for it is full of type-figures: Musa and his gang of delinquent native children, for instance, are recast afterwards as the evacuees in *Charley is My Darling*; the Emir and his Waziri reappear, slightly altered, from *Aissa*; Judith is yet another version of Hasluck; Doctor Schlemm, the German-American missionary, has the same difficulties as Mr Carter ('it was difficult not to hate a man who was capable of so much harm and did it all in Christ's name, who was completely self-satisfied in his ignorance').

The four West African novels, therefore, comprise a world as complete and personal as that created by Edgar Wallace in his too-easily dismissed stories of *Sanders of the River*; and there is, perhaps, a touch of Bosambo in the brilliant portrait of Mister Johnson, the half-educated Negro, with his ingenuous arrogance, his marital difficulties, and his ingrained but lovable dishonesty. Mr Cary, however, never content to rest upon his laurels, then abandoned Nigeria to embark upon his ambitious trilogy of the English scene: *Herself Surprised*, *To Be a Pilgrim* and (his greatest triumph to date) *The Horse's Mouth*, all of them told in the first person. His use of this narrative device is remarkable, for he does not employ it as a 'convenient ventriloquist's dummy', like Mr Christopher Isherwood, or as a detached observer, like Mr Somerset Maugham; but rather as a character-actor assuming his role: his versatility is amazing; as another critic has pointed out, he appears equally at home as an elderly retired solicitor with a taste for indecent exposure, as an intransigent rascally painter of genius, or as that delectable old baggage, Sara Munday. Each of the books may, moreover, be read as a separate novel; there are no tiresome recapitulations, as in the late Ford Madox Ford's Tietjens trilogy, nor does a synopsis of the relationship of the three main characters ever become necessary.

Mr Cary has by now, in eleven novels, exploited almost every method of narration: the flashback, third and first person, the present tense (*Mister Johnson*, *Charley is My Darling*), straight story-telling (as in *The African Witch*); his early descriptive work recalled the paintings of Mr Wyndham Lewis, as the following passage from *Aissa Saved* will exemplify:

> In each wall of the house there was a big square door, ten feet wide, so that to the passer-by outside the councillors appeared like triangular white sacks tied up with black rope and stooked together in the middle shadow of the roof; while to the councillors within the whole land of Yanrin could be seen in four square pictures; to the north all black bush up to the white sky; to the west, old yam fields, tall jungle, and the Niger like an ocean; to the south, the rest camp and the big baobab; to the east, the deep gully of the Akoko river curling upwards into the right-hand corner, with a lacework of bright pools in its muddy bottom and one long crooked pole stuck in the middle of it and gradually falling over.

These angular rhythms and careful grouping gave place to the vivid impressionistic flashes of *The Horse's Mouth*, which resemble shots from a scenario for a super-film in colour, such as Gulley Jimpson himself might have written. In *A Fearful Joy*, however, there is virtually no description; everything is subordinated to telling, at breathless speed and once again in the present tense, the story of Tabitha Baskett's vastly eventful life. The book opens like a parody of a Victorian melodrama, which indeed, in a sense, it is; in next to no time Tabitha has eloped with her handsome seducer and been 'betrayed'; deserted by the scrounging Bonser, she returns home to brother Harry, only to succumb again when the scoundrel reappears with a non-existent job; the job turns out to be selling 'phoney' shares in public houses; soon the poor girl is pregnant and Bonser has vanished again. But a literary racketeer named Manklow now takes her up, and introduces her to Jobson, who acts as procurer for a rich man named Sturge. Tabitha becomes Sturge's mistress, twists the bewildered dupe round her little finger, and persuades him to found a species of Yellow Book magazine called *The Bankside*. Very rapidly she learns the ropes and the jargon of literary decadence, runs Sturge's *salon* for him, sends money to Bonser out of the proceeds, and brings up her son John, later marrying a wealthy industrialist, Lord Gollan. During the 1914 war Bonser emerges as a profiteer, a bit more boozy and flashy and with a big cigar; he reasserts himself as a friend of John's; the boy is crippled in a car accident and afterwards marries a shocking specimen of academic athleticism; Lord Gollan dies and Tabitha at long last marries Bonser and runs a roadhouse. But this is by no means the end: the action is carried right up to the present day; Bonser finally dies, of drink and with persecution-mania, after an intermediate period during which he has established himself as a 'Colonel' of the most reactionary type, and Tabitha falls a victim to her designing, dissolute niece, Nancy, who in turn is a prey to Parkin, a bounder even more neurotic and bad-tempered than Bonser himself. So the pattern is repeated, and Tabitha as an old lady is left praying for a little more time to live, to devote herself to Nancy, after an injudicious fit of laughter has almost finished her off. (The reader recalls Aissa dying, literally, of laughter on the ant-heap, and Gulley Jimpson's last words; for Mr Cary laughter is both a reassertion of the life-force and a form of prayer.)

The author of course revels in those sections which deal with the shady side of literature; the *Bankside* milieu and its hangers-on are superbly done. Bonser too comes off completely: Bonser drunk and munificent ('I've always been generous with money. It's in the blood, I suppose. Money is dirt to a real nob; he just can't take it seriously'); Bonser prosperous and Bonser broke; Bonser brutal and Bonser kind; Bonser in final red-faced retirement, standing a round with fake medals in the Home Guard: Tabitha's 'fearful joy'. For this is a love-story, and Tabitha is as much in thrall to Bonser as Gulley Jimpson was to Sara Munday or Aissa to Gajere; she, like all Mr Cary's heroines, is a dedicated person.

A reader is left wondering what this talented, individualistic writer will do next; it is likely to be something unexpected and important, for, to quote his own words – used in quite another connection – 'the force of life, entering into the delight of the mind, makes an art of all that it communicates'.

Robert Louis Stevenson

*   *   *

'THERE CAN BE LITTLE DOUBT,' AS MR JOHN HAMPDEN REMARKS
quite rightly in his introduction to *The Stevenson Companion*,[1] a selection
from the work of R.L.S. published to commemorate the centenary of
his birth which falls on 13 November this year, 'that it is his novels and
tales which will not only continue to attract the majority of his readers,
but will secure him a permanent place in the history of English literature'. And later he writes at the close of an interesting biographical
essay: 'It is fortunate that Stevenson no longer stands, as he stood for
so long, between his readers and his books'.

The carefully nurtured romantic legend of his lifetime need not
occupy us unduly here, except where, to quote Mr Hampden again, 'a
knowledge of it can quicken appreciation of his work'. The dramatic
moments have been deliberately heightened, selected for their stunning,
vicarious impact like incidents in one of Stevenson's own stories:
the estrangement with his rigidly orthodox family; the leap over the
windowsill into the lamplit room where his wife-to-be awaited him;
the long struggle against illness and financial insecurity; the collapse
on a camping expedition and his rescue by 'a mighty hunter of bears';
success, acclaim, and king-making in Samoa; sudden death super-
vening upon the dictation of *Weir of Hermiston*, and 'the hunter home
from the hill'.

In life as in his work, the inner conflict was more important and
revelatory than the outward action: brought up by his nurse on tales
of hell-fire and Deacon Brodie, these took effect in a manner contrary
to that intended by the good woman, and longing for the sinister

---

1   Phoenix House.

pleasures of a double life alternated with fearful pangs of a puritan conscience; as an undergraduate he renounced the faith of his fore-fathers to plunge into the slums of Edinburgh; the 'strong appetites and unchecked curiosities' commented on by Sir Sidney Colvin at a later date caused him, like Dorian Gray, to seek company which shocked his parents, who were compelled to intervene when their son showed signs of wishing to marry a prostitute. This was a formative period, to whose excesses and attendant remorse we without doubt owe the germ of *Dr Jekyll and Mr Hyde* and the conception of such powerful *tours de force* as *A Lodging for the Night*. Mr Hampden, though he includes this last in his selection as representative of Stevenson's historical fiction, does not do full justice to this, his first published short story, claiming that the imaginative impulses of the author fail in its second half, during the philosophical conversation between Seigneur and thief: yet surely the conclusion, which the editor complains 'peters out', is in a later tradition of anti-climax, thirty-five years at least ahead of its time: 'A very dull old gentleman. I wonder what his goblets may be worth': Villon the poet and master of arts playing at crime, is excusing to himself his cowardice and inability to kill and rob his host, stretching with bravado in the snow-covered street, yet inwardly shrinking from remembrance of the dead man's red hair and the act of genuine violence in the house by the cemetery. 'In many ways,' as Stevenson sardonically has it, 'an artistic nature unfits a man for practical existence'. The sting in this story's tail is therefore psychological, and it is obvious that R.L.S. included much of himself in his delineation of Villon's character; 'some flavour of good birth and training' clings also about the murderer Montigny: 'some-thing long, lithe, and courtly in the person; something aquiline and darkling in the face'. The dissolute monk Dom Nicolas is, however, devoid of nobility: straddling and gross, with his veined cheeks and his distended shadow, he represents the full danger of those evil associations from which Stevenson, at the time of writing, had happily escaped: both he and the president of the Suicide Club are, with Wilkie Collins's Count Fosco, prototypes of those hearty, ruthless rogues who have become inseparable from the contemporary highbrow thriller.

The adventures of Prince Florizel are not included in *The Stevenson Companion*, and Mr Hampden passes them over almost without comment in his introduction: regrettably, since, as Mr V.S. Pritchett has pointed out elsewhere, the satirical dandyism of *The New Arabian*

Nights and the realistic colloquialism of *The Beach of Falesá* represent opposite triumphs of Stevenson's versatility as a narrator. *The Suicide Club* itself is distinguished for many reasons: not only for the sinister joviality of its president or for the portrait of the repulsive paralytic Mr Malthus, the honorary member who 'trifled once too often with his terrors', but for the manner in which the farce of the young man with the cream tarts, the 'familiar' of 'Death's private door', becomes, of a sudden, grim tragedy once that portal has opened and closed behind the visitors. The alternations of mood and the unbroken urbanity of style create a precedent unequalled, since, in the history of English fiction; while the narrative technique of *The Physician and the Saratoga Trunk*, in which the viewpoint is shifted from the foolish Peeping Tom, Silas Q. Scuddamore, to the dashing and chivalrous Lieutenant Brackenbury Rich, foreshadows that of many modern novels where the action is seen through the eyes of minor characters unable, through lack of knowledge, to apprehend the full significance of events. This method is repeated, and amplified, in *The Rajah's Diamond*, whose inspiration is more purely comic – though the vast shadow of John Vandaleur, ex-Dictator of Paraguay, broods in the background to provide the spice of danger essential to the author's scheme.

Its sequel, *The Dynamiter*, is pure light-hearted fooling; it lacks the genuine presence of lurking evil which is not by any means absent from *The Suicide Club*, and is predominant in *The Strange Case of Dr Jekyll and Mr Hyde*, which appeared in print a year later and proved the turning-point of popularity in Stevenson's career as a writer. This was written at top speed and in six days, during a period of dangerous illness and constant attacks of haemorrhage; it is said that Stevenson dreamed the story, and certainly it has much of the quality of nightmare, to which the clarity and dryness of the style lend an added touch of horror. Once again we start off at one remove from the action, with the prim lawyer Mr Utterson as camera-eye; the story is gradually unfolded, a series of short chapters, like the scenes of a play, carrying the reader elliptically on to the final devastating revelation, the shock of which is now lessened by familiarity, but which, to the reader at the time of first publication, must have been extreme. Stevenson, always his own severest critic (*The Black Arrow*, in his opinion, was 'tushery'; *The Pavilion on the Links* 'mere carpentry', *The Wrecker* a 'police machine') considered *Jekyll and Hyde* in the penny-dreadful class, and it was not initially published under his own name; yet the careful craftsmanship and the white-hot speed of execution, allied to the dual personality theme so dear to his heart, argue a degree of urgency and compulsion strangely at variance with so harsh a verdict; it may be that the novel's success made him, always contemptuous of the public ('that great, hulking, bullering whale'), suspect his own integrity for producing a moral allegory in a readable form: 'There must be something wrong in me, or I would not be popular,' he wrote at the time to Edmund Gosse.

Jekyll and Hyde was altogether lacking in the mordant touches of humour scattered throughout the pages of *The Suicide Club*: it is as though the sober spirit of Mr Utterson had entered completely into the author, even as Dr Jekyll was possessed by Mr Hyde. But 'it is said that a poet has died young in the breast of the most stolid', and the book abounds in verbal felicities in spite of the legal severity of its prose: Hyde, with his lean, corded, knuckly hands, cringing back 'with a kind of black, sneering coolness' from the infuriated crowd after he has brutally trampled a child underfoot; the description of Utterson himself, 'cold, scanty and embarrassed in discourse'; the 'haggard shaft of daylight' glancing 'in between the swirling wreaths' of London fog while the swift glimpses allowed us of dingy Soho streets when the fog momentarily lifts are perhaps only equalled by certain descriptive passages in Conrad's *Secret Agent*.

The *nouvelle* was the literary form which perhaps suited Stevenson best; the sustained effort required to complete a novel was, as he well knew, a feat of endurance irksome both to his mercurial temperament and precarious state of health: 'It is the length that kills,' and the novel-length was also inconsistent with the high pressure at which he normally worked: 15 chapters of *Treasure Island* were rushed out in a like number of days; and it was not only the thought of his proofs awaiting correction at the 'Hand and Spear' that spurred him on to such feverish activity, but the consciousness that his energies might flag before the last word was written. He did in fact strike a snag halfway through *Treasure Island*, and the story limps badly through those chapters entrusted, for narration, to the Doctor: recovering only when Jim Hawkins takes up the tale again. But the *nouvelle* presented none of these difficulties: the 30,000 words of *The Suicide Club*, *Jekyll and Hyde*, or *The Beach of Falesá* could be dashed off with scarcely a halt when the 'tide of delighted industry' was flowing fast, and more-over could be treated in the 'summary elliptic method' with which he felt so much at home. For much of Stevenson's best work was done in a manner which, coming from a contemporary writer, would have been labelled cinematic: like a film-scenarist with considerable experience in the cutting-room, he leaped agilely from scene to scene, spotlighting, as a director might, each dramatic moment in the story and deleting in the process all the irrelevant background detail which he so heartily disliked. Whole 'shots' come to mind, presented with perfect timing and from appropriate angles, remaining as vivid in the memory as the lightning-flash that disclosed to David Balfour the trap set for him by his treacherous uncle on the tower stair; Long John Silver's cunning eye gleaming (in close-up) 'like a crumb of glass'; the wind tossing the light of the candle to and fro about the steps of the watchers in Dr Jekyll's deserted operating theatre; the horses' hooves trampling and spurning the body of Blind Pew as the revenue-officers clatter by; the light running along the steel of the Master's sword as he turns the blade against Mackellar's bosom: it was the visual quality of such writing which earned for Stevenson the unstinting praise of Sir John Millais. His most impressive essay in the genre of the *nouvelle*, *The Beach of Falesá*, is rich in camerawork of this order, the effect enhanced by exotic beauty of the setting: Uma awaits Wiltshire in the coral-built station on their bridal night. 'Her shadow went all the way up behind her into the hollow of the iron roof; she stood against it bright, the lamplight shining on her skin...the want of her took, and shook all through me, like the wind in the luff of a sail,' but the story is principally remarkable for its experiment in the vernacular, and for Stevenson's complete identification of himself with the tough narrator: the story has been retold many times, but its characters remain basically the same: the rough but fundamentally decent adventurer and the simple native girl of whom he becomes fond, the designing villain who attempts to shatter their idyll, and the racy idiom in which the tale is told; but never perhaps as adequately or realistically as when Stevenson first sat down to tell it, since his version is devoid of sentimentality and has, unlike its American derivations, an ironical conclusion. 'With Mr Wiltshire,' Mr Pritchett comments, 'Stevenson hands over the keys of the safe to Mr Maugham and to an even younger generation': it is not inconceivable that he handed them also to Mr Ernest Hemingway. Surely the graphic description of Case's murder has not been surpassed even by the killing of the Chinese in *To Have and Have Not*:

'With that I gave him the cold steel for all I was worth. His
body kicked under me like a spring sofa; he gave a dreadful kind
of long moan and lay still…I wasn't going to take chances; I
had his own example too close before me for that, and I tried
to draw the knife out to give it him again. The blood came
over my hands, I remember, hot as tea; and with that I fainted
clean away, and fell with my head on the man's mouth.'

Violence can scarcely go further ('the bullet struck within an inch of
me and knocked the dirt in my eyes'), but it is in portraying the relationship between Wiltshire and Uma as the narrator's fumbling tenderness
awakes that Stevenson particularly strikes home, and in his technical
handling of the colloquial style he by far excels his previous efforts.

The Beach of Falesá belongs to his later period, before he embarked
on the unfinished *Weir of Hermiston*. This, it is generally accepted, would
have been his masterpiece had he lived to complete it; here at last,
critics exclaim, Stevenson had come to maturity: in the portrait of the
younger Kirstie ('this explosive engine in his arms, whose works he did
not understand, and yet had been tampering with') he showed signs of
being able to draw, for the first time, a woman of flesh and blood, for
he had finally realised, against the teachings of his puritan forebears,
that the sexual instinct is nothing to be ashamed of, and, moreover,
that women are not always ashamed of it. Yet it will doubtless be for
the characterisation of the Lord Justice Clerk himself – the mighty
toper, the jeering sadist on the Bench (drawn from Lord Braxfield,
with more than a touch of Judge Jeffries), a grim majestic figure, with
his plebian accent and his smothered affection for the rebellious
Archie that the book will be chiefly memorable; for though Hermiston
belongs superficially, to Stevenson's great gallery of villains, he represents something far more terrible than the pure evil of the Master of
Ballantrae or the vicious cruelty of Mr Hyde – he represents the cold
inhuman principle of abstract justice: and, according to Stevenson's
plan, was to pass sentence of death upon his own son. The whole
existing magnificent fragment is, however, reprinted in *The Stevenson
Companion* that each reader may judge for himself the possibilities of
the novel's final outcome: the style combines the powerful dialect of
Thrawn Janet with the visual method previously commented on:

Little daylight lingered; but on the door being opened, the
strong yellow shine of the lamp gushed out upon the landing
and shone full on Archie, as he stood, in the old-fashioned

observance of respect, to yield precedence. The Judge came
without haste, stepping stately and firm; his chin raised, his face
(as he entered the lamplight) strongly illuminated, his mouth
set hard.

The lighting, it will be observed from this extract, is as good as ever,
but the stark economy of the prose and the new note of doom sounded
in its granite echo, might be profitably studied by a generation of
writers whose chief faults – verboseness and pseudo-poetic 'sensibility'
– are those of which Stevenson most cordially disapproved.

The Surrealist Movement

*   *   *

THE HISTORY OF SURREALISM IS, IN A SENSE, THE HISTORY OF THE whole inter-war period: and its development under the stress of world events, no less than the personal drama of conflicting loyalties played out within the movement itself, constitutes a microcosm of the dilemma with which intellectuals everywhere were faced during those crucial and formative years. To retrace such development, therefore, calls for a re-examination of positions then desperately held and later unconditionally surrendered; one has the illusion of passing through a military post long since abandoned – tattered posters of outmoded propaganda still flutter here and there, a half-forgotten slogan is smudged in chalk upon a crumbling wall, and the air seems, to the receptive ear, full of battle-cries grown faint with the passage of time.

Surrealism was born out of the black period consequent upon the First World War, and without doubt owed much of its inception to the influence upon M. André Breton of the cynical and disillusioned pessimist Jacques Vaché ('lui si pénétré de l'inutilité théâtrale et sans joie de tout'), though Vaché's basic attitude was perhaps closer to the destructive nihilism of the Dadaist group, with which, under the leadership of Tristan Tzara, M. Breton and his friends first became affiliated. The Dadaist programme consisted largely of negation ('Plus rien, plus rien, rien, RIEN, RIEN, RIEN': 'Connais pas, connais pas, connais pas, connais pas'), and of attacks both upon official art and recognised artists: 'If you read André Gide aloud for ten minutes, your breath will smell,' wrote Francis Picabia, though M. Gide's name had appeared earlier, with that of Paul Valéry among others, as a contributor to the first issue of *Littérature*, a little review edited by MM. Louis Aragon, André Breton and Philippe Soupault. Superficially these combative methods appeared highly satisfactory to M. Breton and his comrades, who were also intent upon the destruction of established conventions and reputations, and the Dada technique of attack was later to be adopted by the surrealists themselves against their former allies, for a severance of relations was not long in coming. The initial occasion was the clash between Tristan Tzara and André Breton at a mock-trial of M. Maurice Barrès for crimes against 'la sûreté de l'esprit': a wooden effigy represented the accused in the dock, while Tzara as a witness and Breton as the president of the court crossed swords rapidly: 'Does the witness wish to pass himself off as a complete fool, or is he trying to be committed for contempt?' After this passage of arms the rift swiftly widened until, in 1922, a formal rupture, or dissolution of partnership, was announced.

The primary aims of the surrealists, though André Breton was not to publish his first Manifesto until 1924, were now crystallised: the movement (to quote M. Maurice Nadeau: *Histoire du Surréalisme*, 1945) was not envisaged by its founders as a new school of art, but as a means of charting insufficiently explored continents: the subconscious mind, the wonderland of dreams, dementia and the hallucinatory state: in fact, 'the other side of the logical backcloth'. Its precursors were Baudelaire, Rimbaud, Alfred Jarry, Gérard de Nerval, and, more recently, Apollinaire: some of these were later jettisoned ('en matière de révolte, aucun de nous ne doit avoir besoin d'ancêtres,' Breton was to proclaim in 1929), and the prestige of Rimbaud and Apollinaire fluctuated constantly: but the Marquis de Sade and Isidote Ducasse, Comte de Lautréamont, remained firmly upon their pedestals as idols of the group, whilst Freud of course was its prophet: certain Hegelian doctrines played their part in formulating the surrealist outlook, and André Breton himself has acknowledged his debt to F.W.H. Myers.

Both M. Nadeau and M. Michel Carrouges (particularly the latter) are insistent upon Breton's preoccupation with gothic novelists such as Horace Walpole, 'Monk' Lewis, Ann Radcliffe, Clara Reeve, Huysmans, the mysterious Maturin (whose *Melmoth The Wanderer* was to exercise such a powerful influence upon Lautréamont), and, it goes without saying, Sade who, as M. Carrouges points out, presented in a new form more acceptable to the atheist houses of horror inhabited by men who, themselves, achieved the status of demonic spirits. 'The most sceptical among us inhabits a haunted house', and later, during his Marxist period, André Breton was to regard these *romans noirs* as pieces of symbolism directly related to the social problem: the ruins of the castle, he claims, are a visual expression of the crumbling feudal system; the inevitable phantom which haunts them represents a fear that the previous rulers might return to power: the subterranean passage symbolises man's slow and perilous journey through darkness towards the light: the claps of thunder in the stormy night are but the distant explosions of cannon. Be this as it may, *The Castle of Otranto* had a particular interest for the surrealists, since Walpole claimed that the book was automatically written, and the giant mailed hand which pointed the way to the work has its counterpart in several surrealist productions in the illustrations to the review *Minotaure*, in the paintings of Chirico and Max Ernst, and in André Breton's own *Nadja*, where it appears simultaneously on a poster and, traced by a flash of lighting, in the sky.

To André Breton, self-induced hypnotic trances and automatic writing (with which he had been experimenting since 1919) were the means of freeing poetry from its logical confines. In the domain of automatic writing, however, the aims of surrealism were in direct opposition to those of spiritualism, he wrote in *Point du jour*, for while the medium attempts the disassociation of his own psychological personality, the surrealist aimed at nothing less than the unification of that personality. The poet was to be no longer only a 'sounding echo', a prophet or a seer: he was to become a magician whose main aim was to achieve the complete liberation of mankind through the ultimate mastery of the subconscious mind. Nevertheless, it was 'not a poetic form', it was 'a pure psychic automatism by which it is proposed to express, either verbally or in writing, or by any other means, the real processes of thought. Dictated by the mind, free of any control exercised by reason, and quite distinct from all aesthetic or moral preoccupations.' Surrealism was 'based upon belief in the superior reality of certain forms of association previously neglected, in the supreme power of dreams, and the disinterested play of the mind. It aims completely to ruin all other psychic mechanisms and to substitute itself for them in the resolution of life's principal problems...' It was also, according to M. Aragon, 'a philtre of the absolute'; a 'fatal fermentation'; a 'new vice'; the offspring of 'frenzy and shadow'. Literature was but a means to an end, a total revolution of the spirit. 'We have no talent,' André Breton announced in the *Surrealist Manifesto*, '...we who have made ourselves, in our works, the deaf receptacles of so many echoes, humble *recording machines* which are not themselves hypnotised by the patterns they trace.'

A heroic period lay ahead: the séances, the shared and recounted dreams: the laboratory of surrealist research: the appearance of *La Révolution surréaliste No.1*, followed by the pamphlet *Un Cavadre*, attacking Anatole France on the occasion of his death: the scandals, the sound and fury, M. Soupault swinging on the chandelier at the banquet in honour of Saint-Pol-Roux. The Anatole France pamphlet led, owing to a slighting reference to Moscow made by Louis Aragon, towards a brush between the poet and Jean Bernier, editor of the communist review *Clarté*: in his reply Aragon shrugged aside the idea of the Russian Revolution, which he dismissed as a 'vague ministerial crisis'; nevertheless, the outbreak of the Moroccan war caused a *rapprochement* between the erstwhile antagonists, since the surrealists, too, ranged themselves on the side of Abd-el-Krim: a joint Manifesto was drawn up; the movement had entered upon its '*reasoning*' phase: it suddenly felt, as André Breton wrote afterwards, 'the need to cross the ditch separating absolute idealism from dialectical materialism'. This change of view was principally brought about by the fact that Breton had just read the biography of Lenin, by Trotsky, and had conceived an immediate admiration both for the subject and for the author. (His admiration for the latter was to be a lasting one, and to survive triumphantly a later meeting.)

Aragon, now completely reconciled with Bernier, published in *Clarté* a study of 'Le Prolétariat de l'esprit', which the editor found 'irreproachably Marxist'; a merger of Communists and surrealists in a new magazine, *La Guerre Civile*, was proposed and approved by both parties, but this project failed to come about: for, though Breton made a declaration that his movement 'belonged body and soul' to the Revolution, he declined to renounce his present activities for the more stringent discipline of total affiliation with the PCF. A clash of ideologies now began within the group: Pierre Naville was the first to break away, becoming a co-editor of *Clarté*, in which, however, he printed essays and poems by the surrealists: the breach between them was not yet complete, and André Breton reaffirmed his support to the rival party 'when the time came'; meanwhile a new adherent joined the movement: an unfrocked priest who eventually returned to his former faith denouncing Breton as an incarnation of the Devil, while MM. Antonin Artaud and Philippe Soupault were formally excommunicated for 'incompatibility of aims'.

The year 1928 saw the publication of Aragon's *Traité de Style* and André Breton's *Nadja*, the heroine of which described herself as a lost soul: the first surrealist film, *Un Chien Andalou*, was released, and the collaboration with *Clarté* came to an end. The following year André Breton printed his second *Surrealist Manifesto*: a document more intransigent than ever, for this time he renounced all ancestors of the movement: Poe was spat upon and even Sade went temporarily by the board (though he was later reinstated), while several friends – MM. Jacques Prévert, Raymond Queneau, Robert Desnos, Francis Gérard and André Masson among others – came under the axe. These replied by means of a pamphlet similar to that which Breton had addressed to Anatole France, with this difference: that the 'corpse' featured on the cover was that of their former leader, wearing a crown of thorns and with tears of blood trickling from the corners of his closed eyes. The gaps in the ranks were closed, in 1930, by reinforcements such as Georges Hugnet, Georges Sadoul, and one particularly important addition, Salvador Dali, who brought to the group not only the exercise of his startling talent as a painter, but his whole theory of critical paranoia, in which he proposed to subjugate the reality of the outside world to the reality of the mind.

The year 1931, however, brought about a serious inner crisis, beginning with the return of Louis Aragon from Russia, where he had signed, according to M. Nadeau, a letter to the International Writers' Union denouncing idealism, Freudianism and Trotskyism, and proclaiming his attachment to the party line. Back in France, he complained that this signature was extorted from him and published a manifesto defending the theory of psychoanalysis which, in Kharkov, he had attacked as 'idealistic'. His poem 'Red Front' caused a sensation, and brought the police down on him for incitement to murder, the case against him being based upon certain lines such as 'Let's croak the coppers, Comrades!' and 'Open fire on the dancing bears of Social Democracy'. Breton, rallying to his defence, argued quite rightly that a poem should be considered as a whole and that a prosecution based on lines taken out of their context would be not only unfair but absurd; the case was duly abandoned, but the affair led to Aragon's taking the final step towards membership of the PCF and to his renunciation of the Surrealist creed. In 1934, the year of Stavisky and the general strike, Breton and the group were appealing to the workers for 'unity of action', but they opposed the signature of the Franco–Soviet pact and later signalled their formal defiance 'of the *actual* system of Soviet Russia and its all-powerful chief, under whose régime that system has become the direct negation of what it ought, and used, to be'. In the short-lived revolutionary review, *Contre-Attaque*, Breton gives Surrealism a new definition: 'The fashioning of a collective myth', and while recognising 'the class-war as a historical factor and source of essential moral values,' speaks of his difficulty in deciding what action would definitely reconcile the creation of the collective myth with the more general movement towards the liberation of mankind: 'No shapeless insurrection will succeed in seizing power,' he continued. 'Social destiny today will be decided by the organic creation of a vast medley of forces, disciplined, fanatical, capable of wielding, when the time comes, a pitiless authority,' and indeed the Nazi party was shortly to fulfil, to some extent, this expectation.

There was another, and almost unsuperable, difficulty, though Breton refused to admit it until later: the gap between the revolutionary artist, who has, willy-nilly, benefited from the advantages of a bourgeois culture, and the revolutionary worker who has not; from the date of Breton's reluctant admission that this gap was, for him at any rate, an impassable one, he was forced, however unwillingly, as M. Nadeau shows, into the category of artist, and the movement received therefrom an added impetus: before the Munich crisis it had become world-wide, and Breton was fully employed both in artistic and organisational work. His meeting with Trotsky in Mexico, moreover, must have helped to allay any misgivings he might have had, for Trotsky held the view that the 'struggle for artistic truth' and 'the unshakable faith of the artist in his inner self' were the only conditions in which art could be forged into a serviceable weapon for the freedom of the masses.

The outbreak of the Second World War put an unfortunate term to this period of renewed activity; since then many more changes have taken place in the movement: the most notable of which was André Breton's break, in America, with Salvador Dali (now nicknamed by him 'Avida Dollars'), and the metamorphosis of the latter into a Catholic Fascist: Jacques Prévert has for many years now collaborated with the film director Marcel Carné, his most comprehensive scenario being, perhaps, that of *Les Enfants du Paradis* (there is more than a touch of surrealist 'black humour' in the characterisation of the murderer Lacenaire). Raymond Queneau is the author of several satirical novels, also touched with his personal version of 'black humour'; Louis Aragon has embarked upon a series of vastly successful double deckers, devoid, surprisingly, of any kind of humour, but the painful sincerity of which cannot for a moment be in doubt; Paul Eluard has gone from strength to strength as a poet...André Breton himself appears to place the highest confidence in the work of M. Julien Gracq, author of a biographical and critical study of Breton, whose own novels would appear, on the surface, to belong to the genre of Poe, but whose *Beau ténebreux* (soon to appear in an English translation) has been designated by the Master as 'l'oeuvre maîtresse de la surréalisme'. The gothic side of the movement would seem, then, to be in the ascendancy; but, like Salvador Dali's *Hidden Faces*, also in the tradition of the *roman noir*, M. Gracq's work is closer, in execution, to the style of Quida than to that of Sade or Lautréamont, and exhibits many hallmarks of a romantic *fin-de-siècle* decadence completely at variance with M. Breton's claim that surrealism is still 'a l'avant-garde'.

The time has undoubtedly come, however, for a wholly detached revaluation of the creed. M. Carrouges is too quick to anticipate the reader's reaction to the conclusions which he himself has drawn, leaping touchily into the breach to defend the movement from hostile criticism before any such criticism has been formulated, often at the expense of self-criticism; his partisan attitude contradicts the publisher's claim that 'the time of anathemas and facile enthusiasms is past'. Whether the surrealist contribution is to revolutionary thought, or to art and letters (the soft watches and nightmare canvases of Dali; the worm-cast-strewn sandscapes of Yves Tanguy; the startling images and vertiginous beauty of the prose and poetry, whose strange spell cannot be denied), or whether, as M. Breton would undoubtedly affirm, these activities are indivisible, will be for the objective critic to decide.

André Breton denies that the movement is dead; if a renaissance is indeed on the way, and could recapture some of the earlier vitality, it might well serve as a welcome goad to contemporary inertia.

From a Chase to a View
(Anthony Powell)

*   *   *

ONE OF THE CHARACTERS IN MR ANTHONY POWELL'S LATEST novel,[1] an unsuccessful poet turned schoolmaster, refers to Matthew Arnold's method of 'invoking melancholy by graphic description of natural features of the landscape': this method might almost be described as that of the author himself in the book under discussion, the opening sentences of which depict vividly the drawing in of a winter's day round a group of working men bivouacked on the corner of a London street: the nostalgic quality of the scene thus evoked leads, from a comparison with Poussin's dance of the seasons, to a train of reminiscence in the narrator's mind linking up, by a species of 'verbal dissolve'(though Mr Powell's manner, in this instance, could not be more divergent from the technique of the cinema), with his school-days and adolescence: a period of life untouched upon by Mr Powell in his five previous novels, but from which many of his contemporaries appear never to have wholly broken away.

It was indeed the startlingly adult viewpoint displayed in *Afternoon Men*, and its neglect of the autobiographical subject-matter, which, following the appearance of *Sinister Street*, had become traditional for first novels at the time of its publication twenty years ago, that – together with the brilliance of its execution – caused readers and critics alike to regard the book as a remarkable *tour de force*. Though its material was not new – it was sometimes described as 'the party-novel to end all party-novels' – it avoided the routine delineation of public school and university life which had become so tedious through repe-tition, and though set in Bloomsbury, it avoided also the self-pitying

---

1   *A Question of Upbringing*, Heinemann.

attitude catalogued, at a later date, by Mr Cyril Connolly under the heading 'The Clever Young Man and the Dirty Deal'. Presented in a series of short chapters resembling the sequences of a film ('Montage' was in fact the title of Part One, and the author could not, at this stage, have denied the influence of the cinema, which he was later to shake off so thoroughly), it chronicled, with none of the extravagant satire which characterised *Vile Bodies* but with much the same cumulative effect, the day-to-day doings of a 'Bohemian' group much preoccupied with their love affairs and with the impact of their personalities upon one another; there was little story and no drama (the attempted suicide of the painter Pringle was turned into farce by his return from the sea, having reconsidered his decision to drown himself); and it was solely by the author's quiet irony and wry acceptance of his characters' eccentricities that the reader's interest was successfully held throughout. A third, and most important, factor contributed also to this end: Mr Powell's easy mastery of dialogue used as a means of expressing personality as well as a means of communication; from the raffish locutions of two young men discussing valve-trouble at a bar, to the pretentious 'artiness' of Lola or the labyrinthine drunken discourses of the ubiquitous Fotheringham, each character has a voice, accent and vocabulary recognisably his own. Nor does *Afternoon Men*, reread to-day, give the impression of being a period novel, for the types and situations it describes are perennial, though perhaps restricted more nowadays to the confines of the pub or drinking club, parties of the kind described having become a comparatively rare phenomenon since the outbreak of the Second World War.

Prominent features of the book, besides those already mentioned, were its lack of sentimentality – demonstrated by the principal character's relationships with the various women who figure in the story – and the author's astonishing maturity of approach both to the problems of love and sex which preoccupy most young novelists, and to the feminine protagonists who exemplify such problems; these qualities were again displayed in his second novel, *Venusberg*, though a new delicacy of feeling is present in the hero's emotions towards the two women, similar in type though of vastly different origins, by whom he finds himself captivated. The brief descriptions of the Baltic country in which the book is set prepare the reader by their settled melancholy for the final tragedy which resolves the triangular situation, and for the dying fall of the anti-climactic ending; the sad winter scene so economically invoked resembles in its effect the opening passage of *A Question of Upbringing* already referred to, although this effect is achieved by means diametrically opposite to those employed in the later book. It would not be correct, however, to describe *Venusberg* as in any way 'miserablist' in outlook; there are chapters which are wildly funny without ever degenerating into farce, and a whole gallery of richly comic subordinate characters: the egregious valet, Pope, called by his comrades in the army 'The Duke', the two Russian counts, Scherbatcheff and Bobel; the ingenuous American, Courtenay, and the conscientious Waldemar; there are times indeed when Count Bobel, with his samples of face cream, his amber-scented cigarettes and masterly evasive replies to questions concerning his actual origin, appears, to the enchanted reader, to deserve a novel all to himself, though Mr Powell is too astute a writer ever to allow the Count to get out of hand to this extent.

Venusberg marks an advance on *Afternoon Men*, also, by its symmetry of form: a quality even more amply demonstrated by *From a View to a Death*, perhaps the most satisfying of all the earlier novels, and in many ways the most representative of this author's talent; for here his latent preoccupation with the will to power and its visible incarnations fully emerges in the portrait of Zouch, the ruthless bearded egotist, who uses art as a convenient cloak for his predatory instincts and comes to grief only through the machinations of an even more sinister figure, into whose family he proposes to marry for reasons of social advancement. The background here is again different: the small market town and the hunting field, the country house and the cocktail party at the Fox and Hounds, though Zouch's home terrain is not dissimilar from that already explored in *Afternoon Men* – Chelsea being substituted for Bloomsbury. Obvious indignation is never one of the weapons employed by Mr Powell to explode odious types, and the urbanity with which Zouch's detestable actions and habits of thought are chronicled serves to heighten the horror of the portrait; the carefully planned seduction of the pathetically highbrow Joanna Brandon and Zouch's subsequent conquest of Mary Passenger, which results in Joanna's betrayal to her own devices, are particularly well presented: while the the painter's internecine warfare with his fellow-superman and prospective father-in-law, Mr Passenger, is a masterpiece of superficially polite thrust-and-parry. Nor is the author lacking in sympathy towards Zouch's principal victim, Joanna, though her reactions to her betrayal and Zouch's callous behaviour are tellingly understated, thus skirting successfully the danger of sentimentality implicit in describing more fully her chagrin at the position in which she finds herself.

Comic relief is not neglected either, and the mad Major Fosdick with his two sons, the cloddish Jasper and the cretinous aesthete Torquil, among others, rank high among the subsidiary eccentrics whom Mr Powell invariably provides for our delectation, without, however, allowing their antics to detract from our consideration of the central situation. Of such are the opium-smoking Marquis, the bluff and bewildered Commodore, the shrewd and secretive Schlumbermayer, and the dwarfish German film director with a hook in place of a hand in *Agents and Patients*, a story set in London, Paris, and pre-Hitler Berlin, centring in the attempts of two genial and indigent intellectual adventurers to obtain the financial backing necessary for their schemes from a young man named Blore-Smith, more fully furnished with ready cash but scarcely cognisant, at the start of the book, with the facts of life. Blore-Smith's timid and breathless plunge into the unfamiliar world of Maltravers and Chipchase, and his subsequent immersion in the floodtide of their affairs, followed by his eventual re-emergence on to the dry land of his former dull life – a sadder and wiser, yet oddly benefited young man – is described with brevity and astringent wit (the book contains, incidentally, one of the most scarifyingly funny descriptions of a hangover to be found in modern fiction); yet *Agents and Patients* lacks, perhaps, the deeper insight into human nature present in *From a View to a Death*, though it is consistently entertaining on all levels and the formal structure is as carefully proportioned as before.

Blore-Smith appears to have served as a preliminary sketch for the character of Widmerpool, the dogged, sycophantic prig who seems at first sight destined to become the central figure in *A Question of Upbringing*, though after his initial emergence from the fogs of winter, wearing spiked shoes, he becomes subordinated to a more humble place in the general scheme of the book. Blore-Smith, in a dim, groping way, was not devoid of a lust for power, though he lacked the sharp drive of ambition present in Widmerpool; and in the last analysis only his thick-lensed spectacles and slight impediment of speech would appear to have been bequeathed to his successor. *A Question of Upbringing* is Mr Powell's first novel for 12 years, and both its manner and approach are markedly dissimilar from those characteristic of the earlier work. In spite of the stylistic brilliance of the previous books the reader may find himself unprepared for the distinguished classical prose and rounded periods of the new novel; in composing long sentences Mr Powell has skilfully avoided the morass of circumlocution into which Mr William Faulkner has lately floundered: his meaning remains as sharp and clear as in the curt paragraphs of *Afternoon Men*. An example, from one of Widmerpool's appearances in the first part of the book, may suffice as illustration:

> He stood there in the shadowy space by the slab in a setting of brown-paper parcels, dog-eared school books, and crumbs – a precinct of which the moral and physical cleansing provoked endless activity in the mind of Le Bas – and stood with his feet apart and eyes expanded, his painting, as Templer had justly described it, like that of an elderly lap-dog: his appearance suggesting rather some unusual creature actually bred in those depths by the slab, amphibious perhaps, though largely belonging to this land-world of blankets and carbolic: scents which attained their maximum density at this point, where they met and mingled with the Irish stew, which, coming from the territory of laundry-baskets and coke, reached its most potent force on the first step of the stairs.

Passages as admirably orchestrated as the above abound throughout; the background sights, sounds and smells of school are solidly blocked in behind the action; the faint, fading, melancholic strain conjured up by the method attributed by the housemaster, Le Bas, to Matthew Arnold breathes occasionally over the scene like the sound of a horn blown upon a distant hill, reminding us that the theme is, after all, the passing of youthful preoccupations and their replacement by the corrupt values of the adult world; but the tone is entirely free from the romantic nostalgia with which many writers look back upon their lost innocence, and the narrator is on the whole more concerned with the people who surround him than with self-analysis, though his personal problems are not entirely neglected and the effect of outside pressure is shown at work upon him, too. His visits to the homes of his two school-fellows Stringham and Templer are, for instance, both of a formative nature, as is his intermediate stay with a French family in Touraine, where Widmerpool, who had achieved a measure of notoriety by wearing, on his initial appearance at the narrator's school, an overcoat of an unfamiliar pattern, reappears to state his ambitious creed and give us a glimpse of the main pattern, already foreshadowed by the narrator's encounter, in the Templer household, with the astute intriguer Sunny Farebrother, whose air of shabby resignation to the buffets of fate actually conceals a power-complex analogous to that developing in the character of Widmerpool, and represents a variation of the go-getting type to which the latter will, in after life, belong. Stringham, a more highly strung boy, subject to moods of cosmic depression alternating with outbreaks of feverish high-spirits, of which his practical joke on the housemaster at school may be cited as an example, conditioned and thwarted by the shadow of his mother, a woman of wide social influence and powerful personality, and by constant skirmishes, at home, with his faintly raffish stepfather, is the first to take a real dive into the world of affairs, though Templer is already, by this time, established in his father's firm in the City; but it is suggested that the latter's moral fibres have been hopelessly coarsened by his family environment and that he is now relegated to his proper sphere in life. Stringham, however, is represented as a more unsettled product; and though he is shown, at the close of the book, in the first flush of worldly corruption, when, having become secretary to a financial tycoon through the machinations of a slightly ineffectual Don who belongs basically to the same brotherhood as Farebrother and Widmerpool, he breaks an appointment with the narrator to attend, in preference, a fashionable party at which persons of future use to him may be present, the reader is left with the impression that he is in reality ill-equipped to deal with the forces that surround him, and that he may later come unstuck.

The foregoing account will give some idea of the scope of the book; this, however, is scrupulously focused upon the business in hand, and the incidents carefully selected to illustrate, by the behaviour of a handful of characters, the wider issues of Mr Powell's thesis. It is to be hoped that the author will allow us, in the future, further glimpses of his characters' development: a reference to the reappearance of Sunny Farebrother, twenty years ahead, in the life of the narrator, seems to promise a sequel at some date to come; but, be this as it may, the present volume, whether considered as a study of the obsequious and the self-seeking, a brilliant comedy of manners (there are passages in the book which cause one, occasionally, to laugh aloud, and such lyrical figures as the narrator's Uncle Giles or the self-satisfied, English-speaking Monsieur Debuisson appear only too seldom), or as an analysis of the doom of youth, cannot fail to be regarded as a triumph in its own right.

Mr Powell is, mercifully, a writer without a 'message', either philosophical, religious or political; he is content to examine without comment, and to illustrate through character in action, the changes in human nature brought about by the changing face of the social order in which we live: in other words, he is attempting to fulfil the novelist's only true function.

A Saga of the Deep South
(William Faulkner)

*   *   *

AN ENIGMATIC AND RETIRING FIGURE, WITH A TRUE ARISTOCRAT'S distaste for personal publicity, Mr William Faulkner seems not so much to shrink from the limelight as to stand deliberately in the outer circle of shadow made deeper by its concentrated glare: and even the recent blaze which accompanied the award to him of a Nobel Prize for literature failed to illuminate more of his personality than the faint sardonic smile which may be seen in his photographs.

Nor is he given to those pronouncements about his own work which run so easily from the pens of his more portentous *confrères*: only once has he written a preface explaining how a book of his came into being (to the 'Modern Library' edition of *Sanctuary*), so that it is not easy to hazard a guess as to his methods of working. A clue to these, however, may be found in the first English edition of *Absalom, Absalom*, where the endpapers took the form of a map on which the principal land-marks figuring in the author's novels were charted: for instance, the Old Frenchman's Place, where Popeye, the impotent gunman, murdered the half-wit Tommy: a domicile which figures also, at a much earlier period of its existence, in *Absalom* itself. In one corner of the map was inscribed the legend 'Jefferson County, the sole property of Wm. Faulkner, Esq.'; and since some landmarks were cited as the scenes of incidents in stories which had not yet appeared in print at that time, it seems safe to assume that the main body of Mr Faulkner's work is in the nature of a continuous *roman fleuve*, each volume of which is complete in itself, though the novels exist in the mind of the author as interdependent and inseparable one from the other: the full story is seldom, in reality, told, as there are always new details to be added, though years may pass before the additions are made, and the lives of minor characters in one book are often rounded out in later works, or *vice versa*: thus the Narcissa who makes several brief appearances in Sanctuary is a main figure in *Sartoris*, and the Quentin who commits suicide in *The Sound and the Fury* reappears not as a narrator but as a listener to the long, involved recital in *Absalom, Absalom*: a tale which undoubtedly influences him, consciously or unconsciously, in the commission of his last desperate act. It is much to the author's credit that these additions and developments never appear to be tacked on as afterthoughts, but seem to have been merely held in reserve until the time was ripe for the telling, and from the evidence at our disposal this may indeed be the case.

For there can be little doubt that to Mr Faulkner his imaginary county and the characters with which he has populated it are intensely real, and therefore subject to the changes, both subtle and drastic, which age and time brings to most living beings: changes not always credible at first in the light of our former knowledge of the persons affected, yet seeming, on reflection, to have been predestined from the start. A hint thrown here and there, a quirk of character that may have appeared incongruous at the time, reveals clearly, on looking back, the fate in store, though one might not have believed it then. So a reading of *Absalom, Absalom* is necessary if one is fully to understand the motives which prompt Quentin to kill himself in *The Sound and the Fury* (his last anguished thought, 'I don't hate the South, I don't hate it', strikes the key to his mood on that day so movingly described, in his own words, in the latter book, though this was published several years before the saga of Colonel Sutpen). Much of the work, therefore, is complementary, and the uniform edition now being issued by Messrs Chatto and Windus will give us an opportunity of reassessing the richness and fertility of the author's imagination at its true value.

As with every main stream, there are tributaries, the exploration of which may prove exceptionally rewarding: the group of war stories in *These Thirteen* (which includes also that atmospheric masterpiece 'Minstral') may be quoted as examples, and perhaps some of those in *Dr Martino*: 'Leg' and 'Turn About' being particularly impressive in their evocation of horror, while the picture of utter degradation presented in *Pylon* has still not been equalled by novelists of the dipsomaniac school now in fashion.

Mr Faulkner was once described by Mr Wyndham Lewis as a moralist with a corn-cob, and certainly he may be regarded as a literary descendant, in some respects, of Hawthorne. Lust masquerading as, and mistaken for, love is the theme of many of his most compelling stories, notably *The Wild Palms* (and seldom have the consequences been so terrible); in *Light in August*, too, the effect of passion awakened too late in a spinster of forty is analysed and described in all its alternating phases: here also the penalty is severe, since the affair ends with the spinster's murder by her lover and the mutilation of the murderer at the hands of a bloodthirsty mob. The reporter in *Pylon* (like other members of the male cast, including a maddened police-officer) is bewitched by the woman parachute jumper (who shares with Charlotte in *The Wild Palms* and Joe Christmas's Miz Burden a hard, unyielding, mannish quality); the schoolmaster in *The Hamlet* is undone by his physical longing for a plump, horribly female child, while in reverse Temple Drake in *Sanctuary*, herself an epitome of the feminine principle, is dragged down and almost destroyed by her desire for the gangster Red. Lust, however, and the retribution attendant upon its satisfaction, is not the sole motivation of Mr Faulkner's chief characters by any means; it is merely their closest approach to love. Pride is their ruling passion: in Joe Christmas a perverse pride in being partly coloured; family pride and fear of dishonour in Quentin, and Colonel Sutpen; pride glaring hateful and grotesque in the barn-burning Snopes and the egregious Jones, but attaining a noble stature in the Negro Lucas Beauchamp. Only in the person of Gavin Stevens, the attorney in *Knight's Gambit* and *Intruder in the Dust*, is humility allowed to manifest itself, but Stevens is a later and more sympathetic figure, many of whose utterances may be supposed to coincide with the opinions of the author himself: 'Some things you must never stop refusing to bear. Injustice and outrage and dishonour and shame'; on the Negro problem, to the literature of which *Intruder in the Dust* is perhaps the most notable contribution from either side of the Atlantic, he is also worth quoting because free from hysteria:

> I'm defending Sambo from the North and East and West – the
> outlanders who will fling him decades back not merely into
> injustice but into grief and agony and violence too by forcing
> on us laws based on the idea that man's injustice to man can
> be abolished overnight by police ... I only say that the injustice
> is ours, the South's. We must expiate and abolish it ourselves,
> alone and without help nor even (with thanks) advice.

Among Mr Faulkner's main characters Stevens, perhaps owing to his legal training, is unique in being clear-sighted where the others are only single-minded; he remains detached while they are obsessed, driven. For the most part they are not so much characters as creations, larger than life and, in many cases, monsters. Their mannerisms, their clothes, are part of them, like the protagonists in Mr Wyndham Lewis's *Childermas*, who began to dissolve instantly if a particle of their raiment were removed. It is as impossible to imagine Lucas Beauchamp without his black broadcloth coat or gold toothpick as it is to visualise Popeye dressed other than in his slanted straw hats and tight narrow black suits, not unlike those affected by Joe Christmas, who shares, too, his habit of smoking a cigarette down 'without touching his hand to it once'. These are zombies, walking somnabulistically towards death and disaster, terrible, undeviating, doomed: Popeye does not even try to defend himself when arrested for the wrong murder, while Christmas, on his way to kill, 'didn't think even then *Something is going to happen. Something is going to happen to me*' (though this thought does occur to Temple Drake, couched in these identical words, as Popeye moves towards her in the crib).

That the author persuades us to accept these automata as real, by endowing them with a semblance of galvanic life, is because of his brilliant re-creation of their background, and also his mastery of narrative technique: probably unequalled since Conrad, from whom he may be seen in certain aspects to derive. Conrad's main characters, too, were the puppets of an ironical fate: the degradation to which Willems in *Outcast of the Islands* sinks through his attachment to the beautiful Aissa is closely paralleled by many of Mr Faulkner's characters in the grip of the same emotions, as demonstrated above; while Mr Jones and his secretary Ricardo – to name but two – have much of the blank, savage menace we have come to accept as inseparable from a Faulkner villain. A charge of pretentiousness and wilful obscurantism might be laid against both authors for the tricks they play with time and chronology and the delight they appear to take in telling their stories in what would seem, at first sight, to be the most difficult and roundabout way; yet on closer examination the obliquity of these methods will be found as justifiable as those of a photographer or film-director who shoots his subject from an unfamiliar angle in order to underline or illuminate a particular artistic truth which would remain otherwise invisible.

Of Mr Faulkner's brilliant technical experiments, perhaps the most triumphantly successful is *The Sound and the Fury*, a novel long out of print in this country and which, it may be hoped, will soon be available again in the uniform edition. The choice of a congenital idiot for narrator of the first part is no act of bravado intended to display the author's virtuosity; like everything in this carefully planned book, it has a definite purpose, for Benjy, owing to the mental fog in which he has his being, lives in a continuous stream of time, past and present are all one to him: therefore, though he (and consequently, at first, the reader) understands almost nothing of what is going on around him, clues to the meaning of previous and subsequent events are scattered throughout his confused narrative which can be fully understood by the time the concluding section is reached, thus attaining a final depth of clarity which could not be arrived at by more straightforward story-telling. The book might be described both as a modern essay in Greek tragedy and a detective story of character; and if it requires a second reading for its full cleverness and profundity to be appreciated, the same can be said of few novels nowadays, and should not necessarily be regarded as a drawback.

Allied to this impressive technical equipment (exemplified also, to a high degree, in *Light in August*, next to *The Sound and the Fury* his most powerful novel) there is also the compelling quality of the style. Recently this has been in danger of self-strangulation: the convoluted sentences are sometimes pages long, as in the later work of Henry James; but in the early books it may be seen at its best: the dialogue curt and revelatory as that of his most gifted contemporaries, the rhythm of the descriptive and analytical passages moving as inexorably in their measured periods as his hallucinated protagonists towards their appointed end. A reader forgives the mannerisms, recurrent as those of the characters themselves: the reiteration, for example, of his favourite words, 'sourceless', 'primogenitive', 'inflectionless', 'defunctive' and 'whorled'; the preponderance of adjectives: 'mild, cold, bland, heartless voice', 'a quick, hard, high, close grip', etc: they are the marks of an individuality welcome in an age when most fiction might be written, collectively, by the staff of a newspaper.

Perhaps the simplest, yet most vivid, example of his style may be found in *Sanctuary*, to which his latest novel, *Requiem for a Nun*, is the sequel. According to the 'Modern Library' preface, *Sanctuary* was Mr Faulkner's attempt to write a thriller on the popular plane, and though it has since inspired a school of sensationalism which its begetter may, with reason, hold in abhorrence, certainly the sheer savage tension of the original has not been surpassed by any of its imitators. At the close of that book, we left Temple Drake, the sullen and corrupted victim of outrage, sitting beside her father in the Luxembourg Gardens 'where at sombre intervals the dead tranquil queens in stained marble mused', and the sky lay 'prone and vanquished in the embrace of the season of rain and death'. One would have thought she had been punished enough, but Mr Faulkner, the moralist, was not satisfied: there was still more expiation to come. Now we find her some years later, a young matron married to Gowan Stevens (not to be confused with his uncle, the lawyer of *Knight's Gambit* and *Intruder in the Dust*, who appears also in this book, in his customary role of *deus ex machina*). Gowan's drunken bout in *Sanctuary* was initially responsible for his future wife's meeting with Popeye, and in remorse he has sworn himself to abstinence from liquor; together they are attempting to live down the scandal of the past, when the appearance of a blackmailer and the murder of their baby by the Negro nurse, Nancy (who was herself hunted down by a murderous husband in the story 'That Evening Sun'), combine to set in motion a new series of confessions and abnegations, involving a complete recapitulation of Temple's past to the Governor of the State in which Nancy is to hang, and to whom the bereaved mother is making a plea for clemency. Here, and especially in the utterances of Nancy in the condemned cell, the anonymous and mysterious 'Player' of *Sartoris* and *Light in August* is revealed to be God Himself, and His pawns are now given, as by the Christian ethic, freedom of choice between good and evil. The main theme is majestic and Dostoevskian; but though Mr Faulkner shows that he has not lost his passion for experiment by writing much of the story in the form of a play (each act prefaced by a historical account of the origins of the three respective settings: courthouse, capitol and gaol), his imaginative grip on the reader, during the long dramatic dialogues, is sometimes allowed to slacken. It may even be that his best work belongs to the past, though he will probably prove us wrong in this respect: that already done, however, would more than entitle him to the honour conferred, as a tribute of recognition, to an important and considerable artist in his lifetime.

The Simenon Cycle

*   *   *

M. THOMAS NARCEJAC'S SHORT BUT COMPREHENSIVE STUDY, *The Art of Simenon* (reviewed in these columns on 17 October last), contains, besides other valuable material, a bibliographical table listing 125 titles by subject, published between the years 1931 and 1952, 57 of which have already been translated into English. Even when it is remembered that the majority of these novels – the Maigret stories in particular – are approximately 40,000 words in length such industry is remarkable; the year 1948, moreover, is credited with the appearance – among others – of three full-length books: *Le Destin des Malou*; a semi-autobiographical novel containing 516 pages (not yet translated); and *The Stain on the Snow*, now available in this country, and by some acclaimed as the author's masterpiece.

Already the inevitable comparisons have been made with Balzac, Zola, Edgar Wallace; inevitably, also, M. Simenon's enormous productivity has caused him to be regarded, in some circles, with distrust: 'Even to-day,' M. Narcejac tells us, the French critics 'applaud with reservations'. There is a tendency everywhere among intellectuals to find 'importance' and 'significance' inseparable from slow gestation and small prolificity. At a time when the reputations of many eminent contemporary novelists rest upon a handful of books, we are apt to forget the large output of Shakespeare and Dostoevsky, that many acknowledged classics were written, under a compulsive creative urge, in a matter of weeks; and that, while James Joyce spent seven years in writing *Ulysses*, a comparable amount of time was expended, by their respective authors, on *Gone with the Wind* and *Forever Amber*.

What is, however, as a rule unavoidable in the case of writers as phenomenally fertile as M. Simenon is the occasional publication of inferior work owing to haste and overstrain; his most extraordinary achievement appears to be the total absence of pot-boilers on the appended list: one cannot, of course, speak of the innumerable *feuilletons* which he wrote previously under the name Georges Sim, though it appears on good authority that the standard of these was also high. There is no sign of fatigue in the first ten adventures of Inspector Maigret, which appeared one after another in 1931; on the contrary, there is a steady increase of narrative control and the writing has an almost contemptuous ease: while apart from these admirable stories, the same year saw the publication of *The Man from Everywhere*, a sardonic study of a retired master-criminal which foreshadowed M. Simenon's later manner and must rank high in its own right, though *The Window over the Way*, printed two years afterwards, marks an even more rapid advance in sombre power and psychological tension.

M. Narcejac has made a careful analysis of the Maigret cycle, and also of the methods and personality of that redoubtable police officer, which he equates with those of the author himself. Here, as elsewhere, he reaches some sound conclusions, though as a critic he adopts too often a partisan standpoint and is over-zealous in defending his subject from some fancied slight. It is arguable, moreover, whether (as we are insistently told) 'Simenon has never written a single detective story.' True, the problems posed in the early Maigrets were not the 'classic' crossword-puzzle kind beloved of English addicts and dependent for their interest on tide-tables and apparently unbreakable alibis; they were, refreshingly, problems of character, but detective stories none the less. M. Simenon may have broken some of the 'rules', but he is too good an artist not to accept the discipline, and work within the limits, of his medium; where the identity of the criminal is concealed, he is less unfair in misleading the reader than, in most cases, the members of the Detection Club. His immediate success in this country proved, not only that the older forms were outworn and the public weary of red herrings and 'impossible' crimes, but that the stories, in spite of their unconventional approach, fulfilled the basic principles of investigation, deduction and revelation. For instance, in *Liberty Bar*, with only a small number of suspects, with all possible avenues explored one by one, we are still kept in doubt until almost the end as to who really killed William Brown – and the solution, though seemingly obvious when arrived at, yet comes as a surprise.

The same story contains a typical example of Maigret's mental procedure when confronted with a crime – no doubt, as M. Narcejac claims, comparable with M. Simenon's own in creating character; out of his depth in the South of France, among the white villas and mimosa and the little cafés behind the Croisette, the Inspector examines a photograph of the dead Englishman whose murder he is supposed to solve, and discovers in it a faint resemblance to himself. Instantly 'Brown-the-corpse' is forgotten: here is a man who intrigues him, that he 'must know more of'. By identifying himself thus with the object of his inquiry, and attempting to reconstruct the dead man's thoughts, he eventually succeeds, through this psychological post-mortem, in reconstructing the crime itself; for Maigret shares with his fictional compatriots this national tendency, even though he differs, in other respects, so radically from Rouletabille or Arsène Lupin – and still more from those eccentric French detectives created in this country: he neither twirls his moustaches nor puffs the Maryland.

Incidentally, the absence of traditional Gallic mannerisms may, apart from his other qualities, explain the popularity of the inspector on this side of the Channel: except for an occasional shrug of the shoulders he might almost be English himself. He is solidly built, soberly dressed, respectably married, sparing of speech; smokes a pipe and drinks beer for preference; like ourselves, he is insular and no linguist; asked to investigate a crime in Holland, he finds himself foxed when the suspects talk together in their own language, nor is he at home in *The Flemish Shop*: we have yet to read of his experiences in New York. He is unique among his kind in being a three-dimensional figure, broadly human, becoming more fallible book by book without losing a particle of his original authority; his background filled in with homely, telling detail: as when on holiday, visiting his wife stricken with appendicitis at a convent hospital, he is ill at ease in the presence of the sisters of mercy to whose care she has been entrusted, and plunges into an investigation as a relief from boredom and anxiety: or when, tracking the killer of a clairvoyante during a Paris heat wave, he longs for an iced lager – and stumbles upon the vital clue in consequence.

M. Narcejac states, perhaps with reason, that 'Simenon created Maigret primarily in order to try to reach the inner nature of his characters through this privileged personage', and to develop in this fashion the finesse of his literary technique. It is more than likely that Maigret was also brought into being as a means of freeing the author from financial pressure and leaving him at liberty to choose from a wider field of subject-matter: we are told that Roger, the protagonist of the autobiographical *Pedigree*, took a passionate interest, when at school, in 'Dumas, the poor, unknown scribbler in an office where he was only tolerated out of charity', and it is conceivable that the career of the young Simenon was modelled on that of the author who, by indefatigable publication, solved his economic problems and outlived in popularity many of the more highbrow colleagues who once patronised him.

However this may be, when the inspector had served his purpose he was temporarily abandoned, and the central figures in the stories that followed had more in common with the criminals in the previous series than with the solidly integrated police official: they were, in fact, lost without him. Deprived of anyone to accuse and apprehend them, to lead them with gruff sympathy towards ultimate expiation, they ran around in circles searching for their own destiny, battering themselves against the brick walls of their isolation and despair. These were the rootless and driven (De Ritter, M. Hire, *The Lodger*), but sometimes the walls were cushioned and the character was isolated for our observation in the padded cell of a senseless routine (Kees Popinga, the lawyer Loursat, the grim Burgomaster of Furnes). They are creatures of habit, ringed round by position, environment or family, imagining themselves safe in the asylums of their own choice until some visitation or event from the outside world forces them to engage in the life with which they are so unfitted to cope, and brings about their destruction or redemption. Of these, Popinga, in *The Man Who Watched the Trains Go By*, may be regarded as the type-figure, for he loses at one blow all the comfortable illusions which have buttressed him for so long; and having become a murderer, ends in an actual asylum. Sometimes they attempt to break away of their own accord (Mahé, the *Banana Tourist*, M. Monde), but remain prisoners none the less, since their revolt lacks organisation and aim: only Roger Mamelin escapes, to become, it may be presumed, M. Simenon.

Then there are the turbulent, ambitious young men (Phillipe Dargens, Michel Maudet in *The Magnet of Doom*) peering, these, through walls of glass at the desired objects of money and power, planning smash-and-grab raids into the luxury circles they envy; but once the glass is broken and the sortie successfully carried out they are not appeased, for some unspecified longing (love, integration with their fellow men?) always eludes their eager grasp. Frank Friedmaier, in *The Stain on the Snow*, belongs roughly to this group, though M. Simenon has now arrived at a much later stage of his creative development, and his character has affinities with Stavrogin and the Boy in *Brighton Rock*, while the theme is not dissimilar from that treated by M. Sartre in *Lucifer and the Lord*.

The setting is an anonymous foreign city occupied for the past four years by enemy forces, and Frank, the son of a local brothel-keeper, has grown up protected, by his mother's occupation, from the sordid poverty and misery which oppress most of his neighbours. For this reason – though not until the end of the book, and then only dimly – does he formulate to himself the motive for his behaviour – the boy now aged nineteen, sets out to invite suffering; first, he kills an enemy sergeant to gain experience and exposes himself to an enigmatic figure named Holst in the hope of betrayal, then he murders a miserly old woman from the village of his upbringing, having first robbed her of a collection of watches coveted by an occupying general; and finally he arranges the seduction of Holst's daughter, Sissy (who loves him), by a gross, corrupt black-marketer whom he helps to dispose of the loot. 'It was not that he wanted to become a martyr, nor merely a victim...Fate was lying in wait for him somewhere. But where? Instead of waiting for fate to reveal itself at its appointed time, Frank ran after it, casting about everywhere in his search.'

And, four pages later: 'He had searched for fate in every corner, and fate was in none of the places where he had hunted.'

Holst does not betray him, nor attempt to avenge his daughter; the proceeds of his robbery bring him no happiness: he does not even know what to do with the money, which he carries about loose in his trouser pockets, and is reduced to giving away a large sum to a needy acquaintance, though scarcely of a generous disposition. It is the money which leads to his undoing in the end, for the notes are marked, and he is arrested for questioning by the authorities, who eventually execute him, after he has received forgiveness and absolution from Holst and Sissy and confessed to his crimes.

This story which, treated less expertly, might have proved intolerable to read, does, as presented by M. Simenon, achieve a tragic dignity: in it the author seems to have set out to disprove Mr Edward Sackville-West's assertion that 'the grave issues cannot receive artistic expression save through the medium of characters who are both highly articulate and thoroughly aware of their predicament'. M. Simenon's characters are neither: nor do they 'possess an appreciable education and/or sensibility'. They are people without God, though salvation is not denied them – as in the Christian ethic – so long as they trouble to seek for it: witness, in this connection, that of Frank – outwardly as intractable a case as any to be found in the pages of Mr Greene or M. Mauriac. But salvation must be found, according to M. Simenon, through the realisation of self: we are told that his ambition as a novelist is to create 'a new concept of a man', a new way of looking at humanity. Now, in his fiftieth year and at the height of his powers, he is well on the way to succeeding in this difficult task, and already, perhaps, deserving of the high place in contemporary literature which M. Narcejac claims for him.

Mr Wodehouse and Others

*   *   *

MR P.G. WODEHOUSE COULD SCARCELY COMPLAIN OF HARSH treatment from the critics; as an established favourite he is unassailable: yet since the late Hilaire Belloc's generous tribute there is something superficial, something dismissive, about the crop of short notices which greets the publication of each new work: in spite of the superlatives with which these are studded, the reviewers seem content to pigeonhole him conveniently as ideal light reading for beach, train, or weekend trip, and the simultaneous appearance of five of his novels in the Penguin edition – spanning, from their original publication dates, fifteen years of creative activity – affords a welcome opportunity of reassessing his contribution to contemporary literature.

What strikes one immediately on re-reading these books[1] is the widespread effect exercised by Mr Wodehouse's style on writers of divergent schools, and particularly on those specialising in humorous dialogue: the trick of repetitive utterance, for example, so characteristic of Bertie Wooster at moments of stunned incredulity, is also a marked feature of the early novels of Mr Evelyn Waugh and Mr Anthony Powell, among others; while the locutions of the imperturbable Psmith are echoed in the speech of both Lord Peter Wimsey and Mr Albert Campion: at times, too, there is a suave acidity in Psmith's tone not unlike that of Anthony Blanche in *Brideshead Revisited*:

> 'No, but – well, as I was saying, I'm frightfully keen to get hold
> of a thousand quid.'
> 'So am I,' said Psmith. 'Two minds with but a single thought.

---

1   *Leave it to Psmith, The Inimitable Jeeves, Big Money, Right Ho, Jeeves, The Code
    of the Woosters*, Penguin Books.

How do you propose to start about it? For my part, I must freely confess that I haven't a notion.'

Psmith – the initial letter is silent, 'as in phthisis, psychic, and ptarmigan' – made his début, we are told in a biographical note, in a school story written for *The Captain*: he must have aroused in his housemaster some anxious speculation as to the course of his future: in 1915 he showed signs of embarking on a journalistic career, but in *Leave it to Psmith* (1923) we meet him at a later stage, monocled and wearing 'a morning coat of irreproachable fit', yet in spite of this surface smartness 'broke as the Ten Commandments', standing on the verge of destitution: 'that low moaning sound you hear is the wolf bivouacked outside my door.' His postbag consists of three tempting offers from money-lenders with Scottish pseudonyms, 'a printed brochure entitled "This Night Shall Thy Soul be Required of Thee"', and a circular from an undertaker offering to bury him for eight pounds ten; but by impersonating a Canadian poet, the author of *Songs of Squalor* ('Plumbs the depths of human emotion and strikes a new note' – *Montreal Star*; 'Very readable' – *Ipsilanti Herald*), he secures an invitation to Market Blandings, where a peer's son (also impoverished) involves him in a plot to steal a valuable diamond necklace.

With this book Mr Wodehouse was evolving from an intermediate and less characteristic manner: goofs and golf were left behind, Piccadilly Jim, Sally and Jill the Reckless superseded by characters like Stanley Featherstonehaugh Ukridge, with his ingenious but impracticable schemes for making a fortune. A personal mythology was beginning to emerge – the Drones Club in Dover Street, where bread rolls were bandied across the luncheon table by prominent members named Catsmeat Potter-Pirbright or Barmy Fotheringay-Phipps; and Blandings Castle, the scene of many a future frolic, with its flowerbeds and begonias so beloved by the absent-minded earl, its owner.

Although published three decades ago, *Leave it to Psmith* remains remarkably undated, except for a few phrases of American slang (that ever-changing quantity), and some references to the silent film serials of the time, the comments on which are as pungently satirical as those made later by Mr Wodehouse on talking-pictures and television: the heroine lies bound upon a sacrificial altar at the end of episode eleven, the hero is slipping over a precipice in an attempt at rescue: 'I'm afraid it won't end happily,' Psmith sighs; 'I think he'll save her'. On the whole, this novel is less of a period-piece than *Vile Bodies*, and surely the creation of Colonel Blount, in the latter book, owes much to that amiable dodderer, Lord Emsworth, who, when approached for a loan, believes he is being offered one, and refuses with thanks, saying he has ample money for the moment. The confidence-man with the mottled face and the flowered waistcoat, who accosts Psmith with bogus breeziness in the Piccadilly Hotel, might have stepped straight from the pages of Mr Graham Greene, and indeed a similar incident is briefly sketched in one of that author's 'entertainments', while Anthony Farrant, in *England Made Me*, is a seedier latter-day version of Psmith himself.

The following year, 1924, saw the publication of *The Inimitable Jeeves*, and with this volume Mr Wodehouse had found his proper vein: Bertie Wooster's seemingly artless narration of his own misfortunes foreshadowed the manner of those colloquial writers who later became fashionable in this country through the influence of transatlantic models, and remains far more natural and unforced than the style adopted by his successors: 'I was about fed up with the whole thing. I mean, cats in your bedroom – a bit thick, what? I didn't know how the dickens they had got in, but I was jolly well resolved that they weren't going to stay picknicking there any longer.'

The presence of the cats, originally stolen for a rag by the undergraduate twins Claude and Eustace, and introduced into Bertie's bedroom by his man Jeeves, results in Sir Roderick Glossop, the psychiatrist, believing that he is dangerously insane; consequently the engagement to Sir Roderick's amazonian daughter is broken off, to Bertie's hearty relief; once more Jeeves, by a masterstroke, has saved his employer's bacon. *The Inimitable Jeeves* is in reality a series of short stories loosely linked by a main theme: Bertie's efforts to help his school friend, Bingo Little, whose impetuousness in affairs of the heart lands him invariably up to the neck in trouble. Bingo belongs to the same category as those two delectable ancients, Old Biffy and Old Sippy, whose exploits used to brighten the pages of the *Strand* magazine; and Bertie's attempts to extricate him from the consequences of his folly result in the luckless narrator fleeing to the United States, becoming involved with tricksters on the French Riviera, and posing as a lady novelist whom Bingo afterwards marries. Thanks to Jeeves he emerges from these ordeals safe and sound, but with his sanity more than ever doubted by his acquaintances.

Ten years later, in *Right Ho, Jeeves*, to which *The Code of the Woosters* (1938) forms a sequel, Bertie is similarly entangled, and once more on behalf of a friend: this time Gussie Fink-Nottle, whose single-minded devotion to Madeline Bassett (daughter of a police-court magistrate, Sir Watkyn Bassett, CBE) is no less dangerous than Bingo Little's more widely distributed affections. Bertie's formidable female relative Aunt Dahlia, once the pride of the Quorn, now proprietress of a fashion magazine perpetually on the fringe of insolvency and called *Milady's Boudoir*, takes part in the action; the dragonish, domineering Aunt Agatha, whose main desire is to see Bertie suitably married off, looms in the background; and at one point he finds that he has himself become betrothed to the whimsical Madeline, who alludes to the stars as God's daisy chain and is sometimes described (though not by Gussie) as a 'weird Gawd-Help-Us':

> 'Oh, look,' she said. She was a confirmed Oh-looker. I had noticed this at Cannes, where she had drawn my attention in this manner on various occasions to such diverse objects as a French actress, a Provençal filling station, the sunset over the Estorels, Michael Arlen, a man selling coloured spectacles, the deep velvet blue of the Mediterranean, and the late Mayor of New York in a striped one-piece bathing suit.

It is instructive to note how the Wooster style has changed imperceptibly, from the callower, conversational rhythms of *The Inimitable Jeeves* to a more flexible and sensitive instrument, capable of delineating character in a few rapid strokes without disturbing the impression of entire naturalism. For instance, at the opening of *Right Ho, Jeeves*, we find Bertie grappling with one of the storyteller's major problems: how, effectively, to begin.

> It's a thing you don't want to go wrong over, because one false step and you're sunk. I mean, if you fool about too long at the start, trying to establish atmosphere, as they call it, and all that sort of rot, you fail to grip and the customers walk out on you.
>
> Get off the mark, on the other hand, like a scalded cat, and your public is at a loss. It simply raises its eyebrows, and can't make out what you're talking about.

Compare this with an extract from *The Code of the Woosters*, and the difference becomes immediately apparent:

> One of these well-remembered moments in my own case was the time at my first private school when I sneaked down to the head master's study at dead of night, my spies having informed

me that he kept a tin of biscuits in the cupboard under the bookshelf; to discover, after I was well inside and a modest and unobtrusive withdrawal impossible, that the old bounder was seated at his desk – by what I have always thought a rather odd coincidence, actually engaged in the composition of my end-of-term report, which subsequently turned out a stinker.

Bertie explains this stylistic development by constant association with Jeeves, which, he says, has 'enlarged the Wooster vocabulary considerably', but we are not deceived: we know that it is the narrator himself who has developed. For there can be little doubt at this stage, in spite of the vast and varied portrait gallery exhibited in the other books – in spite of Mr Mulliner, Lord Emsworth, the Biscuit all the Eggs, Beans and Crumpets, and even Uncle Fred – that Mr Wodehouse's real epic creation is Bertie Wooster, and not Jeeves as is generally accepted. A normal Englishman's dislike of frigid efficiency is reflected in the traits displayed by his more unpleasant characters: Sir Watkyn and Sir Roderick, Rupert Baxter the perfect secretary and the rascally astute Steggles; only Jeeves is exempt from this implied censure, but none the less the omniscient valet is too remote, too Olympian a figure to merit more than our grudging respect: all our affection is reserved for his pre-eminently endearing employer. It is difficult not to resent a man who is never wrong, and we cannot help sharing Bertie's hope that the god in the machine will fail one day to deliver the goods. Impossible, of course, to imagine this warm-hearted loyal young man, with his abundant literary gifts, separated from his ubiquitous attendant, but that Jeeves is incapable of holding the stage successfully without Bertie to act as Boswell and record the chilly triumphs of his superhuman piscivorously sustained intellect was made manifest when Mr Wodehouse essayed the experiment in his latest novel, recently reviewed in these columns.

Of the 'Jeeves' series, *The Code of the Woosters* is one of the richest in characterisation and incident and contains, moreover (among the malignant magistrates, obstructive policemen and embryo dictators that people its cast), a captivating portrait of a girl named Stiffy Byng; one of Bertie's many advantages as chronicler is the fact that he rarely falls in love (for his creator's purposes he must remain a bachelor), therefore his judgement of the opposite sex is unclouded by sentiment and, on occasion, tinged with asperity; but even his objective presentation cannot prevent the charm of this delightful, if dim-witted, heroine penetrating to us.

Mr Wodehouse has written more than sixty books to date and is still at the height of his form; indeed, *Barmy in Wonderland*, an acidulous account of a Drones Club member matching wits with shady theatrical promoters in New York, was one of his best non-Wooster novels for many a year. Inconceivable that, during his lifetime, his popularity will ever wane: it remains to be seen how his work will withstand the test of time. His world is, in its way, as formalised as that of Miss Ivy Compton-Burnett; like her, it is with the fundamentals of existence that he is mainly preoccupied: finance and the lack of it, the stern reality of economic pressure, by which – however lightly this problem may be treated – his characters are nevertheless conditioned, as many of his titles, *Big Money, Money for Nothing, Money in the Bank*, amply demonstrate. Such factors, combined with the agelessness of his idiom, the freshness and vitality of his prose, make it more than likely that a future generation will rediscover him, as is happening today in the case of Ronald Firbank – who, in his dandyism, his personal eccentricity and rueful approach to life, had certain superficial affinities with Bertie Wooster and other Young Men in Spats; and who, as a writer, was perhaps not so dissimilar from Mr Wodehouse as might be supposed.

A Totem of the 1920s
(John Buchan)

*   *   *

POPULAR FICTION IS A KIND OF FOLK MYTH, OBLIQUELY symptomatic of current social trends, as George Orwell demonstrated by contrasting *Raffles* (1900), on the one hand, with *No Orchids for Miss Blandish* (1939) on the other. 'The worst books,' he wrote in his essay on 'Boys' Weeklies', 'are often the most important, because they are usually the ones that are read earliest in life', and, referring to the generation that grew up between the two world wars, he added: 'it is probable that many people who would consider themselves extremely sophisticated and "advanced" are actually carrying through life an imaginative background which they acquired in childhood from (for instance) Sapper and Ian Hay.'

The truth of these observations may be illustrated by some examples from the work of Orwell's own contemporaries: W.H. Auden invokes, in the litany from *Journal of an Airman*, the names of several heroes from boys' adventure stories (Dixon Hawke, Nelson Lee, Ferrers Locke); the burlesque super-villain in Christopher Isherwood's unpublished Mortmere stories is called Reynard Moxon; and 'Moxon Ivery' is the alias adopted by the German count posing as a pacifist intellectual in John Buchan's *Mr Standfast*; while the secret agent incident in *Mr Norris Changes Trains* could have been written only by one thoroughly conversant with the spy melodramas which it so cleverly parodies; the namesake of Graham Greene's *Third Man* was the leader of Edgar Wallace's *Fellowship of the Frog* (though in the latter case 'Lime' is spelt with a 'y'); and even Orwell himself was not entirely unaffected, since *1984*, despite its serious purpose, is cast in the basic form of the traditional thriller, with the most-unlikely-person revealed at last as a member of the secret police.

Mr Richard Usborne mentions the passage from Orwell quoted above in the introduction to his 'nostalgic study'[1] of the three romantic writers whose works, absorbed during the formative years of childhood and adolescence, helped (as he freely admits) to condition his attitude to adult life in the manner suggested by Orwell. His particular trio – though Sapper exercised a powerful influence – did not, however, include Ian Hay: its two other members were John Buchan and Dornford Yates.

At the age of forty-three, Mr Usborne decided to re-read the novels and stories of these authors (a considerable task, since there are seventy-eight volumes all told), his object being partly to 'retrace his steps in the favourite reading of his youth', partly to re-examine its remembered magic in the light of later experience. The result will be immensely diverting to those many readers who, in earlier days, shared the same literary tastes, though they may not necessarily agree with the views expressed by him in his entertaining survey.

The author warns us that his approach is purely personal, his judgements highly subjective, belonging to the 'Lower Criticism'; but, despite these modest disclaimers, *Clubland Heroes* contains much shrewd comment on the social climate of the period to which the works in question belonged: Mr Usborne's scrutiny is all the more acute for being unclouded by political bias. His book consists of a general introduction and three parts: one devoted to each author, and subdivided into chapters dealing with the protagonists (Berry, Hannay, Bulldog Drummond etc) who recur most frequently in the various sagas; a final section treats with mock seriousness the fanciful conception of British espionage postulated by the 'Secret Service' writers of the 1920s ('Since authors must live between wars, so must their spies'). Mr Usborne's trio had much in common: all were professional men who had seen war service. John Buchan (later Lord Tweedsmuir, Governor-General of Canada) had been a *Times* correspondent on the Western Front in 1915, a major in Intelligence a year later, and a colonel in 1917, when he was appointed a director of the newly-founded Ministry of Information. Sapper (Lt-Col. Cyril McNeile) was a regular soldier who retired in 1919 and settled down to writing as a career. Dornford Yates (Major William Mercer) had, like Buchan, been called to the Bar and was President of the Union at Oxford: both he and Sapper were obviously much attached to their public-school backgrounds (Yates even dedicated

---

1   *Clubland Heroes*, Richard Usborne, Constable.

a novel to Harrow). Although Buchan's initial adventure story, *The Half Hearted*, was published in the same year as *Raffles*, and the White Ladies group was introduced to magazine readers by Dornford Yates in 1911, Sapper's first volumes of short stories actually appeared during the war, and all three were essentially war-writers; long after the conflict was over, the atmosphere of the trenches pervaded the civilian lives of their characters, all of whom had distinguished themselves in battle and earned decorations for valour: Sapper awarded the DSO and MC to Bulldog Drummond and the VC to Toby Sinclair; Yates gave Jonah Mansel and Boy Pleydell the DSO and MC respectively; Richard Hannay and Archie Roylance both got the DSO from Buchan, who also bestowed a posthumous VC upon Peter Pienaar, the wily old Afrikander, for his gallant death in action with the Royal Flying Corps.

These men were also great sportsmen in both senses of the word, famous at school for their prowess on the playing fields; as adults ('eternally "fit"') they added climbing, hunting, shooting and fishing to their list of accomplishments. Sapper's heroes held, perhaps, the best all-round records in these respects: Ronald Standish and Peter Darrell were scratch golfers as well, Jim Maitland and Bulldog Drummond ex-amateur-heavyweight boxing champions; though this distinction was shared by Yates's Jonathan Mansel, who put his skill to good use by killing a crook 'with a single blow to the jaw': a feat soon duplicated by his devoted chronicler Chandos. (Drummond – equally expert in judo as with the gloves – preferred to despatch enemies 'with his bare hands', by a stranglehold taught him by 'Osaki the Jap'.)

One and all were elected by their authors to membership of West End clubs, which they used as bases for their confidential missions on behalf of the Old Country, and Mr Usborne draws an adroit parallel between this way of life and the public school system, pointing an analogy, also, between the prefects' code, by which corporal punishment may be arbitrarily inflicted with the sanction of the authorities, and the summary executions of criminals and subversive aliens carried out, with the unofficial connivance of Scotland Yard and the Ministries, by Drummond, Mansel and their respective henchmen; it is more probable, however, that the theory of extra-judicial retribution derived originally from Edgar Wallace's *Four Just Men* (1905): though Jonah Mansel, actuated as a rule by talionic motives, is apt to conceal these beneath a show of moral indignation when passing sentence, and lacks, therefore, the cold impartial dignity of George Manfred in similar circumstances, while Leon Gonsalez would doubtless have been dismissed by Bulldog Drummond as a dago.

John Buchan was the first of the three to enter the lists with a novel of international intrigue: *The Thirty-nine Steps* (1915). Until his advent, William Le Queux and E. Phillips Oppenheim had this literary field more or less to themselves; theirs was a less realistic convention, stiff and formalised in manner: the crackle of starched shirts could be heard between the sentences as suave diplomats skirmished with barbed politeness over dinner-tables in cosmopolitan restaurants or in 'the chancellries of Europe'. Buchan's swifter pace and colloquial style, containing homely echoes of *King Solomon's Mines* and *Allan Quatermain*, was to alter all that.

Meanwhile Dornford Yates had already published his first collection of squirearchal tales featuring the Pleydell family, while Sapper's army stories (not dissimilar in subject-matter and *dramatis personae* – the glasshouse boy who atoned by dying bravely on the battlefield, the 'gentleman-ranker', the tough Hibernian sergeant etc – from those written during the more recent war by Gerald Kersh) were well received by critics of the day: '"Sapper's" books will live for generations, and will take their place with the classic literature of the war' – *British Weekly*; 'As good as Kipling's early tales' – James Douglas; 'There is a touch of genius, and more than a touch, in "Sapper"' – Sir W. Robertson Nicoll. (These notices, re-read today, may give rise to reflection on the exaggerated and ephemeral nature of reviewers' praise, especially at the present time, when personal narratives or military and maritime adventure, issued *en masse* by publishers in response to a sudden public craze, are being acclaimed in the press with eulogistic tributes out of all proportion to their literary merit.)

Mr Usborne draws attention, also, to Sapper's novel *Mufti*, published in 1919 (two years before the appearance of Bulldog Drummond), in which, though incipient democratic sympathies are expressed 'and the social problems of war discussed without dogmatism', the young author was at the same time evolving his grotesque conception of the officer type as representative of a master-race recruited solely from the leisure class and endemic to English shores: 'Of such was The Breed'. This doctrinaire ideal, personified by the egregious monocled figure of Jim Maitland, became gradually responsible for the obsessional insularity, sadistic overtones and explicit anti-Semitism which Mr Usborne rightly deplores in his later work.

Similar traits recur to a lesser degree in the characters and situations created by Dornford Yates, but here Mr Usborne, who openly acknowledges his preference for this author's work, is less willing to view them with disfavour. In fact, where the Berry books are concerned, he is quick to anticipate criticism before any has been offered, extolling them as 'a considerable achievement in light literature' and even suggesting, at one point, a comparison with Trollope. He analyses the 'choriambic rhythm' and 'attractive archaism' of the 'unusually studied' style: 'There are frequent moments in both his types of books when Yates calls for silence, and then, in perfect phalanx, wheels his sentences into the Dorian mood. He is writing for special attention, and with special care.'

This solemn assessment of what is obvious tushery, judging by the passage appended as a sample of the so-called 'diamanté prose', would on the face of it seem preposterous, yet, as an epigraph to the section, Mr Usborne quotes from a review by Cyril Connolly, in which the latter professes his admiration for Dornford Yates, postulates the existence of a cabalistic fan club meeting 'at great garden parties, literary luncheons, or in the quiet of an exclusive gunroom', and concludes by praising the author for 'fine writing' and 'a wit that is ageless united to a courtesy that is extinct'.

This review was printed by *The New Statesman* in 1935; and, though Mr Connolly may have conceivably altered his views since then, the invocation of so distinguished a critic in support of Mr Usborne's claims seems to call for a more careful consideration of the work at issue. One finds little trace, nevertheless, of the qualities ascribed: especially that of ageless wit; Berry himself is a pompous, dogmatic buffoon, both his outbursts of rhetorical acerbity and his self-styled 'monographs' being couched in ponderous circumlocutions of a type frequently parodied by Patrick Hamilton ('I am about to contribute to this heterogeneous volume a little dissertation of indisputable value'; 'If I may make bold to borrow Shakespeare's deathless words', etc): though to call one's wife a venomous shrew and to suggest, even in jest, that she is verminous, denotes undeniably a courtesy which is extinct. Fine writing also eludes the most diligent seeker; two passages from *Perishable Goods*, one descriptive, one of dialogue, might be said, on the other hand to display its antithesis:

> I do not believe in Enchantment: but, if there be such a thing,
> it stood at my shoulder that evening upon the ramparts of
> Gath. Castle, spur and thickets, mountains and forests and the

flash of the water below seemed all 'such stuff as dreams are made on,' and I could not shake off the feeling that we were about to quit a fantastic country which, search for it as we might, we should never see again.

'I love you,' he said. 'I love the stars in your eyes and the breath of your lips. I love your hair and your temples and the pride of your exquisite mouth. I love all your peerless beauty. But, most of all, my queen, I love your darling nature and the finest, bravest heart that ever closed a book at the end of one golden chapter – and put it back on the shelf.'

But, as Boy Pleydell truthfully observes in *As Berry and I Were Saying*: 'If you can write, you can: if you can't write, you can't – and you never will be able to…no one can ever teach a person who can't write to write and no one, other than himself, can ever teach a person who can write to write well.'

Mr Usborne is less biased in favour of Buchan: in fact, while stating, correctly, that he was the best writer, storyteller and craftsman of the three, he quite unfairly asserts that the creator of Sandy Arbuthnot, John S. Blenkiron, Haraldsen and the boy Peter John Hannay (to say nothing of Ivery, Colonel Stumm, Hilda von Einem and Dominick Medina, on the opposition benches) failed in character-drawing. However, any disagreement with the views expressed in *Clubland Heroes* must be a purely personal matter, for each reader will have his own particular preferences among the authors it examines; perhaps the passages dealing with the heroines of the period (the open-air types, the 'topping girls') are among the happiest in the book: here Mr Usborne's wryly ironical manner extracts the utmost fun from the material at his disposal. He is weakest in the middle section and, though his textual knowledge of the books concerned is elsewhere encyclopaedic, it is possible to catch him out on several minor points where the Hannay books are concerned; a list of errors is appended below, for correction in future editions, of which we hope there will be many.

Archie Roylance did not join Hannay and Arbuthnot (then Lord Clanroyden) on their expedition to *The Island of Sheep*: Lombard, a former companion of Sir Richard's bushveld days was the third man on that occasion. Lord Artinswell retired from the Foreign Office in the early 1920s and was not, therefore, the Head Man fifteen years later (unless he was recalled to duty after the Medina affair in which he did not plan counter-measures, but took only an onlooker's part); nor did the Graf von Schwabing (Moxon Ivery) appear anywhere in *The Three Hostages*; while Clanroyden's Christian names were not Alexander Ludovick, but Ludovick Gustavus: though he once called himself Alexander Thomson whilst posing as a dramatic critic on holiday. (Sandy – not one of Mr Usborne's favourites – was incidentally the only character created by any of the three authors who would have attended a Bloomsbury party, unwashed, wearing a black sweater, and furnished with 'all the latest Paris studio argot', but there is some excuse for these lapses from the accepted standards of his 'totem': for he was disguised, at the time, as a 'Surréaliste'.)

Out of the Ordinary:
The Novel of Pursuit and Suspense

*　　　*　　　*

'MORE THAN A QUARTER OF A CENTURY HAS PASSED SINCE Richard Hannay found the dead man in his flat and started that long flight and pursuit – across the Yorkshire and the Scottish moors, down Mayfair streets, and along the passages of Government buildings, in and out of Cabinet rooms and country houses, towards the cold Essex jetty with the thirty-nine steps, that were to be a pattern for adventure writers ever after. John Buchan was the first to realise the enormous dramatic value of adventure in familial surroundings happening to unadventurous men...murder in "the atmosphere of breeding and simplicity and stability".'

Thus Mr Graham Greene, in his admirable collection of essays, *The Lost Childhood*, traces the genealogy of a literary genre to whose later development he himself, 'fascinated by the new imaginative form, the hairbreadth escapes in a real world', has contributed so much. Buchan, influenced by the earlier example of Stevenson, adapted the sense of helpless terror conveyed in the first part of *Treasure Island* to a metropolitan setting and surroundings even more prosaic than those described in *The Suicide Club* or *The Rajah's Diamond*: the frightened boy, Jim Hawkins, bracing himself, in the lonely besieged inn, against the onslaught of Blind Pew and his ruffianly gang, was transformed into those prototypes of the unromantic modern-thriller hero: Edward Leithen, the 'dry stick' of a middle-aged lawyer, fleeing from the emissaries of *The Power House* through the London streets lit by June sunlight, or Hannay, the war-seasoned battalion officer (though 'quite safe, looking for a taxi in the middle of Whitehall'), breaking into a sweat of fear at thought of the mission ahead of him: 'I watched the figures in khaki passing on the pavement, and thought what a nice safe prospect they had compared to mine.'

351

These men were human, more than willing to admit to a feeling of 'complete funk', unlike the conventional Bulldog Breed of Drummond and the *Boy's Own Paper*; and though Hannay's victory in a hand-to-hand fight with the formidable Stumm puts a strain on the reader's credulity, there are psychological factors which make such an outcome just possible: the incongruous note so dear to Buchan's successors is struck in the contrast between Stumm's enormous height, gross physique, and pear-shaped Prussian head, and the feminine luxury of his private sanctum, scented and 'upholstered like a lady's boudoir':

> It was the room of a man who had a passion for frippery, who had a perverted taste for soft, delicate things. It was the comple-ment to his bluff brutality. I began to see the queer other side to my host, that evil side which gossip had spoken of as not unknown in the German army. The room seemed a horribly unwholesome place, and I was more than ever afraid of Stumm.

Indeed, not only Buchan's heroes but also his villains are in the modern tradition; nor are they devoid of nobility or even pathos: the leader of the Black Stone, the German agent who could hood his eyes like a hawk, was, 'more than a spy; in his foul way he had been a patriot', and the reader is able to share Sandy (Ludovick) Arbuthnot's pity for the lonely satanic figure of his enemy Dominick Medina, in *The Three Hostages*. That Arbuthnot and Medina seem, in many ways, to be almost counterparts is due to more than the surely intentional similarity between their Christian names, for a curious bond of sympathy and admiration often exists between the antagonists in these books: Hannay himself is strongly attracted to Medina in the initial stages; Sandy is nearly seduced from the path of duty by the evil, imperious Hilda von Einem; Mr Lumley tries to convert Leithen to his empty anarchistic creed, and so on (Buchan's Protestants and Calvinists, like the Catholic protagonists of Mr Greene, are fully alive to the allure of the devil's advocate), while few thriller writers, during the recent war, would have risked unpopularity by drawing a sympathetic portrait-sketch of Hitler, as the author of *Greenmantle* did of the Kaiser in 1916.

In his later novels – *The Three Hostages* in particular – the 'great extra-social intelligences' moving behind the international scene, with a view to world destruction, in *The Power House*, were replaced by 'Wreckers on the grand scale, merchants of pessimism, giving society another kick downhill whenever it had a chance of finding its balance', and

behind these smug exploiters lay the whole dreary wastes of
half-baked craziness...feverish cranks toiling to create a new
heaven and a new earth, and thinking themselves the leaders
of mankind, when they were dancing like puppets at the will
of a few scoundrels engaged in the most ancient of pursuits.

Such utterances, which seem prophetic today (we have seen enough
Pitt-Herons in our own time), did not accord with current intellectual
opinion during the 1930s, and caused Buchan to fall into disrepute
with the more highbrow sections of the public: though they are now,
ironically enough, re-echoed in the thrillers of former left-wing writers
such as Mr Nicholas Blake (*The Whisper in the Gloom*), Mr Julian
Symons (*The Broken Penny*), and Mr Roy Fuller (*The Second Curtain*);
while the settings and scenes in *Mr Standfast* (1918) appear to be almost
contemporaneous in the 1950s (the arty-crafty garden city, peopled
with well-meaning Bohemian eccentrics and 'pacificists', which is used
as a cover for the genuinely subversive activities of rubber-faced, silver-
tongued Moxon Ivery – actually the Graf von Schwabing, and 'the most
dangerous man in all the world'; the chapter in which Hannay, disguised
as a private soldier during a London air-raid, is prevented from capturing
Ivery by the intervention of officious military police, who arrest and
detain him as a deserter).

This last episode might have been devised by Mr Alfred Hitchcock,
whose earlier talking pictures carried the Buchan formula a step farther
(it is no coincidence that one of the most effective was based, however
unrecognisably, on *The Thirty-nine Steps*); and through their influence
upon Mr Graham Greene, were the visual forerunners of a whole new
literary trend. Mr Hitchcock himself had evidently learnt from the
silent films produced in France and Germany during the post-1914–18
War years; as Mr Greene and Sir Carol Reed were, in turn, to learn
from him. So the figure of Fantômas, in the Louis Feuillade serials,
with his sinister hood and slippery skin-tight costume, escaping
eel-like from his pursuers into the black wet labyrinth of the Paris
sewers, was obliquely reflected, three decades later, in the bulky black-
overcoated shape of Harry Lime fleeing through the sewers of Vienna
– just as the character of Sir Marcus, the wicked armament king in *A
Gun For Sale*, faintly recalls Fritz Lang's *Spy* in his role as the powerful
crippled financier. (Lang's melodramas – *Mabuse the Gambler* and its
sequel *The Testament of Dr Mabuse*, to say nothing of *The Spy* itself –
had a strange allegorical Kafkan-nightmare quality and, by an ironic

juxtaposition of background and situation, prefigured the Hitchcock–Greene tradition: an informer stabbed to death in a taxi during a traffic jam, while the strident continental klaxons drown any sound of a scream; the steam-laundry, with its shaking earthquake floor, camouflaging a counterfeiters' den; the spy, in his personality as a famous clown, killed in a gun-duel with the police in the presence of a juvenile audience.)

It was, however, Mr Graham Greene's individual blend of these basic ingredients which provided the standard modern recipe for what Mr Roy Fuller, in a skilful concoction of his own, has called the Novel of Pursuit. His 'entertainments' – among which *Brighton Rock*, in spite of its serious eschatological theme, may be listed for the purpose of this essay, since its technique was an extension of that previously employed in *A Gun for Sale* – included an admixture of the Conrad who wrote *The Secret Agent* and *Victory*: the fanatical Professor, passing 'unsuspected and deadly, like a pest in the street full of men', has his parallels in Mr Greene, and a slight resemblance may be detected between Raven and Plain Mr Jones's 'secretary', the savage Ricardo, who, it will be recalled, also 'went soft on a skirt'; *Romance*, on which Conrad collaborated with Ford Madox Ford, is an even more important precursor (Castro with his dummy wooden hand sheathing the murderous blade; the kidnappers' sack flung over John Kemp's head while the old Don dozes unwitting in his chair), while *The Confidential Agent* occasionally recalls, in style and manner, Ford's own *Rash Act* and *Vive le Roy*. But it was Mr Greene's personal contribution which appealed most to the inter-war generation: the ruthless violence and suspense that seemed to symbolise the impending calamity of which all were conscious; the seediness and squalor, the cinematic narrative technique and swift-moving impressionistic prose; the varied settings and minor characters so brilliantly sketched in; and the sense of love and pity, despairing but still alive in a world well lost for hate.

Mr Eric Ambler's novels of international intrigue also attracted many admirers during the same period, but these, with their dryly ironical, matter-of-fact approach and cosmopolitan backgrounds, derived from Mr Somerset Maugham's *Ashenden* series and diverge in many ways from the direct tradition. Mr Geoffrey Household's *Rogue Male* was much acclaimed in 1939 because of its ingeniously topical basic idea, but proves now to have been overrated, and Mr Greene's 'entertainments' still remain unrivalled in their field. During the war itself, when anything could happen and the Hunted Man had become a popular symbol of the times, he had, oddly enough, few imitators (an almost isolated example being Mr John Mair, whose *Never Come Back* was an interesting and creditable thriller, containing all the essentials); not until the cessation of hostilities, two years after publication of *The Ministry of Fear* (itself inferior, perhaps, to its predecessor in spite of the magnificent opening and closing chapters), did the spa of imitations begin to appear, some of which – Mr Richard Collier's *Pay Off in Calcutta*, for instance – seemed to verge upon unconscious parody in their assiduous aping of the master.

More recently, however, a new school has arisen, whose members may be considered completely in their own right: some of these – such as Mr Michael Innes (*The Secret Vanguard, The Journeying Boy, Operation Pax*) and Miss Margery Allingham (*Traitor's Purse, Tiger in the Smoke*) – had already applied the formula during the war and – like another Oxford recruit, Mr Edmund Crispin (*The Moving Toyshop, Holy Disorders*) – combine the chase, the equivocal characters and uneasy atmosphere of the genre proper, with a detective interest and a mystery problem; Mr Julian Symons's *The Thirty-First of February* and *The Narrowing Circle* belong to the dual category, while *The Broken Penny* is a more uninhibiting pursuit-novel, comprising some excellent English scenes – notably those in a seaside town and a military exercise: though the middle section, set in an Iron Curtain country, is on the whole less satisfactory. Indeed, the species seems to flourish best on British soil; there have been no examples from the continent, few from the United States, exceptions in the latter case being wartime thrillers of Miss Dorothy Hughes (*The Cross-Eyed Bear, The Fallen Sparrow, The Delicate Ape* and Mr Patrick Quentin's *Run to Death* and *The Follower*). This may be because the impact of the abnormal upon the ordinary, on which so much depends, is less striking when the surroundings are too exotic: as demonstrated by Mr Kevin Fitzgerald's *Quiet Under the Sun*, which after a brilliant beginning (a respectable diplomatist returning home in time to see his manservant shot dead by a burglar in a stocking-mask) becomes tedious when we – and the diplomatist – are transported to the headquarters of a Spanish sect, run by a cripple so hideously deformed that even the *Caudillo* shrinks at sight of him. Again, the first half of the author's *A Throne of Bayonets* could scarcely be bettered, but once the scene shifts from the haunts of black-marketeers and the shady drinking clubs behind Piccadilly to mountain climbing in Wales, and a secret organisation of an outmoded type is introduced, we rapidly lose interest. Nevertheless, Mr Fitzgerald is one of our most promising newcomers, possessing an admirable command of dialogue, a rapid colloquial style all his own, and an even more original sense of humour – a gift which he shares with another talented writer, Mr Richard Parker, whose *Gingerbread Man*, with its simple plot-line, ingenious chain-of-incident and freshly observed characters might almost serve as a model for future practitioners.

Humour and satire, in fact, seem to have become common attributes of the novel of pursuit and suspense; even in the intrinsically sombre stories of Mr Fuller, who appears to have chosen the literary under-world as his unhappy hunting-ground, humour is introduced: not to provide comic relief, but as an essential part of his plan; while, in the equally impressive work of Miss Margot Bennett and Mr Bernard Glemser, satirical and humorous sequences of the highest quality abound, without ever detracting from the pervasive ambience of mistrust and fear which is spread about their pages.

Unlike many women novelists, Miss Bennett writes mainly, and convincingly, from a masculine standpoint, though her scenes of feminine malice and occasional tenderness have a correspondingly accurate ring, and the love interest – particularly in *Farewell Crown and Goodbye King* – is often poignantly treated. *The Widow of Bath* contains, also, several highly effective female portraits, with a South-coastal setting, and at least one genuinely terrifying creation: the 'plump, cold Cady' with his hand-ground Boy Scout knife, his 'wistful interest in death' and grot-esque attachment to the public-school code (when threatening the modishly frightened hero, he says: 'I just want you to do the decent thing').

> 'Would you like to walk along the promenade with me?' Cady said.
>
> Everton stood still.
>
> 'Oh, yes; you would,' Cady said. 'Shall I tell you something? I like you. I like you so much I'm going to stay beside you. We two shall see the sun go down, as the poet says.'
>
> 'I hope we shall,' Everton said. 'Anyway, what poet?' He turned and walked away quickly, but he found that Cady, holding his elbow, was still beside him ...
>
> 'All I want to know,' Cady was saying, 'you've been with the police Inspector and that – that woman Leonard. I want to know what she said and when you've told me you can forget my dear familiar face.'

'She didn't say anything,' Everton said. 'She just gabbled.' He turned suddenly and jumped from the promenade towards the beach. A ball rolled towards his feet, and he picked it up and tossed it back to the little girl who had thrown it...

Everton walked towards her and said with an ingratiating smile: 'Throw it back and we'll have a game.'

She gave him a staff manager's look, but said, with some uncertainty, 'Nanny says I'm not to play with strange children, I don't know about strange men.' She looked at him with piercing innocence.

'But I know what she'd say about you,' she shouted, and ran away.

'Since there's no help,' Cady said, 'let's take our walk now. Earth,' he said, waving towards the sea, 'hath not anything to show more fair. What was that old woman saying to the policeman? Take your time. We'll wait here by the harbour...'

Mr Glemser's *The Dove on his Shoulder* is perhaps even more accomplished, centring in the misadventures of a young American, son of a prominent Senator, whose desire to propagate good fellowship among mankind leads him into situations the reverse of peaceful (the description of a pacifist meeting, which turns into a free fight between Communists and Nationalists of various creeds, is particularly delightful). Incident succeeds incident – comic, tragic, menacing and mysterious – at a jet-propelled narrative speed which even Mr Greene might envy; the ill-assorted inhabitants of the Bloomsbury boarding-house where Vincent lives present bewilderingly incongruous facets of their personalities while remaining individuals rather than types (though most of us have suffered in some form from Mr Rhys Morgan and Mr Greenberg). It would need pages of quotation to do justice to this author's gifts: his accurate ear for all kinds of dialogue (from officials of the American State Department and Russian Embassy, to Austrian refugees, English majors, bank clerks and Bond Street shopkeepers); his technical skill; his ability to create a wholly appealing heroine, to name but a few. Such a book as this, and those of Mr Fuller and Miss Bennett, deserve more critical attention than they are accorded, at a time when the so-called 'straight' or 'serious' novel has become a vehicle for ponderous philosophical or sociological theory, and seems in danger of forfeiting its claim to be considered as literature.

The Awful Child
(Jean Cocteau)

*   *   *

IN *THE CONCISE OXFORD FRENCH DICTIONARY* POSSIBLE ENGLISH versions of the phrase *enfant terrible* are listed, variously, as 'terrible child, chatterbox (fam.), regular pickle, plague; holy terror; little devil (especially one whose utter frankness and awkward questions make him an amusing nuisance; in this sense it can be said of young adults).' The phrase has often been applied to M. Jean Cocteau himself, besides providing a title, in the plural, for one of his most remarkable and fascinating works, now available to us in a new translation by Miss Rosamond Lehmann, with the author's own illustrations.[1] (Incidentally, though approximations have already been used by Arthur Machen and H.G. Wells, *The Holy Terrors* seems a more suitable English title than the present one, which may suggest to some readers a study of juvenile prostitution rather than the ferocious innocence of those 'êtres si purs, si sauvages', Elizabeth and Paul.)

*   *   *

It will readily be seen that almost all the above interpretations might be employed to disparage one whose ceaseless revolt against the pompous and the authoritarian could not fail to arouse antagonism in orthodox strongholds, among the established literary pundits and *petit-maîtres* of his time. For M. Cocteau is a brilliant, indefatigable talker and undeniably amusing; his disconcerting frankness as a young adult doubtless had its nuisance value. He has asked many an awkward and unanswerable question; his use of aphorism and paradox, his sophistication and

---

1 *Children of the Game*, The Harvill Press.

elegance, above all his astonishing versatility, have caused him until recently to be viewed with suspicion in his own country as an irresponsible playboy, and in England – where he is known chiefly through his plays and films – as an ingenious jack of all trades or Gallic counterpart of Mr Noël Coward.

We are not concerned here, however, with M. Cocteau's career in general, or the legends that have grown up around him, but with his achievements as a novelist and those attributes of his personality which most affect his performance in this particular literary sphere. The novels have not, so far, been subjected to much examination, save by their author (*Autour de Thomas l'Imposteur*, 1923); they were accorded little space in Miss Margaret Crosland's recent critical study and, except for *Thomas*, scarcely mentioned in Mr Erik de Mauny's article in the Spring Number of *London Magazine*; yet, though written in the 1920s and only three in number (the disquieting symbols of the Eugene-Mortimer sketchbook and the fable of that delightful monster *Le Potomak* – 1913–14 – belonging more properly to *poésie graphique*, or what might be termed *poésie de l'inconscient*), they are in many ways more representative than much of M. Cocteau's work in other media.

* * *

This author has always carefully equated method with subject-matter ('c'est la manière dont j'envisage, dont j'utilise les faits'); and in the above-mentioned article, originally printed in the *Nouvelles Littéraires* as an advance preface to *Thomas l'Imposteur*, he calls attention to the subtitles of *Thomas* and *Le Grand Écart*: 'histoire' and 'roman' respectively ('Le titre renseigne sur les genres, non le métrage. *La Chartreuse de Parne*, deux gros tomes, est une nouvelle'), comparing the structure of *Le Grand Écart* to that of a scenic railway: 'Le lecteur part de haut, tombe assez bas dans une intrigue médiocre, remonte vite de sa propre impulsion et parcourt (épilogue) quelque distance en terrain plat. Le choc des tampons l'arrête au bout.'

Needless to say, this framework is scrupulously designed to fulfil its appointed purpose: the swooping switchback curves, the mounting tension of the steep climb to the summit, the final vertiginous fall (into space, annihilation, eternity?), are all duplicated in the action as we follow anxiously, like the markings on an emotional health-chart, the tragi-comic course of Jacques Forestier's first love affair through its several stages of infatuation, elation, ecstasy, disillusion, despair and anti-climax (his attempt at suicide fails through the dishonesty of the barman who had sold him a diluted drug).

Morbid? Miserablist? Quite the reverse: the perennial dichotomy between the ideal and the actual, the inevitable shipwreck of romant-icism on the sharp rocks of reality, have seldom been demonstrated with such lack of self-pity or sentiment (as distinct from genuine sensibility). Not, perhaps, an unusual or original theme (a young writer's first love and first novel are so often indivisible), but M. Cocteau – the apostle of new art-forms, the champion of Picasso, Stravinsky, and Les Six – asserts in *Opium* his dislike of originality: 'Je l'évite le plus possible. Il faut employer une idée originale avec les plus grandes précautions pour n'avoir pas l'air de mettre un costume neuf.' None the less, *Le Grand Écart* resembles no other novel dealing with this classic predicament, and remains as fresh and dazzling a *tour de force* as when its pristine pink cover first appeared in the Paris bookshops thirty-two years ago.

* * *

At this remove of time, however, it seems less remarkable for its exhilarating high spirits and incisive wit, refreshing though these are at a period of creative inertia and 'consolidation', than for the masterly construction, the deft manipulation of plot and counterplot (presaging the expert stagecraft of *Les Parents Terribles* and *Les Monstres Sacrés*) that underlies the iridescent surface sparkle. On re-reading, too, one is aware of the extraordinary objectivity with which the chief characters are depicted: for though our sympathies are primarily enlisted on Jacques's behalf, his mistress Germaine, whose radiance derives from the dunghill ('de même que la rose offre le spectacle d'une bouche profonde qui puise son parfum chez les morts'), fickle, corrupt, yet capable of a genuinely vernal rapture at each new 'mobilisation' of her heart, is portrayed impartially and without malice: even when she discards him in turn as callously as, on his account, she had previously deceived her rich protector, the Levantine financier named, 'like a brand of cigarettes', Nestor Osiris. The portrait of this last also, complacent, ignoble, obtuse and pathetic, yet rising in the epilogue to unexpected heights of dignity and power, illustrates M. Cocteau's unique gift for displaying character in action without recourse to tedious analysis or text-book psychology.

'Les griefs de petite intrigue, de types connus,' together with the equivocal background and a story-mechanism involving bisexuality, Lesbianism, addiction to drugs and heterosexual promiscuity on a scale unparalleled in 'French' farce (resembling, at times, an erotic Lobster Quadrille or game of Adulterous Chairs), might easily have become sordid or boring in other hands: yet *Le Grand Écart* is protected from either of these labels by the author's peculiar quality of aristocratic innocence, which he shares with the eponymous heroes of *Thomas l'Imposteur* and *Les Enfants Terribles*.

M. Cocteau's early preoccupation with ciné-montage and film technique (he was one of the first important writers to be consciously influenced by the cinema which in *Le Secret Professionel* he christens the Tenth Muse) is reflected in the outward form and actual layout of his fiction: an episodic system of ellipses, transections and carefully regulated changes of tempo, by which the rapidity of the narrative is slowed down when required by the interpolation of aphoristic allegory, as subtitles on the silent screen were inserted to comment on the development of psychology or plot (the well-known parable of the Persian gardener's abortive flight from Death – usually attributed to Mr Somerset Maugham and perpetuated by Mr John O'Hara – figures, in this connection, in chapter two of *Le Grand Écart*, though the fatal appointment is scheduled for Ispahan instead of Samarra).

Thomas l'Imposteur follows superficially the same design: the difference lies in its interior rhythm. 'Le cinématographe devrait dérouler une psychologie sans texte. J'essaie, avec *Thomas*, de dérouler un texte sans psychologie, ou si rudimentaire qu'elle corresponde aux quelques lignes explicatives d'un film modèle,' the author wrote, and later:

> Mon prochain livre se déplace en accélérant sa vitesse. On dirait, au ralenti, le trajet entre une fenêtre du cinquième étage et le trottoir. La victime de cette chute n'en tire pas grand bénéfice … être assez aigu, assez rapide, pour traverser d'un seul coup le drôle et le douloureux, c'est à quoi je m'exerce.

M. Cocteau succeeded in this ambition; *Thomas*, his account of the First World War, written in 1922, has already been praised in these columns as a comic masterpiece, while pain and anguish, both physical and mental – often concomitants of high comedy, as in the films of Mr Chaplin or the early novels of Mr Evelyn Waugh – are by no means absent from its pages. In the hospital at Rheims, where 300 soldiers lay dying from wounds, hunger, thirst, tetanus and enemy bombardment, a gunner was told that his leg must be amputated without chloroform, as the only chance of saving him; while he was smoking a last cigarette before the ordeal, a shell reduced the surgical equipment to powder and killed two staff orderlies. Thenceforward, nobody dared go near the gunner. A sweetish, nameless, nauseating odour was supplemented by the 'black musk' of gangrene in a first-aid tent where Frenchmen and Germans alike sprawled indistinguishably on straw: 'Le luxe des blessés,' according to one medical officer, who refused at first to allow extra treatment for the wounded under his care.

And in the foreground of this horrible chaos, like 'rainbow-coloured flies of the charnel-house', the Princesse de Bormes, a spirited, sanguine, female saint-of-the-world, who has organised a special Red Cross convoy to the battle area, emerges accompanied by Guillaume Thomas, alias de Fontenoy, a lad of sixteen masquerading in uniform and rapt in some ineffable dream, who has added to his own the name of this famous general (also that of his birthplace), which acts as a magic password and open sesame to them on their mission of mercy. Guillaume is a personification of the Divine Fool, 'le poète inconnu', a myth-maker in thrall to the legends he himself has created, wandering somnambulant in his private phantasmal world. He is in no way pathological or perfidious; and it is an acid comment on human nature that, even when his impostures are exposed, characters such as Doctor Verne or the managing editor Pesquel-Duport are forced to cover them up from motives of self-interest. Guided always by some 'star of falsehood', he remains unsullied by the horror and the carnage until one stellar night, carrying a message to the front, he is shot down by an enemy patrol, in 'an apotheosis of fairyland'. ('"A bullet," he thought. "I'm done for unless I pretend to be dead." But, to him fiction and reality were one and the same...')

M. Cocteau feared that he might be accused of portraying the war in too frivolous a light. His fears were realised; and later, in *Opium*, he wrote: 'Tous les critiques officiels ont dit que *Thomas l'Imposteur* racontait une fausse guerre et qu'on voyait bien que je n'y avait pas été. Or il ne se trouve pas un seul paysage, pas une seule scène de ce livre que je n'aie habitée ou vécue.'

He himself, like Thomas, had stood in the Nieuport snow and heard the strange Negro music of the *Nouba*, as he recalls in his account of the 1919 victory parade (*Carte Blanche*); it was the scandal of Rheims that sent him initially to Maurice Barrès for help – an interview that resulted in the celebrated parody. Yet the quality of enchantment that invests his prose transformed the humdrum and horrific reality of war, which he himself had experienced, into the fabulous world of the peerless Princess and her enravished daughter and the ghoulish Mme Valiche: where under the fairy-tale firmament Guillaume was to die for all of them.

It is this individual magic, also, that insulates the Terrible Children, Elizabeth and Paul (a couple prefigured, perhaps, by Tigrane and Idgi d'Ybreo in *Le Grand Écart*), from the ugly implications of incest: the contorted, leering faces that peer through the pane at Paul in his dying delirium – harrowingly depicted in one of the author's most effective sketches in the present edition – may be intended to represent the invidious outside world launching its last loathsome accusation against the brother and sister, until Elizabeth squeezes the trigger and Dargelos steps forward with his deadly snowball (which did *not*, incidentally, contain a stone) to shatter, finally, the dream. But it might be unwise to speculate further, since even M. Cocteau hesitates to plumb the nebulous area enclosing the 'Game', and tells us only that *Les Enfants Terribles* was written in seventeen days – a tremendous feat of concentration and application, even though the novel, as usual, is short – after he had undergone the cure described in *Opium* (itself produced during the same period, December 1928–April 1929), 'sous l'obsession de *Make Believe* (*Showboat*); ceux qui aiment ce livre doivent acheter ce disque et le relire en le jouant,' and that the last pages were the first to be devised.

'Le seul style possible, c'est la pensée faite claire,' the author writes in *Opium*; and speaking of style again in *Le Secret Professionel*: 'Pour bien des gens, une façon compliquée de dire des choses très simples. D'après nous: une façon très simple de dire des choses compliquées… le vrai écrivain est celui qui écrit mince, musclé. Le reste est graisse ou maigreur.' *Les Enfants Terribles*, the most tautly written of the three novels, conforms exactly to these precepts. M. Cocteau has said of translations in *Journal d'un Inconnu*, 'La traduction ne se contente pas d'être un mariage. Elle doit être un mariage d'amour,' and one might add that Miss Lehmann, in rendering this difficult, laconic and trenchant style into English, has managed, on the whole, to achieve this ideal literary-conjugal relationship: though the following comparison of two passages may serve as an example of the over-amplification and elaboration into which she occasionally falls:

La cabine des mannequins est une rude épreuve. On y retrouve l'angoisse du premier jour de classe, les farces des écoliers. Elizabeth, sortant d'une interminable pénombre, monte sur la sellette, sous des projecteurs. Elle se croyait laide et s'attendait au pire. Sa magnificence de jeune animal blessait ces filles peintes et lasses, mais elle figeait leurs moqueries. On l'enviait et on se détournait.

(*Les Enfants Terribles*, chez Grasset, p. 113.)

To be a mannequin requires a harsh apprenticeship; the first day is as terrifying, as humiliating, as one's first day at school. Emerging from a long dark tunnel, Elizabeth stepped up on to the dais, under the glaring arc-lamps. Convinced that she was hideous, fearing the worst, she flamed among the other sophisticated, jaded models in all her untamed alien beauty. Enviously they stared, started to whisper among themselves; but something about her gave her immunity from open persecution, and they decided to ignore her.

(*Children of the Game*, p. 86.)

It is to be hoped that the publication of this outstanding work of fiction will gain new admirers for M. Cocteau in Great Britain; few writers have worked harder, or with such courage, under great handicaps; and it is surely time for us to realise, with his recent election to the French and Belgian Academies, that the Awful Child, the tight-rope talker, the playboy who would not grow up, has in fact been for long a mature artist whose novels alone make him worthy of recognition in other countries that his own has officially accorded him.

Mr Hamilton and Mr Gorse

*　　　　*　　　　*

THE ABOMINABLE ERNEST RALPH GORSE, 'EXPERT AND RESOURCEFUL liar', impostor, defrauder of women, and potential 'slayer' with his reddish hair and toothbrush moustache, his rimless monocle, bogus breeziness, and slightly nasal voice, would – so his creator, Mr Patrick Hamilton, assures us – 'have served, indeed, as a perfect model for, or archetype of, all the pitiless and not-to-be-pitied criminals who have been discovered and exposed in the last hundred years or so in Great Britain'.

According to a fictitious future biographer of Gorse, John George Haigh and Neville George Heath exhibited, compared with him, 'a certain charm, kindliness, generosity and dash', and that 'in the matter of purely repulsive, sustained, and thorough-going evil, Gorse belonged to a sort of upper class'. (This would have pleased the subject of the monograph, himself 'a deep, burning, embittered social snob'.) 'Only such characters as Brides-in-the-Bath Smith, or Sydney Fox, or Neill Cream were his equals.'

These are big claims – the criminological equivalent of declaring a promising young novelist to be the equal of Hardy, Conrad and Henry James – but they will doubtless be justified by the iniquities that Gorse has still to commit: certainly, to readers of the three novels in which he has featured so far,[1] he has already – on the strength of three cunning swindles, three acts of robbery with violence (including one perpetrated at the age of twelve), and the promise of murder-yet-to-come, acquired the status of a real figure in the calendar of crime; and the aforementioned physical characteristics, though not photographically

---

1　*The West Pier* (1951), *Mr Stimpson and Mr Gorse* (1953), *Unknown Assailant* (1955), Patrick Hamilton, Constable.

represented, have become as familiar as the wide toothpaste smile and laughing Irish eyes of Patrick Mahon, the sad Faustian face of Eugen Weidmann, or the single earring and bushy naval beard of Ronald Chesney – one who surely had many psychological traits in common with Mr Hamilton's character.

Mr Hamilton insists several times that Gorse 'had not any sort of good in him', that he 'loved trickery and evil for their own sakes', and that his motives are 'only partially commercial'; we are also told that his ruling passion is social snobbery: he is animated, moreover, by a strong power-complex, which expresses itself in the sending of anonymous letters to his victims (among other methods of spreading stealthy terror), and is symbolised by his 'almost pathological' obsession with militarism and its attendant trappings, manifested initially at his prep-school OTC and causing him, ultimately, 'to masquerade in uniform in the West End of London and elsewhere'.

In addition to these already repellent attributes, he knows more about 'car-buying, car-selling and car-trickery' than any other young man 'in England, Europe or the world', has histrionic ambitions, is powerfully attracted to the theatrical world in general, and passes as either a person of aristocratic connections or an ex-army officer of the 1914 war (awarding himself, during his sojourn in Reading, the Military Cross for gallantry in action). As a boy, addicted to unpredictable brooding silences (when not immersing his white mice in the bath, transferring the property of one school-fellow to the pockets of another in order to observe their subsequent reactions, puncturing the tyres of parked bicycles, or indulging in other acts of gratuitous mischief), he has assumed in adult life a manner of facetious gaiety, performing a 'silly-ass act' when in liquor, and modelling his behaviour and speech on Bertie Wooster, with an admixture – especially in his epistolary style – of the late Jeffrey Farnol.

This latter idiosyncrasy alone reveals Gorse to be a more Machiavellian and sinister descendant of those pretentious and often malevolent bores whose anatomy Mr Hamilton so ably dissected in *The Plains of Cement* and *The Slaves of Solitude*, combined with the raffish and dangerous ne'er-do-wells of *The Siege of Pleasure*, *To the Public Danger* and *Hangover Square*: 'Doctor Margrave' in the radio-play *Caller Anonymous*, the black-mailer in *Money with Menaces*, and Brandon in *Rope* – not to mention the Victorian husband in *Gaslight* – also possessed something of the same patient, tortuous, diabolic temperament.

That such figures as this – even apart from the examples already cited – have in reality existed, any student of crime or the sensational Sunday papers will confirm; but to make an *imaginary* incarnation of evil credible is almost as difficult as attempting to portray a saint in print, and most writers of fiction would hesitate to choose so detestable a protagonist for even a single book, let alone a whole series. Mr Hamilton, notwithstanding, avoids all the obvious pitfalls triumphantly, with more than a touch of the astuteness which has enabled Gorse himself to keep out of gaol hitherto. Both as dramatist and novelist, he has long been occupied with 'that cruelty and inhumanity in the nature of men' which Fielding, before him, 'contemplated with concern': Bob of *The Midnight Bell* in thrall to the irresponsible wanton Jenny Maple; Ella the barmaid tormented and bewildered by the egregious Mr Eccles; George Harvey Bone – that pathetic and amiable schizophrene – captivated and scorned by Netta Longden; Miss Roach confused by the amorous, alcoholic American lieutenant and persecuted by the odious boarding-house bully, Mr Thwaites: the pattern repeats itself endlessly, though without monotony; and while in his plays, where such conflicts are expressed in terms of melodrama, the oppressed are finally allowed to humiliate, in their turn, the oppressor, the underdog in the quieter scheme of the early novels is rarely permitted to rebel: though it's true that Bone eventually kills Netta and Miss Roach does in the end round on Mr Thwaites. In *Hangover Square* and *The Slaves of Solitude*, the author, however, was evidently working towards a synthesis of the suspense-story and the tragi-comic realism of his London trilogy. The obnoxious Gorse, who belongs to both worlds (his predatory instincts and latent homicidal tendencies supplying the necessary element of tension and menace) provided an answer to this technical problem: by allowing him to develop in the anomalous period between the world wars, against a rootless urban background of red brick and fumed oak, slot-machines on fluorescent seaside piers, huge ornate hotel-lounges, equivocal metropolitan cocktail-bars and fake-tudor provincial pubs, Mr Hamilton was able to exercise to the full his outstanding talents as social satirist and historian of the uneasy peace.

While refusing resolutely to endow his chief character with any redeeming or romantic qualities, denying even the legend of his Hypnotic Eyes (also attributed to Haigh and Weidmann in their day), and emphasising constantly Gorse's vulgarity, lack of taste and fundamental caddishness, as well as his more nefarious and lethal potentialities, he succeeds none the less in making the novels consistently diverting and entertaining, in a manner which writers dealing with more likeable characters and pleasanter themes often fail signally to achieve.

Gorse, though now in his thirtieth year, has not yet murdered; his two previous adventures were solely concerned with devious machinations employed by him to deprive two women, diametrically opposed in age, character and upbringing, of their savings: amounting to £68 15s. and £500 respectively. Since his methods are, though suitably adapted in each case, basically identical – involving, apart from an intuitive knowledge of feminine psychology, copious libations of gin and Italian; the gradual inspiring of confidence by alternate injections of anxiety and relief, motorcars ostensibly belonging to Gorse and offered as security to his credulous victims; and nonchalantly cryptic proposals of marriage (which are finally accepted with enthusiasm), the main interest lies in the skill with which the women themselves, and their respective environments, are presented. Esther Downes, the beautiful, slum-dwelling Brighton shop-girl whom Gorse – returning on holiday to the scenes of his boyhood – picks up, in company with two old schoolmates, Ryan and Bell, in *The West Pier*; and Mrs Plumleigh-Bruce, Colonel's daughter and Colonel's widow, the middle-aged 'drawling, fruity, affectedly-indolent', self-styled Lady of Reading, with her horrid brass-bedecked house, opulent bedroom and overworked 'Oirish' maid, whom the young trickster separates, not only from her bank-balance, but from a rival suitor, the boorish, 'subterraneously lecherous' local estate-agent who shares the title-rôle in *Mr Stimpson and Mr Gorse*.

The third, and latest, instalment, *Unknown Assailant*, set 'early in the year 1933', follows the previous examples, beginning with a Defoe-like simplicity and directness: 'Ivy Barton, a Chelsea barmaid, was on Sundays able to stay in bed an hour later than on weekdays. This she relished very much.'

Opening her *News of the World*, Ivy ('a decidedly foolish but very good and loveable girl … twenty-nine years of age') reads an account of a working-girl who was tied to a tractor in the country and robbed of £20 by an 'unknown assailant'. The latter is, naturally, Ernest Ralph Gorse, who had already indulged in a similar exploit when at school in Hove and now, posing as 'the Honourable Gerald Claridge', frequents the pub where Ivy is employed. Later, when she is herself trussed-up in a wood in Berkshire, he compels her to read the revelant extract aloud to him as a concession to his vanity before disappearing with her savings (£50 in cash), plus a cheque for £200 belonging to her 'harsh, vain, grasping and embittered' father: ex-gamekeeper who imagined that he was investing this sum in a musical comedy backed by Gorse's acquaintance, the theatrical impresario Lord Lyddon.

That is the story in outline: on the face of it not a very edifying one; the delight we take in reading it is due, as usual, to the incidentals: the first interview between Gorse and Ivy's father, when they both address each other as 'Sir' and there seems no way out of the tangle; the scene where the odious Mr Barton, anxious to boast in the 'local' of his connection with Lord Lyddon, finds to his fury that the name evokes only *The Last Days of Pompeii*; and the delectable drunken sequence, in Mr Hamilton's happiest vein, when the ex-gamekeeper, being put to bed by his wife after a meeting with a rich industrialist, babbles lyrically 'about hearts of gold, bricks of gold, bricks with hearts of gold, hearts with bricks of gold, golds with hearts of bricks, and, even, half-bricks with halfs of gold' (Mr Stimpson, it may be remembered, when out on the spree in London with Gorse, suddenly became 'rhyming-drunk' in Piccadilly, 'mentioning laboriously, Tact with Bogs, Cogs, Dogs, Fogs, Gogs, Jogs, Logs, Mogs, Nogs, Pogs, Quogs, Rogs, Sogs, Togs, Vogs, Wogs, Yogs and Zogs').

Students of the Gorse saga may notice several technical changes in the new book (apart from its extreme shortness by comparison with the two preceding volumes): the scheme of ironically titled sections ('Gorse the Tempter', 'Gorse the Revealer' 'Gorse the Absent', etc – and, perhaps most amusing of all, 'Gorse of Assandrava') seems, regrettably, to have been abandoned; secondly, the sense of period which Mr Hamilton, as a rule, so vividly conveys is noticeably lacking: despite the year in which the story takes place, there is no allusion (as the Kaiser's war is mentioned in *The Pier* or the General Strike in *Mr Stimpson*), to the encroaching Nazi menace or the world situation generally, to which one would have expected Gorse, with his feeling for incipient evil, to be well attuned; on the other hand, the personal picture is gradually growing darker, and Gorse's unnecessarily vicious treatment of Ivy shows that murder cannot be delayed much longer: the disclosure of his particular sexual 'perversion' – foreshadowed in the first chapter of *The West Pier* – seeming to indicate strangulation as his eventual method of killing.

Of the present trilogy, despite many felicities contained in *Unknown Assailant*, *Mr Stimpson and Mr Gorse* is probably the most rewarding:

the sections dealing with Major Perry's agonised attempts at versification, or Mr Stimpson's struggles with his crossword-puzzles, are among the funniest in contemporary fiction, while the closing chapters, in which motorcars are seen as a sinister coleopterous species that has conquered and enslaved mankind, is an extraordinary piece of *bravura* which might astonish those who have thought of the author as a purely realistic and colloquial writer, with an unrivalled ear for catching the conversational banalities of daily life.

It is perhaps too soon to conjecture closely as to Ernest Ralph Gorse's future career, except to remark that the Haywards Heath dentist and the Rugby watchmaker (hinted at in *Unknown Assailant*) seem to promise special treats in store; it is, however, surely time to second Mr John Betjeman's opinion that Mr Hamilton is one of the best living English novelists.

Affairs of Honour
(from Chekhov to Scott Fitzgerald)

*   *   *

DUELLING SEEMS TO HAVE DIED OUT OF FICTION NOWADAYS, though there was a happy period not so long ago when the Field of Honour figured imminently in the novel, and when long-short stories of over one hundred pages (which would now be published separately at nine-and-six a time) could be written around the subject of one duel alone. Both Chekov and Conrad did this.[1]

The Chekovian duel took place about five miles outside a Caucasian seaside port, at the junction of the Black and Yellow rivers, where a picnic had previously been held and the characters concerned had eaten fish soup cooked on the spot (there were no restaurants in the neighbouring town). The motivation was mutual dislike, eventually turning to hatred between Von Koren, a severe, cold, scientific type who had 'come for the summer to the Black Sea to study the embryology of the medusa', and Laevsky, the ineffectual Government clerk, who taught the local residents (previously practically teetotal) to 'distinguish Kospelov's vodka from Smirnov's No. 21, blindfold'.

Despite the violent storm that breaks out the night before, both the contestants believe that the 'duel will end nothing', and we, knowing that their creator is Chekov, begin to fear the same; but meanwhile Laevsky discovers his mistress in the arms of the Police Captain, who has been blackmailing her, and consequently is in no condition to fight: his shot misses, and Von Koren prepares calmly to kill him, when a shout from a young deacon (who had concealed himself near by, partly with a view to intervening, partly in order to write a comic account of the duel) disturbs *his* aim also, the bullet merely bruising

---

1 *The Duel*, by Anton Chekov; *The Duel*, by Joseph Conrad (*A Set of Six*, 1908).

the right side of his enemy's neck instead of scoring a direct hit. Neither contestant is punished (though the normal penalty is 'a maximum of three years' imprisonment in the fortress'), and Laevsky thereafter suffers a complete change of heart, marries the mistress (whom he'd been about to abandon), and settles down to work like a beaver and pay off his debts; the antagonists are finally reconciled in face of this feverish industry, and Von Koren sails off on a turbulent sea in which we privately hope he may drown.

Conrad's *Duel* (between two young lieutenants of Hussars in Napoleon Bonaparte's army), though approached also in a sardonic spirit by the author, is an altogether different storm-in-a-teacup. The story, beginning in 1801, covers sixteen years, and the participants are middle-aged generals before its course is run, their private quarrel having been interrupted by the Napoleonic wars. Perhaps the title should be in the plural, for during the intervening period five duels in all are fought: one, almost, to mark each step of promotion.

In the fifth, and final, encounter, the generals stalk each other with pistols through a wood at break of day, Feraud technically forfeiting his life after he has missed D'Hubert point-blank with his second shot. D'Hubert, however, not only does not kill him but later sets him free from all obligation, also contributing (secretly) to his enemy's support thence-forward: for, as a man of forty unused to the more tender passions, he would never otherwise have tumbled to the fact that his young fiancée really loved him (she had run two miles from her own house, with her hair down, on hearing of the duel).

Duelling, however, plays a less happy part in the lives of Mr Wyndham Lewis's[1] self-styled 'Freiherr' Otto Kreisler, the boorish Prussian painter, and Louis Soltyk, the Polish art dealer, whose quarrel, initiated among 'bourgeois-bohemians' in Paris before the First World War, came to a tragic conclusion in the Bois de Boulogne, when Kreisler – admittedly by mistake – shot his unarmed enemy dead with a Browning on the Field of Honour itself. But this, owing to the unconventional circumstances attending its inception, the unseemly behaviour of the principals throughout, and the fact that it ended in murder, can scarcely be called a duel at all: nor does Chesterton's *Duel of Dr Hirsch*[2] really merit the dignified title, since this was a publicity

---

1 *Tarr* by Wyndham Lewis, first published 1918.
2 In *The Wisdom of Father Brown*.

stunt organised by a self-seeking politician, and no actual contest could have taken place: the 'challenger' being the wily doctor himself in disguise.

Almost the last instance of a duel in 'serious' fiction (which, as the late Dylan Thomas pointed out, may also be funny) is that, recorded by Scott Fitzgerald, between two of the subsidiary characters in *Tender is the Night* (1934): Albert McKisco, author of the first criticism of *Ulysses* to appear in the United States, and Tommy Barban, a soldier of fortune who, since the age of eighteen, had 'worn the uniforms of eight countries'. McKisco cannot be said to have represented Literature too badly: he showed no sign of overt fright and duly faced the formidable Barban at forty paces.

Later we meet McKisco again, improved and humbled by success, which, we are told, 'was founded psychologically' upon the duel. Thus duelling would appear to have, from most of the examples cited, a salutary effect on the participants; and latter-day writers might do worse than reintroduce it instead of sex or religion when a beneficial transformation is required in the lives of their characters.

The Hunted and the Heather
(John Buchan)

*   *   *

IN SPITE OF HIS DISTINGUISHED RECORD IN OTHER SPHERES OF
life and letters, it seems likely today that the late Lord Tweedsmuir's
final claim to posterity will rest – as so often happens – upon those
works of fiction to which he referred, in his lifetime, with such
unaffected and deprecating modesty.

In the Thomas Nelson edition of John Buchan's novels – ten of which
have now been reprinted by Penguin Books – a list of twenty-eight
titles (excluding the posthumously printed *Sick Heart River*) is appended.
These – according to the admirably concise and informative, though
anonymous, Penguin introduction – were 'written in what leisure he
could get from public life'; while still an undergraduate at Oxford ('too
poor' – at first – 'to dine in Hall') he had already published five books;
and – as early as 1900, at the age of twenty-five – *The Half-Hearted*,
derivative, perhaps, from *The Four Feathers*, but nevertheless an important precursor of his later works: succeeded, a decade afterwards,
by *Prester John*, a tale of South African adventure influenced by
Stevenson and Rider Haggard, yet displaying from the very first sentence
a technical mastery which was to earn it a place as a classic in this
genre and captivate, like *Treasure Island* and *King Solomon's Mines*,
a public much wider than the juvenile audience for which it was
initially designed.

'Read to-day, in the light of contemporary happenings in South
Africa,' as the introduction points out, '*Prester John* can be seen to have
a prophetic importance its author would certainly have disclaimed';
and this element is by no means accidental, for the book was based
upon first-hand experience of the country concerned and a profound
insight into the workings of the native mind. The Reverend John Laputa,

374

evangelist, illicit diamond broker, self-appointed leader of 'the African race to conquest and empire', 'a great genius', 'a second Napoleon', 'as brave as a lion', with 'the heart of a poet and a king', to whose 'fineness and nobility' his enemy, the British intelligence officer Captain Arcoll, is glad to bear testimony', personifies many of the qualities to be found in Buchan's subsequent villains; just as David Crawfurd, the nineteen-year-old narrator (like his creator, a son of the manse) exemplifies the sound common sense, the doggedness and daring, of such later heroes as Richard Hannay and Edward Leithen.

Leithen – whose character and career approximates in many ways to the author's own, and whose death, also in Canada, preceded his by a short time only – made a first appearance in *The Power House*, called by Buchan in the dedication 'a precipitous yarn' and written – though not published – before *The Thirty-nine Steps*, 'found favour in the dug-outs and billets of the British front', and with countless civilians both then and now. Improbable though it might have seemed, however, to readers 'in the smooth days' before the 1914 War, *The Power House* not only created a precedent for the modern thriller of pursuit and suspense, but also – in the disappearance and flight to Moscow of the volatile and talented Charles Pitt-Heron – once again forecast a situation with which we have become only too familiar.

Nor did the author follow him through Central Asia, Bokhara and Samarkand: the real drama was played out in bright June sunshine, against prosaic London backgrounds: Oxford Street, Piccadilly and the Edgware Road; danger stalked Leithen – the future Solicitor-General, at that time 'an industrious common-law barrister' slaving away in 'the dust and squalor' of his working chambers – through underground stations and ambushed him in Bloomsbury restaurants; the book culminated in a desperate daylight chase through Green Park and across Belgrave Square, after he had first been besieged in his Down Street flat:

> It was a blazing hot midsummer day. The water-carts were sprinkling Piccadilly, and looking from my window I could see leisurely and elegant gentlemen taking their morning stroll. A florist's cart full of roses stood below me in the street. The summer smell of town – a mixture of tar, flowers, dust, and patchouli – rose in gusts through the hot air. It was the homely London I knew so well, and I was somehow an exile from it. I was being shepherded into a dismal isolation, which, unless I won help, might mean death...

But Leithen – that 'sober and practical person', whose 'quite irrelevant gift of imagination' was reflected in his precise yet colloquial style – did not die for many years to come, and eventually checkmated Mr Andrew Lumley, *alias* Julius Pavia, the 'great extra-social intelligence' who dreamed of defeating the 'conspiracy of civilisation'; 'two eminent statesmen were among the pall-bearers' at Lumley's funeral, and royalty was represented: 'It was a queer business to listen to that stately service, which was never read over stranger dust.'

It is to be hoped that this incomprehensibly neglected landmark in the history of the thriller will be included in a future Penguin selection: the present series comprises only a lighter-hearted adventure of Sir Edward's, *John Macnab* – where, by the way, he does *not* tell the story, which concerns hunting, shooting, fishing and poaching (for a wager) on moor, river and in glen. *Macnab*, which contains several extremely funny scenes and is consistently entertaining throughout, belongs to the same category as the Dickson McCunn trilogy, *Hunting Tower*, *Castle Gay* and *The House of the Four Winds*, whose blend of dry humour, occasional farce, and Ruritanian romance would provide an excellent basis for a sequence of comic films: it seems odd that producers should have ignored the less serious side of Buchan, though his formula for inducing suspense has influenced the cinema ever since Mr Alfred Hitchcock's version of *The Thirty-nine Steps* – actually, the only book of his to be brought to the screen.

Mr Robert Donat, in the role of Richard Hannay, acquitted himself creditably as the lone man hounded across England and Scotland for a murder which he did not commit; but he failed to suggest those characteristics which were, within a comparatively short space of time, to result in military distinction, a knighthood, and membership of exclusive clubs for one who, before the outbreak of war, was known to few people in Great Britain and had 'no real pal who could come forward and swear' to his character. Hannay – 'an ordinary sort of fellow, not braver than other people' – was none the less a man of parts; he could pass anywhere as a Scotsman, an American, a German, or a Boer from Western Cape Colony; relying, in this direction, not so much upon physical disguise as upon the ability to become the type he was imper-sonating ('A fool tries to look different: a clever man looks the same and *is* different'): a method which he had learned from old Peter Pienaar in Rhodesia and which was also employed by his antagonists, the three German agents of the Black Stone – and in particular by the survivor of the trio, the plump, rubber-faced, lisping Graf von Schwabing, who afterwards reappeared in *Mr Standfast*, as Moxon Ivery, the 'pacificist'.

Having disbanded the Black Stone, Hannay – the South African of Scottish origin – joined the New Army, rose to be a general officer, was awarded the DSO, the Legion of Honour, and a CB: officially for 'his part in the Erzerum business', but in reality for thwarting the *Greenmantle* conspiracy in the Middle East, a mission which he fulfilled with the able assistance of the Honourable Ludovick ('Sandy') Arbuthnot (later Lord Clanroyden), and John S. Blenkiron, the dyspeptic, patience-playing, cigar-smoking 'citizen of the great American republic'.

Sandy Clanroyden – 'tallish, with a lean high-boned face and a pair of brown eyes like a pretty girl's' – was also a master of the histrionic art, who scorned the use of too much make-up and specialised in oriental roles (though he once attended a highbrow party as a French *surréaliste* in a black sweater, equipped with 'all the latest Paris studio argot', and posed successfully as Martel, the Belgian *apache*, sewer-rat, and sneak-thief in *The Island of Sheep*); it was he who impersonated Greenmantle, the Prophet himself, and – eight years afterwards – Kharáma, the evil mystic in *The Three Hostages*: the latter, with such skill that he deceived not only Dominick Medina, but Hannay himself (it was a peculiar facet of their relationship, which might be of interest to Freudians, that Sandy in one of his impenetrable disguises frequently aroused a feeling of violent hatred and loathing in his otherwise devoted friend).

Sandy was – like John Laputa – 'a man of genius...but he had the defects of such high-strung, fanciful souls', and much in common with Lawrence of Arabia: a complex character, able to understand – and sympathise with – satanic opponents such as Medina, Jacques d'Ingraville and Hilda von Einem, since he shared something of their visionary temperament; though an inner core of spiritual toughness – stemming, perhaps, from his Scottish heritage – prevented him from being won over by them, and helped him to resist the blandishments of the imperious Hilda on the Turkish hillside (he 'made a sudden movement as if to defend himself against a blow', when he heard her voice calling to him from out of the mist). He symbolised the romantic, imaginative side of his many-faceted creator, just as Hannay, Leithen and – in a different social sphere – Dickson McCunn epitomised the shrewd, sterling everyday virtues; and Wee Jaikie of the Gorbals Die-Hards, who, through the exercise of industry and application, became Mr John Galt of St Mark's College, Cambridge, represented the Glasgow grammar schoolboy who made good (though, unlike Buchan, Jaikie obtained only a second-class in his Tripos, while Sandy Arbuthnot fell as low as a third in Greats).

It is, however, in the creation of his villains that John Buchan's skill in characterisation is displayed in its most subtle form. His attitude towards these paradoxical figures is curiously ambivalent, none is devoid of grandeur (even Colonel Stumm – with his gross physique and perverted passion for feminine frippery – is allowed a final tribute: 'He was a brute and a bully, but by God! he was a man!'), from Laputa onwards: Hilda von Einem 'might be a devil, but she was also a queen'; the old man who could hood his eyes like a hawk was 'more than a spy; in his foul way he had been a patriot'; d'Ingraville ('whose forebears once owned half Haute Savoie') was 'a scoundrel, but on a big scale'; Moxon Ivery was 'the most amazing actor on earth, the most dangerous man in all the world ... the most cunning and patient and long-sighted' (though he was 'not clean white all through', being a victim of agoraphobia and afraid of bombs in a big city); while Dominick Medina, poet and hypnotist (a 'deity of *les jeunes* and a hardy innovator'), 'as exotic as the young Disraeli and as English as the Duke of Devonshire', with his terrible blind mother and his inordinate ambitions, is built on the biggest scale of all.

Even Sir Richard Hannay – who took 'a modest pride' in his handling of *The Three Hostages* affair, 'because from first to last it had been a pure contest of wits' – fell under Medina's spell at the start (though practically immune from actual hypnotism), and might never have defeated him had it not been for Lady Hannay (Mary Lamington of Fosse Manor in *Mr Standfast*) who, though she herself regarded Medina as 'almost superhuman', saved the day by threatening to throw acid in his face.

The Three Hostages is probably Buchan's best novel, amplifying the method already used in *The Power House* and *Mr Standfast* (a method initiated by Stevenson in *The New Arabian Nights* and since adapted, cinematically, by Mr Fritz Lang, Mr Alfred Hitchcock and Sir Carol Reed), of imbuing realistic settings with a sense of menace and stealthy terror:

> The West End of London at night always affected me with
> a sense of the immense solidity of our civilisation. These
> great houses, lit and shuttered and secure, seemed the extreme

opposite of the world of half-lights and perils in which I had sometimes journeyed. I thought of them as I thought of Fosse Manor, as sanctuaries of peace. But to-night I felt differently towards them. I wondered what was going on at the back of those heavy doors. Might not terror and mystery lurk behind that barricade as well as in tent and slum? I suddenly had a picture of a plump face all screwed up with fright muffled beneath the bed-clothes…

Frank Harris Revisited

*　　　*　　　*

UNDREAM'D OF SHORES: SANDWICHED ON A SIXPENNY STREET book-stall between *Freckles*, by Gene Stratton Porter and an early historical novel by John P. Marquand, silted over with grime and soot from the railway terminus nearby, the oddly evocative title caught my eye. As a young man I had met the author once, and much later wrote an account of my visit to his villa in the south of France, but it was many years since I had opened one of his books. How, I wondered, would he read today?

Out of curiosity I picked up the volume and read on the flyleaf an inscription to a friend: 'these last stories by Frank Harris', and the date 'Dec. '24'. The ink was brown and faded; the handwriting clear, oblique, and curiously delicate for so robust and virile a personality. 'Autographed copy: 6/-' was pencilled above. This seemed a good bargain for sixpence, and so it proved.

Novelist, editor, controversial author of *The Man Shakespeare*, friend and biographer of Wilde and Shaw, literary adventurer, according to some a blackguard and even a blackmailer, Frank Harris – though his autobiography, *My Life and Loves*, on his own valuation at the luncheon-table consisted of 'pure filth', and could certainty be considered a pornographic work – was nevertheless acknowledged in his day as a master of the short story. *Montes the Matador*, and *Elder Cocklin* were everywhere compared to de Maupassant, and Arnold Bennett among others regarded him with respect. On the evidence of *Undream'd of Shores*, comprising twelve stories and a coda – '*My Last Word*' – in semi-Biblical style, this view was not altogether unjustified.

There is no echo of the nineties, no hint of the baroque in his style, which – owing no doubt to the Maupassant influence and, at a further remove, to that of Prosper Mérimé – is graphic and unadorned: though the subject-matter is frequently exotic (since the settings include Paris, Vienna, Samarkand and the ramparts of Heaven), Harris's handling of it remains strictly realistic.

The stories are mostly told in the first person, either directly or recounted by the protagonists to a narrator who is plainly intended to be Harris himself. (When asked by a lunatic whether he writes essays or stories, he replies: 'Both; but I prefer stories and pen-portraits of important contemporaries,' adding: 'You can put as much imagination into a portrait as you like'.) It is not inconceivable that Somerset Maugham may have been influenced by this conception of a tolerant and worldly globe-trotter, treating life as material for literature, always ready to lend a sympathetic ear to the troubles of his fellow men, providing that these are likely to form the basis of an interesting tale.

Harris's narrator, however, is less impersonal, more susceptible and ready to take sides, and (oddly enough) easier to shock. A fair portrait of the author in fact emerges: anxious to show his sensibility, his interest in music and painting, and to display the extent of his culture by discursions on art. ('Everyone can see that Watteau is infinitely more gifted as a painter than Rembrandt; Rembrandt carries it because he was the greater man... The brainwork in Rembrandt is far higher.') In this respect he resembles Aldous Huxley, though at a lower intellectual level. His attitude towards the opposite sex, while ostensibly cynical, is in reality rather naive; and the sentimentality of the born libertine is occasionally revealed in his rapturous descriptions of female beauty, despite the fact that Rachel, heroine of *In Central Africa* and daughter of a powerful Mohammedan chief who lived in a kraal on the slopes of Kilimanjaro, taught him 'to see the ordinary girl without glamour or romance'. (His disillusionment with Rachel began when 'the thigh, properly kept for a fortnight and smoked, of a young girl about thirteen years old' was served up as a delicacy to the Sultan and it became evident that his daughter, too, enjoyed the taste of human flesh; but matters were brought to a head when Rachel proposed marriage, and he deemed discretion the better part of valour: 'matrimony – straight off – without more ado – I was not prepared for it'.)

The smoked thigh caused the teller to 'think better of some prejudices,' we are told, but Harris's other stories also have strong sadistic overtones: especially *A Chinese Story*, in which an Eric-Ambler-like Russian guide named Shimonski, who takes an 'epicurean pleasure in cruelty', shows him the sights of Shanghai. (An elderly Chinese offers to commit suicide for their delectation, in order to provide a ten-dollar dowry for his daughter; the gigantic executioner of a band of pirates points proudly to a headless corpse: 'That's the way I do my work; all you have to do is to keep quiet, chin up, head back.') Harris had an objective interest in violence akin to Hemingway's: indeed, *The Great Game*, a tale of the American boxing world, is a forerunner of *Fifty Grand*. (Dick Donovan becomes a featherweight, then a bantamweight, and finally a lightweight champion, but finds it more profitable to sell fights on instructions of Sid Harriman, 'a betting man, whom the boys thought to be a millionaire'.)

Undream'd of Shores was published by Grant Richards seven years before the author's death; and despite his abundant talent Harris died in disappointment and neglect. It is sad to think of so much gusto, ambition and appetite for life coming to rest at last among the trashy titles, the dust and grit of the sixpenny stall.

A Beginning, a Middle
and an End

*   *   *

'IN COMPILING *MODERN ENGLISH SHORT STORIES: SECOND Series*, the year 1930 has been taken as an approximate starting point, so that the collection is virtually an anthology of the stories of the past twenty-five years,' Mr Derek Hudson writes in his introduction to the volume under review; and later: 'This selection aims only at presenting some of the best modern stories that have been written in their various kinds.' In theory, both are admirable selective principles, since the last two-and-a-half decades produced many outstanding examples of the art and marked the emergence of several trends important to its future development; yet it must be stated, however reluctantly, that the second claim fails signally in practice, for reasons which leap to the eye at a quick glance down the contents list.

There are, to begin with, some notable omissions. Authors from the Commonwealth, and the 'indigenous short stories of Ireland and Wales' are not unreasonably excluded – though inevitable losses are incurred thereby – but it is hard to understand the absence of Angus Wilson, Gerald Kersh, T.O. Beachcroft, Inez Holden, John Sommerfield, C.H.B. Kitchin, L.P. Hartley and John Collier, to name only a few. Rhys Davies and the late Alun Lewis might be excluded on the grounds of Welsh origin, though Lewis's last magnificent stories were not concerned with his native land but with service in the British Army both in England and abroad: while Mr Davies's shrewdly observant studies of London life could scarcely be considered indigenous to Cymric soil or, properly, be spared from any representative anthology. Moreover, if the late Frances Towers is to be included, why not Elizabeth Myers, also deceased; and, above all, why not the late Denton Welch, whose early death was an even more tragic loss, and who, in

'The Judas Tree' alone, wrote one of the finest short stories to appear since the war? Nor do any of Anna Kavan's poignantly uncomfortable asylum pieces or James Hanley's terse, elliptical maritime tales find a place in these pages. Curiously enough, too, though Mr Hudson states that the dominating impression left by the volume 'is of humour... the sense of a humorous perspective of life', no specifically comic writers – apart from Mr Evelyn Waugh – are included: for instance, there is no example of the work of Mr Anthony Carson, whose wit and wryly individual view of the world has been delighting readers of weekly journals for the past couple of years.

Copyright difficulties might explain some, but surely not all, of these omissions; Mr Hudson appears to have made his selection from collections published in book form rather than from reviews and periodicals, which may account for the fact that no material from either the *London Magazine* or *Encounter* has been chosen, and the newest writers represented – also the youngest – are A.L. Barker (1918) and Nigel Kneale (1922), who, as author of the *Quatermass* serials, seems since to have forsaken the short story for sound radio and television.

Of the nineteen authors, three – Somerset Maugham, Elizabeth Bowen and H.E. Bates – have contributed to the previous volume in this series, and at least four – C.S. Forester, Clemence Dane, John Moore and Eric Linklater (an oddly disturbing fantasy about a hirsute and sophisticated seal-man) – cannot really be classed as short-story writers in the true sense, though all have written short stories in the intervals of preparing more novels: their tales have a highly professional gloss, but little connection with the more serious forms of the genre; while the names of the characters in 'The Little Willow' – Simon Byrne, Stephen Elyot, Richard Harkness &c. – can only indicate that the story was initially designed by Frances Towers for publication in one of the better-class women's magazines: a soldier on leave from the desert who speaks to a girl at a party of being 'lost, and parched with thirst, and terribly frightened' is unlikely to find favour with even the most sensitive masculine reader, and the general atmosphere – beautiful cello-playing sisters and Cinderella-like heroine – is reminiscent of those sentimental Victorian products mentioned by the editor himself in his introduction.

Elsewhere, the selection is governed not only by extreme conservatism – Mr Hudson's claim that experiment is not ignored applies only to Rosamond Lehmann's brilliantly impressionistic 'A Dream of Winter'

– but by what must be deemed a lack of initiative: Graham Greene, for example, is represented by his almost universally known 'The Basement Room', when less familiar but no less powerful instances of his talent are readily available; H.E. Bates's curious mixture of romanticism and boisterousness, 'The Woman Who Had Imagination' (1934) is too long and diffuse, lacking the speed and precision which he later acquired; the style is also uncharacteristic, and reads in places like a parody of V.S. Pritchett: while Mr Pritchett himself – with the whole of his *Collected Stories* to choose from – is shown dealing, quite untypically, with Welsh characters in a wartime setting.

William Sansom's 'The Vertical Ladder' is a more successful choice: foreshadowing, in the snatches of shouted dialogue, the change-over from his early Kafkan allegories to the studies in suburban fright-fulness that were to follow; Fred Urquhart contributes a chilling little portrait of a psychopathic parasite; while on the distaff side the technical expertise of Virginia Woolf and Elizabeth Bowen is illustrated, respect-ively, by vignettes of a snobbish self-made jeweller and a spoilt, precocious 'poor little rich girl'. By far the most entertaining, however, is Christopher Sykes's story of a turbulent priest forced to turn jockey in North Africa, as the only means of saving a stolen cathedral chalice from falling into sacrilegious hands: the author's firm grasp of character and situation is amply demonstrated by the fact that not even the most pious of Roman Catholic readers could take offence or fail to be amused by poor Father Macdonnel's predicament:

> The riders stood in the ring, discussing last-minute instructions
> with their patrons, as is the custom. Only one stood apart. He
> appeared on the card as E. Macdonnel. He ground his teeth.
> He was reflecting that for a priest to dress up in this clownish
> costume was very nearly sacrilegious in itself... He wished
> the 'jockeys up' bell would ring and hasten the end of this
> blasphemous farce.

In his ironic and tolerant approach, his unadorned narrative ease, and in the way he catches the authentic accents and the locutions of such characters as Attar, the Syrian-Christian interpreter in 'The Sacred and the Profane', Mr Sykes plainly derives from Mr Maugham, who in 'The Kite' seems to be one of the few writers represented who are aware an urban lower-middle-class exists:

> Some people don't know how lucky they are; thank the Lord,
> I do. No one's ever had a better son than our Herbert. Hardly

a day's illness in his life and he's never given me a moment's worry. It just shows if you bring up somebody right they'll be a credit to you. Fancy him being twenty-one, I can hardly believe it.

Yes, I suppose before we know where we are he'll be marrying and leaving us.

'What should he want to do that for?' asked Mrs Sunbury with asperity. 'He's got a good home here, hasn't he? Don't you go putting silly ideas into his head, Samuel, or you and me'll have words and you know that's the last thing I want. Marry indeed! He's got more sense than that. He knows when he's well off. He's got sense, Herbert has.'

Otherwise, most of the characters in these stories belong to the privileged classes: even in wartime Frances Towers's three sisters are able to entertain 'musicians and artists and writers' in 'a peculiarly gracious room' with an Adam chimney-piece, and Rosamond Lehmann's protagonist lives in a large country house where 'the old Squire' used to have the bee-man up for evening classes; Miss Barker's 'Mr Minnenick', comfortable in a cottage on the eve of Munich, cuts a new white loaf into sturdy slices; Woolf's Bond-street jeweller, in his flat overlooking Green Park, extracts from envelopes every morning 'thick white cards of invitation' from duchesses, countesses, viscountesses and Honourable Ladies; Miss Bowen's awful child – a baronet's niece, incidentally – attends a fashionable school where 'she learnt swimming, dancing, some French, the more innocent aspects of history, and *noblesse oblige*'. All this might lead a foreign reader, unacquainted with present-day conditions in this country, to believe in an almost obsolescent England of butlers and spinsters and girls 'in service'; many of the backgrounds, moreover, are rural, and only Mr Sansom gives us a glimpse of the encroaching mechanised ugliness: 'the scrap-iron and broken brick... the grid of girders, a complexity of struts.'

For Mr Hudson has by-passed completely a whole epoch in the history of the English short story, and one peculiarly characteristic of the 1930s themselves. While acknowledging the influence of American writers such as Irving, Poe, Melville, Bret Harte, Crane and Ambrose Bierce ('the "lend-lease" of a century ago') upon the English writers of the 1890s and their successors, he fails to mention that exercised by Hemingway, Steinbeck, Saroyan (*via* Gertrude Stein and Sherwood Anderson) upon those of a later generation: an influence more potent than any since those of the French and Russian masters, bringing about, as it did, a total revolution not only in style but subject-matter.

> These Americans brought to their developing art a mastery of construction, a terseness and clarity of expression, that gave them authority [Mr Hudson says of the first-named group]. There was to be no room for verbiage or pomposity, none of the novel-reader's indulgence for creaking machinery; each stroke had to be directed to the total effect:

words which apply even more strongly to the heirs of Frank Norris, Theodore Dreiser and Jack London, who formed the bridge between. Still more verbosity was stripped away, description cut to a minimum and replaced by dialogue exchanges; the characters, drawn from a lower social sphere and frequently from the underworld itself, expressed themselves – mostly in the first person – in a pungent idiom to which the emergent English writers began excitedly to seek a parallel. H.E. Bates switched from romantic sensitivity and the countryside to laconic metropolitan realism; James M. Cain, Michael Fessier, Horace McCoy and John O'Hara added impetus from across the Atlantic, and gradually a new vernacular school grew up, of which the principal exponents were Peter Chamberlain ('What the Sweet Hell' and 'Our Lives are Swiss'), Arthur Calder-Marshall ('A Date with a Duchess') and Leslie Halward ('To Tea on Sunday' and 'The Money's All Right') – none of whom are included in this collection; V.S. Pritchett, too, contributed several inimitable examples in the volume entitled *You Make your own Life*.

With the appearance of *New Writing*, under the inspired and eclectic editorship of Mr John Lehmann, proletarian themes and writers were given a chance of publication; factories, the Labour Exchange and public houses replaced the family, the drawing-room and the smart cocktail bar as settings for stories (V.S. Pritchett's outstanding 'Sense of Humour', as well as Christopher Isherwood's Berlin stories, first appeared in this enterprising book-magazine). Mr Halward, who applied the technique of Chekhov and Katherine Mansfield to the lives of artisans and mechanics (and who now, regrettably, appears to have almost stopped writing) at first led the field, with the clipped, cinematic and poetical tales of G.F. Green a close runner-up: a precursor of these, stylistically, was Henry Green's *Living*, which, published a few years before the movement got under way, still remains the best modern English novel of working-class life.

Though payment was made on a small scale, there were plenty of non-commercial markets besides *New Writing*, the *London Mercury, John O' London's Weekly* and *Life and Letters*, among others, offered encouragement to the young writer steering a perilous course – as Mr Hudson puts it – 'between the Scylla of popular journalism and the Charybdis of preciosity', though publishers – as they still do – fought shy of issuing short-story collections and were apt to advocate the writing of a novel instead. During the 1940s, after the inauguration of *Horizon* and *Penguin New Writing*, many other anthologies and book-magazines were founded: alas, of an ephemeral nature, but nevertheless affording an outlet to writers who, perhaps in the forces, perhaps in the general levelling-down entailed by wartime conditions, found inspiration for tales told in the colloquial manner. Fees increased with the cost of living: it was even possible at one time, if one were industrious enough, to earn a reasonable livelihood by writing short stories.

This would not be so today. Not only have many magazines, periodicals and literary reviews ceased publication, but restrictions of length – the most cramping of all to any writer who wishes to develop character and incident beyond the level of mere anecdote – are posed editorially owing to shortage of space. Even *Encounter* and the *London Magazine* are reluctant to print anything over five or six thousand words maximum; an exception to this rule being the short-story magazine *Argosy* which, while retaining a commercial preference for dramatic themes and a strong climax, recently printed one of Mr Bates's longest and most effective *novellas* to date. Small wonder, in these circumstances, that fewer and fewer young writers are being 'discovered' to carry on the tradition of their immediate literary ancestors: the stories selected by Mr Hudson may not, as he insists, 'derive from a dying art', but certainly it is one which – unless existing conditions improve – will soon be menaced with extinction.

Mystery Magazines

*　　　*　　　*

ALTHOUGH, OF COURSE, BOTH G.K. AND JOHN O' LONDON HAD AT one time their respective weeklies, neither Raffles nor Dr Fu-Manchu ever occupied an editorial chair. But as transatlantic movie stars spend more and more nowadays to direct and produce films featuring themselves, so fictional characters have begun increasingly to become editors of magazines bearing their own names. This trend, also of American origin, is at present restricted to various mystery magazines, whose eponymous editors are either detectives or criminals operating in the USA.

Pioneer in the field was Ellery Queen who, as his many admirers know, is not only a detective but the chronicler of his own cases. It was Mr Queen who set the prevailing pattern: the title-page facsimile signature; the semi-humorous comment on the stories included in each issue; the price (35c in the States, 1s 6d for the English edition); and the consistently high standard of authorship (he printed, for instance, the story version of Graham Greene's *Third Man* complete in one number). The American edition, slightly larger and thicker than that sold in this country, has a pictorial coloured cover often depicting incidents – such as a gorilla strangling a girl through the bars of its cage – which have no place in the actual contents; but the British cover has become steadily more decorous, graduating finally from an attractive border design of lethal weapons, spades, skulls, scales of justice, hypodermic needles and coffins to the severely plain white and gold of the October issue.

Mr Queen's example was soon followed from the other side of the fence by the Saint, a chivalrous expatriate English crook and literary descendant of Arsène Lupin and Edgar Wallace's *Four Just Men*, who solves mysteries on the side and metes out retribution to criminals whom the law cannot touch. But Simon Templar, the Saint, does not himself edit the detective magazine which is named after him: instead it is the pleasantly pugnacious, Burt Lancastrian face of his creator, Leslie Charteris, which is pictured on the reverse of the cover. (Ellery Queen, presumably, was debarred from photographic representation by the fact that he was initially the product of *two* men, working in collaboration.)

Mr Charteris, too, has published Graham Greene and maintains a high literary standard: his table of contents is 'multiple-starred with the names of such greats' as William Faulkner, P.G. Wodehouse, G.K. Chesterton, H.G. Wells, Damon Runyon and Ray Bradbury among others. Each issue contains a long, complete adventure of the Saint in addition to material by other writers, and the editor is not inhibited by modesty in referring to these examples of his own work ('I liked it very much when I originally wrote it – I like it just as much now'); he is elsewhere described as 'the incomparable Leslie Charteris', and an advertisement declares that 'there's no more widely known and beloved character in present-day mystery fiction than our own Simon Templar'.

His editorial approach is forthright and even slightly truculent: 'When I consider (as I seldom do),' he writes,

> the flatulent judgement of the egg-heads who affect to look down their long noses at the type of fiction which this magazine is dedicated to merchandising I am usually tempted to retort that the main difference between the so-called 'better' literature and ours is that the former takes a normal and believable situation and problem and wrings it out to a remorselessly dull and predictable conclusion, whereas our writers would never sell us a line if they couldn't start with the same material and rapidly lead through a few novel and original twists to something fairly electrifyingly unexpected.

The Saint has recently developed a companion monthly named *Mike Shayne's Mystery Magazine* (after an Irish-American Private Eye called that); an advertisement depicts the two magazines running along, rather endearingly, hand-in-hand, but though the photograph of Mike's creator, Mr Brett Halliday, shows him wearing a black eye-shade of agreeably piratical aspect, the contents-value has not, thus far, come up to scratch: a long Mike Shayne 'novelet', however, is provided every time to satisfy the numerous fans of this 'tall, compact, sardonic crusader, who is as ready to kick a killer in the stomach as he is to help an old lady across the street'.

Patriotism notwithstanding it must also be stated that the single example of the trend to originate, so far, from this country does not bear comparison with either of the two American pioneers. This is *The John Creasey Mystery Magazine*, whose executive editor (creator of a gentleman-adventurer called The Toff) has an annual output – estimated in words alone – said to put Edgar Wallace in the shade. It includes accounts of factual crimes, costs sixpence more than its transatlantic rivals, and consists mainly of reprints (an excellent historical story entitled 'The Black Cabinet', by John Dickson Carr, published in *The Saint* for April 1957, appeared again in the May issue of Mr Creasey's monthly). In the same number, however, Mr Creasey scored by including Charles Dickens as a contributor and reviewing two of his own novels in a section headed 'John Creasey Looks at Some New Books'.

In the USA the latest editorial recruit is neither detective, criminal, nor fictional character but Mr Alfred Hitchcock, the film director. His *Mystery Magazine* ('New stories presented by the master of Suspense'), now on sale in England, price two shillings, is larger in format than its competitors and more sophisticated in general make-up. The photo-montage cover (by Bsacca/ldea House) shows Mr Hitchcock's head superimposed on a tailor's dummy clad in a mauve-and-white-striped suit, in the act of drawing a gun from an inner pocket. This surrealistic figure, standing on a chessboard floor, is in turn menaced from behind by a revolver held in the hand of a uniformed but faceless cop; while, seen through a panel slid back in the wall, bathers are sporting on a beach below.

As in the TV programme *Alfred Hitchcock Presents*, Mr Hitchcock's shadow and silhouette are used as trademarks throughout.

In the September issue he writes an amusing, chatty editorial, all about the death of his dog ('Myer of Bristol, née Phillips of Magnesia') and a correspondent who wished him to commit the perfect murder; his attitude to the reader is unaffected and even matey ('now that you have finished reading Alfred Hitchcock's *Mystery Magazine*, how did you like it? I should also be very pleased to receive your reactions...'); while his personal taste is strongly reflected both in the stories and his ironically macabre comments upon them. We take leave of him presenting us 'with a most extraordinary subscription offer' (a $5.25

value for only $4.00), and his photograph spreads its hands in resignation: 'Well, now, it's altogether up to you.'

There the trend rests, at present. But suppose it spreads to Great Britain? And beyond the mystery magazine, to other spheres of literary activity? Just imagine what this might result in. *John Osborne's Angry Young Man Mag*, or even *Lucky Jim's* ... But enough.

Hornblower in Command

*　　　　*　　　　*

AS A STORYTELLER MR C.S. FORESTER COULD IN SOME WAYS BE compared with Simenon. Though far less prolific – the Hornblower adventure is his first novel for four years – the taut, spare style, the variety of background and the sense of place, the focus on personal oddities and reactions at times of physical or mental stress, are qualities he shares with the creator of Maigret; while Hornblower is surely the Maigret of the high seas (i.e. Mr Forester has succeeded in humanising the conventional steely-eyed, square-jawed, tight-lipped naval officer of countless novels in much the same way as Simenon has humanised the police inspector of detective fiction: though in both cases the protagonist's professional efficiency remains unimpaired by the process).

Nor should it be forgotten that Mr Forester's career was launched by the success of *Payment Deferred* (1926), a terrifying yet pathetic study of what might today be termed an anti-murderer; or that, four years later, in *Plain Murder*, he followed up with one of the most chilling analyses of a criminal psychopath in modern fiction: both of these worthy of the Belgian master at his later best.

Poor Mr Marble of *Payment Deferred*, the worried bank clerk and family man with the sparse reddish hair, weak grey eyes and bristling moustache (later portrayed on the screen by Mr Charles Laughton), murders his nephew from Australia and buries him in the back garden in order to pay off debts amounting to thirty pounds; remains haunted (even after becoming well off through speculation in the rise of the franc) by the fear that some interfering busybody may dig up the corpse; and ends by being hanged for the murder of his wife, who had actually committed suicide ('in fact, Marble went down through history as an extraordinarily clumsy murderer'). So realistically is the story presented that one often has the illusion of reading the vamped-up report of a real-life crime: one of the sort in which the author presumes to know the words spoken and the emotions felt by the characters at any given time. In spite of his actions Marble engages our sympathy; yet there are moments when he becomes a frightening figure by very reason of his weakness: while the relationship with his wife Annie is rendered with a psychological depth and subtlety which would surprise readers and critics who suppose Mr Forester to be a writer preoccupied mainly with men involved in warfare or other violent action, almost to the exclusion of the opposite sex.

Morris, of *Plain Murder*, is on the other hand a complete, but credible, monster. About to be sacked from his advertising office for taking bribes, he conspires with two other young men to murder the chief clerk who could expose them, succeeds in shooting him on Guy Fawkes night; then proceeds calmly to iron out his accomplices for fear that they might talk. Here is Morris just before the first murder:

> He felt no fear; it might be said with truth that he felt no excitement. The exaltation of spirit which possessed him was something he had never known before; it was rather a delicious feeling. It was splendid to find oneself facing a considerable danger without fear, holding all the threads of a tangled skein without confusion, keeping track of quite a large number of different facts and possibilities without difficulty.

And later, after he has killed one accomplice and failed to hang the other from some hooks on his bedroom wall:

> Morris, with his hand on the rope, stood and hesitated. Someone in the house must have heard that noise; it was penetrating enough. Even if it made no impression now, it would be vividly recalled when Oldroyd was found hanging on those hooks. Even the little rumble made when the bed was jerked across the floor might have been heard. That would lead to Morris's death by hanging as well as Oldroyd's, and Morris's life was a thing infinitely more precious than Oldroyd's. Morris was sane enough still to retain the instinct for safety and retreat. The moment after he had pulled the noose tight again he released it once more...
>
> 'It's all right now, you fool,' said Morris. 'I'm not going to kill you after all.'

Morris is a superman (though Mr Forester describes him, in relation to other murderers, as 'only the best of a very poor lot'), and his relations (of a suburban sado-masochistic sort) with his wife Mary are again depicted with insight. Mr Forester is as much at home among the marble-topped teashop tables and motorbicycles as he is among the Central African natives of *The Sky and the Forest*: a meal of cold mutton, cut thick, and washed down with cups of strong tea is described as lovingly as the feast of iguana ('tender and sweet as chicken') eaten by the men of Columbus's expedition in *The Earthly Paradise*; while it is possible that the manner of presenting this plain murderer may well have influenced Mr Patrick Hamilton in his Ernest Ralph Gorse series.

Sandwiched between the two murder novels was that magnificent *tour de force Brown on Resolution*, followed later by *Death to the French*: a companion-piece in that both are concerned with objective studies of a man alone, facing privation and death out of a sense of duty in time of war. There is a certain similarity between the two stoics, Leading Seaman Albert Brown and Rifleman Matthew Dodd: both willing victims of the patriotism and class systems of their times; and in both books a Flaubertian irony flavours the ending.

Mr Forester is obviously fascinated by the Lone Man, though *two* people are concerned in the strange voyage of *The African Queen*, his next noteworthy novel (it was preceded by one of his least successful, *The Peacemaker*, in which a physics master, who has discovered an anti-magnetic device capable of stopping the traffic, decides by this means to enforce disarmament upon the nations: an unusual concession on the author's part to the anxieties and problems of the 1930s). An excellent film version, starring Katharine Hepburn and Humphrey Bogart and directed by John Huston, will have made many readers familiar with the plot and incidents of *The African Queen*; but the book should be re-read for its tenderness and charm, alternating with spasms of breathtaking excitement (such as the crossing of the rapids) and packed with idiosyncratic detail (Allnut cleaning his razor of its protective grease in order to shave; then smearing cylinder oil on his hair; Rose tucking her skirt up into her underclothes, like a little girl at the seaside, before starting to bail).

Mr Forester has a passion for detail which equals Defoe's. How to fight with battle-axes or how to light fires under primitive conditions, by means of 'a lump of a softish wood, and a foot long stick of hard wood, and some handfuls of the rotting fibre pulled from under the bark of a fallen tree' (*The Sky and the Forest*); how to estimate the speed of a ship by counting one's pulse-beats (a method used by Christopher Columbus in *The Earthly Paradise*); or how to roast mule (*Death to the French*) are not pieces of information of which most novelists are possessed. Yet Mr Forester passes them on not only entertainingly *but as part of the story*; never indulging in know-how for its own sake in the modish modern Ian Fleming manner, or holding up the action while the characters indulge in some gargantuan banquet, every item of which must be named, as in Dennis Wheatley. There is, in any case, little scope for the gourmet or gastronome to make his appearance: one of the most refreshing things about Mr Forester being that his characters rarely come out of the topmost social drawer. *The General* – with *The Peacemaker*, his least satisfactory novel – affords us one of the few sustained views of high life, with dukes and duchesses and characters called Lord George and Lady Constance Winter Willoughby; and of course Hornblower nowadays eats trout off gold plate with the nobs occasionally – though even here we are told that 'a gold service looks very well, but it allows the food to grow unfortunately cold': a piece of information which one reviewer would never have had without acquiring it in this way.

It is many years ago since *Mr Midshipman Hornblower* first made his appearance, but it was immediately apparent that he was not going to be another *Midshipman Easy* (he was seasick while at anchor in Spithead on board HMS *Justinian*). Since then we have got to know him extremely well. We know, for example, that he is 'a tall and rather gangling individual with hollow cheeks and a melancholy cast of countenance', and that his legs are thin and hairy. We know that he first ate lobster when acting as a professional gambler in the Long Rooms, and that he likes blackcurrant the least of all jams. We know that he is tone-deaf, a defect which he strives assiduously to conceal. We know that his French accent remains inadequate, in spite of the penniless noble French refugee who instructed him in boyhood. We know of his literary tastes: Gibbon (the object of his sincerest admiration), Johnson and Swift and Pope and Gray (from the last two he is able to quote), and of his opinion that *The Rime of the Ancient Mariner* should have been rewritten by Pope in heroic couplets, assisted by someone with more knowledge of navigation and seamanship than 'this Coleridge fellow'. We know that only once has he drunk anything stronger than water when by himself, and on that occasion he drank three glasses of claret, 'enjoying every drop'. He once, also, had an affair with a red-headed Vicomtesse called Marie. He dreads mutilation as a result of enemy action because he believes it would make him into a figure of fun. He hates parsons and has great skill with babies.

We have seen him through various stages of promotion, and he is now Rear-Admiral Horatio Lord Hornblower, Knight Grand Cross of the Most Honourable Order of the Bath, one-time Commander-in-Chief of His Majesty's ships and vessels in the West Indies. He has been married twice. His first wife, Maria Mason before their marriage, taught in a school with graduated fees ('readers paid fourpence, writers six-pence, and counters ninepence') and was the daughter of his landlady, who once dunned Hornblower for twenty-seven and sixpence when he was hard up through holding bad cards at whist. (Maria on the other hand had earlier slipped half-a-crown into his pocket.) Both his first children by this marriage – little Horatio and little Maria – died of smallpox, and Maria herself died in giving birth to a third, Richard (her death was announced as that of the 'widow of the late Captain Horatio Hornblower, Bonaparte's martyred victim': Hornblower himself being supposed to be dead at the time).

His second wife is Lady Barbara Wellesley, widow of Admiral Lord Leighton, 'the daughter of an earl, the sister of a marquis and of a viscount who was well on his way towards a dukedom' (one could hardly do better than this, though it was a case of true love with Hornblower, who is the very reverse of a snob). Maria was loyal and tender, but none the less dumpy, with a thick figure, coarse black hair, and heavy red cheeks; and Lady Barbara has it over her all the time when it comes to grace and beauty, but it must be admitted that Lady Barbara is also a trifle wooden (Mr Forester is at his best when portraying ladies of less patrician birth), though she makes a good staunch companion in danger aboard ship or during a hurricane in the Atlantic.

But in *Hornblower and the Hotspur* we are back in a much earlier stage of his career – the time of his first command, before Lady Barbara had even crossed his path. Maria, however, was very much upon the scene: in the first paragraph, in fact, Hornblower is just being married to her (we are later told that the thought of saying 'no' at the altar had passed through his mind). The dumpy figure and heavy red cheeks do not seem to have developed yet, moreover her lips are soft and eager; but even before the honeymoon night (which he manages, however, to make), Hornblower is ordered to sea as a forerunner to the blockade of Brest, and to keep an eye on the French (the date is 1803, when war with France merely awaited declaration, and 'Boney' was being spoken of much as Hitler was during the summer of 1939). Aboard HMS *Hotspur*, having put to flight the French frigate *Loire*, Hornblower is faced with the unwelcome task of answering his bride's letters adequately ('Plunged as he was into professional problems the episode of his marriage was suffused in his memory with an unreal quality'); Maria, however, is an indefatigable correspondent:

> Hornblower read, several times, that he was Maria's Dearest Husband. The first two letters told him how much she missed her Angel, how happy she had been during their two days of marriage, and how anxious she was that her Hero was not rushing into danger, and how necessary it was to change his socks if they should get wet...
>
> The fourth letter began precipitately with the most delightful, the most momentous news for her darling. Maria hardly knew how to express this to her most Loved, her most Adored Idol. Their marriage, already so Blissful, was to be further Blessed... There might be a Christmas Baby, or a New Year's Child; Hornblower noted wryly that much more space in these later letters was devoted to the Blessed Increase than to her Longed-for but Distant Jewel.

But it should not be thought from this extract that the new book is all on this level of domestic comedy (though the comedy seems grim enough when one remembers the fate of the child-to-be). There is a Royal Marines coastal raid by night and some excellent, typically exciting naval engagements:

> At a long threequarters of a mile *Félicité* at last scored an important hit, one hit out of the broadside she fired as she yawed widely off her course. There was a crash aloft, and Hornblower looked up to see the main yard sagging in two halves, shot clean through close to the centre, each half hanging in the slings at its own drunken angle, threatening, each of them, to come falling like an arrow down through the deck. It was a novel and cogent problem to deal with, to study the dangling menaces and to give the correct helm order that set the sails a-shiver and relieve the strain.

And so in the end Hornblower is promoted to Captain ('Maria would be delighted'). This book bridges the gap between *Lieutenant*

Hornblower and *Hornblower and the 'Atropos'*, making the saga complete and up-to-date. Now might be the time for Mr Forester to turn his considerable talents in another direction. Still in his early sixties, his body of published work is impressive by any standards (there are now seventeen volumes in the Greenwich edition of his novels); but of the author himself we know little or nothing. Like Joyce Cary, he has – except for one book – rigidly excluded any personal note: and this in an age of autobiography disguised as fiction. May one hope that *Randall and the River of Time*, once announced as the first of a possibly auto-biographical novel-sequence, may shortly have a successor?

The Black Romances
of A.E.W. Mason

*　　　　*　　　　*

'WHAT A WORK OF ART THE THRILLER CAN BE,' ARNOLD BENNETT
wrote when greeting *No Other Tiger* on its first appearance in August
1927; and there can be little doubt that the improved status of this
particular genre among present-day critics owes much to A.E.W. Mason's
archetypal study in suspense, published three-and-a-half decades ago.

Previously, Mason had achieved spectacular successes with two
detective novels, *At the Villa Rose* (January 1916) and *The House of the
Arrow*; and in his preface to an omnibus volume comprising them,[1]
he shows himself to have already been preoccupied with problems of
characterisation as well as plot:

> Do the people who conduct the story live? Are they elucidated
> by and do they, being what they are, assist inevitably in the
> development of the events? Or are they mere dolls jerked by
> the author into unnatural movements and posed so that
> somehow they may be squeezed into the pattern of thrills and
> surprises which he has designed?

At the Villa Rose, he goes on to tell us, was based on a synthesis of
two real-life cases: the murder of a rich elderly widow, with the connivance of her maid and companion, at her Aix-les-Bains villa (Mason
was shown their two names, scratched by a diamond ring on a window-
pane during a visit to the Star and Garter at Richmond); and the
sordid killing of a spinster shopkeeper by habitual criminals in the
Commercial Road (he attended the murderers' trial at the Old Bailey
and from this derived the idea, incorporated in his novel as a reason
for keeping the kidnapped Celia Harland alive, of the guilty parties

---

1　*Inspector Hanaud's Investigations*, Hodder.

failing to find the hidden jewellery which had been their motive for the crime).

> Then the Memoirs of Monsieur Goron,[1] and of Monsieur Macé, both of them distinguished chiefs of the Paris Sûrété, began to build up for me a French detective, who should be first of all a professional, secondly, as physically unlike Mr Sherlock Holmes as he could possibly be; thirdly, a genial and friendly soul...

Such were the prototypes and genesis of Inspector Hanaud. But Mason – like the master-craftsman which he has often been claimed, quite rightly, to be – was principally concerned with the 'all-important question' of technique and presentation; what in fact resulted were two novels in one: the surprise (itself a staggerer) of the murderer's identity in *At the Villa Rose* occurs at the close of chapter thirteen, and the remaining nine chapters are devoted to a recapitulation of the crime from inside, thus fulfilling the author's 'desire to make the story of what actually happened more intriguing and dramatic than the unravelling of the mystery and the detection of the criminal', or – as he writes of *The House of the Arrow* – 'The solution itself was...so to depend upon the interplay of characters one upon the other and a natural succession of new incidents, that it would provide a second story of greater interest than the story of the mystery solved.'

This method, however, was not altogether original, since Conan Doyle had anticipated it in *A Study in Scarlet* and *The Valley of Fear*; what broke entirely new ground was Mason's manner of achieving his climactic surprises by playing upon the public's acceptance of reconceived character and situation: in *At the Villa Rose*, the conventional handsome young 'hero', calling upon Hanaud to prove the innocence of the girl he ostensibly loved, is in reality a brutal, cowardly and heartless killer; while in *The House of the Arrow*, the position is reversed: the distraught and beautiful young woman, apparently the victim of a blackmailer's baseless accusation, is herself a blackmailer and anonymous letter-writer who had poisoned her benefactress for gain. (Like its predecessor, this book also had real-life parallels, and an actual poison-arrow coated with 'Strophanthus Hispidus' came into the author's possession.)

---

1 Goron figures also as a protagonist in Herr Joachim Maas's *The Gouffé Case*, surely one of the great German novels of the last decade.

Both these cases – and their successor, *The Prisoner in the Opal* (of which, more later) – were set in France (Aix, Dijon, and the Gironde, respectively) and solved on the spot by Hanaud. At this point, it must reluctantly be stated that, like most recurrent fictional detectives (Lord Peter Wimsey, Sir Henry Merrivale, M. Hercule Poirot, to name but three), the French Inspector, with his blue comedian's chin, his buffoonery, and horridly unfunny idiomatic misquotations ('You cannot make a silk purse out of a Bath chap', 'Don't keep me on the tenthook', etc), is an egregious bore.

On the other hand, his 'foil and butt', Mr Julius Ricardo, the retired tea-broker from Mincing Lane – whose capacity for being tedious is frequently commented on by his creator – becomes by contrast an endearing figure, despite his appalling snobbery, dilettantism and old-maidishness:

> 'I may be old-fashioned,' he said, flapping a hand up and down in the air like a fin of a fish, 'but I cannot endure any but the mildest of Turkish tobacco in my bedroom.'
>
> 'Good!' Hanaud answered cordially, without, however, letting him off one single puff. 'Then the more I blow the Maryland, the sooner you will rise from your bed.'

Ricardo, and not Hanaud, is Mason's real triumph in these books. Initially invented as an unusual kind of Watson, a convenient device through whose uncomprehending (though not unworldly) eyes enigmatic and perplexing events might be viewed, he emerges as a truly comic creation, drawn in the round; excluded from *The House of the Arrow*, he makes a brief, welcome reappearance in *No Other Tiger*: but one is nevertheless relieved that he is frightened off the scene before Hanaud can also be brought upon it.

For, though *At the Villa Rose* and *The House of the Arrow* are now considered classics of their kind, establishing precedents for future practitioners to follow, they were – in spite of superior style and careful characterisation – still strongly dependent for their interest on 'the pattern of thrills and surprises'; while the climate of *No Other Tiger* is altogether more atmospheric: the quality of menace, of stealthy stalking terror, is predominant, and the main problem is not the villain's identity (known to the reader almost from the start), but the question of when he will strike and where?

Archie Clutter, the 'gentleman from Cayenne', 'famished, mauled, disfigured, half brute and wholly demon...stripped of all hope here', is very nearly one of the great villains of fiction. He glides soundlessly through the memory like 'the man without a shadow upon a sunlit day', corrupt, ferocious and cunning, yet oddly pathetic despite his dedication to hatred and revenge: one recalls him with a shiver long after the complex machinery of artifice and coincidence which sets him in motion is forgotten. For *No Other Tiger*, while in many ways a precursor of the contemporary suspense novel, remains unalterably a period-piece, with all its period's faults: the plot is melodramatic and stagey, the figure of the heroine, Lady Ariadne Ferne, now appears hopelessly dated and unreal: though perhaps no less than Michael Arlen's Iris Storm.

A.E.W. Mason was born in 1865, and Ariadne with her bobbed boyish hair and ugly impertinent habit of calling 'her friends and her loves by their surnames' was an Edwardian attempt to draw a 'Modern Girl': she tries 'a quite new drug' at a party and eats sandwiches out of a paper-bag at Epsom, but does not convince or come alive in the way that her false friend Corinne, that famous dancer and accomplice to a cruel murder for profit, never fails to do. (Mason, like many more eminent novelists, found it much easier to delineate guilt and evil than to portray goodness and innocence: though later, with Joyce Whipple in *The Prisoner in the Opal*, he did at last succeed.)

Corinne, the *demi-mondaine*, 'hag-ridden by terror' of Clutter's vengeance, acquisitive and treacherous yet none the less human and appealing, is the real heroine of the book: we feel sadness when at the end she is found hanging from her own chandelier, just as we cannot help feeling sympathy for Clutter himself when he is shot dead like a jungle beast by Ariadne's stolid prosaic suitor, Colonel John Strickland.

Never before or afterwards, however, were one's sympathies engaged by the evil-doers in Mason's work: this may not have been at all his intention even in *No Other Tiger*, but it is because he succeeded – perhaps unwittingly – that the novel seems prophetic in the light of present-day fictional trends, where the twisted and the damned are prone to arouse the reader's pity. But who could pity Betty Harlowe the poisoner, clapping her hands with a clear joyous laugh 'like the trill of a bird' as she contemplates her prospective victim trussed up in a sack? Or handsome Harry Wethermill (note how the Christian names are artfully chosen to suggest honesty, while the Wodehousian ring of Archie Clutter's lends a touch of grotesquerie to the fear he inspires) screaming as the body of the woman he had strangled fell against him 'with her whole weight', and the instigator of the crime, the 'cruel, masterful, relentless' peasant Hélène Vauquier looked contemptuously on? Corinne, the 'pagan to her fingertips' (she kissed the feet of an amber Christ while falsely protesting her innocence of a murder by remote control) and Clutter, the sometime dandy, degraded by circumstance and eight years' confinement in a cage to the point where he volunteered for duty as the penal colony executioner, are pitiable because in a sense they are victims of life and their own weaknesses, whereas the others were actuated from the beginning by black envy and malice and something perilously close to pure evil.

Perilously close to: with his next Ricardo-Hanaud adventure Mason took a step towards pure evil itself. Few if any readers could sympathise with the members of the secret satanic cult from *The Prisoner in the Opal*: with Tidon the ambitious examining magistrate who used his official handcuffs to shackle a girl who had assisted unbidden at the forbidden ceremony; or Cassandre de Mirandol, the degenerate Vicomte with his 'full, mincing lips', dimpled childish face, and thin piping voice; or Robin Webster, the prematurely white-haired renegade priest and amateur Casanova, who might have been an incarnation of Satan himself: Robin being one of the Devil's names and Adonis – as Mason is fond of telling us – another.

Not even Mason's graphic description of Webster writhing in the torment of his passion for Joyce Whipple ('I can't help myself. I am like the man in hell. I want my drink of water beyond anything in the world – you, Joyce, you!') can persuade us to feel anything but repulsion in his case. Nor is much sorrow inspired by the murder-victim Evelyn Devenish, stabbed to death while her naked body served as altar for the Black Mass (as Madame de Montespan once had lain for the Abbé Guiborg) and stuffed into a wicker basket with her hand hacked off: for had she not designed a more horrible end for the girl she hated? Entombment alive:

> They [Evelyn's eyes] had flashed with an implacable fury then, and they had moved up from the slim foot in its slipper of silver brocade to the knee, with a veritable hunger of hate. Oh, without a doubt Evelyn Devenish had been thinking at that moment of the distorted figure of that youth in the Cave of the Mummies! She had been putting Joyce Whipple in his place, had been watching her knee pressed in a despairing agony against the coffin-lid. Yes, it was Evelyn Devenish who had

sighed. [Sighed, we have been told earlier, with 'a passionate longing that such a penalty could still be exacted'.]

Hanaud 'could not but respect thoroughness, even if it were a thoroughness in cruelty', and his creator obviously shared this trait (the heroine of *They Wouldn't be Chessmen* forced to make the fishing-net in which she herself was to be enmeshed) though in Mason the French detective's 'reluctant admiration' was magnified into something approaching fascination, especially where the opposite sex was concerned. His work contains a long gallery of hideously cruel women (Vauquier with her flask of vitriol, Harlowe with ready hypodermic, Clara von Paten grinding her heel between the dying Königsmark's teeth) culminating in his portrait of the abominably wicked Frances Scoble who, among other horrors, tried 'like a witch' to poison her twelve-year-old half-brother's dreams in the historical novel *Musk and Amber*. But in *The Prisoner in the Opal* he depicted for the first time a deeper malevolence: Evelyn Devenish is a woman actively possessed, driven by more than sexual jealousy: as genuinely evil as Joyce Whipple is genuinely good. (Moreover, the resourceful and courageous Californian Cinderella is real as Lady Ariadne was not: her personal radiance shines like a beacon through 'as black a business as Hanaud could remember', and we are shaken with relief when she finally comes through more or less unscathed.)[1]

'Black', by the way, is the operative word. Mason started his career as a romantic writer in 1895, but he had travelled far since the rehabilitation of Harry Feversham (though as early as 1902 *The Four Feathers* included blindness, humiliation, and bloodshed in plenty); the ethics of cowardice and heroism interested him no longer, but the romantic's basic pessimism and ambivalent attraction to the dark side of the moon remained. (Who but a romantic of this type would have chosen, at the age of seventy-seven, to write the extraordinary tale of a boy dispossessed of his birthright and gelded – owing to the greed and cruelty of women, naturally – who becomes a great operatic soprano and later returns to seek the *Musk and Amber* of revenge on those responsible for his deprivation?)

---

1 The device of the gate varnished by Joyce with mustard gas in order to trap all those who attended the Black Mass was used – as Hanaud relates – to identify German agents in 1917; and according to his biographer, Roger Lancelyn Green, it was Mason himself who in real life employed it. (He was a Major in the Secret Service of 1914.)

As in the case of Hugh Walpole, it is with these Black Romances, written in the guise of thrillers, rather than his 'straight' novels, that we come close to the themes which obsessed him. No novelist could have been less subjective, and this is the nearest we get to the expression of a personal philosophy: the vision of this world as a vast opal inside which the observer stood: 'An opal luminously opaque, so that I was dimly aware of another world outside mine, terrible and alarming to the prisoner in the opal.'

Mason, like Hanaud, may have been 'inclined to believe that at times the other hidden things outside…break through to punish or to save', but we are at any rate certain of his belief in the 'terrible and alarming' denizens peopling, also, this other world, dimly glimpsed beyond a firmament shaped like a prison dome.

Seventy Years of Sexton Blake

*　　　　*　　　　*

'SEXTON BLAKE, FOR INSTANCE,' GEORGE ORWELL WROTE IN HIS essay on '*Boys' Weeklies*', 'started off quite frankly as an imitation of Sherlock Holmes, and still resembles him fairly strongly; he has hawk-like features, lives in Baker Street, smokes enormously and puts on a dressing-gown when he wants to think.'

Certainly it is thus that most members of my generation will remember him pictorially represented: long and lean and aquiline, a permanent forty, relaxed in an armchair with a curved briar pipe between his teeth and one sinewy hand fondling the ears of Pedro the bloodhound stretched at his feet; beside him stands his boy-assistant Tinker, who in those days addressed him with respectful affection as 'Guv'nor': much in the same manner that Bram Stoker spoke to Sir Henry Irving.

But Sexton Blake began his public career as more than an imitation of Holmes: he was obviously intended as a substitute. For Blake must have been born as a fictional character in the same month of the same year – December 1893 – when, in the pages of the *Strand* magazine, Holmes and Professor Moriarty, locked together, fell to their death in the Reichenbach, 'that dreadful cauldron of swirling water and seething foam'.

Of course Holmes did not really die; but even Conan Doyle did not know that then. He had thought himself finally rid of his character, whom he had wanted to kill off two years earlier, only his mother, outraged, put a stop to that. (It was not until 1903 that, yielding to an offer from the United States of five thousand dollars a story – for the American rights alone – he was persuaded to bring Holmes back to life.) Meanwhile the news of Holmes's death was regarded as a nation-wide calamity: 'In London,' one biographer of Conan Doyle tells us, 'sporting young City men went to their offices with crepe bands tied round their hats.'

The story of *The Final Problem* was written, however, some months before (April 1893); and George Newnes and Greenhough Smith, acting editor of the *Strand*, must have been appalled when they received the MS.[1] The periodical world and Fleet Street being what they always have been, it is inconceivable to suppose that rumours of the approaching disaster failed to leak out. The appearance of Sexton Blake (in *The Marvel*, published by Alfred Harmsworth and succeeded by *The Union Jack*, 1894, price one halfpenny) at precisely such an opportune moment is a coincidence too hard to credit otherwise: as a piece of journalistic timing it remains in any case hard to beat.

At this time, too, Blake must have been intended for a predominantly juvenile public. I myself first became aware of him at the age of eight, having already read most of the Sherlock Holmes short stories, and eagerly accepted him as a replacement. My father, a year older than Conan Doyle himself, was not so eager, Blake had not been part of his boyhood (as he was to become part of mine); he was thirty-five in 1893 and had married my mother the year before: the advent of Holmes's successor may even have escaped his notice in the general pressure of events. On the other hand he did not actually refuse Blake entry to the house, as he did with Blake's colleague and competitor Dixon Hawke and the American detective Nick Carter, whom one saw occasionally in newsagents' windows firing off revolvers or knocking out an opponent.

The Sexton Blake Library novelettes (founded 1915 and succeeding *The Union Jack*) at this period cost fourpence apiece and were issued at the rate of four volumes a month. They were printed in double columns by what was then the Amalgamated Press (now Fleetway Publications Ltd) and each contained approximately 60,000 words. The first one I ever read was called *The Valley of Fear* (issued five years after the Sherlock Holmes novel of the same title, and bearing no relation to it in scene or content); the cover illustration depicted a man struggling desperately in the grip of a gigantic carnivorous plant (part

---

1   About Sherlock Holmes's fall over the precipice Newnes used such terms as 'dreadful' and 'unhappy': as, to a meeting of shareholders, well he might (John Dickson Carr, *Life of Sir Arthur Conan Doyle*).

of the story was set in the jungle of Patagonia or some such place) and this excited my father's disapproval less than the lurid covers of Blake's contemporaries (the only Dixon Hawke which I had attempted to buy had on it a motorcyclist masked by goggles and going all out with a gun in his hand). It is possible that he did not quite realise what kind of book this was, and imagined it to be an adventure story along the lines of Henty or Mayne Reid.

The Sexton Blake authors then, and for some years after, remained anonymous; so the name of the writer cannot be given here, nor can I at this remove of time recall the plot. I do remember, however, the eerie atmosphere of the tale, which was concerned perhaps with the effects of some exotic drug (it is even probable that the protagonist on the cover – not, I think, either Blake or Tinker, introduced in 1904, a year after Holmes's resurrection – went to the fearful valley in some kind of dream or vision rather than in the flesh). Soon after we all went to France, where the Sexton Blake Library was more difficult to obtain; but on our return two years later I bought at a railway bookstall two new volumes, one of which, entitled *The Red Dwarf*, was subtitled 'by the author of *The Valley of Fear*'. Even without this, the authorship would have been unmistakable: *The Red Dwarf* dealt too with weird happenings, this time in the dungeons of a haunted castle, and the eponymous villain's name was Yedax. (Both these stories may have been the work of the late Gwyn Evans, said by some to have originated the character of Sexton Blake,[1] and certainly the creator of one of his principal antagonists, the sinister Hindu Gunga Das. Evans, whose stories I afterwards read in boys' weeklies such as *Pluck* and *The Rocket*, specialised in the bizarre – waxwork murderers coming to life, vanishing omnibuses, and a figure of terror behind a bead curtain which had the face of a newborn baby;[2] another possibility is Eric W. Townsend, who wrote for the same weeklies as above – all published by the Amalgamated Press – and once created a murderous dwarf named Steffal: he specialised in tropical settings and the man-eating Patagonian plant would have been right up his street, though in my experience his name never in later years appeared on a Sexton Blake.)

---

1 The name of Blake's first chronicler was actually Hal Meredeth.

2 The rat-torture used on Winston Smith in George Orwell's *Nineteen Eighty-four* occurs identically in this particular Gwyn Evans story, 'The Vengeance of the Pharoah', published in *The Rocket*, 1923.

For in the early 1930s, when I again renewed acquaintance with the great detective (or 'consultant criminologist' as we are told he is listed in *Who's Who*), anonymity had been discarded – though the format of the volumes remained the same – and the names of Gwyn Evans, John Hunter, Anthony Skene, Warwick Jardine etc, were printed plain for all to see. The first three writers also produced full-length, hardback thrillers for adult readers: in Anthony Skene's case three excellent examples come to mind, *Five Dead Men*, *The Masks* and *Gallows' Alley*; he was also, for the Sexton Blake Library, the creator of Zenith the Albino, a strange criminal with his own curious code of honour who sometimes even lent Blake a hand in defeating villains of a deeper dye. John Hunter – probably the best boys' writer of his day, and certainly the most varied in subject-matter: he could encompass anything from football to *The Quest of the Giant Sloth* – was perhaps less successful in his adult products (though *The Three Crows* and *When the Gunmen Came* are not to be despised), but the Sexton Blake novelettes which he wrote are so memorable that some contemporaries of mine are able to quote from them today.

Both Hunter and Anthony Skene were stylists worthy of study, for the former in the early 1920s was writing for the boys' magazines in the manner now attributed to Dashiell Hammett (but which originated with pulp-magazine writers of the period such as Carroll John Daly); while Skene – on his own admission strongly influenced by *The Maltese Falcon* and *The Glass Key* – was introducing to English readers, via Sexton Blake, many concepts of the modern thriller now taken for granted, long before they were vulgarised by *No Orchids for Miss Blandish* or adapted by Peter Cheyney. Skene's style was sharp and dry – less melodramatic than that of Hunter, who even at best was highly charged and apt to bring in the Angel of Death a shade too often. Violence was handled by Skene in a throw-away, matter-of-fact manner not always to his readers' tastes, and he was frequently taken to task by correspondents for making Blake himself feel fear in the face of danger. But both he and Hunter could create convincing, off-beat villains (one of the main tests of a good thriller-writer: Ian Fleming has never succeeded in making his other than grotesque and unbelievable) and their power, apart from this, lay in the actual method of narration: as distinct from Gwyn Evans, who relied upon horrific gimmicks and startling situations to rivet attention on the page. (Another Sexton Blake author of the Thirties was Gerald Verner, whose Wallacian mystery-yarns

– written under the pseudonym of Donald Stuart – were afterwards published for adults by Messrs Wright and Brown: Sexton Blake being changed into a dramatist named Trevor Lowe and Tinker becoming his secretary, Arnold White.)

Most of these writers contributed as well to *The Thriller* (which published Edgar Wallace himself, many of the early Leslie Charteris-Saint stories, and serialised a short Dashiell Hammett novel, *The Great Knock-Over*), and its companion-paper *Detective Weekly* (defunct 1940), which carried a complete 20,000-word Sexton Blake story in every issue. Of these, Orwell writes: 'Both of these papers admit a certain amount of sex-interest into their stories, and though certainly read by boys, they are not aimed at them exclusively.' This was true also of the Sexton Blake Library at this time: girls – and even seductive ones – were often introduced, though Blake personally was not allowed to be captivated (in common with most fictional detectives, including Sherlock Holmes, Inspector Maigret and – until almost the end of his career – Philip Marlowe) and Tinker was considered to be far too young.

By the mid-1930s, the parallels between Blake and Holmes had become less marked, though he still shared the physical characteristics and residential area of his prototype (as Holmes was looked after by Mrs Hudson, Blake was served by a landlady named Mrs Bardell, doubtless a descendant of Mr Pickwick's, and addicted to monstrously unfunny Malapropisms). There was still an occasional, token mention of 'deduction', as contrasted with the routine police-methods of Scotland Yard Inspector George Coutts (the Blakeian equivalent of Lestrade), but in the main Blake's cases were solved by more direct action and he was of course operating in what were at that date present-day conditions.

As Dickson Carr reminds us, Sherlock Holmes remained rooted for the most part in a period even earlier than 1885, when he was first conceived: he really belonged to the London Conan Doyle had seen eleven years before as a lad of fifteen: 'the vast eerie city … with its lamps glimmering through brown fog and its curtained mystery-haunted streets'; in 1905 Sir Arthur rejected indignantly the suggestion that Holmes and Watson should undertake cases mounted on a motorcycle, though he himself was riding one. But even Holmes had to emerge from retirement in 1914 to outwit the German agent Von Bork: no thriller series of any kind can ignore contemporary reality for long; and the SBL authors, within the limitations imposed on them, strove hard to bring their material up to date. While world politics were not, as I recall, overtly mentioned, Blake more than once opposed Fascism in the form of a Ku-Klux-Klan type organisation called the Black Legion, which then actually flourished in the United States (Anthony Skene's novel *The Masks*, though not a Sexton Blake story, was serialised in *Detective Weekly* and dealt with a derivative of this society, practising mysticism and magic of a Wagnerian sort similar to that propagated by Hitler).

It should be noted that most of these writers were turning out several almost full-length novels a year for a flat fee of 60 guineas a time, and probably as well several novella-length stories for *Detective Weekly*, which also paid a guinea per thousand words. The stint is halved and remuneration much higher these days. An entry in *The Writers' and Artists' Year Book* for 1963 reads, under the heading 'Sexton Blake Library':

> 1s. 2 each month. – Complete detective stories of about 35,000 words, with sustained interest, dramatic action and strong characterisation. The same central characters – Sexton Blake, Paula Dane and Tinker – are invariably involved in these stories which should set out to be as different and as unusual as is consistent with plausibility. Locations should be accurately described, and the writing must be of a high standard…
> *Payment*: 100 guineas to 150 guineas per story on acceptance.

Not bad, considering the new length (halfway between the *Detective Weekly* and the old SBL) and the average advance on royalties made by publishers of crime novels, which in many cases is often all the author will ever get from diminishing sales to lending libraries: plus – if lucky – a payment for paperback rights, half of which falls due on publication only – two years after the hardback edition appears. Intrigued by this entry, 'Who,' I wondered, 'is Paula Dane?' and having believed Blake to be like Holmes long dead, I finally located three examples of the new-style SBL on a Paddington bookstall, hidden in among copies of the Schoolgirl Picture Library, Thrilling War Pictures, and something entitled simply 'Bombs Down!'

It was immediately apparent that they were in the wrong place: 'boys', in the true meaning of the word, were obviously no longer aimed at. These Sexton Blakes were pocket-size, printed in small type but not double columns, 64pp. long (format introduced, I found out later, in December 1962). For a shilling each they seemed – and proved to be – excellent value. The names of the respective authors, Philip Chambers and Howard Baker (in collaboration), Richard Williams and Martin Thomas were unfamiliar to me (though most had an impressive list of titles in the series to their credit). It was plain that 'resident villains' such as Zenith the Albino would no longer stalk across the pages (with his white hair, crimson eyes and the cyanide cigarette, kept in case of capture and stamped with a red circle to distinguish it from the others he carried: perhaps he had smoked it at long last). Two of the cover designs (no worse and in some cases better than the average half-crown paperback, where the predominant symbols are also a blonde, a corpse and a gun: sometimes a montage of all three) featured contrasting photographs of Sexton Blake as played on film by the screen actor Geoffrey Toone; one bore also a photo of Leslie Charteris, quoted as saying: 'I hope the Saint is as full of life as Sexton Blake when he has reached the same staggering total of successfully concluded crime cases.'

Tributes have been paid also by Dorothy Sayers, Agatha Christie ('Delighted to see Sexton Blake still going strong…and with such aplomb!); the former chief of Scotland Yard's ghost squad; ex-Chief-Supt. Cherrill, CID; Raymond Francis (AR TV's Supt. Lockhart); and Rupert Davies (BBC TV's Inspector Maigret); the latter echoing Agatha Christie word for word, except for the aplomb.

Another cover informed me that Sexton Blake was translated into, and published in, German, Spanish, Norwegian, Dutch, Swedish, Finnish, Portuguese, Danish and Hindustani. On the third, *The Daily Mail*, after stating that Blake's sales have exceeded 500 million copies, continued: 'Sexton Blake is a changed man…undergoing rebuilding and modernising.' The texts bore out this latter claim. Blake now has an ultra-modern suite of offices in Berkeley Square (a plan is given on the backs of later issues), a staff to match (the mysterious Paula Dane turned out to be his personal secretary), a silver-grey Bentley Continental for his own use (replacing the old 'Grey Panther') and a Jaguar to chase criminals in. He also owns a seal-point Siamese cat named Millie, with a taste for sweet sherry (Pedro the bloodhound is in retirement, though brought back recently in a hunting-background story called *Killer Pack*). His Baker Street consulting-rooms have become a luxurious, centrally-heated penthouse flat in the same thoroughfare, and the erstwhile landlady Mrs Martha Bardell (with, mercifully, fewer Malapropisms) is now his 'daily woman' and doubles as cook. In the flat below lives Edward Carter, alias Tinker, his 'junior partner and associate', who now like the rest of the staff calls him 'chief', having reached the age of twenty-six. (Blake, however, has stuck as usual about the forty mark, but has acquired a number of new skills: he practises judo and karate, can pilot a plane, sing baritone, speak Swedish and Afrikaans and readers are reminded that – going one better than Holmes – he is a qualified physician.)

His physical attractions too have been pointed up lately (to such an extent that the beautiful but crooked Duchess of Derwentwater addresses him as 'Sexy'): much is made of his 'tanned, eagle face', black widow's peak and grey-blue eyes; crisp, incisive (or deep, resonant) voice: sometimes a note of woman's-magazine hysteria enters in ('There was a virile magnetism in his lean masculinity' and so on) or an attempt is made to turn him into a 'rakish' swashbuckling figure, like the Saint. Despite all this, he remains emotionally uninvolved, though there was a dangerous moment when Adèle, the Duchess, told him he had lovely eyes down at Deadleigh Abbey, where the Lifetakers Murder Syndicate was secretly in action (see SBL No 514, *A Corpse for Christmas* by Wm A. Ballinger).

Frequent controversy, in the correspondence section called 'Mailbag', rages round his status quo with the devoted, tall, honey-blonde Paula Dane. Some readers think she should have 'a closer relationship' with her employer; others complain vehemently about authors who 'drool over her' (it is true that her 'long, showgirl legs' have taken the place formerly occupied, in John Hunter's case, by the Angel of Death); there is an extremist faction who want to have her cut out altogether (this is composed mainly, but not entirely, of women; on the other hand it is a woman reader who would like to see more of the old, warm Paula who was so openly in love with an appreciative Blake). Meantime Blake has been known to take Paula to lunch in Fleet Street and to the Oriel Room for dinner on the same evening, their luncheon date having been spoilt by a girl hurtling to her death from a window above as they were making towards the Cock Tavern (SBL No 402, *Murder Most Intimate* by W. Howard Baker – who incidentally introduced Paula in an earlier story, SBL No 359, *Frightened Lady*: a male reader in Jamaica is anxious to obtain a copy and willing to pay costs and postage to any-one who has one to spare; requests for autographed photos of Paula also abound).

The grown-up Tinker treats Paula with brotherly affection, but indulges in flirtatious horseplay with Marion Lang, the pretty brunette receptionist: though not with Miss Louise Pringle, the 'more mature'

Sexton Blake Investigations Company Secretary (described by one reader as 'a mixture of Mrs Pym and Miss Marple'); Miss Pringle seldom plays an active role, apart from exercising Millie the Siamese. Tinker is said (by Martin Thomas in *Death in Small Doses*, a tale of the Los Angeles drug traffic with a female transvestist surprise ending) to believe that 'anything – anything at all – could be brightened by the presence of an attractive girl'. But, while he is a tall, blond broad-shouldered and personable young man, it is one of the new conventions that he never gets very far with women, and indeed often makes a temporary mess of his assignments owing to this predilection for the opposite sex (given knock-out drops by glamorous decoy or a black eye by girl suspect's jealous admirer etc); he has, however, protested in a recent story against being made by his biographers to 'look a proper Charlie'.

Aside from members of the staff, the Duchess of Derwentwater and her ducal husband (described by Tinker as 'an upper-crust Ted'), other new 'pool' characters – as a Transvaal reader aptly called them include:

Arthur ('Splash') Kirby, the 'Around and About' Fleet-Street columnist, who works for *The Daily Post* (owner: Lord Charmwood, né Silas Cudmore, 'The Baron'; editor: Paul Jorgensen, enough said).

Eustace Craille: old, skeletal, unpleasant and ruthless Director of the Inter-Service Co-Ordination of Strategic Intelligence and National Security ('Disco Sinsec'), also chief of the British espionage network PAN-SAC (of which Blake is a senior operative).

Nick Reuter: thin dark dapper private detective, to whom Blake occasionally farms out leg-work and surveillance jobs.

Deputy Commander Gimwald: Scotland Yard's grizzled, distinguished Liaison Officer with MI5.

Another CID officer is the 'headline-seeking' and foppish Superintendent Theodore Dunkelow; while *Chief* Detective Inspector Coutts, thus promoted, is still very active, bowler-hatted and bulldog-jawed as ever: he has retained, too, his pipe, though Blake's has been abandoned in favour of cigarettes carried in a 'slim gold case'. ('It's Sherlock Holmes who smokes the pipe,' he told an American actor impersonating him on TV, 'I gave it up years ago.')

These characters are used impartially by any of the new-style Blake authors. Their outward characteristics have been well assimilated by all and are proudly trotted out on every possible occasion ('Splash' Kirby's 'rugged crumpled face', thinning hair, filter-tip fags and raffish speech; Craille's claw-like hands and dry, throaty chuckle, due to incessant smoking of Egyptian cigarettes, etc). Even Millie's 'lustrous blue eyes' and 'dark V-shaped mask' are constantly plugged (she has, by the way, been kidnapped and held as hostage twice: once by voodoo-worshippers in Notting Hill Gate and once by Chinese restauranteurs in Mayfair; a chapter in the latter novel began: 'Had Sexton Blake eaten Millie?').

Of the authors themselves, the most notable is perhaps Jack Trevor Story, a sort of 'rogue' writer (in the sense of 'rogue' elephant), on whose novel the Hitchcock film *Trouble With Harry* was based. One of his Sexton Blake stories, *Collapse of Stout Party*, was subtitled 'Shady Doings in Darkest Suburbia'; another, *Nine O'clock Shadow* (about a beatnik wrongly convicted of murder) was rewritten for the screen and produced as a film featuring Adam Faith, the role of Blake (transformed into a lady psychiatrist) being played by Anne Baxter. The book of the film was published as a hardback novel entitled *Mix Me a Person*: since when he has written the screenplay for the highly successful hire-purchase film, *Live Now, Pay Later* (also published in novel form). Story is sometimes attacked by 'Mailbag' correspondents who find his flip approach and zany, oddball humour a bit beyond them (one of his opening chapters is told from the viewpoint of a woodlouse which witnesses a gang-murder), though he has supporters too. In any case, the future for him seems to lie in other, more lucrative spheres of literary activity and he has not contributed to the SBL for some time, though his name is now used to advertise the series.

Desmond Reid, by far the most prolific regular contributor (twelve out of twenty-eight consecutive issues, according to our Transvaal correspondent), specialises in fantastic themes and offbeat settings (an English village infected by a wave of irrational violence; a Cape Town blood-cult; murder in a method-acting academy); but his staccato style is too febrile and he suffers, like many of his colleagues, from a reversion to the manner which Orwell complained of in the boys' weeklies, by which a simple statement is rammed into the reader by repeating and paraphrasing it in several different ways.

W. Howard Baker's forte is realism (Brighton, Wardour Street, Earl's Court etc: the latter is indeed a locale favoured by almost all group-members); besides Paula Dane, he has also introduced Blake's father, Dr Barclay Blake; and he has written the only story, *The Big Smear*, in which Blake is represented as overworked and feeling his age(!); the scene where Blake's staff, trained by their chief to respect evidence, discuss the possibility that he is really guilty of sexual assault is particularly true-to-life (the charge is of course a frame-up, but it brings Blake to the verge of ruin and suicide). Richard Williams is a kind of SBL Julian Symons; his backgrounds – such as a big department store (where the 'Easter Bunny' is murdered) or, in one case, a publishing house of lurid paperbacks – are always admirably documented: he has also drawn an unsentimental portrait of 'fictioneer, second class' ('one of the faceless, near-anonymous army ... who, without benefit of prestige-paper reviews and Sunday-press profiles, provide the main mass of popular reading') which does him great credit.

Wm A. Ballinger occasionally bends over backwards to fulfil the 'different and unusual' editorial requirement: this led him once to introduce the grim grey monolithic figure of 'E', the SBL Editor in person, employing Blake to find two actual authors (Peter Saxon and Arthur Maclean) who had disappeared without delivering their MSS ('We don't do that sort of thing! We're not running the *Gem* or the *Magnet*!') But his 'B'-picture producer, 'Magic' Wand, from *Murder in Camera*, has the right quality of dreadful resilience, the studio atmosphere and detail are authentic; and the bowler-hatted, brief-case-carrying professional killers in *A Corpse for Christmas* cast about them a genuine chill. (In the latter story there is, as well, a startling account of a giant pike attacking Blake underwater in a quarry-pool, which shows not only considerable imagination, but real descriptive power in presenting the personality of the pike himself.)

It must be admitted that the new group of writers contains no stylist comparable to Hunter and Skene. But, with the new freedom accorded to its members, the nature of the material has become infinitely wider and more varied. Nobody could now accuse the SBL of turning its back on the present state of the world: there can be few centres of unrest which these later tales have not covered (one correspondent writes: 'I have liked your bang-up-to-date novels dealing with the Congo troubles, the Algerian situation, and behind the Iron Curtain'). Even the existence of culture is acknowledged, and readers presumed to have knowledge of Picasso, Matisse, Mozart: abstract painters also (though Blake does not personally admire abstract art).

The Sexton Blake Library, for whatever readership it was designed, has always afforded a microscopic cross-section of the thriller of its time; and the thriller has today come to reflect, as in a distorting mirror, not only the trend of serious literature (in which more and more thriller themes are being absorbed) but – as proved by public events over the past two decades – the actual tenor of the times. Blake himself celebrates his seventieth anniversary of publication this coming Christmas. As a character whom almost everyone has heard of, he antedates Dracula by four years, Raffles (created, incidentally, by Conan Doyle's brother-in-law) by six.

And over the years a portrait (as promised in an early editorial) has been built up, crudely perhaps and by many different hands, yet not differing in essentials: the portrait of a man who, though not an idealist, represents nevertheless an ideal; who is not, like most of his fictional colleagues, devoid of compassion, a sadistic brute, or an eccentric bore; but who continues, in the human interest, to combat injustice and crime: a man doing at any rate, to the best of his ability, the work he set himself to do, and adhering still to the principles he formulated in *The Marvel* seventy years ago: 'if there is wrong to be righted, an evil to be redressed, or a rescue of the weak and suffering from the powerful, our hearty assistance can be readily obtained…'

> NOTE: After this article had gone to press, I learned with regret that the Sexton Blake Library was to cease publication with No 526 of the new series (*The Last Tiger*, by Wm A. Ballinger), which includes a farewell message from Blake himself, and leaves him hand-in-hand with Paula Dane 'on the golden glistening beach in the bright Honolulu sun' – and a visit to the Vicar of a Thameside village tacitly agreed between them for the very near future…

Mary McCarthy and
the Class of '33

*   *   *

WE ALL KNOW, AND MANY OF US HAVE WRITTEN, THE ONE ABOUT
the intelligent man who falls for a silly vulgar girl and is ironically
aware of her every fault while remaining in thrall to the magnetism she
exerts. During scenes of seduction and sex, such a protagonist is apt to
be especially observant: detachment occasionally extends to a complete
mental dissociation from the physical act, as when even Graham Greene's
hardly intellectual Anthony Farrant thought about bicycles and changing
trains at Rugby while embracing the young woman he had picked up
in Stockholm. It came, therefore, as a salutory shock to male readers
(and also writers) when in the early 1940s we were shown by Mary
McCarthy that a woman could do it too.

Miss McCarthy's bland, impersonal, down-to-earth approach to
the mystery of sexual attraction, and indeed to the sex-act itself, was
radically different from that of our own women novelists, by whom it
had always been taken for granted that the objects of their hallucinated
heroines' affections were madly glam: Eddie, for instance, in Elizabeth
Bowen's *Death of the Heart* possesses a diabolic disorganised charm,
while that of Rollo in Rosamond Lehmann's *The Weather in the Streets*
enslaves practically every woman in the book. Miss McCarthy's heroine
was not hallucinated, and her *Man in the Brooks Brothers' Shirt* represented not only the opposite of what she admired but was, moreover,
not even young. After twenty years, no story quite like this has been
produced by a woman in this country: the ostensibly 'masculine' and
'realistic' attitude of a contemporary female writer such as Doris Lessing
assumes that the woman (though as a rule intellectually superior) is
almost always a victim and the man automatically an insensitive clot,
by the very fact of being a man. Miss McCarthy has no implicit bitterness

or antagonism towards the opposite sex: she is merely clear-sighted; there is little malice in the way she coolly takes the wind out of her males. The nearest comparison would be with Muriel Spark; both Miss McCarthy in her new, long-awaited novel[1] and Mrs Spark, in her recently published *The Girls of Slender Means*, have taken a group of assorted young women for subject-matter and followed their fortunes over a crucial period of change: Mrs Spark's being linked by their fortuitous association, in 1945, at the May of Teck Residential Club in Kensington, Miss McCarthy's more closely by belonging to the Class of 1933 at Vassar (apparently a kind of American Cheltenham Ladies' College), while both novels contain a character of literary-world leanings who – in neither case the most appealing member of the group – finally achieves material success through dogged application to the business in hand: Mrs Spark's fat Jane Wright as a gossip-columnist 'for the largest of woman's journals', Miss McCarthy's Libby MacAusland as a leading literary agent.

There are other, personal similarities between the two novelists, sometimes in reverse (Mary McCarthy is a cradle-Catholic, long since lapsed; Mrs Spark, like Miss McCarthy's mother, is a convert to the faith; Miss McCarthy's grandmother was Jewish, Mrs Spark's also, as she has informed us in a recent broadcast), but the literary affinity is one of quality and temperament alone. Miss McCarthy shares Muriel Spark's objectivity without a trace of the latter's predilection for fantasy (disembodied voices, ghostly apparitions, young men with embryo horns on their heads, and doppelganger-type murderers who turn into dust-devils after death) or formalism of style: her narrative is nothing if not straightforward.

The activities of the eight graduates making up her group cover seven years, from the wedding of one of them in 1933 to the time of the London Blitz in 1940, when they foregather again at the funeral of the bride. Dynamic Kay, having run round the table at the Class Day dinner (a curious custom by which Vassar girls announce their engagements to contemporaries) marries a monster called Harald who keeps his *sang froid* even in bed ('he did the multiplication tables to postpone ejaculating – an old Arab recipe he had learned from an Englishman'). All members of the group except she are virgins at this time, despite their 'progressiveness' and surface sophistication, and fastidious little

---

1   *The Group.* Weidenfeld and Nicolson.

Helena Davison remains so throughout; but after the wedding breakfast, 'twinkling' Dottie Renfrew from Boston (a devout Episcopal communicant and the last person one would expect to succumb to a sudden physical passion) is deflowered by a misogynistic, unhappy painter in an attic room smelling of cooking fat. There follows the famous contraceptive sequence (which will be already familiar to some readers from its publication some years ago in *Partisan Review*); the fitting of the pessary in the dedicated birth-control doctor's office, and the cruelly but superbly funny climax when Dottie, after waiting six hours for her lover to return home, finally abandons the apparatus, douche bag and all, under a bench in Washington Square. ('Imagine the junkman's surprise!' she exclaims afterwards when confessing the incident to her mother, Class of 1908, who has tried to send her back to the birth-control bureau on the eve of her wedding to an eligible but much older man.) These pages are unique in present-day fiction and likely to remain so: it is, incidentally, doubtful whether Miss McCarthy herself, without her Catholic upbringing and Convent education, could have written them.

The shadows, meanwhile, are already closing in on newly-wedded Kay. The horrible Harald comes back one evening, grasping a pint of gin, with the news that he has lost his job in the theatre and an excuse which will be recognised by anyone who has worked with stage people: 'When he told the director, softly, where to get off, the nance gave him notice'; and not long after, having sold an option on one of his own unproducable plays, he starts an affair with the graceless, sluttish Norine Schmittlap Blake, an unpopular hanger-on of the group, who wears 'a peculiar garment made of old grey wolf' and is married to a 'registered Socialist' (impotent unless his wife dresses up as a whore and even then he ejaculates prematurely). Helena Davison, a prig whose awful purist mother (not actually 'a college woman') has 'the heart of an alumna' (Helena herself is Class Correspondent for the *Alumnae Magazine* and her reflections are sometimes couched in a parody of its idiom) surprises Norine and Harald locked in an embrace in Kay's kitchen and attempts to intervene on the latter's behalf but is defeated by Norine's pachydermatous passive-resistance to any interference with the course she has set herself. Kay suspects the liaison but remains faithful to Harald, who continues to impress her as a misunderstood genius partly because of a suicide attempt which he claims to have made before their marriage: though in fact the borrowed car turned over on him while he was driving drunk (he also burns his play-script exhibitionistically at a party, knowing that other copies are on file at his agent's office).

Libby MacAusland, the literary one, when not making love to herself on the bathroom mat, aspires to a career in publishing with a determination equal to Norine's own ('not just copy editing, but creative rewriting': it is an awful thought that authors in the States may have their MSS rewritten by girls just out of college); but abandons this (ending up as a successful literary agent) after mistaking a revolutionary Sicilian novel, published in 1912, for a tract in favour of Mussolini. (One of the funniest chapters, next to that on contraception, concerns her narrow escape from rape at the hands of a Norwegian baron: the description of this is proof positive that humour is always an aphrodisiac.) The leftish publisher at whom Libby had initially set her cap embarks on an affair with Polly Andrews, another classmate, but returns to his Communist wife when he finds that sexual satisfaction leaves him without dreams to recount to his analyst; Polly later marries happily a psychiatrist at the Medical Centre where she works, who first tries to persuade her to have her melancholic father certified as a lunatic. It is this husband who, later still, exerts himself to have Kay freed when Harald has had her committed to an asylum after beating her up while drunk. She is too far gone, however, for anyone to save her; released at last, she falls to her death from the window of the Vassar Club while 'aeroplane spotting' after the outbreak of the Hitler war: Harald of course is a rabid isolationist while Norine, now married to a prosperous Jew, has given up politics in favour of comparative religion: 'Society is finished if it can't find its way back to God. The problem for people like us is to rediscover faith. It's easy for the masses; they never lost it. But for the élite it's another story.'

The friends assembled at Kay's funeral are joined there by the beautiful expatriate Elinor Eastlake ('Lakey') who has returned to her native shore as a confirmed lesbian, accompanied by a butch-baroness 'boy'-friend, said to employ brass knuckles on any male arousing her jealousy. It is uncertain what Miss McCarthy is trying to prove here. Some critics have taken the theme to be the defeat of liberalism: certainly the background of the period in which the New Deal became *vieux jeu* is brilliantly sketched-in. ('You can't make any progress in medicine unless you're willing to be hard,' a paediatrician who is trying to get his wife to breast-feed their baby tells her. 'It's the same with your friend Roosevelt and those soft-headed social workers in the White House. The economy would have recovered by itself if they'd left it alone, instead of listening to the whimpers of the down-and-outs,' while Norine opines: 'The New Deal is rootless – superficial. It doesn't even have the dynamism of fascism.') Kay is undoubtedly defeated: but could she, or any of the group for that matter, be said to stand for progress? As often in real life, the shoddy and the untalented, the pushers and the thrusters (Norine and Libby), make their way to the 'top' while the loyal and the trusting go to the wall: on the other hand the egregious Harald remains conspicuously unsuccessful, embittered, and finally miserable at the very end.

Apart from its inconclusiveness, the novel has other faults. It bears internal evidence of having been written over too long a period: certain chapters contain unnecessary repetition (Dottie Renfrew also 'twinkles' a shade too often), the one concerned with the question of breast-feeding versus bottle could have been cut to advantage, and fourteen pages dealing with the English family butler of the dimmest member of the group have little relevance to the whole. Miss McCarthy is at her best as an episodic writer, in *The Company She Keeps* or in the autobiographical pieces making up her *Memories of a Catholic Girlhood*; here, in a long novel of 360 pages, the pace tends inevitably to flag. But she has given us much to be grateful for, and her uncompromisingly amused attitude to sex points the way to a real breakthrough in fiction: unlike the muddled members of her group, she is a true pioneer, and progress will not really be defeated so long as she remains with us.

The Dark Glass of
Sheridan Le Fanu

*   *   *

Something like a stunted, blackened branch was sticking out
of the peat, ending in a set of short, thickish twigs. This is what
it seemed. The dogs were barking at it. It was, really, a human
hand and arm, disclosed by the slipping of the bank, under-
mined by the brook, which was swollen by the recent rains...
In this livid hand, rising from the earth, there was a character
both of menace and appeal; and on the finger, as I afterwards
saw at the inquest, glimmered the talismanic legend 'Resurgam
– I will rise again!'

IT WAS DOROTHY L. SAYERS, QUOTING FROM *WYLDER'S HAND*[1] IN
the Introduction to her first anthology of Detection, Mystery and
Horror, who put me on to the works of J. Sheridan Le Fanu. I was then
sixteen, living in the south of France; and in the dim musty room,
behind a bright modern bookshop that served as English Lending
Library on the Place Macé at Antibes (itself, atmospherically, a Le
Fanu-like place) among the rebound Tauchnitz and damp spotted
Victorian volumes on the shelves from which, four years before, I had
first taken Poe and Wilkie Collins, I found without much difficulty the
book I sought.

And after a long elapse, here it is again, a replica, inside of the
edition (first published a hundred years ago) which I held then – 387
pages of close clear print, with wide margins and ornamental capitals
at each chapter-opening – but wrapped now in the same yellow dust-
jacket and reissued under the same publisher's imprint as the
anthology which introduced to me its author.

---

1   Victor Gollancz.

From their background of 'sombre old trees, like gigantic hearse plumes, black and awful' or tall hedgerows gilded by 'slanting beams of sunset', while billiard-balls are clacking and brandy-and-water is being drunk at the village hostelry, the protagonists emerge once more: the 'very gentleman-like' Captain Stanley Lake, that 'sly, smooth terrorist', with his yellow eyes 'very peculiar in shape and colour his scented matches and gliding step'; his 'insubordinate and fiery' sister Rachel and cold, apathetic cousin Dorcas, whom he later marries and who, 'had she been a plain woman...would have been voted an impertinent bore but was so beautiful that she became an enigma': to say nothing of Jos. Larkin, the shifty 'eminent Christian' lawyer of Gylingden, who finally 'was dismissed, in a tempest, with costs' and 'vanished from court, like an evil spirit, into the torture-chamber of taxation'.

It comes again as a disappointment that the passage Miss Sayers quoted is to be found only on page 369 and that the actual secret, on which this apparent edifice of evil is so blackly built-up, turns out simple enough to be summarised in two pages at the end; but here, as with so much of Le Fanu's work, *Wylder's Hand* is a forerunner of a literary genre, the atmospheric novel of menace, not fully developed in his own day (incidentally, different versions of the plot later provided a basis for *The Door with Seven Locks* by Edgar Wallace and Dashiell Hammett's *The Thin Man*).

Born in 1814, senior by a decade to Wilkie Collins and only three years Poe's junior, an Anglo-Irish newspaper owner and editor who did not embark on a career of authorship until the age of forty-four (after the death of his wife in 1858), Le Fanu remains above all an innovator. In his novel *Checkmate* (1870) a criminal for the first time altered his appearance by means of plastic surgery; his tale of a Lesbian vampire, *Carmilla*, antedates *Dracula* by twenty-five years and contains, not only the complete paraphernalia of *nosferatu* legend, but a sure-fire method of extermination (the head struck off after the stake through the heart) which, if used on the Carpathian Count, would have effectively prevented his return in so many screen-sequels of our time. But it is in *Green Tea* (written a year before the author's death in 1873) and the other strange stories collected under the title *In a Glass Darkly* that he seems most of all, not so much a prophet, as to be peering, himself, through a clouded pane into the future. These tales, ostensibly forming part of the case-histories amassed during a lifetime by a practitioner of 'Metaphysical Medicine' named Dr Hesselius, and posthumously published by his secretary, can no longer be taken for the ghost stories they were once believed to be.

If Captain Barton, the retired naval-commander in *The Familiar*, is really hounded and finally frightened to death by the ghost of a sailor whom he had 'sanguinarily punished', who then writes the eerie notes signed 'The Watcher', by which the persecution is initiated? And what are we to make of Mr Justice Harbottle – a sort of Judge Jeffreys – who in 1746 is arraigned, in what purports to be a dream, before a phantom court and condemned to be hanged by 'Chief-Justice Twofold', whom even he recognises as 'a dilated effigy of himself'? Who drew up 'in angular scrivinary', on parchment, the indictment signed 'Caleb Searcher, Officer of the Crown Solicitor in the Kingdom of Life and Death', and what became of the original of this interesting document? (Not surprisingly, after Harbottle has duly carried out the sentence on his own person, only a copy – 'of an illusion, incident to brain disease?' asks the narrator – in the judge's own handwriting was found.) Then there is the Rev. Mr Jennings, haunted by a small black monkey, first encountered in an omnibus, which only he can see. After this clergyman's suicide, Dr Hesselius comments: 'The complaint under which he really succumbed was hereditary suicidal mania', but the doctor seems a colossal old humbug, a precursor of the worse type of psychiatrist, expressing his theories in jargon which Le Fanu may have even intended as parody. In modern terms he only occasionally talks sense ('If the patient do not array himself on the side of the disease, his cure is certain'); at other times he appears to believe in a kind of cerebral third eye opened, in Mr Jennings's case, by the drinking of too much green tea (Le Fanu may himself have believe in something of the sort: Captain Lake in *Wylder's Hand* – an opium addict, incidentally – felt the Sword of Damocles was suspended 'over his pineal gland').

We today can see past the elaborate ventriloquist's dummy of the 'metaphysical physician' and recognise these for the early studies in schizophrenia and sexual aberration that they are, written in lucid prose (except when the Doctor is expounding his own opinions) by a true poet of the uncanny, dark catacombs of the mind. As a pioneer of the psychology of terror, Le Fanu will have a permanent niche: even Henry James, creating the fearsome presence of Miss Jessel in *The Turn of the Screw* twenty-five years after the Irish author's death, may have been influenced by memories of her prototype, the French governess in *Uncle Silas*, grinning at her panic-stricken pupil from beyond the dark glass.

Chandler and Hammett

*   *   *

RAYMOND CHANDLER DID NOT, AS SOME PEOPLE BELIEVE, INVENT the 'hard-boiled murder story'. Moreover, he specifically denied having done so. 'I have never made any secret of my opinion that Dashiell Hammett deserves most or all of the credit,' he wrote to a confrere in the posthumous collection of his letters, *Raymond Chandler Speaking*; and he might, since Hammett's first full-length novel, *Red Harvest*, was published in the USA in 1929: ten years before the appearance in England and America of Chandler's *The Big Sleep*.

Chandler and Hammett, so often bracketed together, met only once and both are dead now: Chandler in 1959, at the age of seventy-one; Hammett, six years his junior, in 1961. Both of them began by writing crime-novelettes for the pulp magazine *Black Mask*, under the editorship of Joseph Thompson Shaw; though Hammett started considerably earlier than Chandler, whose first story *Blackmailers Don't Shoot* (18,000 words, for which he was paid 180 dollars) did not appear until 1933, a year before Hammett's fifth and last novel, *The Thin Man*, was published: so that he was in fact beginning his career when Hammett had already ceased to write.[1]

No two authors' backgrounds could have been more dissimilar. Hammett, born in Maryland, brought up in Philadelphia and Baltimore, left school at fourteen; and, after a variety of odd jobs, worked for eight years as an operative for Pinkerton's Detective Agency. 'The First World War,' we are told, 'in which he served as a sergeant, interrupted

---

1 The last 20,000-word Hammett suspense novella to be printed, *Woman in the Dark*, bears all the signs of having originally been a Hollywood 'treatment' for a film to feature, possibly, Luise Rainer.

his sleuthing and shattered his health' (a very early story is concerned with a TB patient in a US military hospital); after his discharge, 'he resumed detective work', and left it, he is believed to have told an interviewer, because (like his own character Nick Charles) 'he got sick of poking his nose into other people's business'.

Hammett therefore had, over most of his fellow mystery-mongers, the advantage of first-hand detective experience, of which as a writer he made undoubted use. Although, unlike Chandler (as Somerset Maugham pointed out in an essay entitled *The Decline and Fall of the Detective Story*), he created a different detective for each novel, his initial protagonist (also anonymous narrator of many novelettes) was an operative for the Continental Detective Agency in San Francisco, an organisation controlled by the bland and ruthless 'Old Man' and roughly resembling the average reader's conception of Pinkerton's.

Actually, according to the statement of a former US Secret Service officer, Donald Gerrard Hughes, recorded in Frederick Oughton's admirable 'portrait of the private detective', *Ten Guineas a Day* (which contains a potted history of the agency), Pinkerton's function is quite other: 'It's a kind of private army where the employers can hire any number of hard fist artists whenever they need them… They can supply you with an armed riot squad inside of a couple of hours.' It is not suggested that Hammett served in any such capacity; but in 1892 Pinkerton's men were called in as strike-breakers at one of the plants owned by a powerful industrialist Henry Clay Frick, 'the Coke King' (plainly a prototype of Elihu Willsson, 'the Czar of Poisonville' in *Red Harvest*), who as a result was shot through the neck in his Pittsburgh office by an attacker carrying, also, a capsule of fulminate of mercury in his mouth, enough to blow up the whole building. Despite his wound, Frick summoned clerks to 'secure' the gunman, and the Coke King recovered, to be 'hailed as a true martyr' by the workers, Mr Oughton tells us, 'enabling him to go on with his unholy war against the labouring classes who now considered him a true tough guy'. (A similar incident is related, in reverse by Hammett, where the Poisonville Czar – who had employed gangsters as strike-breakers instead, and now wants the Continental Op to clear them out of his city – shoots his assailant, also through the neck, and leaves the corpse lying on his bedroom carpet for the corrupt police to collect.)

It is typical of Hammett's method that the Continental Op (whose name is never revealed) was physically the direct opposite of his creator, also five or more years older: aged forty, 5 feet 6 inches in height and weighing 190lb 'not all of them fat' (Hammett himself was very tall and lean); typically, too, he is described indirectly, by comparison with other characters. Tough, cheerful, and full of rude common sense, he bears a stamp of authenticity that causes the reader to accept the not-always-credible course of events in which he takes part; and of course Hammett's knowledge of the underworld, derived from his days as an actual detective, helped to build up the illusion of reality.

Apart from these beginnings, however, little is known of his private life, except that he married Lillian Hellman, the dramatist (author of *The Little Foxes* and *Watch on the Rhine*, to whom *The Thin Man* is dedicated), and departed for Hollywood in the 1930s, to write nothing but film-scripts thereafter. He seems to have left behind him no body of correspondence for publication, and his true personality must remain an enigma save to those who were his friends.

Not so with Raymond Chandler: far less reticent, whose collected letters amount almost to a compressed autobiography and whose origins and early life, for an American tough-mystery writer, were in many ways less likely than those of his predecessor in the field. Born 1888, of Quaker descent, in Chicago, he was brought to England at the age of eight and attended Dulwich College as a day pupil (much is made, in the Foreword to *Raymond Chandler Speaking*, of his 'classical education': in fact he reached the Sixth Form on the 'Classical Side', having already gone 'up the Modern Side to the top', and left Dulwich at the age of seventeen). Afterwards he studied for a year in France and Germany, passed a Civil Service exam (third out of six hundred), went into the Admiralty but resigned after six months and 'holed up' in Bloomsbury, where he heard Shaw, his beard still red, lecture on Art for Art's Sake, wrote verse for the *Westminster Gazette* (then edited by J.A. Spender) and reviewed Jeffrey Farnol and Eleanor [sic] Glyn for *The Academy* (previous owner Lord Alfred Douglas: Chandler made contact with the new owner by pretending he wanted to buy an interest in the magazine).

Between 1912 and 1914 he returned to the States (California); at the outbreak of war enlisted with the Canadian Gordon Highlanders, commanded a platoon in France, then in 1918 joined the Royal Flying Corps and was demobilised in England a year later, arriving back in California 'with a beautiful wardrobe, a public school accent, and had a pretty hard time trying to make a living (he was far from well-off and had, moreover, a mother to support). None the less he 'finally became an officer or director of half a dozen independent oil-corporations...small companies but very rich...everyone called me by my Christian name'.

He began to write again after losing his job in the depression, and joined the Black Mask group which included Erle Stanley Gardner, Carroll John Daly (whom Gardner claims was the real originator of the hard-boiled style, and whose trigger-happy private eye Race Williams was certainly the forerunner of Mickey Spillane's Mike Hammer), and Lester Dent, who with his strangely oblique approach to violent themes and staccato but subtle style might have rivalled Hammett and Chandler had his output been larger.

The narrative technique adopted by these men, quite apart from their use of colloquial and underworld idiom, was difficult to follow because unusual in those days (Mr Maugham confesses that he is sometimes 'not a trifle confused' by Hammett and, as late as 1939, *The Big Sleep* was deemed 'obscurantist' by the crime critic of the *Observer* on its first appearance over here). Yet their work was addressed to – and presumably understood by – ordinary people who, according to Chandler, 'thought they were getting a good meaty melodrama written in the kind of lingo they imagined they spoke themselves'. Dramatic values were put before plot: 'a good plot was one which made good scenes. The ideal mystery was one you would read if the end was missing.' He adds: 'Some of us tried pretty hard to break out of the formula, but we usually got caught and sent back. To exceed the limits of a formula without destroying it is the dream of every magazine writer who is not a hopeless hack.'

As already stated, Hammett however had escaped and was famous in two continents before Chandler arrived on the scene, though he is included in a group photograph of a Black Mask dinner published in *Raymond Chandler Speaking* (his great height and prematurely white hair must have been severe drawbacks in his former profession, which may be why the Continental Op was designed to be less conspicuous). Chandler is standing in the back row too (it was the occasion of their one meeting): unsmiling and solemn with pipe and spectacles, high of brow, dark hair backswept, he wears a jacket lighter in shade and of smoother cloth than anyone else; the others, selfconsciously smirking or widely grinning, face the camera, sleekly groomed and soberly clad – though one has a tartan tie – with glasses in their hands or on the table before them (no bottles of bourbon or rye are visible: prohibition must still have been in force). Like the majority of writers, they might be bank clerks, insurance salesmen, even business executives: all look pleasant and intelligent, certainly none looks tough; nor do they seem the sort of men to initiate a literary revolution (but the same would apply to photographs of Bolshevik leaders in another sphere).

Yet the revolution by this time had already taken place. Publication of *The Maltese Falcon* (Hammett's third novel but his first to appear in Great Britain: *Red Harvest* and *The Dain Curse* were not imported until 1950, in Cassell's *Dashiel Hammett Omnibus*) had brought it about, though its effects in some quarters were not so far to be fully felt. In this country, for instance, the vernacular first-person style had not really taken hold, even in the 'straight' novel or short-story magazines (I remember my own initial efforts being rejected, by editors and literary agents with exclamations of puzzled distress and sometimes outrage), and the detective-mystery novel was infinitely more hide-bound by tradition and harder to remake in a new mould (it was the hey-day of the flippant, debonair 'amateur sleuth' so rightly decried by Chandler: his Christian name was usually Anthony, Trent, Gillingham, Gethryn, etc; there was also Roger Sheringham (but invented by Anthony Berkeley) – and any of these might indeed have been played on the stage by Anthony Carson, when he was being an actor during this period).

The Maltese Falcon, however, was not written in the first person or the vernacular, except for the dialogue, and had made a considerable impact over here; an ingenious gentleman alias 'Henderson' even typed it out verbatim, changing only the characters' names ('Cairo' became 'Cohen') and the locale (from San Francisco to London), and had the 'novel' published under the title *Death in the Fog,* which led to an action for plagiarism in the early thirties ('Henderson' having mysteriously disappeared beforehand). A few years, nevertheless, would have to pass before the spate of imitations in pseudo-transatlantic idiom began, with Peter Cheyney and later James Hadley Chase: a speakeasy brawl from *The Thin Man* (after Arthur Barker printed the first English edition in 1934) was repeated almost word for word in a 'wide-boy' novel by an author who must, alas, be nameless, since no action was taken in his case. (Chandler has said that Hammett 'wrote scenes that seemed never to have been written before'; not only this, but his phrasing sticks so vividly in mind that one finds more than mere echoes of it in the work of writers who would certainly not stoop to conscious literary theft:

the same is true, to a lesser degree, of passages in Chandler himself; but, as he points out in a letter to Cleve F. Adams, a fellow crime-novelist: 'The law recognises no plagiarism except that of basic plots'.)

In the letter mentioned above (dated 1948) he also writes: 'Everybody imitates in the beginning. What Stevenson called playing the "sedulous ape"'; twelve years before, he had been an emulator of Hammett:[1] on one occasion producing a novelette (*Guns at Cyrano's*) which, without a hint of parody, so resembled Hammett in his *Glass Key* manner that the protagonist – a boss politician's son rebelling against the debased traditions of his birth and environment – might have been a close, but richer and more influential, relation of the gambler Ned Beaumont (even his name, Ted Malvern, has an identical ring). In the same year, however (1936), he published *Goldfish*, a trial run of the Philip Marlowe-type story (though the detective-narrator is named Carmady); from then on, his own manner developed and he sloughed the skin of the sedulous ape, becoming, within his self-imposed limits, a master of evocative prose, and the odd yet graphic simile, although his odiferous comparisons were often of a nature outside most readers' experience: involving dead toads, boiling alcohol under a blanket, or a fairly clean Chinaman.

But *Guns at Cyrano's*, surprisingly, is one of his early best (which seems regrettably to prove that the 'lifting' of another writer's 'personal tricks, stock in trade', etc, a method he was later to denounce, can be justified by results); and he himself thought well enough of the story to consider, in his 1939 *Plan of Work*, adapting it as a future full-length novel, blended with another Black Mask novelette, *Nevada Gas*; Chandler called this technique 'cannibalisation': the gaming-room sequence from *Fingerman* (1934) figures, with a few alterations, in *The Big Sleep*; a shorter version of *The Lady in the Lake* appeared in *Dime Detective* (1939), etc; and he was not the only one to practise it. Hammett had once more anticipated him, transforming *The Whosis Kid* from the story of that title into Wilmer, Mr Gutman's boy-henchman in *The Maltese Falcon*, while the Fat Man first appeared (as

---

1   Kenneth Millar, whose first Chandleresque novel (published under the pseudonym John Ross Macdonald) was dimly viewed by the Master (*vide Raymond Chandler Speaking*), described his own prentice work as 'Chandler with onions' and Chandler himself as 'Hammett with Freud potatoes', adding: 'We all came out from under Hammett's black mask.'

a sinister Greek) in the tale *Gambler's Wife*; the Russian 'princess' in *The Gutting of Couffingal* shares characteristics with Miss Wonderly, and so on. 'Cannibalisation', in Hammett's case, may be the reason why so many mysteries in *Red Harvest* (the murders of Donald Willson and Police Chief Noonan's brother, for instance: committed for different reasons by two different killers) are solved one by one; even *The Dain Curse* (on the face of it a masterpiece of plotting, in which each of the three parts contains a surprise solution to a series of apparently unrelated crimes, revealing at last the real criminal's identity and the fact that these problems form part of a previously hidden whole) may have been initially constructed from three other Continental Op adventures connected by a freshly forged story-link. Again, a new mystery, with new characters, seems to start up in the second half of the little-known, 30,000-word Hammett novel *The Great Knock-Over* (sometimes entitled *Blood Money*) but proves to be but an extension of the first.

Chandler might have disapproved of this latter method (in his 'Casual Notes on the Mystery Novel' he inveighs against something of the sort), and to him *The Dain Curse* may not have seemed 'credibly motivated', since the criminal behind the scene is obsessionally insane: moreover the final revelation could savour of a 'trick' or 'least-likely-person' ending ('To get the surprise murderer you fake the character,' he wrote in 1940, thus putting in a nutshell the honest mystery-writer's principal dilemma). On the other hand, the device of translating portions from previously published novelettes into later novels, or combining two subjects into a new pattern must have been a godsend to him, for he appears to have always been plagued by the necessity for plot (that of *The Little Sister*, he wrote to Hamish Hamilton, 'creaks like a broken shutter in an October wind', and elsewhere describes himself as 'one subject from early childhood to plot-constipation').

Farewell My Lovely, for example, which Chandler believed to be his best book, is compounded of two novelettes, *Try the Girl* and *Mandarin's Jade* (both 1937); and from the latter is obviously derived the story of Lindsay Marriott and the Fei Tsui necklace, introduced in Chapters 7 and 8 and linking up afterwards with the main theme of Moose Malloy and his search for the Girl from Florian's (Chandler's original name for this novel: the American publishers disapproved strongly of his later choice, although *Farewell My Lovely* was actually to set a new fashion for mystery-story titles).

Chandler frequently wrote that he was looking only for 'an excuse for certain experiments in dramatic dialogue'; that the mystery and its solution were to him but 'the olive in the martini'; or simply that he did not 'take the mystery element as seriously' as he should; but other letters to fellow craftsmen and his 'Casual Notes' (compiled in 1949), not only show his conscientiousness in this respect, but his immense preoccupation with the very rules he affected to despise (to the extent of drawing up new ones of his own). The acclaim he received led him in the end (despite earlier protestations of modesty) to take an exaggerated view of his literary position, precisely because he persisted in considering himself primarily a *mystery* writer, as extracts from his correspondence show: 'Once in a long while a detective story writer is treated as a writer, but very seldom'; 'What greater prestige can a man like me (not too greatly gifted, but very understanding) have than to have taken a cheap, shoddy, and utterly lost kind of writing, and have made of it something that intellectuals claw each other about' (1945); or: 'Many writers, although not all, concede that I did manage to re-create a worn-out medium and that, but for me, they would hardly be able to exist' (1957); and again: 'To accept a mediocre form and make something like literature out of it is in itself rather an accomplishment. They tell me – I don't say this on my own information – that hundreds of writers today are making some sort of living from the mystery story because I made it respectable and even dignified.'

By 1954 this megalomaniac note had crept in: 'I might be the best writer in this country, and with two exceptions I very likely am, but I'm still a mystery writer. For the first time in my life I was reviewed as a novelist in the London *Sunday Times* (but Leonard Russell is a friend of mine and may have leaned a little out of kindness).'[1] It was in this country that he enjoyed his greatest reputation (and also, in the 1950s his largest sales): 'Over here,' he wrote to Hillary Waugh from London, 'I am not regarded as a mystery writer but as an American novelist of some importance... a thriller writer in England, if he is good enough, is just as good as anyone else... People – well-bred English people – come to me in this rather exclusive hotel and introduce themselves and

---

1 Leonard Russell, then literary editor of the *Sunday Times*, did not lean out of anything. I was doing the novels at the time and specially asked to review Chandler under General Fiction, though in the event my notice – doubtless for space reasons – was cut to a bare precis of plot and incident.

thank me for the pleasure my books have given them...' and before this, in 1947, 'over there the top flight critics, like Desmond MacCarthy and Elizabeth Bowen, review them' (his books). But he had a low opinion of critics in general and did not hesitate to express it ('I think most critical writing is drivel and half of it is dishonest'); if adversely criticised he defended himself by quoting facts about the work in question that only its author could know, or by saying the critic had failed to understand the element of burlesque in his writing.[1]

Nor did he, despite his early sojourn, care much for England and the English: one of his recurrent ambitions was to write *English Summer*: 'a short, swift, tense, gorgeously written story verging on melodrama... The surface theme is the American in England, the dramatic theme is the decay of the refined character and its contrast with the ingenuous, honest, utterly fearless and generous American of the best type' (a type, incidentally, not much represented in the novels which he did write). The 'refined character' (a woman of title to be called Lady Lakenham) 'has about as much sex as a capon,' he wrote as late as 1957, for even after a recent visit to this country he evidently considered most of us, male or female, as completely effete: not surprisingly, in view of the fact that he seemed to read no modern English novels except detective fiction of a rather outmoded kind.

He also considered English inferior to American because less flexible as a means of expression: 'I had to learn American just like a foreign language. To learn it I had to study and analyse it'; but during his last two years, he wrote to the editor of the *Atlantic Monthly* that he had been trying to learn English, '...almost a mandarin language, but it is beginning to loosen up and I think I might possibly do something with it, since I am beginning to feel that I have done about all I can do with the mystery story'. This may well have been true (it must be remembered that Chandler was fifty-one when his first novel was published); the fragment of the Philip Marlowe story on which he was working at the time of his death is compounded of elements with which he has made us familiar in the past (more than a hint of civic corruption, antagonistic police, a club-owning racketeer with gun-toting hoods who attempt unsuccessfully to hijack our hero, etc), except for the fact that Marlowe is this time on honeymoon: Chandler's friends

---

1   He did both in a letter to James Sandoe with reference to a 'panning' which a screenplay of his received in a film article which I wrote for *Penguin New Writing*.

having prevailed upon him to marry his character off at last, and to a fabulously rich woman at that. (One might say that Marlowe began his career – in *The Big Sleep* – by 'calling on four million dollars', and ended it by marrying eight.)

It is idle and perhaps unkind to speculate what he might have done had he lived (apart from a play to be based on the *English Summer* theme, which would plainly have been disastrous). A posthumously published short story, written in 1951, shows him to have had little aptitude for the straightforward study of psychological conflict, while the novel he once hoped to write ('ostensibly a mystery and keeping the spice of mystery… actually a novel of character and atmosphere with an overtone of violence and fear') had already been written, twenty years before, by Dashiell Hammett in *The Glass Key*. It is doubtful, however, whether Chandler realised this; indeed (while never ceasing to praise his predecessor) he doubted 'whether Hammett had any deliberate artistic aims whatever', possibly because these were never overtly expressed.

Hammett expressed nothing overtly. Long before he went to Hollywood, he was writing in the manner of a film: we are left to deduce his characters' emotions only from what they do or say (and often from what they do not say). The reader of *The Glass Key* realises that Ned Beaumont is in love with Senator Henry's daughter only when he rewrites a letter to her because the original draft contained a split infinitive: a piece of subtlety of which Chandler, with all his considerable gifts, would have been incapable. Hammett could convey the essence of a relationship between two people purely through dialogue and action and convince us of its reality in a way that Chandler never succeeded in doing: compare the atmosphere of genuine love and trust conjured up by the affectionate banter of Nick Charles and his wife in *The Thin Man* with the embarrassing honeymoon exchanges of Marlowe and Linda ('Don't be nasty or I won't – you know.' 'Oh, yes you will. You can hardly wait'; 'Goddamn you! I'll get my white whip out if you're not polite. It has steel inserts in the lash.' 'The typical American wife', etc). Or compare the friendship between Marlowe and Terry in *The Long Good-Bye* with that, in *The Glass Key*, between Madvig, the political boss, and Beaumont the gambler (whom even Somerset Maugham, persuaded that Chandler is the better writer, acknowledges to be 'a curious, intriguing character whom any novelist would have been proud to conceive'.) The latter is a friendship rare in Anglo-Saxon fiction in that it comprises no suggestion of latent homosexuality: we believe as implicitly in Beaumont's selfless devotion to Madvig as Beaumont himself believes in his friend's innocence of murder despite all evidence to the contrary.

The Glass Key, however, is not only a study in loyalty, but also of betrayal: Madvig's daughter betrays her father; Taylor Henry is only prevented from betraying his by the fact of his murder; Mrs Mathews betrays her husband, the newspaper publisher, and is morally responsible for his suicide; the moronic bodyguard Jeff betrays and strangles his boss; the gangsters and politicos, the bookies and their floosie girlfriends, double-cross each other constantly; and Beaumont in the end betrays his friend with the girl he is engaged to, though the symbolic dream from which the title is derived warns them that there can be no happiness in store. Here indeed is a milieu where – in Chandler's words – 'the law was something to be manipulated for profit and power' and 'the streets were dark with something more than night': but, while Chandler could never forbear to make, through the mouth of Marlowe, some 'social' comment, however oblique, the corruption and darkness of Hammett's world are all the more frightening because his characters accept it completely and without protest, as a normal state of affairs.

Hammett's fame is eclipsed nowadays; his passing, in this country at any rate, created little stir. He abdicated at the height of his powers from the literary scene, and this Rimbaud-like renunciation, his three decades' silence, may have been due – as Chandler suggested – to the fact that he might 'have come to the end of his resources in a certain style and have lacked the intellectual depth to compensate for that by trying something else'. None the less, his achievement has not so far been properly assessed, and it is possible that the contribution which he made, not only to the mystery novel, but to American literature in general, may be considered greater than Chandler's own. Which of the two, however, will eventually be rated Tops for Posterity scarcely matters now; certainly not to Chandler and Hammett: sleeping as they are, themselves, the Big Sleep.

The World of Robert Bloch

*   *   *

THE PRACTICE OF AUTHORS WRITING DIRECTLY FOR PAPERBACK
publication has become increasingly widespread in the United States.
Among writers of suspense and mystery stories it is no longer confined
to purely sensational and sub-pornographic 'fictioneers' of the Hank
Janson–Carter Brown type, and was indeed strongly advocated by the
late Raymond Chandler, who at one time seriously considered it himself.
The reason for this is a simple matter of finance, since by writing a
paperback 'original', an author receives the usual percentage of royalties
on an edition of thousands of copies, instead of halving the profits
with a hardback publisher, as is still the case in the USA (despite the
efforts of the Authors' Guild of America to enforce a more equitable
state of affairs) and certainly in Great Britain, where a fifty-fifty clause
is taken for granted in every contract.

Two startlingly individual novelists accessible for the most part in
paperbacks are John Roeburt, superficially a tough detective writer in the
Dashiell Hammett tradition but specialising in formalised dialogue which
extracts a kind of poetry from the rhythms of demotic and underworld
speech; and David Goodis, whose books are often adapted as unusual
motion pictures – Jacques Tourneur's *Nightfall* and François Truffaut's
Tirer sur le Pianiste, to name but two – and whose off-beat professional
criminals appear to behave almost arbitrarily until the very end, when
their actions are shown to be dictated by some underlying psychological
pattern which only then becomes apparent. But even more outstanding
is the work of Robert Bloch, principally known in this country as the
author of *Psycho*, the novel on which the famous Alfred Hitchcock film
was based.

Only three of Bloch's books – a novel, *The Dead Beat*; a collection of tales called *Blood Runs Cold*; and *Psycho* itself – have so far been published (by Messrs Robert Hale) in an English hardback library edition. His other American paperback originals are not easily obtainable over here unless one is constantly on the look-out; stocks imported are soon exhausted, and another recent selection of stories entitled *Yours Truly, Jack the Ripper* eluded my own vigilance altogether, though a new volume of his science fantasy tales, *Atoms and Evil*, a Gold Medal original distributed by Frederick Muller Ltd at 2s. 6d. was on sale last year. ('The Gold Medal seal on this book means it has never been published as a book before.')

SF has become respectable since Ray Bradbury, and in this country has even been worked up into a highbrow cult, the merits of which, as extolled by Kingsley Amis among others, were not long ago called into question by the editor of the *London Magazine*. The genre is, however, only a sideline nowadays with Robert Bloch, and used by him in the present volume mainly for purposes of satire. These stories (the titles sometimes betray the denouement, as in *Change of Heart, You Got to Have Brains* etc) are representative of his lighter side, his second-string role as a 'teller of tall tales...the inventor of a thousand possible tomorrows'. His sardonic imagination readily projects itself into a future where robots collect the rent from obsolescent psychiatrists, manpower has been replaced by mechanical men, 'End-Docs' (endoctrinologists) supply shots to soothe or stimulate as required, 'ulcerisors' are constantly sucked, and automobile showrooms are devoted to the sale of 'auto-erotics' (synthetic mistresses) instead: 'just push a button to select your speed, all the attachments including a voice-tape and a built-in heater...And take a look at that rear end! She's got the biggest bustle on the market today.' (Such a 'possible tomorrow' might welcome my own invention, Instant Woman, which only lack of financial backing prevents me from marketing immediately.)

Except for this particular tale, *Wheel and Deal*, not much bawdiness is included, unlike the faintly similar SF excursions of Frederic Brown, two of which concern the difficulties of doing it with a mermaid or a visitor from outer space in male humanoid guise but physically endowed in such proportions as to render sex with terrestrial beings impossible. *Atoms and Evil* concentrates on black comedy: the macabre gift bestowed on a benefactor by a 'prosthetic' guest incapable of understanding metaphor; a screen-struck human chameleon who mutates into a monster sixty feet high after seeing a science-fiction film; a *crime passionel* of the twenty-second century, with the parties double-crossing each other by means of 'personalised surrogates'. Verging on the farcical is the Runyonesque account of two card-sharps outwitted by a college professor employing ESP; perhaps the most disquieting is *You Could Be Wrong*, in which a returned serviceman revolts against the preponderance of shams inherent in contemporary life, becoming gradually convinced – and finally proving – that the world we know is an illusion peopled by dummies stuffed with sawdust.

Equally uncomfortable in its effect is another story, *Word of Honour*, contained in the earlier collection *Blood Runs Cold*, and describing a temporary outbreak of 'honesty' brought about by the dissemination of a truth-gas over a big city; this volume comprises also the devastating *Sock Finish*, in which a silent-film slapstick comedian, duped by the latter-day producer who had promised him a comeback, demolishes the blonde star who helped in his betrayal with a home-made custard-pie filled with TNT; and *Is Betsey Blake Still Alive?*, where a Hollywood public relations man, deemed capable of murdering his own mother if it would advance his career, turns out to have done just that: in the last two stories, the corrupt standards, the status-seekers, climbers, crawlers and entrepreneurs of the studio city are mercilessly spotlighted and stripped of their pretensions in the space of a few pages, as opposed to the massive bestsellers which take 200,000 words or more to perform, less effectively, the same function.

Social criticism – on occasion a sharp questioning of our 'civilised' values as a whole – is implicit in most of Bloch's work; nor is the problem of Identity – so important to our own younger dramatists – neglected. The short tale *I Do Not Love Thee, Dr Fell* features a disorientated press agent, unable to express his thoughts except by means of clichés and catch-phrases, who creates an imaginary analyst into whom his own self eventually becomes absorbed: by this solution, and in 'their' previous dialogues, the entire nature of 'personality' is obliquely queried.

Schizophrenia – the mirror image of the mind – forms one of Bloch's predominant themes: first finding expression in such stories as *Lucy Comes to Stay* (where the narrator's drunken excesses and destructive impulse are encouraged by a companion who proves to be a projection of herself) or *The Bad Friend* (where the war comrade of the title – again an alcoholic mirage – volunteers to rid the protagonist of the wife whom he subconsciously hates), culminating in the psychotic Norman Bates's non-existent homicidal mother. He has been called a 'master of the dark world of the warped mind', and those who read or saw *Psycho* (Joseph Stefano's screenplay follows the novel faithfully save for Janet Leigh's long opening escape sequence) will not consider this an exaggerated description. Phantasmal and forbidden urges, aberrations born of guilt – often unfounded – haunt the brains of his characters as in another age they might have been hounded by Heaven or haunted by ghosts: manifestations, apparitions – as mentioned above – actually appear and are real to them.

This type of peculiarly modern horror-story originated, perhaps, with Helen Eustis's *The Horizontal Man* or John Franklyn Bardin's *Devil Take the Blue-Tail Fly*, which in turn derived from Maupassant's *Le Horla*,[1] that astonishing *tour de force* that reads today like a transcript from some psychopathic case-history:

> I was living the mysterious double life that raises the doubt whether there be not two selves in us, or whether, in moments when the spirit lies unconscious, an alien self, unknowable and unseen, inhabits the captive body that obeys this other self as it obeys us, obeys it more readily than it obeys us.

Maupassant's narrator, that 'sane-minded, educated, thoroughly rational man', first – rightly – suspects that he is going mad, but later blames the hallucinations from which he suffers on the presence of 'a new being' (Bloch would say, from another planet), whose 'immaterial body' at one point swallows up his reflection in the glass. (Francis Steegmuller, Maupassant's biographer, rebukes critics who, 'confusing creation and autobiography', have seen in this story 'the beginning of Maupassant's own hallucinatory end', but intimations of 'the syphilis that was to destroy him' are clearly shown in the text: 'this presentiment which is doubtless the warning signal of a lurking disease germinating in my blood and my flesh' etc; the whole of *Dorian Gray* is the expression of a similar intimation on the part of Oscar Wilde.)

Young Larry Fox, Bloch's *Dead Beat* (who for most of the book is very much, and unpleasantly, alive) is an attempt to portray a new

---

1   Since this article was written, an American film based on *Le Horla* has been shown under the title *Diary of a Madman*, which, though redeemed from utter failure by the constant presence on the screen of Vincent Price, fails to realise the full potentialities of the subject as Bloch would have done had he written the script.

kind of being, an only too material Horla of the contemporary scene. One of the characters, a middle-aged man, defines him as belonging to the *Off*-Beat Generation, a mutant resulting from the Hiroshima Bomb:

> It fell years ago. And the mutations began. Not in the bodies of the unborn, but in the minds of the living. All our youngsters weren't affected, but enough of them mutated, and as a result we have the juvenile delinquent and his older brother, the Beatnik. You can't explain them as the products of poverty, or ignorance, or depression. The bomb created them. The bomb exploded their security. Its mushroom cloud obscured the future, set off a chain reaction of neurotic behaviour. Sure, we've had our Lost Generation before, after other wars, but that was only a label. This time our young people are really lost, without values or perspective...

A gruesome theory, to fit a gruesome phenomenon; but Larry as a creation is scarcely strong enough to support the weight of significance thus laid upon him: *The Dead Beat* and *The Couch* (a clinical study of a compulsive ice-pick killer who chooses his victims at random) are Bloch's least successful books; though both would – and most probably will – make excellent films, especially the latter, which with its Hitchcockian situations and *mise-en-scène* seems to have been written with the screen in view. I would rate as his finest achievement (though there are still several listed titles of his which I have as yet failed to obtain) a novel equally cinematic in subject and atmosphere but far more mature in other respects: *Firebug* (1961), the story of the search for a crypto-pyromaniac. (Issued by Regency Books, of Evanston, Illinois, it is also one of the best-produced paperback originals I have ever seen, despite the sensational warnings which precede the text: 'THIS IS NO BOOK FOR THE SQUEAMISH. If you want to read a soft pink-and-white bunny rabbit story, get out of here, quickly! *This is a book of terror. A novel of absolute evil*' etc, etc.) Besides – and most unusually with a work heralded in this fashion – the warnings are in fact justified. *Firebug* IS a frightening book. The smell of burning seems to pervade its pages. And more horrific, perhaps, than the actual events recorded (though these are scarifying enough) are the implications which the author draws from the sightseers who gather to gloat at the scene of a conflagration:

> And always the Mob came. The Mob came to savour smoke as incense, to view the burnt offering and offer adoration to what gods of death?...They'd quietly root for the flames and

silently boo the firemen and stare without pity or sympathy when a volunteer staggered to the sidelines to cough the smoke out of his lungs. It didn't matter whether it was the impersonal façade of the State National Bank being destroyed by the licking flames or Uncle Harry's lingerie shop...

Underneath the gay assertions – 'I always look out of the window when I hear the fire-engines go by' and 'I don't know what gets into Tom, the minute he hears the siren, off he goes in his car' and 'There's just, oh, something about a fire that gets me' – underneath the commonplace, everyday expressions of opinion there was a need. A flaming need for a flaming deed. We're all fire-worshippers at heart. And we rejoice when we see a sacrifice.

But Phil Dempster, the narrator of *Firebug*, is the reverse of a fire-worshipper; he is a *pyrophobe*, in prey to a recurrent nightmare which causes him to fear that he may be, unknown to himself, the incend-iarist who's terrorising the city: all the more since he has been assigned as a journalist to investigate certain crank religious cults, and it is precisely the temples of these which are being burned down. (Needless to say, as with all Bloch's work, the history of actual cults has been carefully studied – the I Am Movement, run by a paper-hanger claiming to sell 'electronic essence', which grossed over three million dollars before its founder's widow was convicted of defrauding the mails – and the ritual procedures of those he has invented are fully documented: the Church of the Golden Atom, where VITAL CREAM and ATOMIC ENERGY CAPSULES – spelt always in capital letters – are on sale at six dollars apiece and Professor Ricardi – *née* Clutt – a 'Cosmic Scientist' trained in 'the secret laboratories of Tibet', heals the sick by laying-on of hands; or the Temple of the Living Flame, where the Negro prophet Ogundu walks on live coals beneath a representation of the Phoenix: members of the Inner Circle are branded with the image of this Resurrection Bird.)

Firebug combines in a satisfactory manner the neurotic-casebook-novel, subjectively told, with that of action, mystery and suspense: for if Phil Dempster is not the arsonist, then who is? Phil suspects everyone in turn, even his own editor ('Figuring Cronin for a firebug, seeing a man hiding under every bed; a man with a torch and a knife'), until the burning question is unexpectedly answered and the firebug's real 'features formed and altered like a waxen mask melting in the heat of the flames' (naturally there has to be a final flare-up); but even then, there is a further and more subtly horrid twist in store. The oppressive obsessional climate is maintained throughout: Dempster's fear follows him everywhere, his surroundings are completely coloured by it; innocent clichés – the 'commonplace, everyday expressions' previously referred to – take on new and terrible associations ('Ball of fire. Firewater. Hellfire. Creative fire. Spark of genius. You're fired. Playing with fire. Hot seat. You burn me up. Fight fire with fire. Better to marry than to burn' etc, etc); when he makes love to a girl, a carelessly dropped cigarette catches the brush-wood alight; shishkabob on a spit and *crêpes suzette* are served near their restaurant table, the steak is charred, the girl's copper curls resemble living flames, and the car radio gives out the Ritual Fire Dance.

An analogous situation occurs in Bloch's novel *The Will to Kill*, published by Ace Books Inc. in 1954, but almost as fascinating as *Firebug* in its way. Here the hero (this time suffering from blackouts induced by traumatic shock during the Korean War) imagines that he is responsible for the local Ripper murders: Tom Kendall is haunted, however, by knives: a poniard is stolen from a case of curios in the shop he owns and may have been used to kill a prostitute, his attorney has scimitars and cutlasses hanging on the wall of his private office (and *Justine* as a desk-side book), even a blind man selling pencils on the street corner has been a sword-swallower in a fairground carnival; and when Tom is finally exonerated, Lieutenant Cohen of Homicide presents him with a carving set as a wedding present. We are all subject to obsessions, and Bloch's method in such books lies in persuading us partly to identify with his hallucinated victims while remaining smugly aware that our own fixations are of a less serious sort (he himself has a mild one in connection with something called 'Crullers', which Americans apparently eat for breakfast in drugstores or at places called Nick's. Tom Kendall 'wouldn't be caught dead with a cruller in his hand'; a campus-student of the class of 1978, in the story *Egghead*, feels a similar distaste, and refuses crullers as a gesture of rebellion; even in a dessert restaurant, crullers are piled on the counter for flies to alight on etc).

Bloch's most significant work to date, however, is not a novel or short story, nor yet a piece of science fantasy or satire. It is in fact his screenplay for the Hollywood remake of *The Cabinet of Dr Caligari* (1962). The film based upon this was incomprehensibly received by English critics, when released, with hostility, contempt, or virtual silence.

They seem in the main to have expected a complete carbon copy of the great German original, with perhaps a dialogue soundtrack thrown in, when reflection should have told them that this was simply impossible. (For one thing, the novelty which struck audiences in 1920 was partly due to the expressionist sets and décor, which even the most uninformed public of today would scarcely regard as *new*.) From the evidence of his fiction alone, Bloch has obviously made a study of motion picture history in general, and the Hans Janowitz/Carl Mayer/Robert Wiene version of *Caligari* in particular (starring Conrad Veidt and Werner Krauss, as the sadistic lawyer in *The Will to Kill* reminds us with nostalgic relish: he also runs, as a 'home movie', episodes from Paul Léni's *Das Wachsfigurenkabinett*, featuring the same actors, with Krauss in the role of Jack the Ripper). Any remake of such a film, if attempted at all, would clearly have to be in a completely different manner.

Bloch quite rightly proceeded to change everything; the mentally disturbed male student from whose viewpoint the events – largely products of his distorted imagination – are presented, became Jane (Glynis Johns), a young woman on holiday whose car breaks down on a coastal road, forcing her to take refuge in the mansion of the bearded, handsome Caligari (Daniel O'Herlihy). The resulting film was announced on every poster as 'by Robert Bloch, author of *Psycho*', in the way that a play for the theatre would be: an advance in itself, since screenwriters are seldom admitted to have this type of responsibility; and it is, therefore, as a new work by Bloch that the picture should have been judged.

Little remains of the original except a vague resemblance to the central situation and the basic theme of Tyranny, as expounded by Dr Siegfried Kracauer in his invaluable work on the history of the German film, *From Caligari to Hitler*. The interiors are contemporary, with a metal staircase spiralling upward from the living-room and an enormous aquarium tank of tropical fish through which the characters are sometimes seen. There is no fairground, no homicidal somnambulist, in fact no murders at all (though at one point we believe we see one committed), and little actual violence: save for one hideous climactic act of cruelty, following swiftly upon an extraordinary transformation staged to show Jane that 'things are not always what they seem' (a truth amply illustrated in the closing sequences, when the real meaning of the film is at last made plain). Action is confined to the grounds (patrolled by savage dogs) and the house itself, filled with a heterogeneous assortment of people, including an elderly bewigged lady who devours chocolates in secret (it is she who appears later to be brutally murdered before our very eyes), and Paul, a kindly tweeded father-figure who bends a sympathetic ear to Jane's problems while sucking on the stem of a comfortable pipe.

The action is concerned with Jane's attempts to escape from the house, where it soon becomes evident that she is being held prisoner, and from Caligari himself, who quickly sheds his initial attitude of suave politeness and embarks on a regime of ruthless persecution, handing her obscene postcards to look at, spying on her nudity through the bathroom ventilator and continuing to read a book when, reduced to desperation, she finally strips off her clothes in an effort to seduce him. From this incomplete account it will already be apparent that a study of sex-antagonism is intended. But this is by no means all: I will not spoil the pleasure of those who may not have seen the picture by revealing the basic theme (one, indeed, which the many influential female film critics who condemned the picture may not have cared to be confronted with). It seems sufficient to say that the tension throughout is such that the film holds one riveted for almost two hours, *without knowing what it is really all about.* (This is due not only to the absorbing nature and visual mastery of the script, but to the almost constant presence on the screen of Glynis Johns: one of the few supremely talented actresses whose beauty is of a sort to survive the large frequent close-ups and her appearance in the final scenes, which many women would have balked at.)

The Cabinet of Dr Caligari, new style, explores with a sharper accuracy the psychological and physical pressures and conflicts between the sexes than do many so-called 'adult' dramas in which naked lovers, by no means always attractive, are shown disporting themselves in bed. It marks, also, a new departure for its author, who has already shown us not one, but several, worlds and may now be on the verge of further discoveries which, with luck, we may all share.

Ernest Hemingway

*   *   *

IN HIS POSTHUMOUSLY PUBLISHED BOOK OF MEMOIRS,[1] Hemingway takes us back to the Paris of his – and the century's – early twenties. Here we have again the two-roomed apartment in the rue du Cardinal Lemoine where Harry, the drunken failure dying of gangrene in *The Snows of Kilimanjaro*, having traded in his talent for security and comfort, also lived; the green autobus and the Café des Amateurs (packed with poverty-stricken, sour-smelling local drunks) in the Place Contrescarpe; and the 'cheap tall hotel where Paul Verlaine had died', on the top floor of which both Hemingway and Harry wrote their early work: the room cost Harry, at any rate, sixty francs a month, though Hemingway – possibly because Harry was at work in it – seemed to prefer writing in a café on the Place St Michel or, later (when he moved to the rue Notre Dame-des-Champs), at the Closerie des Lilas. He shares many memories with this There-but-for-the-Grace-of-God-type other self: for instance skiing at Christmas in Schrungs in the Vorarlberg, Austria (where Hemingway was known to peasants as 'the Black Kirsch-drinking Christ'), and playing poker with Herr Lent of the Alpine Ski School as described in both the story and the last chapter of *A Moveable Feast*; but one feels that Paris during this period (1921–26) would have been Hemingway's own chosen happy-hunting-ground rather than Kilimanjaro, as with Harry.

I too was in Paris then, living not far away in a flat formerly belonging to the Irish poet James Stephens and, like Hemingway's, over a sawmill: indeed I must often have seen him, without knowing it, walking hungrily about the Luxembourg Gardens while I was

---

1 *A Moveable Feast*, Cape.

watching Guignol and Grangalet at the age of ten, a time of life when one's perceptions are particularly sharp where the sights, smells and weather in a foreign city are concerned, so I can vouch for the truth of how he says it was in the winter and summer; though (from later experience) for only the partial truth of what he says about the value of being 'belly-empty, hollow-hungry'.

'Hunger,' we are told, 'is good discipline and you learn from it.' (Yes, how to try and avoid getting into this unpleasant state again.) A lot of nostalgic nonsense is often written about poverty and hunger by successful authors who no longer have to experience them, and Hemingway here is no exception ('I learned to understand Cézanne much better and to see how truly he made landscapes when I was hungry. I used to wonder if he were hungry too when he painted; but I thought possibly it was only that he had forgotten to eat', etc, etc). Incidentally, the book is so full of descriptions of eating that perhaps the best place to read it would be in a restaurant or after a heavy meal.

About Hemingway's actual methods of writing, and theories concerning his craft, which he was always unwilling to discuss, one learns little more than can be found, rather more fully expounded and on the whole better expressed, in the interview with him in *Writers at Work* (Second Series, 1963[1]), much as the Paris and Austrian backgrounds are re-created just as vividly, in microcosm, during the Kilimanjaro flashbacks: 'A writer can be compared to a well … The important thing is to have good water in the well and it is better to take a regular amount out than to pump the well dry and wait for it to refill.' (The well fills of itself with 'juice' overnight, providing you stop writing at a point where you know what is going to happen next.) There is also the simile of the iceberg ('seven-eighths of it underwater for every part that shows') first encountered in *Death in the Afternoon*. ('If a writer of prose knows enough about what he is writing about he may omit things that he knows and the reader, if the writer is writing truly enough, will have a feeling of those things as strongly as though the writer had stated them. The dignity of movement of an iceberg is due to only one-eighth of it being above water.') In *A Moveable Feast*, we are given an example of the iceberg-principle when the author casually informs us that one of his most effective early stories, *Out of Season*, really ended with the old Tyroler Peduzzi hanging himself (suicides

---

1 Secker & Warburg.

have always been a prominent feature of Hemingway's work): the imaginary Old Lady who acted as conversational sparring-partner in *Death in the Afternoon* would complain that the 'wow' or pay-off had once more been left out, but this non-stated climax, quite unsuspected by the reader until now, may be seen to account for the oppressive atmosphere of guilty malaise informing what on the face of it seems a semi-comic character-study.

A few more glimpses of the young writer at work are vouchsafed us: bringing *The Three-Day Blow* into being because of the wind outside the café where he wrote; deciding to start a long story about coming back from the war without mentioning the war itself (this seems to be *Big Two-Hearted River*, though certainly no one could guess the true subject from internal evidence); and once when interrupted by a homosexual bore ('Take your dirty camping mouth out of here') whom he attempts unsuccessfully to turn into a critic. The relationship with his first wife (who at one stage lost by accident all his MSS: an almost insurmountable setback) never seems entirely credible because presented too idyllically in his later manner – rather like the Colonel's relations with Renata in *Across the River and Into the Trees* – and Mrs Hemingway is portrayed as far too admiring and acquiescent for a flesh-and-blood woman, however much in love: a fault which first began to show during the conversations with a different 'Mem' in *Green Hills of Africa*. Only in the closing pages does the marriage, under the shadow of imminent dissolution, spring suddenly to life; and perhaps the finest passages are those in which Hemingway, with an abrupt return to his best form, draws up a terrible indictment of 'the good, the attractive, the charming, the soon-beloved, the generous, the understanding rich' who were in some way, during 'a nightmare winter disguised as the greatest fun of all', responsible for the break-up.

The real interest of the book lies, however, in his portraits of the famous contemporaries with whom he came in contact, and the self-revelation contained in the personal reactions which he now claims they aroused in him: for example, the force of loathing conjured up by his first sight of Wyndham Lewis (compared among other things to toe-jam and an unsuccessful rapist) seems out of all proportion until we remember the 'Dumb Ox' essay in *Men Without Art* (1934). Certainly Lewis seemed unaware of any antagonism: they evidently shared a distaste for the 'Dark Laughter' racial theories of Sherwood Anderson (according to Gertrude Stein, one of Hemingway's formative influences, whom he afterwards publicly repudiated in the parody *Torrents of Spring*); and in his autobiography *Rude Assignment* Lewis quotes a letter from Hemingway dated October 1927 in which the latter congratulates him on publication of *Pale-Face* (also an attack on Anderson), adding: 'I have always had a great respect for Hemingway...he is the greatest writer in America.' The subject of Lewis ('the nastiest man I've ever seen') appears by the way to be the only one on which Hemingway's and Gertrude Stein's accounts agree; according to his, she said: 'I call him "the Measuring Worm". He comes over from London and he sees a good picture and takes a pencil out of his pocket and you watch him measuring it on the pencil with his thumb. Sighting on it and measuring it and seeing exactly how it is done', while *The Autobiography of Alice B. Toklas* states: 'He used to come and sit and measure pictures. I cannot say that he actually measured with a measuring-rod but he gave all the effect of being in the act of taking very careful measurement of the canvas, the lines within the canvas and everything that might be of use.'

About Miss Stein herself, Hemingway is considerably more guarded (though quoting as new an anecdote about the death of Apollinaire already told in *Alice B. Toklas*, as well as his own interpretation of Ezra Pound and the injured armchair, and the origin of the celebrated 'lost generation' label, which he seems to think inapplicable yet adopted as an epigraph). He admits grudgingly that she gave him good advice about writing (the story *Up in Michigan*, dismissed by her as *inaccrochable*, is evidence of this); she also attempted without much success to make him take a more tolerant view of genuine homosexuality, and recommended for after-work reading the novels of Mrs Belloc Lowndes (which he seems, astonishingly, to have enjoyed). From their respective styles it is still hard to tell who influenced whom: whether Hemingway learned to simplify his prose from proof-reading *The Making of Americans* or Miss Stein learned to write dialogue from *The Sun Also Rises*, and probably both claims are justified. He states that their friendship folded because he inadvertently overheard her quarrelling with a lesbian friend: her version is that the breach occurred when she told him that 'remarks are not literature' (*Alice B. Toklas* actually gives two separate reasons for this observation: (1) that Hemingway had written that Miss Stein 'always knew what was good in a Cézanne'; (2) that, having previously accused E.E. Cummings of 'having copied everything', he had then praised *The Enormous Room* as 'the greatest book he had ever read'). But the truth will never be known now, since as Hemingway himself says in another connection: 'All those people are dead.'

He was obviously a good hater, and one who never forgot a fancied slight: Aldous Huxley's essay 'Foreheads Villainous Low' is remembered after all this time, even though the last destructive word is delivered obliquely, through the mouth of Miss Stein in a reported conversation. Joyce, Pound and Pascin come off scot-free (he is nevertheless extremely funny about Pound's well-meaning efforts to rescue 'Major' T.S. Eliot from the bank in which he was then employed); the full blast of his malice is reserved for a phoney poet and literary con-man named Ernest Walsh, now dead (of TB), forgotten and seemingly scarcely worth the trouble,[1] and Ford Madox Ford.

In a very amusing chapter, where the 'wow' is certainly not omitted, Ford is shown obtusely explaining the location of a Bal Musette above which Hemingway had lived for two years (and where he enjoyed with the taxi-driving proprietor the same drink recalled by Harry in *Kilimanjaro*). It is doubtful, however, that Ford would in reality have mistaken Aleister Crowley for Hilaire Belloc (see the section on 'Starting a Review' in his *Selected Memories*[2]), or that he would have gloried in 'cutting' Belloc as a 'cad'; what seems more likely is that he got their names mixed up, an inherited failing admitted in his 'Table Talk'. It is also possible that Ford, in pontificating upon the definition of a 'gentleman' (Hemingway did not qualify), believed that an American would be genuinely interested in an analysis of this quaint form of English snobbery, or that he was simply sending himself up; an example of Ford's poker-faced fun is given in Harold Loeb's recent reminiscence printed in the *London Magazine*: a young woman was startled on being informed with apparent seriousness that she could now tell her grandchildren she had danced with Ford Madox Ford, whereas he was plainly paraphrasing Liszt's remark to himself as a child; moreover, he would be unlikely to have 'severely' corrected a waiter for a mistake which he had not made, after dilating upon the existence of waiters as human beings in another Selected Memory entitled 'A Shameful Episode'.

---

1 Alice B. Toklas mentions: 'Kate Buss brought Ernest Walsh, he was very young then and very feverish and she was very worried about him. We met him later with Hemingway and then in Belley, but we never knew him very well.'

2 *The Bodley Head Ford Madox Ford*, vol. 1, John Lane.

Hemingway's insistence on the 'heavy, wheezing, ignoble' presence of a man who had helped him as an editor (he even tastes his brandy cautiously to see if Ford's coming had fouled it) remains puzzling, although the reason for it may be found in Alice B. Toklas, where Ford is also reputed to have said of Hemingway: 'He comes and sits at my feet and praises me. It makes me nervous.' But if he is unfair to Ford, one cannot complain of the picture presented of Scott Fitzgerald, the golden boy of American literature, who arrived slightly tarnished upon Hemingway's scene wearing a Guards tie, and proceeded to turn straight-away into a living death-mask under the influence of alcohol. Fitzgerald emerges as a tiresome hypochondriacal nuisance when drunk ('You can sit there and read that dirty rag of a French paper and it doesn't mean a thing to you that I am dying'), yet none the less endearing and a victim of his wife's literally insane jealousy of his talent: showing with impersonal pride when sober a ledger listing all sales, royalties and other sums received for his stories, or giving 'a sort of oral PhD thesis on Michael Arlen', whose books Hemingway found unreadable, although there is an odd occasional echo of the Armenian's mannered facetiousness in some of his dialogues with the Old Lady in *Death in the Afternoon*:

> Old Lady: That's a very nice line, about lust.
> Author: I know it. It came from Andrew Marvell. I learned
> how to do that by reading T. S. Eliot.

Fitzgerald, however, outlived his meteoric fame as chronicler of the Jazz Age, and died too early to become a legend in his own lifetime, which does a writer more harm than too much whisky; Hemingway, on the other hand, did: and came to put almost as much work into perpetuating his personal myth as he had previously put into per-fecting his style. *Death in the Afternoon*, containing much of his purest writing and most exact observation, equal in precision to the skill of the bullfighters which it celebrates, forms a bridge across the river and into the trees growing – figuratively – on the *Green Hills of Africa*.

In this latter book the self-made legend may be seen to start, with Hemingway in a newly created 'Personal Appearance Artist'[1] role as a gruff, laconic hunter on safari, complete with Little Woman (or, as he actually called her, 'Mem-Sahib') as feed. The opinions on literature so

---

1 Wyndham Lewis's phrase.

clearly expressed in *Death in the Afternoon* have become dogmatic pronouncements (though in his *Writers at Work* interview he attributed this to the character of his interlocutor, the Austrian Kandisky); rancour towards confrères – Gertrude Stein and Thomas Wolfe among them – first shows itself, and the ability to laugh at himself (conspicuous in the account of his bullfighting misadventures) has largely atrophied. *To Have and Have Not*, the most underrated of his novels, was a partial recovery, comprising some interesting technical experiments and the last two women (Helen Gordon and Marie Morgan) whom he was able to imbue with life (compare Maria, the 'Little Rabbit' of *For Whom the Bell Tolls* with Brett Ashley and Catherine Barkley, or Maria's love affair with Robert Jordan to that between Catherine and Frederic Henry in *Farewell to Arms*); the minor characters – Mr Sing, Eddy the rummy, Bee-Lips the lawyer, the drunken Vets, the mad Spellman, even the murderous Cuban, to say nothing of the occupants of the yacht basin so harshly arraigned in the fast sequence – constitute a gallery of portraits very different in calibre from the Hollywood stereotypes of the Spanish War novel; while in *Across the River and Into the Trees* there are no minor characters, except the egregious Grand Master and other admiring flunkies whose function it is to further glorify the already inflated ego of Colonel Cantwell, plus a pock-marked grotesque embodying Hemingway's inexplicable grudge against a distinguished (though, in his day, overrated) fellow-writer.

This novel represents a penultimate phase in Hemingway's development which few readers of *Farewell to Arms* could possibly have envisaged: not even the author's appearance in the play *The Fifth Column*, thinly disguised as a pseudo-drunken newspaperman who turns out to be a kind of Scarlet Pimpernel, like the dual-role protagonist of a Doug Fairbanks silent, could have prepared us for his complete self-identification with the Colonel, a professional soldier as romantically conceived and lovingly treated as any woman's magazine hero, whose stiff upper lip approximates closely to that of the British officer-type which he derides and despises, and whose sexual prowess with his titled Italian 'thoroughbred' daydream-girl is so embarrassingly plugged:

> 'This is good for you, Daughter. It is good for all the ills that all of us have and for all sadness and indecision.'
>
> 'I have none of those,' she said… 'I am just a woman, or a girl, or whatever that is, doing whatever it is she should not do. Let's do it again, please, now I am in the lee.'

One would have imagined from passages such as this, which read as if written by one of his less-talented imitators, that Hemingway was forever sunk, but he possessed a built-in buoy which allowed him to rise again to the surface (he also, by implication, claimed possession of a 'built-in, shock-proof, shit detector', but this must have been out of order during the writing of *Across the River and Into the Trees*.) His physical metamorphoses in private life may be traced, in Leo Lania's *Pictorial Biography*, from the photograph (captioned 'The Successful Author') resembling a handsome Hollywood actor in the rôle of the young Al Capone, to the rugged, bearded incarnation of Nobel prize-winning 'Papa': a character-part to be played, obviously, by Edward G. Robinson; yet, hidden somewhere behind these strangely chosen masks, the fastidious, dedicated inventor of the iceberg-technique lived and worked on: here is *A Moveable Feast*, in which he reverts briefly to his real, former self, to prove it.

The acceptance of *My Old Man* for the *Best Short Stories* anthology, and the dedication of the volume to him by Edward J. O'Brien ('a gentle shy man, pale, with pale-blue eyes, and straight lanky hair he cut himself, who lived then as a boarder in a monastery up above Rapallo') was a turning-point in those far-off days when he had to be tough indeed to survive the lost MSS and the rejection slips; for, unlike Scott Fitzgerald, he never compromised by altering his endings to suit editorial requirements.

He knew, however, that he must soon write a novel: '... it seemed an impossible thing to do when I had been trying with great difficulty to write paragraphs that would be the distillation of what made a novel... When I had written a novel before, the one that had been lost in the bag stolen at the Gare de Lyon, I still had the lyric facility of boyhood that was as perishable and as deceptive as youth was.' (Gertrude Stein had found this first effort wanting: 'There is a great deal of description in this, she said, and not particularly good description. Begin over again and concentrate.') So Hemingway went into training by writing 'longer stories as you would train for a longer race', and the result was *The Sun Also Rises*: first draft 'written in one sprint of six weeks', and rewritten during the winter of 1925–26.

It is quite customary nowadays for critics to state that Hemingway was not really a novelist at all, on the grounds that *To Have and Have Not* and *Across the River and Into the Trees* were started as short stories (while *Farewell to Arms* can of course be read in a potted form – with an even more downbeat ending – as *A Very Short Story*). Possibly no definitive verdict on this point can be reached until his huge novel of the Second World War is published at last. Nevertheless *The Sun Also Rises* stands up extraordinarily well to a re-reading. One of the author's ambitions was to convey 'experience to the reader so that after he or she has read something it will become a part of his or her experience and seem actually to have happened': not only does he succeed in this, but whole passages of dialogue have sunk deep into one's memory, so that it comes as a shock to realise, on finding them here, that they were not overheard in real life at some time in the past. As a summing up or sort of testament, no satisfactory equivalent exists for the activities of subsequent generations, and only one attempt to do for the fifties what Hemingway did for the twenties comes to mind: Chandler Brossard's *Who Walk in Darkness*, one of the first American hipster or 'Underground'-type novels, couched in the Hemingway idiom and starting with a sketch of an unsympathetic character's background in much the same way as *The Sun Also Rises* begins with an outline of Robert Cohn's. One's opinion of the latter opening, which seemed at first reading a marvellous technical device, leading to the devastating and apparently deliberate throwaway by which we are only told of the narrator's terrible disability in Chapter IV, is naturally qualified now in view of the knowledge that the first two chapters were suppressed: presumably because they dealt outspokenly with the operation performed on Jake (an amputation, incidentally – like that self-inflicted by the boy on Christmas Day in *God Rest You Merry, Gentlemen* – Hemingway has explained, rebutting a critic's assertion that 'Jake was emasculated like a steer'). But the original impact is in no wise weakened, and the choice of Jake's predicament (apart from the dimension of tragedy lent thereby to the novel) remains an inspired one, by which he is both onlooker and participant up to a point: thus avoiding the snag present in many first-person narratives where the protagonist as detached observer often seems too remote from the people and events he describes to be entirely human.

Hemingway's career began and ended with suicide: 'Indian Camp', the first story printed in the volume *In Our Time*, featured a prospective father who cut his throat rather than endure the sight of his wife's sufferings in labour, and the ensuing dialogue between the boy who witnessed this and his own father, the doctor, assumes an added poignancy now. *In Our Time* and *The Sun Also Rises* are seminal works and their early influence (as Hemingway said of Joyce) 'was what changed everything, and made it possible for us to break away from the restrictions': all writers of his own and future generations have cause to be grateful to him. Had he never written the magnificent volumes of stories which followed, he would be assured of another kind of immortality than that which poor Nick Adams, as a boy, believed to be his on that morning up in Michigan: 'on the lake sitting in the stern of the boat with his father rowing, he felt quite sure that he would never die.'

The Strange Realm
of M.P. Shiel

*　　　*　　　*

SHIEL'S CENTENARY FALLS NEXT YEAR. NOVELIST, SHORT-STORY
writer, poet, prophet and philosopher, his work was held in high
esteem by critics and fellow-writers during his lifetime: Victor Gollancz,
re-issuing four of his books simultaneously in 1929, proclaimed him
'author of some of the most wonderful novels in the English language'
(though 'a name unknown to the general public'); Arnold Bennett
called him 'A scholar, a linguist, an inventor, a stylist', Hugh Walpole 'A
flaming genius...the best romantic writer we have in England today',
L.P. Hartley 'A master of the written word'; to H.G. Wells he was
'Colossal...brilliant', and to Dashiell Hammett 'A magician', Dame
Rebecca West, claiming him to be 'A writer of imperial imagination,
who combines the scientific qualities of Wells with the mystery of Poe',
stated that 'sensible people ought to have a complete set of Shiel'.

His own personality was almost as colourful as the characters he
created. He was born in the West Indies (Montserrat, a place of
'hurricanes, earthquakes, brooks bubbling hot, 'soufrieres' – sulphur-
swamps – floods'), of Irish descent, nine years before the death of
Sheridan Le Fanu (a writer with whom he had some affinity); at the
age of eleven he was compiling and issuing his own newspaper ('a
penny-periodical, seven copies a week for seven "subscribers", written
by *hand*'); on his fifteenth birthday, his father, Matthew Dowdy Shiel,
a wealthy trader, ship-owner and local Methodist preacher, had him
anointed and crowned King of Redonda by the Bishop of Antigua.

The Island of Santa Maria La Redonda (or Rodundo: Shiel used both
spellings), between Nevis and Montserrat in the Caribbean Sea, was
discovered and named by Columbus on his second voyage in 1493.
Circular in shape, as the name implies, it is a mile and a half in length

by a mile in breadth ('nine square miles', according to Shiel), with an altitude of 1,000 feet. Now uninhabited (except by rats, seabirds, iguanas and a wild herd of a hundred goats, 'with beards nearly reaching the ground'), almost uninhabitable, the island at one time 'supported a mining operation and had about 130 people living on it', Dr Richard A. Howard informs us – in his 'Botanical and Other Observations on Redonda' (reprinted, as a pamphlet, from *Journal of the Arnold Arboretum*, January 1962). Ores containing phosphate ('Redondite', currently considered to be variscite, and included in a porphyritic or olivine basalt) were discovered there prior to 1860, and the material mined between the year of Shiel's birth and 1912 (visiting geologists had to be hauled up the cliff-face in iron buckets operated by pulleys). Two hurricanes, however, in 1899 and 1929 respectively, blew away the buildings which housed the workers, and the mining company's lease was finally relinquished – apparently with reluctance – in 1930.

In his autobiographical essay 'About Myself', Shiel, describing his kingdom, makes no mention of the miners:

> My subjects were troops innumerable of Boobies deciding to swoop with sudden steepness into the sea like streams of meteors streaming, together with eleven poor men who gathered the Boobies' excrement to make 'guano' (manure). And these were *American* people! Moreover, not long after my coronation the British Government, apprehensive that America might 'annex' the rock, 'annexed' it itself, i.e. stuck a little flagstaff on it; and though my parent irked heaven and earth with his claim of 'priority', there the flagstaff remains, if it has not now gone to heaven on some gale's gallop.

King Felipe the First, as he was crowned (presumably a Spanish version of his middle name, Phipps: in Redondan matters he would sign himself variously, Matthew R., Phipps R.), was nevertheless disinclined to forfeit his throne; indeed Oswell Blakeston has suggested that he became a novelist through practice in writing letters of protest to Whitehall. According to Bradley Smith's book *Escape to the West Indies* quoted by Dr Howard's pamphlet, Charlesworth Ross, recently commissioner on Montserrat, reported that the British Colonial Office eventually 'tacitly admitted' his claim, although actually Redonda remains under the administration of the Antiguan Government.

To a deeply religious child such as Shiel obviously was, brought up in a strict Methodist atmosphere to read every morning with his father a chapter of the Bible, which he came to know by heart (though he soon abandoned his conventional faith), 'to see the palm of the Rev. Dr Semper,[1] of Antigua, daub me with the balm of anointment' must have been a tremendous formative experience, which profoundly influenced the choice of his later literary themes:

> ... this notion that I am somehow the King, King of Kings, and the Kaiser of Imperial Caesar was so inveterately suggested to me, that I became incapable of expelling it. But to believe fantasies is what causes half our sorrow, as not believing realities causes half, and it would have been better for me if my people had been more reasonable here; nor can I forgive myself now for the solemnity and dignity with which I figured in that show.

He continued all the same to hold court in exile, and in 1936 decreed that his literary executor, the poet, editor and bibliographer John Gawsworth (Terence Ian Fytton Armstrong) should succeed him as Monarch, 'so a quick blood transfusion with a pen-knife' was made between their right wrists, and the first proclamation of His Majesty King Juan the First, on 29 June 1947, four months after Shiel's death, conferred Duchies of the Realm of Redonda upon A.E.W. Mason, E.H.W. Meyerstein, Eden Phillpotts, Frank Swinnerton and Dylan Thomas, among others; also confirming Duchies conferred, during Shiel's own reign, upon literary men including Philip Lindsay (Duke of Guano), Lawrence Durrell and Henry Miller; Victor Gollancz, Edward Shanks and that unjustly neglected American novelist Carl Van Vechten were Grand Dukes of Nera Rocca, the Arch Duke was Arthur Machen, and G.S. Fraser as Chamberlain signed the proclamation. The Court of Redonda, under King Juan, is held to this day (Diana Dors, Dulcie Gray and Dame Rebecca West are Duchesses, Viscount St Davids, Sir John Waller, Bart., J.B. Priestley and Fabian of the Yard are Dukes), pledged to perpetuate the memory and works of Shiel.[2]

Shiel seems to have been an exceedingly industrious and scholarly boy, as well as an infant prodigy: at school in Devon, aged eleven, after a spell at Harrison College, Barbados, he had devoured 'most of what is written in Greek', written a Rider Haggard-like novel at twelve, and

---

1   Elsewhere he says that the rite was performed by a Dr Mitchinson.

2   Julian Maclaren-Ross was himself Grand Duke of Ragusa in the Realm of Redonda.

published his first newspaper serial (in the *St Kitt's Observer*) at seventeen ('It was called "Madame": she was described as "fat and forty", and committed suicide'). Having taken a degree at King's College London, he taught mathematics for two years at a School in Derbyshire, studied medicine at Bart's Hospital for six months (but gave it up after witnessing an operation for strabismus, on the eyeball, which 'sickened and hypnotised me into a dislike for knifing'); then, through his knowledge of 'six or seven languages', became interpreter to the International Congress of Hygiene and Demography and became secretary to Florence Nightingale: 'Meantime I was getting to know the literary people, like Dowson,[1] Machen, Loüys ... Harland, Wilde, Stevenson, while the periodical people were getting to know me.' (Actually he only met Stevenson – 'The most underrated English writer living or deceased' – in a Soho restaurant where he later dined with Wilde, whom he afterwards categorised in a questionnaire as the 'deceased man of letters whose character he most disliked'.)

But the 'periodical people' were indeed getting to know him: W.T. Stead, the crusading journalist who went down with the Titanic, was first on the scene; soon Fleet Street, Pearson and Harmsworth had him in their grip: he wrote serials 'for *People*, *Chronicle*, *Leader*, *Red*, and the rest – easy labour by which one makes two or three thousand pounds a year; but then, to make real books out of the serials, one must needs rewrite, and that is trying'.[2]

For Shiel was the reverse of a newspaper or magazine hack; he was, in fact, a dedicated writer even at this time. His first book appeared in 1895, when he was thirty. *Prince Zaleski*, published in the Keynotes Series by John Lane, with title page and cover design by Aubrey Beardsley (whom, incidentally, he never met) consists of three stories which could be roughly classified as 'detective', since each comprises a mystery solved by the powerful intellect of the Prince: a *fin-de-siècle* figure compounded of the Chevalier C. Auguste Dupin and Stevenson's Prince Florizel, who lives in a ruined abbey in Monmouthshire, attended by a gigantic Ethiopian named Ham, plays the organ and smokes *cannabis*

---

1 With whom he later roomed at a boarding-house in Guilford Place, and who appears in his novel, *The Weird O' It*.

2 During this period (1891), he translated Villiers de L'Isle Adam's *A Torture of Hope* for the *Strand* magazine (the author of *Contes Cruels* and *L'Eve Future*, in which Edison was a protagonist, would naturally appeal to him).

sativa ('the base of the *bhang* of the Mohammedans') while thinking things out, reclining on a couch beside an open sarcophagus containing the rotting mummy of an ancient Memphian.

The early influence of Poe, admitted by Shiel, is obvious if one compares the description of Zaleski's 'vast mansion...gloomy in its lunar bath of soft perfumed light' with Dupin's 'time-eaten and grotesque mansion' lit by 'a couple of tapers which, strongly perfumed, threw out only the ghastliest and feeblest of rays'. It is in the strangeness and intricacy of the actual problems confronting the Prince that Shiel's originality and imaginative force are shown, for the first time, at work. One of them features murder in a locked room containing a corpse which has apparently been murdered twice (stabbed *and* shot), plus one of the murderers (a woman whose fingers have been severed, while attempting to escape, by the 'trenchant edge' of a sash-window designed as a trap) but no pistol; the second concerns a sacred torquoise which changes colour with the approaching death of its owner; a descendant of Hasn-us-Sabah, the Shaikh-ul-Jubal or Lord of the Assassins; and an elderly baronet frightened into a fatal seizure by seeing his Persian secretary in a mirror, *disguised as himself*: the third, and most remarkable, involved a world-wide epidemic of suicides, many of which are really murders committed by a secret cabal (the Society of Sparta or 'SS') sworn to the extermination of the old and unfit (the address of their subterranean meeting place – underneath the Thames – is contained in their motto 'Mens Sana in Corpore Sano': at first sight incongruous in a *Greek* Society). The American *Encore* magazine, reprinting this tale in 1946, editorially comments: 'Mr Shiel was actually inventing a kind of brutal international Fascist society, forty years before its protagonists appeared in Europe in the form of Mussolini and Hitler'; but while Shiel's prophetic vision – as later examples will show – cannot be denied, the philosophical content of the story is much more paradoxical and complex: the SS is far from 'brutal', in fact extremely high-minded and idealistic; and Zaleski himself shares its concept of a potentially pure human race, untainted by disease, to the extent of condemning medical science, as a destructive pestilence, for preserving the lives of the afflicted and 'perpetuating the incurable'. None the less the Prince (who has solved the first two cases by pure reasoning without going outdoors or meeting any of the participants) on this third occasion sallies forth to uncover the culprits and face death at their hands before causing the Society to disband (with Shiel's usual inconsistency, we are not told why the SS, considering its views, should employ an aged, stone-deaf door-man).

Zaleski believed that war would die out, eventually, altogether: 'We no longer have world-serious war,' he stated in 'The SS'; but by 1898 Shiel at any rate no longer shared his opinion: *The Yellow Danger* (subtitled 'The World's Greatest War'), telling of a Chinese who 'manages to pit the European powers against each other and then swoops out of the East at the head of a yellow horde and devastates Europe,'[1] is the first of a trilogy forecasting a situation which, as things are at present, might yet arise. *The Yellow Wave* (1905), 'a novel written without adjectives' (very unusual for Shiel), postulates Japan at war with Russia: Baron Murino, the Eastern leader, *versus* Prince Devilroff (whose family is warned of impending disaster by an overpowering scent of violets) in the West, with a plot to involve other, non-belligerent nations; and *The Dragon* (1913), retitled *The Yellow Peril* when reissued by Gollancz in 1929, predicted global war a year before its actual outbreak, with Edward Prince of Wales, up against another Chinese Li Ku Yu, invading Germany on a flying boat and stealing the national treasure; there are airship battles, bombs, and a blinding ray to save England in the end (a plague killing off a million and a half Chinese turned the trick in *The Yellow Danger*).

Large conceptions came easily to Shiel: though sometimes docketed as a writer of science fiction, romantic or gothic fantasies, he was built on the grand scale, and his best novels are apocalyptic in scope. The themes of international conflict and world domination recur constantly: the latter was often attempted and achieved for the good of humanity by one of his 'Overman' characters – he eschewed 'the misbegotten term superman (latin and anglo-saxon) for Ubermensch' – but his ruthless and basically benevolent Overmen were different from the Teutonic variety: one of them, Richard Hogarth (*The Lord of the Sea*, 1901[2]) was really a Jew whose father's name was Sir Solomon Spinoza.

Shiel himself had Overman qualities, and this grandiose general conception plainly stemmed from his being an exiled king: often the Overmen became Kings of the World, like young Hannibal Lepsius in

---

1 I quote from Shiel's American bibliographer, A. Reynolds Morse, to whom I am much indebted for material. (*The Works of M.P. Shiel*, Fantasy Publishing Co. Inc., Los Angeles, 1948.)

2 Reprinted, 1964, in Gollancz's Rare Works of Imaginative Fiction.

The Isle of Lies (1909),[1] who never learned the meaning of the word 'forget', and lived without seeing a woman until his nineteenth birthday; or Hogarth – an escaped convict condemned for a murder he had not committed – who found a meteorite stuffed with diamonds, built steel forts which made him master of the oceans, put a stop to war ('Germany, France, Russia against England'), and was made Regent of Great Britain: ending up, when his past and true parentage were revealed, as a Shophet or Judge who 'for sixty years ruled over Israel'. Being a Shiel Overman was no picnic, and Hogarth is the only one who dies dancing his way to Heaven: Lepsius is blinded by vitriol flung by a jilted French governess; wealthy Jack Hay in *The Weird O' It* (1902) – Shiel's longest novel (725 pages), in which one character 'laughs himself to death' – after a strenuous life of suffering is immolated in a Christ-like fashion (Reynolds Morse compares this book to Maugham's later *The Razor's Edge*, and indeed Shiel named Maugham 'the best living English novelist, male'); Robert Hartwell in *The Evil that Men Do* (1904), a workingman-philosopher who impersonates a rascally financier, forgives his enemies after starting out ruthlessly to 'eradicate' them; Langler in *The Last Miracle* (1906) is killed in a duel of poison pills by the Baron who schemes to discredit Christianity by producing mocked-up 'visions' of the crucifixion in churches etc: in *This Above All* (1933), Prince Surazal cannot die, since he is Lazarus spelt backwards and made immortal by the touch of Jesus, but he is not allowed to possess the equally immortal Rachel, for whom time has stopped at the age of twelve (though she 'keeps a gallery of portraits of her lovers over the centuries').

Lazarus was always a favourite character of Shiel's: as a boy he spent much time shouting for him to come forth, and in his last, so far unpublished, work *Jesus*, 'a truer translation of Luke', he claimed to prove that Lazarus was the Apostle Paul 'who in his anti-sadduccee craze for resurrection stayed four days in a tomb'. Jesus himself was made explicitly incarnate in Richard Hogarth at the end: '...our greatest are really one...Proteus his name, and ever the shape he takes is strange, unexpected, yet ever sharing the same three traits of vision, rage and generousness – the Slayer of the Giant – Arthur come back – the Messenger of the Covenant – the genius of our species – Jesus the Oft-Born.' All the Overmen really strive towards Christhood, but are foiled by the human traits they possess, which Morse sometimes

---

1   Also reprinted in Gollancz's Rare Works of Imaginative Fiction.

mistakes for foolishness: 'The author often tries one's credulity with the self-immolation of his heroes.'

The Lord of the Sea and *The Purple Cloud*,[1] published in the same year (1901), are possibly Shiel's best-known and most popular novels, especially in the USA. Adam Jeffson in *The Purple Cloud* surpasses all other Overmen: finding himself alone in a world where everyone has been killed off by a wave of cyanogen gas, he imagines himself to be 'the Arch-one, the motive of the world', and sets out to 'ravage and riot' in his kingdom like the Caesars. It is typical of a Shiel creation that, in Morse's words, Jeffson's 'fear that he will finally find someone else alive mounts page by page' and that when he does come upon his Eve by a streamlet in Istanbul, 'his first impulse is to kill and eat her'. (The Eve motif recurs in many of the novels, notably *The Isle of Lies*: Shiel's women – many of them Jewish, and one patterned after his first wife, 'a Parisian Spaniard' who resembled his mother – are extremely realistic, though wayward and contrary to an infuriating degree, and the course of true love is rarely permitted to have its run.)

Containing not only some of Shiel's most magnificent scenes and set pieces, *The Purple Cloud* illustrates one of his greatest strengths: the ability to buttress his situations with selective and specific detail which – despite the melodramatic plots, missing wills, lost heiresses, hidden treasures etc – causes the reader to suspend disbelief. As Morse says, 'He has no equal when it comes to accounting for extraneous objects found in a coffin, to killings by a pistol set off by the sun, or to catching a slayer in his own electric trap'; there is nothing of 'with one bound Bond was free' about his heroes' escapes from danger: the means by which they are effected are made clear and credible (the rope trailing from a balloon, with 'a loop to be slipped under the arms' by which the convict Bates hopes to get away from prison in *Lord of the Sea*; the 'opening covered with a disc of stone kept in place by magnetic force' through which Calvo 'vanished from King Harry' in the historical romance *Cold Steel*), and the Crusoe-like isolation of Adam Jeffson touring the desolate cities is depicted with a realism equal to Defoe's: for instance, when in a deserted mining village, he dresses himself 'in a flannel shirt, trousers with circles of leather at the knees, thick boots and a miner's hat having a socket into which fits a candle', but almost every page provides an example of this method. The effect of

1 Also available from Gollancz: Rare Works no 1.

identification which both Defoe and Shiel sought to bring about is particularly strong today when Jeffson's plight might become that of any of us, and the novel is uncomplicated by the tortuous intrigues and plot-convolutions forced upon Shiel by the conventions of his time and the financial necessity for serial publication, which after all coloured also the work of Dickens and Dostoevsky (his favourite Russian novelist) before him.

It is as though he had set himself to make literature out of the late Victorian romantic mystery, much as Stevenson did with Captain Marryat or Raymond Chandler with the material of the *Black Mask* novelette; and, as with the latter, an element of burlesque was perforce present in the result. But even in a short tale like *Monk Wakes an Echo* (1911), in which Shiel is consciously sending up the sensational stories of his day, the realistic touch and odd detail is not omitted: the Scots baronet-vivisectionist ('the only exact biologist in the world') who, having trapped the investigator, 'sat to a repast of potatoes, boiled cod, black bread, whisky' with a revolver beside him on the table, is almost a Hitchcockian figure, and in the story's mere sixteen pages enough incident is packed to supply several episodes of a series like *The Avengers*.

Cummings King Monk (note the middle name) lives like Zaleski in an abbey, has a weakness of the eyes for which he wears a button in one ear and at times 'would cower for days over a library-fire, tamed, a "shade" over his nose'. But unlike Zaleski he is a man of action, and his way of snapping out of the mood described above is to plunge straight into adventure:

> 'Do you know what I have been thinking there? That one of the big crimes would rouse and excite us.'
> 'No doubt of that,' I said. 'Against whom shall we commit it?'
> 'One needn't commit it oneself,' he said. 'What I mean is that we should first conceive the crime, construct it, then find out someone who is somewhere committing it in the world, and mix ourselves up generally in the trouble.'

In fact, since his friend the narrator has 'no wish to be shot', Monk goes off alone to beard on his lonely farm the sinister baronet, who insures his paying guests for large sums to satisfy the greed of two misers – one of them his sister – living in his house. Sir Saul, having cut out the tongue of a young parson from Cambridge, is driving him mad in order to experiment upon his living disordered brain:

'So how do you drive people mad?' Monk asked.

'Fear, torture, horror, other things; have snakes, a jaguar, a monster grouse with four legs; simply solitary confinement sometimes. Depends on diathesis of subject.'

No writer save Shiel would have thought of the monstrous grouse with four legs, nor the manner in which, with the gun-cotton and phosphorus destined for himself, Monk disposes of the baronet and the misers, blowing up the farm after having caused the sister to murder her brother by accident ('for Monk, who could be ruthless, had doomed all the three'), and escaping with the speechless clergyman slung over his shoulder:

> Wilson's arm clasping his neck, choking him, a whimpering moaning from the dumb throat, while Monk, gasping beneath his load, ran onward in random trepidation, till, spying a gleam like moonshine through a crack, he again and again drove his back against some boarding, tumbled outward, and down fifteen feet, and was rolling downhill in bracken.

One can see, even from this semi-parody, what a great popular entertainer Shiel would have made had he chosen (a Cummings King Monk series on TV is devoutly to be hoped for), and why his friend Louis Tracy (with whom he 'wasted himself' concocting several pseudonymous detective stories) said that he could 'make as much money as Bernard Shaw and Edgar Wallace put together'. But Shiel was above all a *writer*; his textual revisions for later editions consisted mainly of deletions: pruning, cutting, aiming for a more concentrated effect: he defined great writing 'simply as "expressive writing". Can the man express himself – in a few words? For one must add "in a few words", since George Eliot could certainly express herself, only in many words, a fact which puts her outside the very small circle of literary people who have lived.'

His *Best Short Stories*, selected by John Gawsworth and published in 1948, a volume one hopes will be reprinted shortly, offers a splendid cross-section of his macabre invention and literary progress. New readers will find there not only Zaleski (who knew 'forty-three – and in one island in the South Seas, forty-four – different methods of doing murder', all undetectable), but an Indian Maharajah who lives to 120, snatches his future wife from her husband's funeral pyre, and is consumed, finally, in a more horrid manner; a Cockney husband raped on the wedding night by his dead sister-in-law (another Rachel); an embalmed corpse which turns into a gigantic vermilion-feathered cat; a dissertation on tit-bits of the tomb by one who knows (contrary to expectation, the uvula, not the eyes, is the delicacy of the vault); and a son with supernormal hearing who listens to silver bells tinkling in a crypt containing his dead mother, as rats gnaw their way through successive layers of the coffin (Shiel liked to have rats around: a troop of them flees squealing from a turgid pool in Zaleski's downstairs hall, and Redonda itself is rat-infested: an American naturalist who climbed the rock to gather plant specimens in 1958 was nearly eaten alive, and sleep is impossible, says Dr Howard, owing to their attacks).

But it is Shiel's journey as a stylist that can be charted through these tales: from the impassioned rococo eloquence and beautiful bizarrerie of the early examples to the cool – indeed chilling – mosaic of words which makes up *The Primate of the Rose*; he had come a long way from Poe and the archaic adjective in his final phase. He took enormous pains, suiting his style to content: a scene of passion or pursuit is panted out in short breathless gasps; his innumerable tempests – perhaps reminiscent of those roaring round Redonda – literally crackle; his vocabulary, already immense, was enriched by knowledge of many languages and his startling similes were sometimes direct translations from them. He accounted Job the greatest genius and greatest poet who ever lived, and M.P. Shiel the best living prose writer (but, 'no reader … will be sufficiently simple to think me "conceited", for I am over twenty-five and, at that age, if one has lived a fast spiritual life, one only pretends to be conceited'); many critics in his lifetime, however, endorsed the latter opinion, and certainly one has only to compare his best work with a sham modern-gothic attempt at a 'powerful' or 'elemental' novel such as *Radcliffe* by David Storey, to see where the difference lies, or his one real piece of science fiction and last published novel (1937) *The Young Men Are Coming* (containing evanescent beings from outer space with body-temperature so high that they excrete sticks of carbon) with the modern product so highly praised.

Ten years after *The Young Men Are Coming* appeared, Shiel died, at the age of eighty-one, in receipt of a Civil List pension (Sir James Barrie, J.D. Beresford, A.E. Coppard and W.H. Davies were among those who signed the necessary petition, apart from literary figures I have already mentioned). But only thirteen mourners gathered to hear Edward Shanks's funeral oration at Golder's Green. Enigmatic to the last, he never revealed to even his closest disciples the full nature of his 'religion of science', designed to replace outmoded Christianity; but now that the missing MS notebooks which were a bar to the publication of *Jesus* have at last come to light, his message may shortly be deciphered (John Gawsworth found the notebooks last year at Sotheby's: they had been in the possession of the daughter of Grant Richards, one of Shiel's original publishers). But however important the message may prove, it would be a shocking waste if he were to remain the centre of a philosophical and private cult. A revival is in any case due, and it is as literature that his works are likely to be remembered, which is what he would most have wanted.

LITERARY PARODIES

Of Gorse: An Incomplete Story
(Patrick Hamilton)

*   *   *

PART ONE – GORSE THE PUBLISHER

1

MISS ELIZABETH BOOTE, A LADY NOVELIST AND 'STUDENT OF crime', was all her life what is foolishly called an 'omnivorous' reader. She did not, of course, in the literal sense, 'devour' books, even those described by reviewers as being 'crisp as lettuce', etc: but the fact remains that she did read a great deal.

One of the main ingredients of her literary diet was a series of novels dealing with a character named Ernest Ralph Gorse.

Though often described as a 'very serious criminal', a potential murderer destined to become a 'nationally famous figure', etc, etc, Ernest Ralph Gorse had confined himself, in the trilogy about him which had already appeared, to preying upon women by means of trickery, and had not actually killed anyone so far.

Apart from her 'professional' concern with Gorse (as a 'criminologist'), Elizabeth Boote was especially interested in him because, according to the third volume in the series, she was herself to write his biography at some unspecified time in the future. She was therefore anxious for him to start murdering and be caught and executed as soon as possible, so that she could fulfil her appointed role and add to her reputation thereby – to say nothing of earning large sums of money in the process.

It might have come as a severe shock to this vain, foolish, greedy, avaricious, affected, utterly unlovable and even detestable woman had she known that she was personally acquainted with Gorse, and that he was already planning to defraud – if not actually to murder – her.

Unlike his prospective victim, the reddish-haired, reddish-moustached, slightly freckled, nasal-voiced, monocle-wearing, car-driving Gorse was not a 'great reader', though acquainted superficially with the works of Jeffery Farnol and P.G. Wodehouse, whose styles he was 'wont' (as he would have expressed it) to employ in conversation as well as in letter-writing.

He had not failed, moreover, to learn of the series of books devoted to him, which he had purchased and read without liking at all, since almost every page contained some derogatory reference to himself, his innate vulgarity, 'commonness', lack of good taste, etc. Nor had he relished the idea of being written about by Elizabeth Boote – apparently after his death – as 'abominable', 'odious', and 'repulsive', or of being finally 'comprehended' and 'forgiven' by her.

He had in fact seriously considered murdering her (since it seemed he would have to murder eventually), thus preventing the future biography from being written at all, and putting – as he phrased it in the peculiarly vulgar, debased, capital-letter-studded coinage of his private thoughts – a Whacking Great Spoke in the author's Wheel. But some instinct told him that he would be unable to interfere – at any rate, to such an extent – with the course laid down for him.

Gorse, moreover, was anxious to postpone murdering for as long as he could. Not from any moral scruples – in which, of course, he was entirely lacking – but because murder entailed some sort of punishment or retribution which he was naturally keen to avoid. He therefore contented himself with deciding to 'Put the Boote In', and 'Make the Old Trout Rue the Day She Was Born'.

It did not take the astute and purposeful Gorse long to track down the flat-chested, bony, lank-haired, indeterminate-aged female 'student of crime' (whose photograph, suitably etherealised, 'adorned' the back-jackets of her own 'criminological' works), and who combined – as he at once realised – the most nauseatingly foolish characteristics of all the women he had ever victimised, without any of the unhappy Esther Downes's beauty or the endearing simplicity of poor deluded Ivy Barton.

Elizabeth Boote possessed, in addition, an affectedly 'arty', pseudo-'Bohemian', pretentious quality that was all her own. She was, of course, addicted to wearing long, trailing, brightly coloured scarves and 'barbaric'-style earrings, and frequently went about in 'slacks', especially when 'in the house'.

Her 'house' was, in fact, a mews flat in the Regent's Park postal district, and – not surprisingly, in view of her complete lack of any physical or mental attractiveness – she lived alone.

3

Having made the acquaintance of Miss Boote in a neighbouring 'coffee house', to which she often 'repaired' for a 'strong brew' at the end of her 'day's labours', Gorse represented himself to her as a publisher. Or rather not as an established publisher but as a young man with money, desirous of starting a publishing house and seeking 'Names' to have on his 'List'. As Gorse was well aware (from gossip overheard in those public houses frequented by the duffle-coated, bitter-drinking know-alls of the literary fringe), the foolish, yet outrageously complacent and rapacious Miss Boote had just quarrelled with her own publishers over the question of a larger 'advance' – a frequent cause of dissension between author and publisher. She was therefore 'all over' Gorse from the start, recognising (as was undoubtedly true) that her monocled, re-moustached, faintly nasal, Bertie-Wooster-resembling *vis-à-vis* was largely ignorant of the type of business in which he proposed to invest and might, if properly 'handled', prove to be a 'chicken' ready for the 'plucking'.

Here, of course, she was woefully wrong. In fact – as Gorse in his ostensibly debonair, yet somehow evilly facetious, manner would undoubtedly have said – the Boote was emphatically on the Other Foot.

PART TWO – GORSE THE ACTOR-MANAGER

1

It has already been suggested that, had those writers who afterwards scoffed at the credulous folly of Gorse's victims been subjected to his wiles themselves, they might well have reacted in very much the same way.

Certainly this was true of Elizabeth Boote, and might also have been true of Gorse's other biographer, G. Hadlow-Browne, had Gorse been able to get hold of him too: but Hadlow-Browne, fortunately for himself, was 'wintering abroad' at the time and therefore out of reach. (This may account for the fact that Hadlow-Browne's attitude towards Gorse was more 'humorous' than that of Miss Boote, who had every reason to adopt a 'serious' approach to the subject: though – perhaps because she did not care to advertise the extent of her folly – she was careful never to mention her personal connection with the afterwards celebrated criminal.)

Gorse, however, often spoke of his efforts to contact Hadlow-Browne and 'sign him up' as one of 'his' (Gorse's) prospective authors, thereby stimulating to the full the jealousy and envy which the inwardly mean-spirited (though outwardly 'liberal' and 'advanced') Miss Boote entertained towards her rivals.

2

The mews flat in which Elizabeth Boote lived had a 'gaily' painted blue door, flanked by window-boxes containing scarlet geraniums. And on the bright-polished brass knocker, Gorse – having driven up in one of the rakish sports-cars which he hired daily from a shady second-hand dealer off Great Portland Street – was soon sounding every evening a debonair *rat-tat-tat*. Yet, to a sensitive ear, the rhythm of this knock would have sounded somehow 'common' – *nasal*, in fact – even vaguely menacing.

The lank, flat-chested, straggly-haired, bonily sexless Miss Boote was not, however, sensitive. She was, in fact, foolishly and obtusely insensitive to a high degree.

Inside the flat the most 'delicious' dialogues (Miss Boote was obsessively – in fact 'deliciously' – fond of this misplaced and outworn adjective, which she pronounced, moreover, in a peculiarly intolerable, lank-haired and 'arty' way) would take place over the peach brandy and strong black coffee 'brewed' with the authoress's own 'lily-white hands' (which were in reality sallow, skinny, predacious, and darkly veined).

These conversations as a rule concerned the Ernest Ralph Gorse novels and the 'ultimate fate' reserved for that 'fictional personage' (which was 'wrapt' so far – as Miss Boote put it with the most hideously foolish and simpering coyness – in the deepest Mister E.).

'Well – what do you suppose will become of him?' asked Gorse, who disliked intensely being called a Fictional Personage, and concealed his irritation only with the greatest difficulty. 'In the end – I mean?'

'Oh – he'll be hanged of course,' said Miss Boote firmly.

'Why "of course?"' said Gorse with unwonted sharpness, for he disliked even more the idea of being hanged.

'Well,' said Miss Boote, 'murderers usually are – aren't they? At least – such has been my humble experience, anyway.'

'I bow to your superior knowledge, gracious lady,' Gorse, who really felt more like kicking her, now went all Teutonic, clicking his heels, kissing her hand and screwing his monocle deeper in a facetiously 'Prussian' way. 'But Gorse hasn't murdered yet – you know,' he added.

'Yes – but he will,' said Miss Boote, blissfully and 'deliciously' unaware that she might herself be the corpse at any moment, 'Besides – it says he'll die painlessly and quickly … doesn't it? And hanging's painless and quick – isn't it?'

'Well,' said Gorse, 'I couldn't say. Never having been hanged – that is.'

'Oh – but *everybody* knows that hanging's quite deliciously painless, darling,' said Miss Boote. 'Besides, Gorse *likes* being tied up and tying other people up – doesn't he? So it's only poetic justice … really … *n'est-ce pas?*'

'*Pouvait être,*' replied the hypocritical Gorse. 'Ye say well, and worshipfully, fair maiden – *je* trow.'

None the less, had Miss Boote not made that last remark about hanging, he might have let her off more lightly than in fact he did.

3

The resemblance between the reddish-haired, vocally nasal, monocled young 'publisher' and her favourite 'Fictional Personage' had not escaped Miss Boote, who – though inconceivably 'dumb' in the colloquial, transatlantic sense – was not actually blind. Gorse, with his usual acumen, had turned this drawback to his own advantage and proposed not only to 'sign on' Miss Boote as a partner in the publishing firm (for he needed someone of 'experience' to advise him, and she would then be in a position to 'put out' large editions of her own books) but to finance a play based on the career of Gorse, to be 'adapted' and produced from the novels by his 'ladye fayre' with himself playing the principal part.

To this end he often 'rehearsed' in the presence of Miss Boote – bemused for the occasion with copious 'libations' of peach brandy, laced on the sly with benzedrine – his 'silly ass' act, also taking her, on 'free' tickets supposedly supplied by the management, to the 'Little Theatre' where this entertainment was, 'in the near future' to be staged.

In fact Gorse handled her as a skilful actor-manager 'handles' his cast; and the night came at last when her cheque – converted, at the suggestion of her 'knight errant', into hard, 'deliciously' expendable cash – was safely in his pocket and the sash-cord was being wound around her wrists: the 'delicate' wrist of flat-chested, sexlessly bony, pretentiously foolish, female 'criminologist' – in whose faded eyes fear began eventually to dawn.

PART THREE – GOOD OLD GORSE

1

Those already familiar with the Gorse saga – and particularly with the fate of the wretched but loveable Ivy Barton – will not need to be told of the sickening relish with which the nasal-voiced, slightly-freckled and reddish potential 'slayer' revealed his true identity to the lank and 'arty' woman in the mews-flat – who, it must be added, took the unwelcome 'tidings' considerably less calmly and courageously than her sister-in-misfortune. (It may be because of the memory of her own humiliation that Miss Boote made no reference to the case of Ivy Barton in her biography of Ernest Ralph Gorse.) She was also made to read aloud not the mere cutting from *The News of the World* but the whole of the three Gorse novels, and to speculate endlessly upon not only the destiny of Gorse himself (this was turned into a happy and prosperous one, from which hanging was altogether excluded) but upon such minor 'Mister E.s' as the fate of Mrs Plumleigh-Bruce's liver-coloured spaniel which, last mentioned on page 84 of Volume II, vanished thereafter from the book without explanation from the author.

'Now then,' said Gorse. 'Are you going to call me abominable? Or odious? Or repulsive? Eh, you old Boote?'

'No,' gasped Miss Boote, whose voice had by now begun to fail. 'No – I'm not . . . as a matter of fact.'

'No,' said Gorse. 'Instead, you're going to call me "Good Old Gorse" – understand?'

'Good old Gorse!' quavered Miss Boote obediently.

'Louder,' said Gorse. 'Let the jolly old welkins ring,' and added '…to Boote.'

Miss Boote was made to repeat 'Good Old Gorse' three more times, after which Gorse gagged her with adhesive tape and drove away in his car, leaving her for the daily woman to find next morning.

2

Miss Boote did not keep her promise and did in fact use, in her biography, the words 'abominable,' 'odious' and 'repulsive' instead of the more complimentary 'Good Old Gorse'. It says much, however, for her chastened frame of mind that she could also speak of the possibility of eventual forgiveness for her erstwhile tormentor.

Meantime Gorse – who, it will be remarked, had *still* not murdered anyone – drove on towards the next phase of his criminal career, the Haywards Heath Dentist: and to that 'ultimate fate' which will be revealed when the author has finally decided what it is in fact to be.

Good Lord, Jeeves
(P.G. Wodehouse)

*   *   *

ALL UNCONSCIOUS OF IMPENDING DOOM I WAS GNAWING A solitary bone at the Drones Club and wistfully recalling that golden age when coves like Catsmeat Potter-Pirbright and Barmy Fotheringay-Phipps had reigned supreme, filling the air around with snappy dialogue and bread rolls bandied to-and-fro. I'd reached the point, after a few shots of cognac imbibed to assist the gastric juices, when a less reserved chappie would have burst into the chorus of 'Auld lang syne' or wondered, with the poet, where the jolly old *neiges* of *a.* had got to nowadays, and it was in this mellow mood that I became suddenly aware of two birds in formal attire bearing down on me from across the banqueting hall – now, alas, empty save for the last of the Woosters.

Though the advancing figures were clearly recognisable as Sir Roderick Glossop and Sir Watkyn Bassett, CBE, JP, respectively, it took me some moments to realise that these knights were actually present in the flesh, and by the time it'd sunk in that they weren't mere shades conjured up from the mists of m. or the pages of a cheap edition chronicling some past kick of the heels, they were already standing over my table with expressions that betokened business.

Sir Watkyn was the first to give tongue, and at his tone of voice even my iron nerve began to describe a graceful arc. I felt a kinship with those private eyes of American lit., who glance up from a newly discovered stiff to find the boys from the Homicide Squad standing around, idly swinging their blackjacks in preparation for a cosy chat about the case.

'Mr Wooster,' said the former bane of Bosher Street, 'we are from the Ministry of Rehabilitation. We were informed that the club secretary was to be found lunching in this room.'

'I'm the Hon. Sec., Sir Watkyn,' I said: an honest admission received by Sir Roderick with what brothers of the P.E.N. qualify as a mirthless chuckle.

'A suitable nominee for an institution so-named, do you not concur, Bassett?' he said.

'Especially apt in view of the establishment's future function,' Sir W. agreed. 'You are, of course, aware, Mr Wooster, that these premises have been requisitioned w.e.f. today's date as a State Home for the Mentally Deficient...'

'... and that I, as Government Psychiatrist,' said Sir Roderick, coming in pat on his cue, 'will be in charge of the scheme, which is to be implemented forthwith.'

'Here, I say,' I protested, rallying from the ropes, as one who recovers from a right cross, 'you can't do that, you know! The members won't stand for it!'

'There are no members, Mr Wooster,' Sir Watkyn said, planting another *banderillo* in the quivering hide. 'We've already ascertained that. And if it is the free board and lodging which as club secretary you receive here that causes your patent anxiety, why, you are in no danger of losing it. Sir Roderick, I am sure, will gladly sign the certificate insuring your future as an inmate of the Home – eh, Glossop?'

It was the KO delivered with full force to the softer parts of the anat. I had crumpled over the table, gasping for breath, when through the loud singing in my ears a familiar and well-loved voice spoke sharply, scattering the opponents to right and left.

'Gentlemen,' it said, 'I wish to have a word in private with Mr Wooster, if you please.'

The big fight was over. Before you could say Sugar Ray Robinson, Sir Roderick and W. Bassett had beaten it, murmuring, 'Yes, Minister,' and 'Certainly, Lord Jeeves,' in the most obsequious of accents, and the hand, it seemed, of a ministering angel was holding a beaker of brandy to my lips.

'Jeeves,' I said fervently, 'lives there a man with soul so dead as to resist the incomparable Jeeves?'

'Thank you, sir. The tribute is much appreciated.'

'I merely quote from the *Daily Herald*. But wait a sec.,' I said, as full consciousness flooded back to the brain, 'didn't I hear those two blighters address you as Minister? And Lord Jeeves? Or was it a dream?'

'The Government has been kind enough to reward my trifling services with a peerage, and also by inclusion in the Cabinet, sir.'

'As Minister of Re-Thing?'

'Habilitation, sir. A little more brandy, if I might so suggest? I fear this news has come as a grave shock to you, sir.'

'Worse than that, Jeeves. The loss of this job would be the last straw.'

I raised my measure on high. 'To your success, Jeeves, which you dashed well deserve.'

'Thank you, sir. But you were saying about your position as secretary here, and its importance to you...'

'Supreme importance, Jeeves, financially speaking. Nationalisation and sur-tax have taken their toll. The Wooster millions are, in fact, down the drain. Need I say more?'

'It is a plight shared by many in these times, sir. Your friends are unable to assist?'

'*Friends*,' I echoed bitterly. 'Shall I show you the typed note I had from Mrs Bingo Little's secretary? Or the stern refusal received from Stiffy Byng's spouse, the Bishop of Blandings, formerly the Rev. Stinker Pinker? The receipt of such missives is souring to one's sunny nature, Jeeves.'

'Man is an ungrateful animal, sir. But perhaps I might be of some little help, if you'd allow me...'

'How?'

'The offer of employment, sir.'

'What kind of employment?'

'I hesitate to say, sir.'

'Don't hesitate. Out with it. Beggars can't be c., Jeeves.'

'Well, sir, the post of secretary to the Junior Ganymede Club has fallen vacant in the past week. I could confidently promise you the appointment if you so desire.'

'But the Junior Ganymede's a club for gentlemen's personal gentlemen. How could *I* get in?'

'By accepting a temporary position as my personal attendant, sir... If I may say so, you would not find me too exacting an employer.'

We Woosters are nothing if not adaptable. My hesitation was of the briefest. 'Jeeves,' I said, 'you're on! Let's drink to that!'

'Thank you,' said Jeeves, as I ladled out liberal portions. 'Er –... not all the soda, Wooster.'

'No, sir,' I said, falling without effort into this new way of l. 'I will endeavour to give satisfaction, sir... I mean, m'lord.'

Reading
(Henry Green)

*   *   *

ON AN AFTERNOON IN JUNE, THE TIME BEING THE PRESENT AND
the tense the past, John Doe, a novelist who like most of his generation
wrote under the name of Green, entered a public library to see how
many copies of his latest were stocked thereby.

Electric globes, already lit a foggy lemon, yet eclipsed that dimmer
day closing down grey outside what windows were shut fast in turn on
mist and rain without.

'For this is London, England, where is no summer,' Mr Doe appeared
to mutter, dialogue being, as he always had it, for use at once if not
much sooner – by which he meant conversation, any voice enabled to
talk, speak out loud, the author.

Being alone he had no answer, then turned to sight the pimply junior
librarian slumped graceless hard by those grain-wood drawers, card-
indexes of fiction for borrowers' eyes to feast upon, as with a start of
recognition the elder man's did now on the girl expostulating with that
lout, Phoebe Dickson by name, who, recently 'out', had lately learned
to read.

'Then do awake and lend a hand,' the young female was pouting in
a kind of moan. 'I declare, you're just being aggravating, refusing to
aid! So sucks,' she echoed, the Phoebe, and frowned adorable. 'But
Green was the name and you can't tell me other. Yet how's a girl to find
just one among so many, or to tell, feminine intuition aside, which of
these wretched cards has reference to who?'

Whereupon Mr Doe could scarcely wait, but bustled in where she,
the angel, feared to tread.

'There, there, mustn't take on, you know!' he ejaculated in a resonant
voice. 'Tell me the trouble, what ails you that is, and we'll soon set the

matter at rest! By Green, then, is it?' He looked to be enchanted at the girl's sly murmur. 'And who's this great author you're so eager to get that pretty little nose buried into, pray?' To which raillery the darling riposted with spirit.

'Just about the best novelist writing we have today, that's all!' she told him, grand. Whence that librarian opened eyes to emit a chortle, oafish. 'All nineteen of 'em I shouldn't wonder,' was what he might have been understood to dryly opine.

'Well Mummy and my confidante say so, and they ought to know!' the wench cried in a withering tone. 'There's to be a – a – revival or something, I mean of interest in this author, and, oh, you must consider me an awful goose, having such a memory, or rather the lack of one, that I can't even call to mind which Green was intended!' she concluded contrite, with what sounded a sob of sweet self-pity.

'Then look, Phoebe, no offence meant,' apologised the author, this Doe. 'Or it should be Miss Dickson I'm aware, but a chap of my mature years has certain latitudes, or anyway he ought!' John completed, avuncular.

'Well, none taken,' Miss Phoebe accepted. 'And anyway you're not, well not old anyway, like you implied, hoping I'd contradict like your sweet young ladies always do, or should I have expressed that last bit,' she amended, when that librarian spoke up with a grin that might have been malicious, though with a half-wit none could tell.

'Why, it's Mr Green I mean Mr Doe,' he speedily corrected and gave a hoarse guffaw, proletarian.

'Now that's enough!' Mr Doe told him. 'A joke's a joke, but that'll do!' At which the oaf retired with a mumble behind his counter amid the books put by.

'Why should he call you Mr Green, Mr Doe, or I mean John?' the Dickson demanded limpid. 'Don't tell me you've taken to authorship, though that might be wonderful?' she added casual, glancing round.

'Got confused, made an error, I don't doubt,' this man averred ruefully. 'Why only imagine, Phoebe, just the other day the head waiter failed to recognise me in an expensive place I'm accustomed to lunch at, though what the world's coming to I couldn't like to tell!' he wound up with apparently real exasperation.

'And just when you had someone with you,' that débutante demurely agreed, 'some angelic child I expect, that had to be impressed as well as lunched, don't trouble to deny it now! And there's poor little Phoebe just aching to be asked to a real expensive meal but having to be content with a read of Mr Green instead.' On what, with a despairful whinny, she made off with the Doe panting hard behind.

'No, now listen, Phoebe! If what you claim is true, escorts with the wherewithal being, it could happen, in short supply, then if you happen to be free tonight I'd count it a privilege,' he ended by muttering, confused by the brilliant smile of seeming delight she turned upon him.

'Oh, John I'd adore to! Tonight? As never was?'

'The better the day, the better the deed!' was this writer's fervent response.

'And somewhere really posh? A night-club I mean, after? Not that I want to rush you, but that'd be simply delish!!'

'The poshest going!' John announced in ringing tones. 'One must pay for one's pleasures nowadays, you know,' he added into her hair that emanated a great niff of scent, at which the fellow almost swooned.

'Oh I'm aware!' was her winsome answering murmur, which may have sounded sad. 'But my book!' she looked about wide-eyed. 'I mustn't, whichever the outcome, not go home without my darling Mr Green's opus under my arm, or what would my confidante think then?'

'That'd never do indeed,' John Doe nearly shouted, and gripped her arm forthwith. 'Now let's see if I can be your guide. Not that I've much cognisance of Modern Lit. mind,' he added deprecating, but despite this modesty was able to lead the deb. right over to the requisite department – those rows of bindings stamped all with, it seemed, the same author's name, lit a misty yellow by these dependent moons above.

'Hmm yes, a daunting sight! Yet all's not as black as might appear. They've different Christian names, and then there's a matter of spelling. With or without an E at the end, that seems the question, if I may so paraphrase the Gloomy Dane,' Doe finished, and regarded the girl with what looked like lively anticipation.

'But how can one possibly!' Miss D. burst out. 'Though wait! It's coming back to me, something Mums said, about a major and diamonds and Africa could it have been? Now tell me, is there a novel, by which I mean a work of fictional prose, by any Green or Greene that would contain those elements?'

'Could be,' Mr Doe said dryly. 'Try this.'

'Oh you are an angel, such a help,' the young woman gasped, puckering her lovely forehead over the pages. 'But what heart can this, then, be the matter of?' she proclaimed. 'No, there seems to be religion here, and I don't remember Mummy, so I fear Mr Greene with an E is not the answer,' on which her senior breathed out loud as though relieved.

'Now these are spies,' Phoebe went on, moving of her own sweet will along the shelf. 'I'm sure my confidante would not, and here's a Frenchman, Julien, I could swear that wasn't it. Now look what fun!!' she pursued, and John appeared at this point in considerable suspense. 'All these wizard oneword titles, *Loving* and *Nothing* and yes, *Doting*, whatever will such authors imagine next! Conversations too, just like a play and yet it's not, how clever!! But still they're not either what Mummy meant,' she continued, not heeding the man's fierce expression. 'And yet what's this!?! *The Major – Knight Errant*, by L. Patrick Greene! Yes, here's the one! A major and diamonds, and I do believe Africa! There, I knew darling Mum could not be at fault,' the Miss called triumphantly. 'Greene with an E after all, why didn't you tell me right away?' she queried, then caught sight of Mr Doe's darkened face.

'Why what's the matter?' Phoebe exclaimed in concern. 'Don't tell me it's all off! The dinner you know,' she added with impatience, as the man seemed not to comprehend. 'And our night-club, and all the marvellously expensive champagne to drink in buckets after,' she reminded him reproachful.

'Oh, of course,' Mr Doe concurred. 'Though I'm not sure about champagne. Even lager beer's pretty expensive in these haunts, if you take my meaning, and I'm told you can get quite gay on it,' John wound up decisively, at which the Dickson's face appeared to fall.

And so together those two left that library, and lived unhappily never after.

A Cable
(William Faulkner)

*   *   *

EVER SINCE IT (THE BOOK) HAD ARRIVED, WHICH FOR WANT OF
accurate terms in which to categorise it would have to be described,
classified, as fiction, a novel – perhaps not unjustly so as no one
protagonist figuring in its 392 pages (this aggregate not including those
printed sheets setting forth the title and the name of the author and the
list of his – the author's – previous works, or those devoted to the dedication and various acknowledgements) could possibly or even impossibly
have lived, breathed, or moved upon any continent or earthly terrain
known to man outside the uncharted moonscape of the author's
imagination; and would certainly have to be criticised, reviewed, as such,
he (the reviewer) – who was not yet the reviewer of this particular work
since he had not thus far put pen to paper on the subject and indeed
could not have done without violating his infrangible rule that books
sent to him for review should first be read, but who could be said to
belong to that trade or what was even sometimes defined as a profession (though invariably and only by persons who themselves practised
it), by virtue of literary essays, articles, written, printed, and even –
astonishingly – paid for, in the past, had been reading: first – on the
initial day – by light refracted by a window-pane behind the chair in
which he sat and later – when it (the light) swam grey, defunctive,
beyond the glass – by the fringed circle cast effulgent upon the prose and
the sentences and paragraphs from a standard lamp whose shade was
raggedly and brownly punctured at the back where it must have been
at some time tilted too far forward against the recalescent heat of the
hundred-watt electric bulb: closing the book only (the reviewer) when
a clock, sourceless, somewhere in some street, road, avenue, outside
struck thrice and yet again; and then only, as a somnambulist might,

485

to rise and climb into bed and place the book carefully within a hand-stretch and pull up the sheet and close his eyes: which (the eyes) flew once more open after what seemed to him but an instant fleeting and impermanent, yet the whirr of vehicular wheels outside – maybe a milk-float passing – promulgated as a lapse of several hours and the start (even, perhaps, meridian) of another day, since his watch had stopped and he did not rise to draw the curtains, but clicked on the bedside lamp and reached without even looking for the book and opened it at the exact line where he had stopped reading, his glance continuing on down the moil of print while his free hand fumbled unerringly for cigarettes and matches and placed a paper tobacco-filled cylinder between his lips and struck and held a vesta to its (the cigarette) tip and inhaled the dry and bitter smoke: all the while concentrating upon the page with a kind of cold and incredulous and recusant outrage, thinking *Yes, that's it. It's not that I don't understand, don't believe in it any more: it's that I can't, do not know how to now, not any longer:* remembering how once he had carried this writer's books with him everywhere, even in his kitbag when there had been a war and he (the reviewer) who had not been a reviewer then but had wanted to be a writer – that is, one whose scribblings upon paper with a quill or fountain-pen or perhaps a stub of even pencil would eventually undergo the alchemy of printer's ink, be transmogrified into print, and bound between cloth-covered boards, as opposed to ephemeral circulation in the columns of a sheet that might be purchased for one small silver coin, itself the equivalent of a half-dozen coppers – though he was in those days not even that kind of a writer but a private soldier in the army of His Gracious Majesty, King George VI, perusing implacably whenever his duties allowed, amid the brazen shouts of swaddies and lance-corporals and full corporals and sergeants and warrant-officers, transected by the occasional curt command of one who wore a single or two pips or maybe sometimes a crown sewn on his khaki shoulder in lieu of chevrons on the sleeve, the works now catalogued in a uniform edition on the dust jacket of the book that the reviewer grasped, thinking (the private) fifteen years back *if only I could get to write like that,* thinking:

> To be or not to be;
> That is the question

but it was not to be: no – had not been: and now the reviewer who had once been the private sat bolt upright in the unmade bed, his sight absorbing the supererogative prose without assimilating the sense any more than he would have had the book been written in Croat or even Coptic, thinking *even the one about the idiot, told by him too, but this not*; that was on the third day or perhaps the fourth, since he neither rose nor drew the curtains on what could have been sunshine or rain or just as probably a fall of snow, for the season was summer and the country that so-far unknowledged (by its inhabitants, anyway) satellite of the United States which they (the inhabitants) persist in terming – perhaps ironically, for all anyone knows – 'Great' Britain: and not until the last page was turned, did he (the reviewer) climb from between the covers and march upon the wash-basin in a corner of the room, putting a hand upon faucet and toilet accessories in turn with the same unerring glanceless automatic motion with which he had each morning reached for the book and cigarettes and matches upon waking; drawing with an inflexible scythelike sweep the razor across the fimbriated stubble of his chin; later striding down metropolitan streets and traversing traffic junctions with his eyes fixed in the same somnambulant stare and the book clutched in the crook of his tweeded arm; coming at last to a narrow chasm blocked by scarlet omnibuses pulsating and flanked by façades of steel and glass and black midnight-coloured shining marble in which his (the reviewer's) silhouette passed reflected, furious and as if forlorn: his long scissor-like stride carrying him ultimately past a uniformed bemedalled commissionaire illuminated behind glass, like some waxen symbolic hero or maybe an example of the taxidermist's art, intended it could be as a savage and sardonic comment upon the futility of war or the impermanence of martial glory: and up (still the reviewer) a staircase of stone, past a protesting female figure, perhaps a secretary, who rose in his path and whom he did not so much brush aside as walk through like she might have been a mirage or impalpable phantom thinking

To be

and knowing the answer to the unpropounded question even as he pushed open the door marked EDITOR and placed the book carefully on the polished desk-top in front of the seated swivel-chaired figure which did not raise its blanched and silken head at his entrance any more than he himself had glanced at the secretary outside, thinking *like a scene from one of his (the author's) books. The one about the air-circus, the stunt-flyers, only he ought to wear a shade:* 'You ought to wear a green eye-shade,' he (the reviewer) said – 'You know, like a croupier, with a peak at the front' and only now the editor looked up, with his mild bland blue heatless stare, first at the book and then at the reviewer, saying (the editor) in a voice as mild bland and heatless as his eyes, though not as blue since it was devoid of all colour and indeed inflexion, a voice blanched and silky as his glazed and centre-parted hair, 'You've come to resign?' and the reviewer, in a gust of tense and outraged appeal: 'The horse. That's all. Just explain to me about the horse,' thrusting the book forward towards a hand which, however, was snatched instantly away as though it had maybe been menaced with the touch of incandescent steel '– the three-legged horse. And the Negro. And the groom,' he (the reviewer) seemed now to plead, in a voice suddenly broken and despairing and fatigued: 'Because you are the editor. Because maybe you can tell me, make it plain. What they were at, or thought they were at, I mean –' and the editor – inquiring, inflexionless, impersonal – 'There's a three-legged horse? In this book?' and the reviewer, nodding: 'It runs races. On three legs. So I figured you'd have read it, you would know –' tailing off, thinking

not to be;

and the editor: 'My child, why should you suppose I've read it?' leaning back, the white silky hair and the mild bland eyes, with maybe the sketch of a smile mirrored way back in their heatless blue: 'Since as you say I am the editor, it is one of the prerogatives of my position: no, better: perquisites, almost: that *I do not have to read the books*,' and leaning forward suddenly, the pools of his eyes frozen abruptly over and the indubitable crackle of ice in his tone which now was not so much heatless as frigorific: '*I don't have to read them.* Not now. Not anymore. Never. Can you grasp, comprehend, understand that?' and the reviewer, after a pause: 'Yes. I understand all right,' and the editor: 'You want to resign?' mild and bland and almost mellifluous again, since he knew in advance the answer as the reviewer had when he entered the office, before he (the reviewer) replied: 'No. No, I reckon not,' turning with his trance-like step towards the door, and the editor: 'Wait. You've forgotten something,' moving a finger towards the book on the desk though taking care still not to touch it; and the reviewer moved somnabulistically back; and the editor: 'So sorry I couldn't help. About the horse, I mean. Did you say three legs?'

A World of Women
(Elizabeth Bowen)

*   *   *

THE SUN, THIS NOONTIDE, BLEACHING WITH A GLARE INCAN-descent the vacuum sky above the park, lambently was refracted by the lake whose waters, once upon a winter almost two decades bygone, segments of ice had brittlely floated in. That, however, was a whilom era, global-war-transected: now was a different season, another o'clock – summer heat presently blistered the seedy stucco Regency façades of houses which seemed in more than one sense to have come unstuck.

The pilasters of 2 Windsor Terrace in particular were peeling, pie-bald with flaking plaster; spikes of bird-droppings like stalactites depended from the crumbling cornices overhead. 'We paint every four years,' Thomas Quayne quondamly had declared, but a buzzbomb'd accounted for him before the quaternary was up; it is unwise to set a term to anything in times so skittishly unstable, since Anna, Thomas's widow, excluding the kind she put on her face, developed thereafter into not much of a one for paint. The residence's interior too progres-sively went to another kind of pot: it was currently filled with chipped marble, cracked mirrors in tarnished frames, cabinets shedding veneer in strips, and the occluded fumes of gin; beneath rugs worn tatty, the parquet, unwaxed or polished as of yore, with a splintery upgrowth bristled – the various clocks, never wound, held time arrested on their dusty dials. Most of the upstairs was long out of commission, sheeted in soiled linen behind doors irremediably warped; the basement where, before pegging out, austere Matchett had held sway was now the house-hold's hub – yet, on this as many other morns, from a barred window (attic? nursery?) way on high, a girl might have been seen mooning down.

Indisputably a beauty (not flawless, but which of us after all is?), her hair lopped at arbitrarily with what may have been the garden shears (though happily this is a mode in fashion), belted up in a frock of pre-war period, she clutched to her incipient bosom a black, moiré-covered book of a type that at the time she was born might be bought for a shilling, but may nowadays rush you more than double. Of an age traditionally sweet, she'd been named after the sixth month of the year – in fact that in which, now June is introduced and the scene all set, this story can be said to at last get under way.

Late risers all, the inhabitants of No 2 were none the less at this hour astir. Anna Quayne, up in her bedroom, lit the sodden stub of last night's fag and took a sip of gin and meth to cut, as she'd have put it, the phlegm: sardonically ogling the reflection her fly-stippled cheval-glass flung back, like an insulting gift quite rightly rejected. Straggles of *ci-devant* ash-blonde hair, now cinder-grey, she shoved from sight beneath the silk turban, never day or night removed – any more than was the make-up whose successive substrata made her face stand out, as it were, in relief. Buried below this, her initially opaque magnolia skin'd become so to speak browned at the edges: in especially round the lips, where cigarettes constantly relit had singed. A dirt stain by her jugular scrubbed off with cologne, she was ready to slop downstairs: her door opened on the sporadic inexpert clumping of her half-sister-in-law's typewriter echoing up uncarpeted shaft of stair – Anna's smile, however, was not more than ordinarily derisive as she listened; for though the house under Thomas's will was hers, Portia with the novels and stories she desultorily yet profitably turned off might indubitably be termed the breadwinner, now her husband Dickie, retired from the bank, did damn all but blow his pension on whisky, the dog-track, or the pools.

Portia Heccomb's body, once concave and linearly jerkily fluid, had coagulated somewhat since her marriage and wobbled now, like an imperfectly *reussi* blancmange, as she stabbed on at the recalcitrant keys, stiffly stamping out on paper mauvely smudged from the moist carboned fingers of the creatrix another descriptive bit. The excessive sensitivity, which in youth'd been a torture and was become her stock-in-trade, had not forsaken her: never was its aura so palpable as during these acts of composition, when the air around her seemed positively – well, to *quiver*. It was not a quality her daughters outwardly abounded in – June, yes, may perhaps have inherited a portion: Madge, the six-year-old, who now thrust in through the study door, had in this respect been – left altogether in the cold. The backward kick she closed the entrance with set draggled curtains – pristinely Picasso-blue – swinging skewiff upon broken poles: dust engirded Portia crouched, guiltily conscious of kippers uncooked, over what'd been her brother's desk.

As if stuffed, Madge stood accusatory, under one arm the Grand Grimoire, crooked within the other her waxen Voodoo doll, spiky as a porcupine with pins pierced through and modelled in the likeness of her dad. Peer preoccupiedly at her prose though she might, Portia could not for long ignore the mite's unwinking stare – and broke silence by inquiring: 'Is that a louse I see upon your pinny?'

'Not, it's to be hoped. Nits I find one thing, lice are quite another. Aunt Anna agrees – unless of course *she*…'

'D'you not feel an urge to scratch your herpes against the pillars in the hall?'

'They have ceased, Lucifer be thanked, to irritate – it's the witches' broth we brewed' – Madge picked instead at the stuffing extruded by the sofa; idly her mother interrogated: 'We?'

'I and Jolly Gilles de Rais, my doppelganger. He's Undead, you see, for impiety like Dracula – going breakfastless may be part of the punishment, but our inner woman feels the pangs.'

'Now *I'd* have adjudged' – Portia resignedly scooped herself upright – 'Gilles de Rais undoubtedly a male. However, being Undead makes him perhaps unmanned. I wouldn't be aware.'

'*Are* you going to get us, now, some grub?'

'Well, a wink, it's said, is the equivalent of a nod where a blind horse is concerned – or am I,' Portia wondered, 'in reverse?'

'Blinkers before Dobbin, it could be,' dryly the kid cracked back – 'Mother, could I be described as, d'you think, a chip off the Compton-Burnett?'

'Why, whoever did!'

'Anna, of course – the similarity I admit's perceptible sometimes in speech' (as Portia dollied indignantly towards the door). 'She also says you did not ought to have married Father ever –'

'Miss Compton-Burnett?' Portia exclaimed, adrift.

'Silly, no – I said Aunt Anna. Naturally, I see her point; but then one thinks, "Where'd I come in, if not?"'

'And whom did I ought to have wed, in your aunt's opinion?' the mother with more than a spice of irony inquired, longing none the less to know.

'Someone called, if I'm not mistaken, Eddie. Only he was it seems a bounder, and anyway got blown, later, ingloriously up – Aunt's own phrase – and now she feels to blame for having chucked you, as she says, into daddy's arms –'

'Madge, I absolutely forbid –'

'Though I cannot see even an Oxonian Eddie as much improvement; and even supposing, would I've been certain to get hatched?'

Portia, moving forward sharply to reprove – even, it might be, chastise – caught her heel in a goaty rug: at the desk's edge blindly clutched: an over-hanging cliff of books crumbled at her touch, foothold slid from under; suddenly prone beneath Madge's astonished stare, she found her own drawn as if by some fateful pointing finger to the bureau above. There, avalanche'd set up in earnest: an edifice of influences rained down – Henry James, De la Mare, inevitably Austen, struck, bounced off, piled up pyramidally on her as June and Anna, attracted by the awakened echoes, burst in some seconds later. Portia, still prone, gazed unbelievingly overhead at the empty open drawer that until last night had housed her Diary: the black, moiré-covered book abstracted by Anna, eighteen years before, from an escritoire upstairs – and which, at this very moment, fell – open at the name of Eddie – out of June's corsage plump in her mother's lap.

Hearts can kick the bucket but once: the smack of a second betrayal's superficially harder, yet doesn't bruise so deep.

'And not one bit abashed,' Portia, pacing agitatedly about, apostrophised. 'One cannot *not* compare – but, to boot, my own daughter!' out – for *that* was what did rankle – she reproachfully burst.

June replied, resentful: 'Is it sense to suppose I should be? Abashed, I mean – for I'm beyond doubt your offspring…'

'Albeit, I often wonder!' Portia flashed rather idiotically back, disregardful of Anna's murmured '*You*, if anyone, should know.'

'What sent me, principally, was the style,' the indubitable daughter unheedingly continued, 'and not at all your silly old Eddie – though I'll admit he's, as you present him, *alive – a man –*' the detestable suggestion that living males could be desirable, except by their absence, in this female world drew Portia and her sister-in-law momentarily together, as though uniting against invasion: even Madge signified agreement by driving a nail into her doll – 'Yes, and Daddy, and Major Brutt, and Uncle Thomas too!' defiantly went on the girl; 'All living, at least then

– Daddy you did for between you a long time ago; *men*, not ghostly lovers, dim traitors, or just presences unseen! – I never dreamed you could at any time have written naturally, to make people really talk – Oh, I don't mean that never-to-be-heard-on-land-or-sea twaddle you palm off as dialogue today…' She scanned scornfully the sheet of typescript cockled up with heat in the jaws of the machine: ' 'I now do wonder how I so long endured this!' – that, sister, or I should say mother – goes for me also. And why the inverted syntax – this Welsh effect when Ireland your scene here, if anywhere, is?'

'It's, I'd hazard, June, hard cheese on any writer whose dialogue's affected by the Jamesian spell, still more when this comes over one in mid-career,' Portia gently and sadly interjected; whereat the girl's head drooped, maybe in shame. 'The screw's then too tightly turned for the coffin-lid to ever lift: the lesson of the master only – alack! – too tardily learnt.'

'Oh, but I *liked* the ghosts!' Madge, who'd perhaps human feelings after all, loyally cut in. 'The smell of evil could be plainly sniffed – all the reviewers concurred!'

'St Quentin always *said* you'd style,' Anna murmured. 'Just imagine him – in Westminster Abbey, well who'd have thought?'

'I know,' Portia nodded proudly – 'After that, I could not, could I, *not* be a novelist?'

But the question was forever to remain unanswered; for key clicked in latch outside, the hall door banged agape then, noisily, shut: loud voices were heartily – gruffly! – upraised: heavy feet – unmistakably masculine, encased in hobnailed boots at that by the sound of them – stumbled and skidded on the stone floor and could be heard clumping up the staircase in the direction of the drawing-room.

'Dickie!' Anna dramatically hissed. 'He's brought some brutes back from the pub!'

'Heavens!' Portia's hands flew to her head – 'No dinner ready and my hair not done' – Madge's mouth hung lopsided and she grabbed at the Grand Grimoire; only June seemed unaffected by the invasion – could, even, an expression of anticipated pleasure have flickered across her lovely features?

'June, do something, can't you!' rapped Anna at her: it was as if men being somewhere in the offing had already subtly coarsened the patterns of her speech – 'Head those bar-sinisters off whilst we change – before they guzzle all the gin!'

No sooner ordered than obeyed: June had beetled like an antelope off up the stairs, pausing infinitesimally outside with a hand on the knob before softly pushing the drawing-room door ajar. Alas! – on the order of her entrance, as she made her smiling way towards those awkward, uncouth shapes (all, her father included, of an insensitivity outrageous), the story, when about to become interesting, abruptly ended.

The Peach
(H.E. Bates)

*　　　*　　　*

HE LIVED ALONE THROUGH THE CHANGING SEASONS IN A HOUSE
that was designed to look from outside like a hangar, and in spring as
he sat working at his desk that was shaped like the cockpit of a plane,
he could see the peach tree blooming pink in the orchard beyond the
long windows of his study that shimmered in the morning sun.

The walls of the house were sprayed freshly every year with camouflage paint, and the inside of his study was decorated with models of
the various aircraft in which long ago, during the war, he had been
taken up so as to learn what it felt like to fly. When the writer recalled
this sensation he would sometimes strap himself into the cockpit before
reaching out urgently to where, instead of the controls, his typewriter
stood beside the stack of clean white quarto sheets on which he
recorded the lambent and lyrical prose that had brought him his fame.

That was at first, when he wrote the books about the RAF, and the
memory of his flying hours was still so vivid that at times he would
have to pause at the typewriter keys and lean over to void his churning
stomach into the paper bags that were hung for that purpose at the
sides of the cockpit. Nowadays he seldom buckled the straps around
him and the paper bags remained unused. He wrote stories now about
transient love affairs in idyllic country settings that were serialised in
women's magazines before becoming book-club choices and being
filmed; and the four-figure cheques and the fan-mail in illiterate
purple scrawls piled up on the desk, but his day's routine did not alter.

Throughout the fresh and fading springtime he typed on, looking
occasionally out at the peach tree beyond the pane, and when winds
shook down the pink blossom and the fruit began to burgeon on the
branches he would know the time had come to bring about the poignant

495

climax to his tale and parcel up the typescript to reach his publishers for inclusion in their autumn list. In the summer months he took things more easily, sitting down in the cockpit only to answer his morning mail and strolling in the thermal afternoons through the orchard where the peaches glowed increasingly warm and golden with the rose flush on their fullness like the rich bloom on a girl's round young cheek. He was not a tall man, though he had himself photographed always to look bigger, and he could only reach the fruit when the branches became bowed down under its weight, but sometimes when this happened he would stretch up his short arm and pass his fingers over one of the peaches, feeling for a brief instant the soft, downy surface brush tinglingly against his own skin. It was this contact that he would recall when writing a love scene in spring, and even in summer it would sometimes drive him back to his desk in a sudden urge to create. He never actually ate a peach himself, though occasionally, in bed at night, he would imagine the firm, furry flesh against his teeth and feel the warm, sweet juice spurting out on his tongue.

That was before the photograph came. It was towards the close of one spring, with the pink peach-blossom petals already strewn on the grass outside and the new novel nearing its inevitable dying fall, that he slit open one of the fan-letters and the photograph fell out. It was an enlarged snapshot, crudely tinted, of a sort he often received, yet it seemed to him that the creamy gold of the rather coarse face and the red flush on the full round cheeks resembled the colouring of a peach. The girl's eyes, curiously bold and impersonal, stared back at him in a way that caused his stomach muscles to flutter and contract and the cockpit of his desk to heave sickeningly over and down. When he had used one of the paper bags he went out on a sudden impulse to look at the peach tree. The fruit was still unripe, green and small, too high for him to reach, but he felt already his teeth biting into sweet pulp and the fragrant juice flooding over his dry lips.

He did no more work that morning or on the days that followed, but sat staring out at the tree waiting for the fruit to ripen. Letters marked 'Urgent' and stamped with his publishers' colophon remained unopened and unanswered, and the sheet of paper in the carriage of his typewriter cockled up and turned yellow in the heat of the sun. He did not even write to the girl, but every morning he took out her photograph and passed his fingertips over its surface as though feeling beneath them the downy flesh of a peach. But it was not until the fruit blazed sanguine and gilded on the tree that the girl herself arrived.

He came upon her suddenly one afternoon, sprawled out under the tree, a rucksack from which a cheap reprint of one of his novels protruded thrown casually in the grass beside her. She wore a thin khaki shirt open at the throat and a pair of old stained khaki shorts, and the skin of her strong limbs was golden in the warm flood of summer sunshine.

'Hullo,' she said. 'Seeing's you didn't answer my note, I reckoned I'd best drop in and call on you. Being as I was passing by, like.' Her eyes roved over him in that bold impersonal glance, and he could feel the tide of his blood rising and his stomach dropping as when the plane dived suddenly towards its target.

'You're not as big as you look in your snaps,' she said. 'Older, too. Still, I reckon you'll have to do.' It was then that he noticed the half-eaten peach in her hand and saw, as she smiled lazily up at him, that her lips and teeth were sticky with the juice from it.

'Don't mind me pinching one of your peaches, do you?' she said. 'Didn't have no dinner today, what with hitching lifts and that.' Still he stood rigid, unable to speak, watching the furry down on her strong golden legs and the faint bloom on the firm sun-flushed cheeks.

'Look as if you could do with a good feed yourself,' she said. 'Here, sit down and have a bite.' She smiled again, holding out the peach invitingly. 'Go on,' she said. 'It's real lush. Like them yarns you write.'

He spoke then, his voice sounding choked and unreal as he stooped, groping with sudden eagerness towards her in the grass.

'You're like a peach yourself. A peach,' he managed to get out, before her golden furry arm crooked firmly round his neck and drew him down to the bold, impersonal, faintly mocking stare and the warm, sweet, pulpy fruit thrust tenderly against his avid and thirsting mouth.

'Like a peach,' he often told her as the days went by and they lay side by side beneath the tree, on the ground scattered with the stones of the fruit they had eaten, 'a sweet, luscious, sun-ripened peach,' and his stomach would turn over in a delicious nose-dive as her lips rounded sensuously to spit out yet another stone.

'You old silly,' or 'Soppy thing,' she would say to him softly, leaning her bare strong throat back to stare impersonally up into the branches of the tree that swung heavy-laden with fruit just above their drowsing heads.

So the camouflage paint blistered on the hangar walls and the post piled up unread, and the publishers came down from town to batter on the door and return baffled in expensive cars to their Bloomsbury offices and unfulfilled autumn lists; and in the writer's study, the model planes, the Mosquitoes and Spitfires and twin-engined bombers, began to rust and the girl's skin was tanned to a darker tint than any peach.

One afternoon he woke abruptly to find that she was no longer beside him under the tree. Her rucksack was gone too, and only the paper-covered copy of his novel lay, its pages gummed together with dirt and dew, crumpled among the peach-stones scattered on the ground. Sitting up, he called her name hoarsely, but there was no reply; and his writer's intuition told him that if he searched the house he would not find her either. He remembered the rough downy feel of her skin against his face and the sweet, warm juice trickling into his mouth, and despairingly he looked up into the branches of the tree as though expecting to see her there.

Only one peach remained on the bough, and he reached towards it avidly as if it contained the full and final essence of their summer for him to bite into and lingeringly savour. But as his finger-tips brushed it, the fruit fell heavily to the ground and helplessly his arms dropped to his sides as the small worm wriggled from the hole in the round, mushy, over-ripe cheek and crawled, looping, away over his photograph staring up at him from the grass.

It seemed then that there was only one thing left: to write the story; but as he walked slowly back towards the rusting aircraft, the unoiled typewriter, and the broken contracts, it seemed to him also that he had written it only too often before.

So Long, My Buddy[1]
(Raymond Chandler)

*   *   *

1

YOU OUGHT TO KNOW YOUR WAY BY NOW. THAT IS, IF YOU WANT in. Down the deadbeat end of a fashionably shabby corridor, in the sort of building that was new about the year the all-American ace took murder out of the Venetian case and dropped it in the alley where the rest of us had to root around looking for it ever since, Dash him.

Push the pebbled glass door with the flaked black lettering, inhale the down-to-the-minute dust in the waiting room, but don't be surprised if the smell of self-pity turns you kind of sick once you're past the inner door. Because, Brother or Sister as the sex may be, that's right where you'll find me. Sitting by the phone in the suitably sordid office, at the worn desk with the stained brown blotter and the bottle of Old Forester and the Luger holed up in it somewhere and maybe some dame's handkerchief scented with stale cheap sentiment and an old brown bloodstain smeared across that I have instead of a sachet of sweet memories packed away in lavender. Philip Marlowe, the guy who put the 'I' in Private Investigator. Forty bucks a day and expenses when I can get it, or fifteen British bob a read in the UK Omnibus Edition, and cheap at the price. That's me. Or rather, I. Spit right in the Public Eye, folks. Only, if you're a fiction book-critic, tread softly as you cross the threadbare carpet, because you may be treading on the magazine-pulp life made of my lovely boyhood dreams.

---

1   From a hitherto-unpublished collection, *The Simple Art of Marlowe*.

It was a typical Californian summer's day, hot as a mobster's rod or the pants of a Hollywood cutie. Smog crept like a B-movie gumshoe down the blue distance over Beverly Hills. Below, on the dusty boulevard, the buncoboys and the con-men, the hustlers, the heisters, the dope-peddling doctors and vice-czars, the wrong-doers and the rightly served, stewed wearily in their own stench.

I was parked in my swivel chair, reading about woman-slaughter in the works of Sir Thomas Malory that a London female film-reviewer sent me for a last year's Christmas gift. 'The modern equivalent of a parfait and gentil knight,' she'd written one time when Bogart was standing in for me on the screen, and maybe she figured I ought to catch up on the way these characters used to act back in the days when they were bold. 'Ryght,' I read, 'so com hys ladye oute of a chambir and felle over hym, and so he smote of hir hede by myssefortune.' It didn't sound quite ryght or over-chivalrous to me, and the killer's excuse that the death-blow was really meant for the fayre ladye's husband would have been rated a trifle cynical by even a downtown DA. Old Sir Tom himself didn't seem to have been exactly a law-abiding citizen either. In and out of the hoosgow most of his life, though according to the Intro that could have been a frame. 'At a time when legal process was not uncommonly used as a means of achieving private or political vengeance an innocent man might well find himself charged with any crime.' Mr Editor, that goes for me too. After five hundred years, crooked sadistic cop, with heavy sugar from wire-pulling jerks-in-office bulging out their billfolds, can still bust heaven out of guiltless suspects while the grafters and the sharpies, the shakers-down and the beaters-up, the two-timing, treble-dealing four-flushers go for free. Sir Phillip Marlowe, Kt, I thought. The C-green incorruptible.

Now then, Marlowe, cut the moral angle. That's plenty social comment for today. You haven't 125,000 words to play around with this trip. Pseudo-poetical pessimism's out from here on. Provide the goo and the gore, Marlowe. Make the silvery laughter and the blood bubble up. Let the phone ring or the buzzer sound. Have a guy come through the door with a gun in his hand.

The phone rang. The buzzer sounded. A guy came through the door with a gun in his hand. 'Make with the mitts, peeper,' he said in a rasping voice. 'But fast.'

'Just a minute while I take this call,' I said. I lifted the phone and a woman's voice said urgently in my ear: 'Mr Marlowe, you must aid me. Please.' Way back in the voice you could hear frogs croaking somewhere down in Southern France. Her silvery laugh sounded a cracked peal. 'I do not wish to die.'

'Mademoiselle,' I said, 'that makes two of us. Maybe later I can fix your problem, but right now I got a client.'

I hung up and looked at the man with the gun. He was a tall man with a glabrous yellow face and eyes that were as honest as a fellow-writer's praise. The crease in his striped pants was sharp enough to slice through a front-office executive's heart. He probably stropped them every morning after he got through honing his cut-throat razor. I glanced from the short black gun and the short black jacket to the shining black derby he held in his other hand.

'I suppose you call it a bowler,' I said. 'Back in the old country, don't you know.'

The man smiled, a soft apologetic smile. 'Begging your pardon, sir. I had forgotten you were a detective.' The rasp was wrapped in velvet now. His voice was suave and deferential and veddy, veddy British. 'My travesty of a tough American accent could not hope to deceive you for an instant.'

'I did detect a strong odour of limes.'

He made a respectful bow. 'Of course, sir, you yourself can still speak English. If there's any demand for it.'

'Olde Englysshe, too,' I told him. 'Even less demand for that.' The Malory in my left hand caught him square on the side of the jaw. There were 919 printed pages of it not counting the introduction and preface, and he'd have been laid out flat if I hadn't held him up with my right hand clamped round his gun wrist. His bowler hat fell off on to the desk and I shied it over my shoulder, out the open window, into the street far below. He gave a gasp and the pistol slid from suddenly limp fingers. I often wondered why they got called heaters. They always put the chill on me. The man swayed groggily and I pointed the gun at his head and squeezed the trigger.

'Click,' I said. 'That's all. No bang. No blood. No brains. You got to thumb back the safety-catch on these things, or they just won't go off.'

He didn't fold. He had guts. Only he'd have called it pluck. Sound, solid British pluck. Veddy, veddy pukka. The perfect gentleman's gentleman. He started across me at the open window and whispered 'Oh, my hat.'

'Sorry, old top,' I said. 'You can't blame me for feeling a little sore.'

'Oh, no, sir. It is I who should apologise.' The pain and loss went out of his eyes. The respectful smile returned. 'For inefficiency. I fear that I am not really at home with firearms, sir.'

'How about cold steel?' I said. 'The jolly old chiv, what?'

'Too messy, sir. I have always favoured a life-preserver myself. In certain circles it is referred to as a cosh.'

A length of rubber tubing appeared suddenly in his hand. He bowed humbly before bringing it down on my left temple. A galaxy of movie-stars swam up towards me in a Technicolour haze. Bogey, Dick Powell, Fred MacMurray, Bob Montgomery. All those that had once been me who now no longer was. Their faces span in a general mix and merged for the final fade. The screen went dark. I fell into a bottom that had no pit.

3

Somebody was tapping out a bad review on the top of my skull. The typewriter keys fell heavy as sledge-hammers. My brain was the black and red ribbon running through the spools, my nerves were the stretched tension-cord. A bell rang for the end of the line. Every book I got to go through this, I groaned. All because the Continental Op had that laudanum-jag dream in *Red Harvest* and got himself gassed in *The Dain Curse*. Some Brytysshe creep had strekyn of my hede by myssfortune, and every time I tried to fit it back on it dissolved into the head of the jane Sir Gawayne had accidentally sleyne. Jantyll Phil Marlowe, I thought, the Head Hunter of Un-Holywood. I opened my eyes to get a better focus and the head smiled at me from across my desk. 'Mon ami,' it said throatily, 'you are okay again, yes?'

'No,' I growled. The smiling head floated nearer. It appeared to be sheathed in flame. The perfume of mimosa was wafted along with it. Now a drawer slid open and the bottle of Old Forester was tilted level with the mouth I didn't have. I wrapped my non-existent lips round the bottle's neck and took a long swallow. Fire throbbed in my throat and belly and licked the bump that swelled on my forehead, my vision cleared and my head snapped back in its appointed groove. But the other head was still there. Its enormous anxious eyes stared into mine. It had got itself attached to a body too, and the body was sitting in my lap. A bare arm the colour of an old ivory chessman curled around my neck. The sheath of flame was a scarlet play-suit that matched her vivid painted lips. Her lips were hot as sealing-wax. Somewhere beyond the mimosa lay the blue Mediterranean that was reflected in her eyes. Her mouth came unstuck from mine to whisper: 'Aid me, please, dear friend. I do not wish to be murdered.'

'Who's going to murder you, chérie?' I asked.

'I do not know.' Her shape shivered in my arms. 'It is all in the plot.'

'And passions spin it?' I suggested. We kissed again. Time passed slow as the action in a Henry James novel, but more excitingly.

'But I am serious,' she said, pulling away. 'I do not want to be a cadaver that you will stumble on towards the end of the story. I would like to be the girl that is still alive in the last chapter. Not she who assassinates. The client whom you protect, the woman who would make you happy if your profession did not come between.' She leaped up suddenly. 'Keyhole-peeper, cheap shamus, shyster, dirty rubber-souled sneak, son of a snitch.' She slapped both sides of my face. 'See,' she said. 'I will treat you as you like to be treated. I will call you Marlowe if you wish. I will be all those women you have known and loved and lost, Marlowe.' The silver bells of her laugh pealed out for a wedding, and one of them rang somewhere way back in my brain.

'Okay,' I said, standing up. 'Now listen. Stay right here in the office till I get back or ring through. Lock the door. Let nobody in. Drink all the Scotch you want and keep plugging away at this book.' I put the bottle by her side and the Malory in her hand.

'It is in code, yes?' she asked, flicking over the pages. 'It contains some vital clue?'

'Could be,' I said. 'Later I'll buy you a copy in the original Frensshe.' I finished buckling on the Luger in its shoulder-holster. 'My shield and my armour,' I said. 'I am a lonely knight setting forth upon a quest.'

'Not lonely,' she said in my arms. 'Not anymore. Chéri. Marlowe. You will not be killed, mon ami, no?'

'Not me,' I said. 'I'm the guy that's telling the story. I'm the one guy they can't rub out.'

It wasn't until I got downstairs that I realised I didn't even know her name. And by then it was already too late to ask.

The gentleman's gentleman in the short black jacket was surprised to see me when he opened the door. He was so surprised he even forgot to bow. But his reactions were fast. I didn't wait to see if it was the gun or the cosh he was reaching for, or whether he merely meant to carve me up with the crease in his pants. I socked a hard one into his gut and, as he doubled over, slammed the heel of my hand down on his nape. I leaned forward and frisked him quickly as he lay writhing on the floor. He'd a stiff upper lip all right. Never let out a peep. Or maybe he hadn't enough wind left. His mouth was open, gasping like a fish on land, and the glabrous yellow face had gone the colour of verdigris.

'How green was my valet,' I said. 'A poor gag but not, I'm glad to say, mine own. Heard it on the radio donkeys' years ago, old bean.'

I dropped the pistol and the rubber hose into my side pocket, and went on up the wide curving stairway. On the thick carpet my feet made no sound. I ascended light and airy as thistledown. He was in the study on the first landing, just as I expected. I could hear the typewriter ticking behind the oak-panelled door and the lump on my left temple began to ache like a bump of memory. As I lifted the latch and stepped softly into the room, the black cat he was sometimes photographed with shot out past me down the stairs.

He was hunched as usual over his platinum writing-desk, under the emerald shaded lamp, putting a fresh sheet of hand-made vellum into the solid hall-marked eighteen-carat-gold machine, but when I spoke he let go the jewelled platen knob and whirled about in his pneumatic swivel chair to face me.

'Type no more, buddy,' I said. 'This is the pay-off. The last link in the chain. The last piece of the puzzle. The lovely, long-awaited, last-minute dénouement. Only you're not going to be here to write it, buddy. That's where the big surprise comes in.'

'Marlowe,' he said. 'Have you gone crazy, disturbing me at my work? You're supposed to be busy on a case. I sent along some new clients this afternoon –'

'Oh go to Bay City,' I said. 'I'm out on a case all right, and this is it. Marlowe's last case, buddy. Or rather, yours.' I took the valet's short black gun from my pocket and let him look down the muzzle as I thumbed back the safety-catch. He'd made me look down so many guns in his time. But seeing his eyes widen behind the spectacles and his hands tighten on the arms of the chair didn't give me the kick I expected. I felt tired, pooped out. I was a remaindered paperback on a dusty bookshelf in a bankrupt bookstore in a bombed-out city. I went on:

'It's going to be a beautiful frame. Better than any you ever got me tied up in. World-famous toughie-writer, the toast of the intellectuals, found bumped by his own valet. Prints on the gun, every little thing.' I put my hand in the light to show the thin silk handkerchief I was holding the gun with. 'That lug downstairs'll have a police record long enough to reach from here to Baker Street. And who'll turn in the alarm? Why, your very own creation Philip Marlowe, private dick and equally famous corpse-finder. Maybe I'll get a going-over from the cops, but that won't be any new experience, and they know I always turn out in the clear –'

'Listen, Marlowe,' he said with sudden urgency. 'It's been a profitable partnership. You'd be a sap to break it up –'

'Profitable for who?' I said. 'All I ever got out of it was a sore head and a seedy office, a solitary life and a heart with a crack in it that the cold wind blows through. Okay, stay alive if you must, only count me out in future. Get yourself another fall-guy. Marlowe means to retire from this moment. So-long, buddy.' I tossed the gun in his lap and turned towards the door.

'You forget one thing,' the voice said behind me. 'You reckon you can't die, but you're wrong, Marlowe. Because it's I who tells the stories, not you. I'm the one man who can destroy you, just as I gave you life –'

'You're right,' I said. 'I'd forgotten.' I turned and saw the green light glinting on his spectacles and his finger tightening on the trigger. I got the Luger out and fired as the stab of flame tore into my chest. His swivel chair span round and he slopped forward with his face down by the typewriter, one hand trailing out along the keys. 'Sende me good delyveraunce,' I coughed into the Aubusson carpet, as the scent of mimosa faded in my nostrils. 'Me and Tom Malory both.'

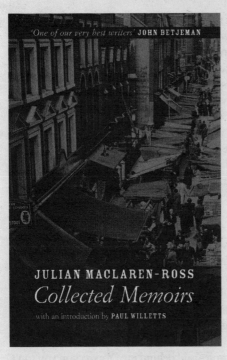

Julian Maclaren-Ross
Collected Memoirs

with an introduction by
Paul Willetts
£8.95 softback
ISBN 0-948238-30-5; 464pp

'Those who have yet to discover this wonderfully stylish and sardonic writer should start here'
PETER PARKER, *DAILY TELEGRAPH*

'Nothing has given me greater pleasure than the continuing revival of one of my favourite writers, Julian Maclaren-Ross, with his *Collected Memoirs*'
PHILIP FRENCH, BOOKS OF THE YEAR, *OBSERVER*

'a substantial account of his great talent'
INDEPENDENT ON SUNDAY

'excellent anthology'
MAIL ON SUNDAY

'Were he writing now…he would be a star'
IAIN FINLAYSON, *TIMES*

Julian Maclaren-Ross was one of the most colourful inhabitants of the Soho and Fitzrovia of the forties, fifties and sixties. He knew and wrote about some of the most memorable characters of the time, among them Dylan Thomas, Graham Greene, Cyril Connolly, J.M. Tambimuttu, Nina Hamnett and Woodrow Wyatt. A dandy, with his overcoat and silver-topped malacca cane, and a gifted raconteur, his life, often chaotic – and related unsentimentally by him in these memoirs – veered between the fringes of the literary establishment and occasional homelessness.

These atmospheric stories are a rare insight into a world now gone, and this collection includes in full Maclaren-Ross's best-known work of non-fiction, *Memoirs of the Forties*, along with many other less known but no less interesting works, some published here for the first time in book form. His poignant memoir of childhood, *The Weeping and the Laughter*, also appears here in full, for the first time since its original publication in the 1950s.

the acclaimed biography

Fear and Loathing in Fitzrovia
Paul Willetts
Dewi Lewis Publishing
£14.99 softback
ISBN 1-899235-69-8; 416pp

'An inspiring read'
JOHN KING, *NEW STATESMAN*
BOOKS OF THE YEAR

'Diligent, painstaking and bleakly hilarious'
GUARDIAN BOOK OF THE WEEK

'Historical profiling of a high order, richly and racily done'
PHILIP OAKES, *LITERARY REVIEW*

'Very striking, very strange and altogether fascinating'
RICHARD HOLMES, AUTHOR OF
DR JOHNSON AND MR SAVAGE

'Gloriously readable'
MAIL ON SUNDAY

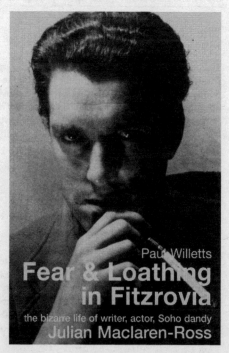

Paul Willetts
Fear & Loathing in Fitzrovia
the bizarre life of writer, actor, Soho dandy
Julian Maclaren-Ross

Julian Maclaren-Ross Selected Stories
Introduced by Paul Willetts
Dewi Lewis Publishing
£9.99 softback
ISBN 1-904587-17-8; 256pp

The world of Maclaren-Ross's short fiction tends to be the dingy, down-at-heel world of smoke-veiled bars, rented lodgings, blacked-out streets, and wartime army garrisons, first-hand experience lending his work a frisson of authenticity. Whether they're narrated in the breathless, slangy voice of an uneducated soldier, or the clipped cadences of a colonial 'expat', whether they're set on the French Riviera or wartime England, they're imprinted with Maclaren-Ross's unmistakable literary logo. The prevailing tone is casual, matter-of-fact and laconic, with his characteristically humorous asides failing to conceal the melancholy that seeps through their hardboiled surfaces.

The Lost Weekend *Charles Jackson*
£6.99 paperback; ISBN 0-948238-27-5; 224pp

Having cunningly contrived his own abandonment, Don Birnam begins the five-day alcoholic bender that may, just may, be the one that ends it all... Subject of Billy Wilder's classic Hollywood movie, which won four Oscars – among them best picture and best director – *The Lost Weekend* captures the atmosphere of Manhattan in the late 1930s – huge tenements, small smoke-filled piano bars, teeming streets beneath rattling elevated railways – with a haunting, cinematic vividness.

'Marvelous and horrifying... the best fictional account of alcoholism I have read' KINGSLEY AMIS

'His character is a masterpiece of psychological precision' NEW YORK TIMES

The Tenant *Roland Topor*
£6.99 paperback; ISBN 0-948238-26-7; 176pp

A masterful psychological thriller, *The Tenant* tells of Monsieur Trelkovsky, an ordinary man with ordinary desires against whom apparently ordinary circumstances conspire until he is enmeshed in an extraordinary and terrifying situation, a nightmare world of paranoia, collusion, horrifying injury and suicide – a world which, we come to feel, is separated from the normality of everyday life by the merest sliver of sanity. Roman Polanski made a film based on the book in 1976.

'hallucinatory classic of literary horror somewhat akin to a fusion of Patrick Hamilton and Edgar Allan Poe' GQ

'unforgettable, gripping' RONALD FRAME, LE MONDE

'a powerful fable set in the twilight zone' OBSERVER

'As cold and quiet and deadly as a snake in the bed' NEW YORK TIMES

The Big Brass Ring an original screenplay *Orson Welles with Oja Kodar*
£9.95 paperback; ISBN 0-948238-16-X; 160pp

Consciously conceived as a companion piece to *Citizen Kane*, here Welles is again concerned with the idea of the great man, and with what happens at the convergence of great talent, public ambition and the undertow of obscure, private longings rooted in the past. A film of *The Big Brass Ring*, its script heavily edited, appeared in 1999, with William Hurt in the lead role.

'The script in its present form, with its witty and extensive stage directions, gives a tremendous sense of what it might have been like in the company of the great raconteur himself... and the authors have taken great care to let us "see" what the film might have been – enthralling, sexy, funny, and politically as trenchant as anything being made today.' SIMON CALLOW

'a living, breathing, finished work on the page... one of the most remarkable and revealing works in the entire Welles canon' SIGHT AND SOUND

'playful, witty and moving' TIME OUT